LINEAR NETWORK THEORY

Analysis, Properties, Design and Synthesis

MATRIX SERIES
IN CIRCUITS AND SYSTEMS

Andrew P. Sage, *Editor*

LINEAR NETWORK THEORY

Analysis, Properties, Design and Synthesis

Norman Balabanian and Theodore A. Bickart
Department of Electrical and Computer Engineering
Syracuse University

Matrix Publishers, Inc.
Beaverton, Oregon

ISBN: 0-916460-10-X

Library of Congress catalog card number: 80-85066

Matrix Publishers, Inc.
11000 S.W. 11th Street
Beaverton, OR 97005

Typesetting: Harrison Typesetting, Inc.
Illustrations: Scientific Illustrators
Printing: Pantagraph Printing
Production: Patricia Miller
In-house Editor: Merl K. Miller

CONTENTS

Preface

This book provides a comprehensive and careful development of linear network theory on a linear graph theory base and utilizing matrix-vector formulations of analytical methods. No attempt is made to provide the needed mathematical tools: matrix theory, functions of a complex variable, Laplace transforms, numerical methods, or programming. However, some reference texts in these areas have been included in the bibliography (Appendix B). Active and nonreciprocal components (controlled sources, gyrators, operational amplifiers, general converters, etc.) are treated side-by-side with passive reciprocal components. A careful treatment of Tellegen's theorem and adjoint networks is the basis for the extensive chapter on computer-aided design.

Both analysis and synthesis are treated, including an extended chapter on contemporary methods of active-RC synthesis. Concepts of sensitivity are used both to determine variations of response to changes in parameter values for specific network realizations and as a basis for optimization in computer-aided design.

Also included are several chapters describing the representation of linear networks as multiterminal and as multiport networks and the analytical properties displayed by these representations. Topics include two-port matrices, the indefinite admittance matrix, scattering parameters, and frequency- and time-domain representations of network functions.

After the introductory chapter, the remainder of the book is divided into four parts, each devoted to one of the themes of the book's subtitle: *analysis*, *properties*, *design*, and *synthesis*. A feature of the book is the scaling and ordering of the work to be done by students. Each part (and the introductory chapter) of the book contains several types of work to be done. *Exercises* are routine applications of the methods and concepts developed in that part. *Problems* include a number of categories of activities: extensions of results to different or more complicated situations, theoretical derivations of collateral results, and treatment of topics that might have formed part of the text but for space limitations. *Programs* suggest the development of computer program routines or subroutines for use with specific analysis or design methods. Finally, *Projects* guide students to study specific pieces of other literature to become acquainted with interesting topics not included in the book.

The present book has some features in common with our earlier book, *Electrical Network Theory*, which has gone out of print. However, it differs in a number of important ways: (a) it does not include a treatment of nonlinear and time-varying networks, and (b) it includes some major topics not treated in the earlier book, namely, adjoint networks, computer-aided design, and active-*RC* network synthesis. An extensive bibliography is provided, grouped under specific topical headings.

The book is used as Syracuse University at the early graduate level, although selected parts could be used at the advanced undergraduate level.

Over the years, we have benefitted from the comments and criticisms of many colleagues and students. To them we express our appreciation.

N. Balabanian
T. A. Bickart
22 February 1980

CHAPTER 1
Fundamental Concepts

1.1 INTRODUCTION

Electric network theory, like many branches of science, attempts to describe the phenomena that occur in a portion of the physical world by setting up mathematical models. These models, of course, are based on observations in the physical world, but they also utilize other mathematical models that have stood the test of time so well that they have come to be regarded as physical reality themselves. As an example, the picture of electrons flowing in conductors and thus constituting an electric current is so vivid that we lose sight of the fact that this is just a theoretical model of a portion of the physical world.

The purpose of a model is to permit an understanding of natural phenomena; but, more than this, we expect that the logical consequences to which the model leads will enable us to predict the behavior of the model under specified conditions. If we can duplicate in the physical world the conditions that prevail in the model, the predictions can be experimentally checked. If the predictions are verified, we gain confidence that the model is a good one. If there is a difference between the predicted and experimental values that cannot be ascribed to experimental error, and we are reasonably sure that the experimental analogue of the theoretical model duplicates the conditions of the model, we must conclude that the model is not "adequate" for the purpose of understanding the physical world and must be overhauled.*

---

* An example of such an overhaul occurred after the celebrated Michelson-Morley experiment, where calculations based on Newtonian mechanics did not agree with experimental results. The revised model is relativistic mechanics.

In the case of electric network theory, the models have had great success in predicting experimental results. As a matter of fact, the models have become so real that it is difficult for students to distinguish between a model and the physical world.

The first step in establishing a modeling procedure is to make detailed observations of the physical world. Experiments are performed in an attempt to establish universal relationships among the measurable quantities. From these experiments, general conclusions are drawn concerning the behavior of the quantities involved. These conclusions are regarded as "laws" and are usually stated in terms of the variables of the mathematical models.

Needless to say, we shall not be concerned with this step of the process. The models have by now been well established. We shall, instead, introduce the components (or elements) of the models without justification or empirical verification. The process of abstracting an appropriate interconnection of the hypothetical components of a model in order to describe adequately a given physical situation is an important consideration, but also outside the scope of this book.

This book is concerned with the theory of *linear electric networks*. By an electric *network* is meant an interconnection of electrical devices forming a structure with accessible points at which signals can be observed. It is assumed that the electrical devices making up the network are represented by *models* or hypothetical *components* whose voltage-current equations are linear equations—algebraic equations, ordinary differential equations, or partial differential equations. In this book we shall be concerned only with lumped networks; hence, we shall not deal with partial differential equations.

The properties of networks can be classified under two general headings. First, there are those properties of a network that are consequences of its structure—*the topological properties*. These properties do not depend on the specific components that constitute the branches of the network but only on how the branches are interconnected; for example, it may be deduced that the transfer function zeros of a ladder network (a specific topological structure) lie in the left half-plane regardless of what passive components constitute the branches. Second, there are the properties of networks as signal processors. Signals are applied at the accessible points of the network, and these signals are modified or processed in certain ways by the network. These *signal-processing properties* depend on the components of which the network is composed and also on the topological structure of the network. Thus if the network components are lossless, signals are modified in certain ways no matter what the structure of the network; further limitations are imposed on these properties by the structure. The properties of lossless ladders, for example, differ from those of lossless lattices. We shall be concerned with both the topological and the signal-processing properties of networks.

The digital computer is an important tool both in the analysis of networks and in network design. Since the advent of integrated circuits and the increasing complexity of networks, the computer has become almost indispensible. In this book we shall assume a degree of literacy in computer programming and numerical computational techniques. We shall not, however, spend time in the text discussing programming and computation, although we shall provide algorithms which can be implemented as programs. Instead, a large number of projects will be outlined in some detail so as to guide you in acquiring skill in using programming and computational techniques in network analysis and design.

1.2 NOTATION AND REFERENCES

The signals, or the variables, in terms of which the behavior of electric networks is described are usually voltage and current, although sometimes electric charge and magnetic flux-linkage are useful. These are functions of time t and will be consistently represented by lower-case symbols $v(t)$ and $i(t)$. Sometimes the functional dependence will not be shown explicitly when there is no possibility of confusion; thus v and i will be used instead of $v(t)$ and $i(t)$.

The Laplace transform of a time function will be represented by the capital letter corresponding to the lower-case letter representing the time function. Thus, $I(s)$ is the Laplace transform of $i(t)$, where s is the complex frequency variable, $s = \sigma + j\omega$. Sometimes the functional dependence on s will not be shown explicitly, and $I(s)$ will be written as plain I.

In steady state analysis, the variables are not functions of s but *phasors* representing sinusoids. No special notation will be used for phasors other than capital letters. The context should make clear whether V represents a phasor or a Laplace transform in a particular case.

Scalar quantities will be shown in the usual way, with italic letters. Vectors will be indicated by bold face letters. Thus, $\mathbf{V}$ is a vector whose elements are Laplace transforms of voltages (since they are capitals).

$$\mathbf{V} = \begin{bmatrix} V_1 \\ V_2 \\ \cdot \\ \cdot \\ \cdot \\ V_n \end{bmatrix}$$

The fundamental laws on which network theory is founded express relationships among voltages and currents at various places in a network. Before these laws can even be formulated it is necessary to establish a system for correlating the sense of the quantities i and v with the indications of a meter. This is done by establishing a reference for each voltage and current. The system of references adopted in this book is shown in Fig. 1(a). An arrow indicates the reference for the current in

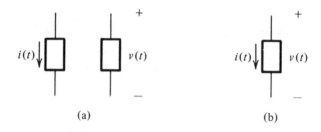

(a)   (b)

Fig. 1   (a) Current and voltage references; (b) Load references

a component. This arrow does not mean that the current is always in the arrow direction. It means that, whenever the current is in the arrow direction, as indicated by an appropriate instrument, $i(t)$ will be positive. Similarly, the plus and minus signs at the end of a component are the voltage reference for the branch. Whenever the voltage polarity is actually in the sense indicated by the reference, as indicated by an appropriate instrument, $v(t)$ will be positive.

For a given component the direction chosen as the current reference and the polarity chosen as the voltage reference are arbitrary. Either of the two possibilities can be chosen as the current reference, and either of the two possibilities can be chosen as the voltage reference. Furthermore, the reference for current is independent of the reference for voltage. However, it is often convenient to choose these two references in a certain way, as shown in Fig. 1(b). Thus, with the current-reference arrow drawn alongside the component, if the voltage-reference plus is at the tail of the current reference, the result is called the *load reference*. If it is stated that the load reference is being used, then only one of the two need be shown; the other will be implied. It must be emphasized that there is no requirement for choosing load references, only convenience.

1.3 KIRCHHOFF'S LAWS

An electric network consists of an interconnection of two or more electrical components, each of which has two or more terminals. An example of a network is shown in Fig. 2. The components numbered 1

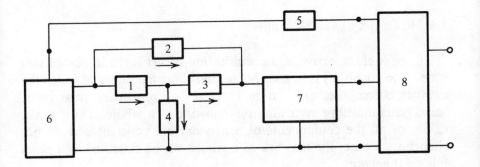

Fig. 2   Illustration of a network

through 5 have two terminals each; such *two-terminal components* are often called *branches* – a name derived from the association of electrical networks with linear graphs, as discussed in Chapter 2. The pair of terminals constitutes a *port* through which access is gained to the branch. Components 6 and 7 have 3 terminals each and component 8 has 5 terminals. Any pair of these terminals can be viewed as a port. The points at which two or more components are connected are the junctions or *nodes* of the network.

Independently of the nature of the components in the network, the currents and voltages are constrained by the manner in which they are interconnected. These constraints are known as *Kirchhoff's laws*.

Kirchhoff's current law (KCL for short) states that the algebraic sum of the currents leaving each node in a network is zero. At the node where objects 1, 3 and 4 are connected, for example, application of KCL leads to:

$$-i_1 + i_3 + i_4 = 0$$

Kirchhoff's voltage law (KVL for short) states that the algebraic sum of the voltages on each closed path or loop in a network is zero. Assuming voltage references to form load references with the currents, application of KVL to the loop formed by components 1, 2, and 3, for example, leads to:

$$-v_1 + v_2 - v_3 = 0$$

Kirchhoff's two laws are the fundamental relationships on which network theory is based. They will be central concerns of ours in subsequent chapters.

1.4 NETWORK CLASSIFICATION

It is possible to arrive at a classification of networks in one of two ways. One possibility is to specify the kinds of components of which the network is composed and, on the basis of their properties, to arrive at some generalizations regarding the network as a whole. Thus, if the values of all the components of a network are constant and do not change with time, the network as a whole can be classified as a *time-invariant* network.

Another approach is to focus attention on the points of access to the network and to classify the network in terms of the general properties of its responses to excitations applied at these points. In this section we shall examine the second of these approaches.

1.4.1 Linearity

Let the excitation applied to a network that has no initial energy storage be labeled $e(t)$ and the response resulting therefrom $w(t)$. A *linear* network is one in which the response is proportional to the excitation and the principle of superposition applies. More precisely, if the response to an excitation $e_1(t)$ is $w_1(t)$ and the response to an excitation $e_2(t)$ is $w_2(t)$, then the network is linear if the response to the excitation $k_1 e_1(t) + k_2 e_2(t)$ is $k_1 w_1(t) + k_2 w_2(t)$.

This scalar definition can be extended to matrix form for multiple excitations and responses. Let $\mathbf{e}(t)$ and $\mathbf{w}(t)$ be excitation and response vectors defined as

$$\mathbf{e}(t) = \begin{bmatrix} e_a(t) \\ e_b(t) \\ \cdot \\ \cdot \\ \cdot \end{bmatrix} \text{ and } \mathbf{w}(t) = \begin{bmatrix} w_\alpha(t) \\ w_\beta(t) \\ \cdot \\ \cdot \\ \cdot \end{bmatrix},$$

where e_a, e_b, etc., are excitations at ports a, b, etc.; and w_α, w_β, etc., are responses at ports α, β, etc. Then a network is linear if the excitation vector $k_1\mathbf{e}_1(t) + k_2\mathbf{e}_2(t)$ gives rise to the response vector $k_1\mathbf{w}_1(t) + k_2\mathbf{w}_2(t)$, where $\mathbf{w}_i$ is the response vector to the excitation vector $\mathbf{e}_i$.

Linearity is an idealization. The physical world is nonlinear; responses are generally not proportional to excitations. For example, devices saturate as excitation signals increase in amplitude. Fortunately, responses are very often approximately linear for small values of excitation — small signals. This book is limited to linear networks. Many of the concepts and analysis procedures can be extended to nonlinear networks but rather often only numerical methods are adequate for such networks.

1.4.2 Time Invariance

A network that will produce the same response to a given excitation no matter when it is applied is *time-invariant*. Thus, if the response to an excitation $\mathbf{e}(t)$ is $\mathbf{w}(t)$, then the response to an excitation $\mathbf{e}(t - t_1)$ — which is $\mathbf{e}$ delayed by t_1 seconds — will be $\mathbf{w}(t - t_1)$ in a time-invariant network. This definition implies that the values of the network components remain constant.

1.4.3 Passivity

Some networks have the property of absorbing and/or storing energy. They can return their previously stored energy to an external network, but never more than the amount so stored. Such networks are called *passive*. Let $E(t)$ be the energy delivered to a network having one pair of terminals from an external source up to time t. The voltage and current at the terminals, with load references, are $v(t)$ and $i(t)$. The power delivered to the network will be $p(t) = v(t)i(t)$. We define the network to be passive if

[handwritten: $p(t) = v(t) \cdot i(t)$]

[handwritten: energy delivered to element $= \int_{t_1}^{t_2} p(t)\, dt$]

$$E(t) = \int_{-\infty}^{t} v(x)i(x)dx \geqslant 0 \qquad \text{[handwritten: passive element]}$$

or *[handwritten: energy given to an element =]*

$$E(t) = E(t_0) + \int_{t_0}^{t} v(x)i(x)dx \geqslant 0.$$

This must be true for any associated voltage and current for all t.

Any network that does not satisfy this condition is called an *active network*; in this case

$$\int_{-\infty}^{t} v(x)i(x)dx < 0 \text{ for some time } t.$$

If the network has more than one pair of terminals through which energy can be supplied from the outside, let the terminal voltage and current vectors be $v(t) = [v_k(t)]$ and $i(t) = [i_k(t)]$, with load references. The instantaneous power supplied to the network from the outside will then be

$$p(t) = \sum_{j=1}^{n} v_j(t)i_j(t) = v'(t)i(t). \tag{2}$$

The network will be passive if, for all t,

$$E(t) = \int_{-\infty}^{t} v'(x)i(x)dx \geqslant 0 \tag{3}$$

1.4.4 Reciprocity

Some networks have the property that the response produced at one port of the network by an excitation at another port is invariant if the positions of excitation and response are interchanged (excitation and response being properly interpreted). Specifically, in Fig. 3 the network is assumed to have no initial energy storage; the excitation is the voltage $v_1(t)$ and the response is the current $i_2(t)$ in the short circuit. In Fig. 4, the excitation is applied at the previously short-circuited port, and the response is the current in the short-circuit placed at the position of the previous excitation. The references of the two currents are the same relative to those of the voltages. A *reciprocal* network is one in which,

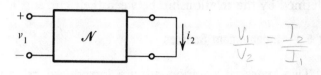

Fig. 3 Reciprocity condition

Fig. 4 Reciprocity condition, excitation and response interchange

for any pair of excitation and response ports, here labeled 1 and 2, $i_1 = i_2$ if $v_2 = v_1$. If the network does not satisfy this condition, it is *non-reciprocal*. This concept will be elaborated in Chapter 9.

In this book we shall be concerned with networks that are linear and time-invariant. However, the networks will not be limited to passive or reciprocal types. The latter types of networks do have special properties, and some procedures we shall discuss are limited to such networks. When we are discussing procedures whose application is limited to passive or reciprocal networks, we shall so specify. When no specification is made, it is assumed that the procedures and properties under discussion are generally applicable to both passive and active, reciprocal and non-reciprocal networks.

1.5 NETWORK COMPONENTS

Now let us turn to a classification of networks on the basis of the kinds of components they include. We assume that all electrical effects are experienced immediately throughout the network. With this assumption we neglect the influence of spatial dimensions in a physical circuit and we assume that electrical effects are "lumped" in space rather than being distributed; the network is said to be *lumped*.

In the network model, we postulate the existence of certain components (or elements) having one or more pairs of terminals that are defined by the relationship between their currents and voltages.

1.5.1 Independent Sources

Two types of components are introduced as models of electrical generators. They are defined as follows:

1. A *voltage source* is a two-terminal device whose voltage at any instant of time is independent of the current through its terminals. No matter what network may be connected at the terminals of a voltage source, its voltage will maintain its magnitude and waveform. (It makes no sense to short-circuit the terminals of a voltage source, because this imposes two conflicting idealized requirements at the terminals.) The current in the source, on the other hand, will be determined by this network. The diagram is shown in Fig. 5(a).

2. A *current source* is a two-terminal device whose current at any instant of time is independent of the voltage across its terminals. No matter what network may be connected at the terminals of a current source, the current will maintain its magnitude and waveform. (It makes no sense to open-circuit the terminals of a current source because this imposes two conflicting requirements at the terminals.) The voltage across the source, on the other hand, will be determined by this network. The diagram is shown in Fig. 5(b).

(a) (b)

Fig. 5   Voltage and current sources

Everyone is familiar enough with the dimming of the house lights when a large electrical appliance is switched on the line to know that the voltage of a physical source varies under load. Also, in an actual physical source, the current or voltage generated may depend on some nonelectrical quantity, such as the speed of a rotating machine, or the concentration of acid in a battery, or the intensity of light incident on a photoelectric cell. These relationships are of no interest to us in network analysis, since we are not concerned with the internal operation of sources, but only with their terminal behavior. Thus our idealized sources take no cognizance of the dependence of voltage or current on nonelectric quantities; they are called *independent sources*.

1.5.2 Basic Components

The three basic elements are the resistor, the inductor, and the capacitor. Their diagrammatic representations and voltage-current relationships are given in Table 1. The resistor is described by the resistance parameter R or the conductance parameter G, where $G = 1/R$. The inductor is described by the inductance parameter L. The reciprocal of L has no name, but the symbol Γ (an inverted L) is sometimes used. Finally, the capacitor is described by the capacitance parameter C. The reciprocal of C is given the name elastance, and the symbol D is sometimes used.

A number of comments are in order concerning these elements. First, the *v-i* relations ($v = Ri$, $v = L\,di/dt$, and $i = C\,dv/dt$) satisfy the linearity condition, assuming that i and v play the roles of excitation and response, as the case may be. (Demonstrate this to yourself.) Thus networks of R, L, and C elements are linear. Second, if the parameters R, L, and C are constant, networks of such elements will be time-invariant. Third, assuming load references, the energy delivered to each of the elements starting at a time when the current and voltage are zero will be:

$$E_R(t) = \int_{-\infty}^{t} Ri^2(x)dx \tag{4}$$

$$E_L(t) = \int_{-\infty}^{t} L\frac{di(x)}{dx}i(x)dx = \int_{0}^{i(t)} L\hat{i}d\hat{i} = \tfrac{1}{2}Li^2(t) \tag{5}$$

$$E_C(t) = \int_{-\infty}^{t} C\frac{dv(x)}{dx}v(x)dx = \int_{0}^{v(t)} C\hat{v}d\hat{v} = \tfrac{1}{2}Cv^2(t). \tag{6}$$

Each of the right-hand sides is non-negative for all t. Hence networks of R, L, and C elements are *passive*. Finally, networks of R, L, and C elements are *reciprocal*, but demonstration of this fact must await later developments.

It should be observed in Table 1 that the inverse *v-i* relations for the inductance and capacitance elements are written as definite integrals. In other publications this inverse relationship quite often is written as an

Table 1

Element	Parameter	Voltage-Current Relationships		Symbol
		Direct	Inverse	
Resistor	Resistance R	$v = Ri$	$i = \dfrac{1}{R}v = Gv$	
	Conductance G			
Inductor	Inductance L	$v = L\dfrac{di}{dt}$	$i(t) = \dfrac{1}{L}\displaystyle\int_0^t v(x)dx + i(0)$	
	Inverse Inductance Γ			
Capacitor	Capacitance C	$i = C\dfrac{dv}{dt}$	$v(t) = \dfrac{1}{C}\displaystyle\int_0^t i(x)dx + v(0)$	
	Elastance D			

indefinite integral (or antiderivative) instead. Such an expression is incomplete, unless there is added to it a specification of the initial values $i(0)$ or $v(0)$, and in this sense is misleading. Normally, one thinks of the voltage $v(t)$ and the current $i(t)$ as being expressed as explicit functions such as $e^{-\alpha t}$, $\sin \omega t$, etc. and the antiderivatives as being something unique: $-(1/\alpha)e^{-\alpha t}$, $-(1/\omega) \cos \omega t$, etc., but this is certainly not true in general. Also, in many cases the voltage or current may not be expressible in such a simple fashion for all t; the analytic expression for $v(t)$ or $i(t)$ may depend on the particular interval of the axis on which the point t falls. Some such wave shapes are shown in Fig. 6.

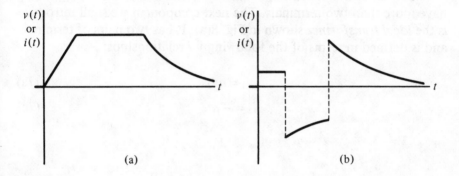

Fig. 6   **Signal waveshapes**

The origin of time t is arbitrary; it is usually chosen to coincide with some particular event, such as the opening or closing of a switch. In addition to the definite integral from 0 to t, the expression for the capacitor voltage contains the initial value $v(0)$. This can be considered as a d-c voltage source in series with an initially relaxed (no initial voltage) capacitor, as shown in Fig. 7. Similarly, the expression for the

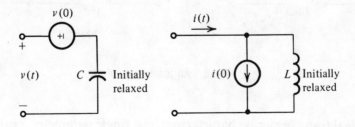

Fig. 7   **Initial values as sources**

inductor current contains the initial value $i(0)$. This can be considered as a d-c current source in parallel with an initially relaxed inductor, as shown in Fig. 7. If these sources are shown explicitly, they will account for all initial values and all capacitors and inductors can be considered to be initially relaxed. Such initial-value sources can be useful for some methods of analysis but not for others, such as the state-equation formulation.

1.5.3 Transformers

The R, L, and C elements all have two terminals; other components have more than two terminals. The next component we shall introduce is the *ideal transformer* shown in Fig. 8(a). It has two pairs of terminals and is defined in terms of the following v-i relationships:

$$v_1 = nv_2 \tag{7a}$$

$$i_2 = -ni_1 \tag{7b}$$

or

$$\begin{bmatrix} v_1 \\ i_2 \end{bmatrix} = \begin{bmatrix} 0 & n \\ -n & 0 \end{bmatrix} \begin{bmatrix} i_1 \\ v_2 \end{bmatrix} \tag{7c}$$

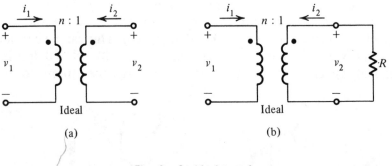

(a)   (b)

Fig. 8   An ideal transformer

The ideal transformer is characterized by a single parameter n called the turns ratio. The ideal transformer is an abstraction arising from coupled coils of wire. The v-i relationships are idealized relations expressing Faraday's law and Ampere's law, respectively. The signs in these equations apply for the references shown. If any one reference is changed, the corresponding sign will change.

An ideal transformer has the property that a resistance R connected to one pair of terminals appears as R times the turns ratio squared at the other pair of terminals. Thus in Fig. 8(b) $v_2 = -Ri_2$. When this is used in the v-i relationships, the result becomes

$$v_1 = nv_2 = -nRi_2 = (n^2R)i_1. \tag{8}$$

At the input terminals, then, the equivalent resistance is n^2R.

Observe that the total energy delivered to the ideal transformer from connections made at its terminals will be

$$E(t) = \int_{-\infty}^{t} [v_1(x)i_1(x) + v_2(x)i_2(x)]dx = 0. \tag{9}$$

The right-hand side results when the v-i relations of the ideal transformer are inserted in the middle. Thus the device is passive and lossless; it transmits energy, but neither stores nor dissipates it.

A less abstract model of a physical transformer is shown in Fig. 9.

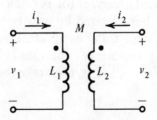

Fig. 9 A transformer

The diagram is almost the same except that self and mutual inductance values are shown instead of a turns ratio. The *transformer* is characterized by the following v-i relationships for the references shown in Fig. 9:

$$v_1 = L_1 \frac{di_1}{dt} + M \frac{di_2}{dt} \tag{10a}$$

$$v_2 = M \frac{di_1}{dt} + L_2 \frac{di_2}{dt} \tag{10b}$$

Thus it is characterized by three parameters: the two self-inductances L_1 and L_2, and the mutual inductance M.

The total energy delivered to the transformer from external sources is

$$
\begin{aligned}
E(t) &= \int_{-\infty}^{t} [v_1(x)i_1(x) + v_2(x)i_2(x)]dx \\
&= \int_{0}^{i_1} L_1 \hat{i}_1 d\hat{i}_1 + \int_{0}^{i_1 i_2} M d(\hat{i}_1 \hat{i}_2) + \int_{0}^{i_2} L_2 \hat{i}_2 d\hat{i}_2 \\
&= \tfrac{1}{2}(L_1 i_1^2 + 2M i_1 i_2 + L_2 i_2^2)
\end{aligned} \tag{11}
$$

It is easy to show* that the last line will be non-negative if

$$\frac{M^2}{L_1 L_2} = k^2 \leqslant 1. \tag{12}$$

Since physical considerations require the transformer to be passive, this condition must apply. The quantity k is called the *coefficient of coupling*. Its maximum value is unity.

A transformer for which the coupling coefficient takes on its maximum value $k = 1$ is called a *perfect* (or *perfectly coupled*) *transformer*. Such a transformer is characterized by only two parameters. A perfect transformer is not the same thing as an ideal transformer. To find the difference, turn to the transformer equations (10) and insert the perfect transformer condition $M = \sqrt{L_1 L_2}$; then take the ratio v_1/v_2. The result will be:

$$\frac{v_1}{v_2} = \frac{L_1 \dfrac{di_1}{dt} + \sqrt{L_1 L_2} \dfrac{di_2}{dt}}{\sqrt{L_1 L_2} \dfrac{di_1}{dt} + L_2 \dfrac{di_2}{dt}} = \sqrt{L_1/L_2} \tag{13}$$

---

* A simple approach is to observe (with L_1, L_2, and M all non-negative) that the only way $L_1 i_1^2 + 2M i_1 i_2 + L_2 i_2^2$ can become negative is for i_1 and i_2 to be of opposite sign. So set $i_2 = -xi_1$, with x any positive real number, and the quantity of interest becomes $L_1 - 2Mx + L_2 x^2$. If the minimum value of this quadratic in x is non-negative, then the quantity will be non-negative for all values of x. Differentiate the quadratic with respect to x and find the minimum value; it will be $L_1 - M^2/L_2$, from which the result follows.

This expression is identical with $v_1 = nv_2$ for the ideal transformer† if

$$n = \sqrt{L_1/L_2} \ . \tag{14}$$

Next consider the current ratio. Since (10) involves the derivatives of the currents, it will be necessary to integrate. The result of inserting the perfect-transformer condition $M = \sqrt{L_1 L_2}$ and the value $n = \sqrt{L_1/L_2}$, and integrating (10) from 0 to t will yield, after rearranging

$$i_1(t) = -\frac{1}{n}i_2(t) + \left\{ \frac{1}{L_1}\int_0^t v_1(x)dx + [i_1(0) + \frac{1}{n}i_2(0)] \right\}. \tag{15}$$

This is to be compared with $i_1 = -i_2/n$ for the ideal transformer. The form of the expression in brackets suggests the v-i equation for an inductor. The diagram shown in Fig. 10 satisfies both (15) and (13). It shows how a perfect transformer is related to an ideal transformer. If, in a perfect transformer, L_1 and L_2 are permitted to approach infinity, but in such a way that their ratio remains constant, the result will be an ideal transformer.

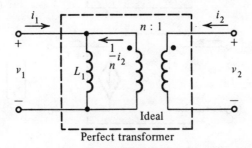

Fig. 10   Relationship between a perfect and an ideal transformer

1.5.4   Controlled or Dependent Sources

Independent sources cannot account for the signal-amplifying ability of some devices. Another class of components is now introduced: These are called *controlled* (or *dependent*) *sources*. A *controlled voltage*

---

† Since for actual coils of wire, the inductance is approximately proportional to the square of the number of turns in the coil, the expression $\sqrt{L_1/L_2}$ equals the ratio of the turns in the primary and secondary of a physical transformer. This is the origin of the name "turns ratio" for n.

source is a source whose terminal voltage is a function of some other voltage or current. A *controlled current source* is defined analogously. The four possibilities are shown in Table 2. These devices have two

Table 2

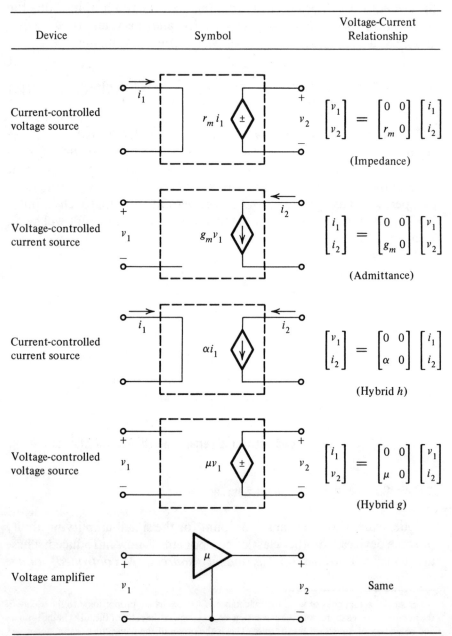

Device	Symbol	Voltage-Current Relationship
Current-controlled voltage source	$r_m i_1$	$\begin{bmatrix} v_1 \\ v_2 \end{bmatrix} = \begin{bmatrix} 0 & 0 \\ r_m & 0 \end{bmatrix} \begin{bmatrix} i_1 \\ i_2 \end{bmatrix}$ (Impedance)
Voltage-controlled current source	$g_m v_1$	$\begin{bmatrix} i_1 \\ i_2 \end{bmatrix} = \begin{bmatrix} 0 & 0 \\ g_m & 0 \end{bmatrix} \begin{bmatrix} v_1 \\ v_2 \end{bmatrix}$ (Admittance)
Current-controlled current source	αi_1	$\begin{bmatrix} v_1 \\ i_2 \end{bmatrix} = \begin{bmatrix} 0 & 0 \\ \alpha & 0 \end{bmatrix} \begin{bmatrix} i_1 \\ i_2 \end{bmatrix}$ (Hybrid h)
Voltage-controlled voltage source	μv_1	$\begin{bmatrix} i_1 \\ v_2 \end{bmatrix} = \begin{bmatrix} 0 & 0 \\ \mu & 0 \end{bmatrix} \begin{bmatrix} v_1 \\ i_2 \end{bmatrix}$ (Hybrid g)
Voltage amplifier	μ	Same

pairs of terminals—one pair designating the controlling quantity; the other, the controlled quantity. In each of the components in Table 2, the controlled voltage or current is directly proportional to the controlling quantity, voltage or current. This is the simplest type of dependence; it would be possible to introduce a dependent source whose voltage or current is proportional to the derivative of some other voltage or current, for example. However, detailed consideration will not be given to any other type of dependence. Note that a different symbol—a diamond-shaped one—is used to designate a controlled source in order to distinguish it from an independent source. A voltage-controlled voltage source is nothing but a voltage amplifier for which another symbol is often used, as indicated in Table 2. The connection to ground is often omitted, for convenience.

For certain ranges of voltage and current the behavior of certain bipolar and field effect transistors can be approximated by a model consisting of interconnected dependent sources and other network components. Figure 11(a) shows such a model. This model is not a valid representation of the physical device under all conditions of operation; for example, at high enough frequency, the junction capacitances of the bipolar transistor would have to be included. A more extensive model is shown in Fig. 11(b).

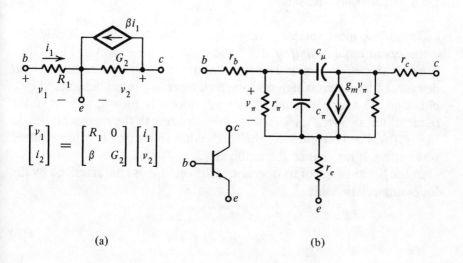

(a)   (b)

Fig. 11   Models of bipolar transistor

The last point brings up a question. When an engineer is presented with a physical problem concerned with calculating certain voltages and currents in an interconnection of various physical electrical devices, his first task must be one of representing each device by a model. This model will consist of interconnections of the various components that have been defined in this chapter. The extent and complexity of the model will depend on the type of physical devices involved and the conditions under which they are to operate. A relatively simple model will lead to ease of calculation but may conceal important characteristics of a device. On the other hand, a complex and detailed model may require tedious calculations and thus tend to obscure the essential features of the device. Considerations involved in choosing an appropriate model to use, under various given conditions, do not form a proper part of network analysis. This is not to say that such considerations and the ability to choose an appropriate model are not important; they are. However, many other things are important in the total education of an engineer, and they certainly cannot all be treated in one book. In this book we will make no attempt to construct a model of a given physical situation before proceeding with the analysis. Our starting point will be a model.

1.5.5 Operational Amplifier

One of the most versatile and widely used modern electronic devices is the *operational amplifier*. Its basic features are shown in Fig. 12(a). There is an output terminal and two input terminals: the *inverting input* designated by a minus sign and the *non-inverting input* designated by a plus sign. The supply terminals are not normally shown, at least in the range of linear operation of the *op-amp*, leading to the representation in Fig. 12(b). For convenience, the connection to ground is often omitted when there is no chance for ambiguity.

In the linear range of its operation, the op-amp is characterized by the following relationship:

$$v_o = A(v_{i+} - v_{i-}) \tag{16}$$

That is, the output voltage is proportional to the *difference* between the two input voltages; the proportionality constant, called the *open-loop gain*, being a large number, typically larger than 10^4. The supply voltage

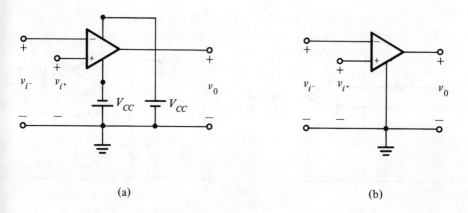

(a)

(b)

Fig. 12   Operational amplifier

V_{cc} is typically of the order of 10 volts and linear operation is restricted to inputs satisfying

$$|v_{i+} - v_{i-}| \leqslant \left| \frac{V_{cc}}{A} \right| \tag{17}$$

That is, for linear operation, the differential input must not exceed about 100 microvolts. (The output saturates at $|v_o| \cong V_{cc}$.)

An *ideal op-amp* (or *infinite-gain op-amp*), obtained as the gain A tends to infinity, is characterized by zero differential input voltage (or $v_{i+} = v_{i-}$), and zero current into both input terminals. It is a decidedly distinct component, since it cannot be modeled by previously defined components. The condition of zero voltage and zero current at a pair of terminals cannot be realized by any interconnection of the previously considered components. (See Prob. 3.) For many practical purposes, physical op-amps approximate this ideal acceptably well.

It is possible to construct many of the other device models to be introduced in this section with the use of ideal op-amps. A preview of this is provided in Fig. 13, which shows both an inverting and a non-inverting voltage amplifier constructed with a single ideal op-amp and a few resistors. An alternate model of Fig. 13(a) is shown in Fig. 14. Thus, the inverting voltage amplifier of Fig. 13(a) can be viewed as a realization of a non-ideal—finite input resistance—voltage-controlled voltage source.

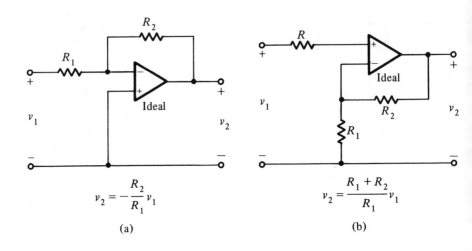

$$v_2 = -\frac{R_2}{R_1}v_1 \qquad\qquad v_2 = \frac{R_1+R_2}{R_1}v_1$$

(a)   (b)

Fig. 13   Voltage amplifiers: (a) inverting; (b) non-inverting

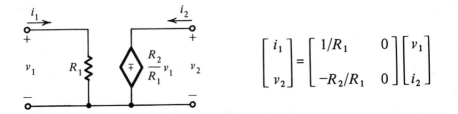

$$\begin{bmatrix} i_1 \\ v_2 \end{bmatrix} = \begin{bmatrix} 1/R_1 & 0 \\ -R_2/R_1 & 0 \end{bmatrix} \begin{bmatrix} v_1 \\ i_2 \end{bmatrix}$$

Fig. 14   Alternate model of inverting amplifier in Fig. 13(a)

1.5.6   Gyrator

A gyrator, whose symbol is shown in Fig. 15, is a component having two pairs of terminals and the following v-i relations:

$$\begin{bmatrix} v_1 \\ v_2 \end{bmatrix} = \begin{bmatrix} 0 & -r \\ r & 0 \end{bmatrix} \begin{bmatrix} i_1 \\ i_2 \end{bmatrix} \quad \text{or} \quad \begin{bmatrix} i_1 \\ i_2 \end{bmatrix} = \begin{bmatrix} 0 & g \\ -g & 0 \end{bmatrix} \begin{bmatrix} v_1 \\ v_2 \end{bmatrix} \qquad (18)$$

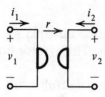 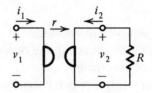

Fig. 15   A gyrator   **Fig. 16   Gyrator terminated in a resistance**

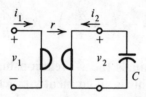

Fig. 17   Gyrator terminated in a capacitance C

Like the ideal transformer, the gyrator is characterized by a single
parameter, the *gyration resistance*, $r = 1/g$. It has a number of very
useful properties. Specifically, if first the right-hand side is short-
circuited and a voltage $v_1 = v$ is applied to the left side, and if next the
left side is shorted and the same voltage ($v_2 = v$) is applied to the right
side, then it will be found that $i_2 = -i_1$. Thus the gyrator is not a
reciprocal device. In fact, it is antireciprocal.

On the other hand, the total energy input to the gyrator is

$$E(t) = \int_{-\infty}^{t} (v_1 i_1 + v_2 i_2)dx = \int_{-\infty}^{t} [(-ri_2)i_1 + (ri_1)i_2]dx = 0 \qquad (19)$$

Hence, it is a passive, lossless device that neither stores nor dissipates
energy. In this respect it is similar to an ideal transformer.

In the case of the ideal transformer, it was found that, when one pair
of terminals is terminated in a resistance R, the resistance at the other
pair of terminals is $n^2 R$. The ideal transformer thus changes a resistance
by a factor n^2. What does the gyrator do in the corresponding situation?
If a gyrator is terminated in a resistance R (Fig. 16), the output voltage
and current will be related by $v_2 = -Ri_2$. When this is inserted into the
v-i relations, the result becomes

$$v_1 = -ri_2 = -r\left(-\frac{v_2}{R}\right) = r\left(\frac{ri_1}{R}\right) = (r^2 G)i_1. \qquad (20)$$

Thus the equivalent resistance at the input terminals equals r^2 times the conductance terminating the output terminals. The gyrator thus has the property of *inverting*.

This inverting property brings about a very useful result when the gyrator is terminated in a capacitor as shown in Fig. 17. In this case $i_2 = -C dv_2/dt$. Therefore, upon combining with the *v-i* relations associated with the gyrator, we observe that

$$v_1 = -ri_2 = -r\left(-C\frac{dv_2}{dt}\right) = rC\frac{d(ri_1)}{dt} = r^2 C\frac{di_1}{dt} \qquad (21)$$

Thus at the input terminals the *v-i* relationship is that of an inductor with inductance $r^2 C$. This is an eminently practical form of *inductance simulation* in those applications where the design calls for an inductor but it is impractical (for reasons of size, weight, etc.) to use an actual inductor.

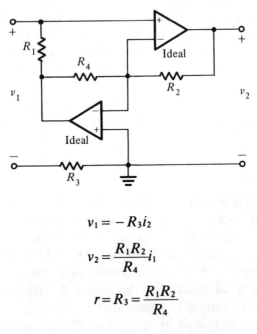

$$v_1 = -R_3 i_2$$

$$v_2 = \frac{R_1 R_2}{R_4} i_1$$

$$r = R_3 = \frac{R_1 R_2}{R_4}$$

Fig. 18   A practical gyrator design

The gyrator, although introduced as a basic component, is not distinct, independent of those previously defined. There exist many different designs of gyrators using ideal transistor or ideal op-amp circuits. A simple design is shown in Fig. 18. Routine calculations show that the network will be a gyrator with gyration resistance $r = R_3$ if $R_1 R_2 = R_3 R_4$. Clearly, r can take on values over a wide range.

Although in the preceding design there is no common terminal between input and output, such a common terminal is often called for in certain applications of gyrators. In such cases, a design other than the one in Fig. 18 must be used.

We will guide you through a study of ideal op-amp and ideal transistor (a new component) models of gyrators in Probs. 6-8. We will also have you examine the impact of using non-ideal components.

1.5.7 General Converter

One of the properties of an ideal transformer is that it transforms, or *converts*, a resistance R terminating one of its pairs of terminals to another value; namely $n^2 R$, where n^2 is a positive constant. We would like to consider generalizing this concept so that the conversion is not simply a multiplication by a positive constant but by a negative constant, or even (in the complex frequency domain) by a function of s.

A *general converter* (GC for short) is a component with two pairs of terminals defined by either one of the following v-i relations:

Current General Converter   Voltage General Converter

$$\begin{bmatrix} V_1 \\ I_2 \end{bmatrix} = \begin{bmatrix} 0 & 1 \\ -f(s) & 0 \end{bmatrix} \begin{bmatrix} I_1 \\ V_2 \end{bmatrix} \qquad \begin{bmatrix} V_1 \\ I_2 \end{bmatrix} = \begin{bmatrix} 0 & f(s) \\ -1 & 0 \end{bmatrix} \begin{bmatrix} I_1 \\ V_2 \end{bmatrix} \qquad (22)$$

These are frequency domain equations as indicated by the use of capitals for the variables. (Compare the equations with those of an ideal transformer.) The distinctions between the two specific cases is clear. In the one on the left, the voltage at the output is the same as the input voltage; only the current has been converted. Hence the name *current GC*. In the case on the right, where $I_2 = -I_1$ — which means the input current goes through the converter and out unchanged — only the voltage is converted; hence the name *voltage GC*.

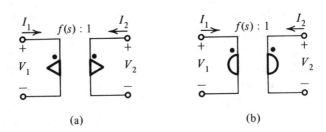

Fig. 19   General converters: (a) current GC: $I_2 = -f(s)I_1$;
(b) voltage GC: $V_1 = f(s)V_2$

The general converter is represented by the diagrams in Fig. 19. Suppose that either of the two general converters is terminated in a resistance R; then $V_2 = -RI_2$. When this is used in the V-I equations the result is

$$V_1 = f(s)RI_1. \tag{23}$$

We see that the load resistance has been converted to an impedance at the input terminals which is proportional to R but the proportionality "constant" is a function of s. Interesting results occur depending on the specific function $f(s)$, as shown in Table 3. The case represented by the last line of the table will be amplified further in the next section.

Table 3

GC Load	$f(s)$	Input Equivalent	Simulates
R	ks	kRs	an inductance, kR
R	k/s	kR/s	a capacitance, $1/kR$
R	ks^2	kRs^2	?
R	$-k^2$	$-k^2R$	a negative resistance, $-k^2R$

Like gyrators, general converters can be realized by previously defined components. A relatively simple ideal op-amp realization of a current GC is shown in Fig. 20. It is obtained from the gyrator design in Fig. 18 by connecting a two-terminal branch across the output terminals in that figure, removing R_3 to create a new output port, and replacing

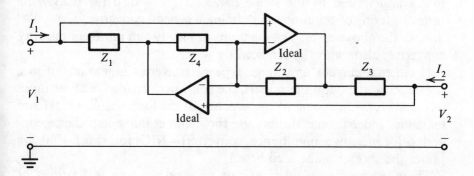

Fig. 20   **A general converter design for** $f(s) = \dfrac{Z_1 Z_2}{Z_3 Z_4}$

the other resistors by other branches. With ideal op-amps, branches 1 and 4 constitute a loop as do branches 2 and 3. It is easy then to show $f(s)$ in terms of the branch impedances to be

$$f(s) = \frac{Z_1 Z_2}{Z_3 Z_4}. \tag{24}$$

In particular, the conversion functions in the first three lines of Table 3 can be obtained as follows:

Line 1: $f(s) = ks$; branch 3 or 4 a capacitor, all others resistors.
Line 2: $f(s) = k/s$; branch 1 or 2 a capacitor, all others resistors.
Line 3: $f(s) = ks^2$; branches 3 and 4 both capacitors, 1 and 2 resistors.

1.5.8   Negative Converter

The particular case of a general converter represented in the last line of Table 3 deserves special treatment. We define a *negative converter* (NC for short) as a component with two pairs of terminals having either one of the following relationships:

Current NC   Voltage NC

$$\begin{bmatrix} v_1 \\ i_2 \end{bmatrix} = \begin{bmatrix} 0 & 1 \\ k^2 & 0 \end{bmatrix} \begin{bmatrix} i_1 \\ v_2 \end{bmatrix} \qquad\qquad \begin{bmatrix} v_1 \\ i_2 \end{bmatrix} = \begin{bmatrix} 0 & -k^2 \\ -1 & 0 \end{bmatrix} \begin{bmatrix} i_1 \\ v_2 \end{bmatrix}$$

It is characterized by the single parameter, k, called the *conversion ratio*. In terms of the function defining a general converter, $f(s) = -k^2$ in both the above cases. The diagrams in Fig. 19 can represent negative converters also, with $f(s)$ replaced by $-k^2$.

If either a current or voltage type of converter is terminated in a resistance at the output terminals, the equivalent resistance at the input terminals is proportional to the *negative* of the load resistance. (Hence its name. Indeed some authors use the name negative impedance converter [or negative immittance converter]—NIC for short—but we prefer the shorter name used here.)

There exist many ideal transistor or ideal op-amp realizations of negative converters, even though the general converter design shown in Fig. 20 does not reduce to a negative converter for any choice of the branches. One possible design for a current NC is shown in Fig. 21. With an ideal op-amp, the current in R_1 (reference to the right) is i_1 and that in R_2 (reference to the left) is i_2. The two resistors form a loop, so we find $v_1 = v_2$. Hence $i_2 = (R_1/R_2)i_1$. Thus, k^2 is the ratio of the two resistances.

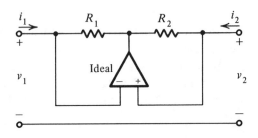

Fig. 21   A negative converter design

1.6   GENERAL COMMENTS

A considerable number of multiterminal components have been introduced in the previous section. (Others are introduced in the problems.) It is useful to make some observations about them. First, the components are not mutually exclusive. That is, some of them can be obtained by suitable combinations of others; for example, ideal op-amps can be combined so as to form ideal component realizations of an ideal transformer, a gyrator, a negative converter, or a general converter. The latter is also realizable with controlled sources if we extend the idea of controlled sources to include a functional relationship other than a real proportionality between controlled and controlling variables. Second, practical implementations of many of the components can be achieved through use of (non-ideal) operational amplifiers in ideal op-amp designs, as in Figs. 18, 19 and 20.

The reason for introducing components other than controlled sources and ideal op-amps is that the functions which they perform — conversion or inversion — are useful in design. Physical implementation of these components exists and a number of different network design procedures incorporate such components.

EXERCISES

1. A network has the excitation and response pair shown in Fig. E-1. A second excitation is also shown. If the network is linear and time-invariant, sketch the response for this second excitation.

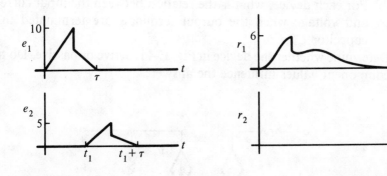

Fig. E-1

2. Suppose the output current of a linear, time-invariant, and reciprocal network, subject to excitation only at the input, is as illustrated in Fig. E-2(a). Find the input current i_1 when the network is excited as shown in Fig. E-2(b).

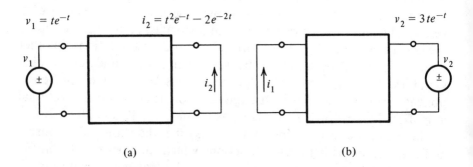

$v_1 = te^{-t}$ $i_2 = t^2 e^{-t} - 2e^{-2t}$ $v_2 = 3te^{-t}$

(a)   (b)

Fig. E-2

3. Two devices have the following sets of voltage-current relations:

$$\begin{bmatrix} v_1 \\ v_2 \end{bmatrix} = \begin{bmatrix} 0 & -r_1 \\ r_2 & 0 \end{bmatrix} \begin{bmatrix} i_1 \\ i_2 \end{bmatrix}, \quad \begin{bmatrix} v_1 \\ v_2 \end{bmatrix} = \begin{bmatrix} R_3 & -r_1 \\ r_2 & 0 \end{bmatrix} \begin{bmatrix} i_1 \\ i_2 \end{bmatrix}.$$

$E(t) \geq 0$ passive

(a) Determine whether the devices are active or passive.
(b) For each device, what is the relation between the input current and voltage when the output terminals are terminated in a capacitor C?

4. Determine whether the device in Fig. E-4 is active or passive. Do the component values influence the answer?

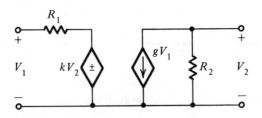

Fig. E-4

5. Let the branch relations of a device be the following:

$$\begin{bmatrix} v_1 \\ i_2 \end{bmatrix} = \begin{bmatrix} 0 & ak \\ k/a & 0 \end{bmatrix} \begin{bmatrix} i_1 \\ v_2 \end{bmatrix}$$

k and a are real numbers. Specify the nature of the device if (a) $a = 1/k$, (b) $a = -k$, and (c) a has other values.

6. Suppose the orientation arrow on the gyrator in Fig. 17 is reversed. What influence does this have on the voltage current relations of the gyrator? What influence is there on the result in Equation 21?

7. Determine whether general converters, the negative converter in particular, are passive or active.

8. Establish the terminal equations for the networks shown in Fig. E-8.

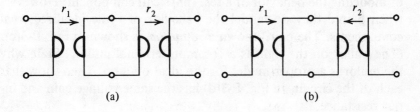

(a)   (b)

Fig. E-8

9. A customer requires a $1000 \mu F$ capacitor. Can you suggest what to ship?

PROBLEMS

1. Draw a diagram containing only controlled sources to represent (a) an ideal transformer, (b) a gyrator, and (c) a negative converter.

2. The inductance simulator of Fig. 17, using the gyrator design in Fig. 18, yields an inductance with one terminal grounded. It is desired to simulate the "floating" inductor shown in Fig. P-2(a) whose voltage-current relation is $v_1 - v_2 = Ldi/dt$. Show that the structure in Fig. P-2(b) with two gyrators "sandwiching" a capacitor is equivalent to a floating inductor.

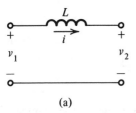

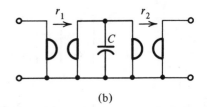

(a)   (b)

Fig. P-2

3. A component with the property that the component voltage and the
    component current are both identically zero is known as a *nullator*
    and schematically represented as in Fig. P-3(a). A component with
    the property that the component voltage and the component cur-
    rent are both arbitrary is known as a *norator* and schematically
    represented as in Fig. P-3(b). Neither component exists in the sense
    of modeling the behavior of a real (physical) component. However,
    when paired they do model the behavior of some idealized, real
    components. The pair, known as a *nullor*, is shown in Fig. P-3(c).
    (The nullor on the right is a common-terminal nullor.) State why
    the nullor is a proper model for the ideal op-amp. Then show that
    each of the circuits in Fig. P-3(d) has the same voltage gain and in-
    put resistance.

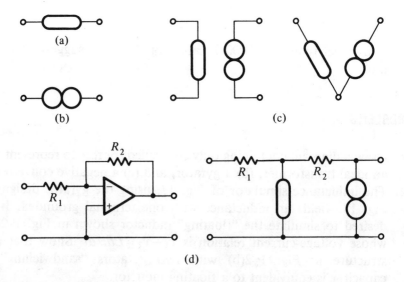

Fig. P-3

4. An ideal transistor has zero base current, zero base-to-emitter voltage, and infinite β (common-emitter base to collector current gain). State why the common-terminal nullor (see Fig. P-3(c)) is a proper model for the ideal transistor. Then show that the circuits of Fig. P-4 have the same voltage gain and output resistance.

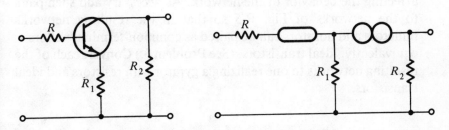

Fig. P-4

5. Verify that the networks of Fig. P-5, containing nullators and norators, each realize a gyrator. Specify the gyration conductance or resistance.

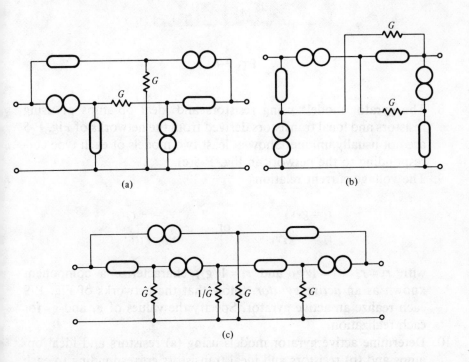

Fig. P-5

6. By pairing a nullator and a norator as a nullor—equivalently, an ideal op-amp (see Problem 3)—convert each of the networks of Fig. P-5 to one realizing a gyrator with resistors and ideal op-amps.

7. A series-connected nullator and norator can be connected between any pair of nodes in a network, as illustrated in Fig. P-7, without affecting the behavior of the network. As necessary add such pairs to the networks of Fig. P-5 so that in the resulting networks nullators and norators can be paired as common-terminal nullors—equivalently, ideal transistors. (See Problem 6.) Convert each of the resulting networks to one realizing a gyrator with resistors and ideal transistors.

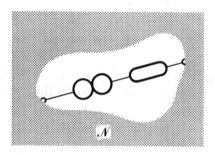

Fig. P-7

8. The gyrator models using resistors and ideal op-amps or using resistors and ideal transistors derived from the networks of Fig. P-5 are not usually unique. Show at least two models of each type corresponding to the network in Fig. P-5(c).

9. The voltage-current relations

$$i_1 = g_1 v_2 \qquad\qquad v_1 = -r_2 i_2$$
$$\text{or}$$
$$i_2 = -g_2 v_1 \qquad\qquad v_2 = r_1 i_1$$

with $r_1 \neq r_2$ ($r_1 = 1/g_1$ and $r_2 = 1/g_2$) characterize a component known as an *active gyrator*. Show that the networks of Fig. P-9 each realize an active gyrator. Specify the values of g_1 and g_2 for each realization.

10. Determine active gyrator models using (a) resistors and ideal op-amps and (b) resistors and ideal transistors corresponding to each network in Fig. P-9.

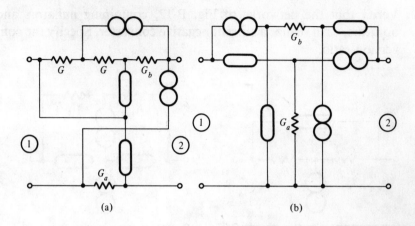

(a)

(b)

Fig. P-9

11. In the resistor and ideal transistor models of the gyrators of Problem 5 and of the active gyrators of Problem 9, replace the transistors by (i) the non-ideal transistor of Fig. P-11(a) and (ii) the non-ideal transistor of Fig. P-11(b). What have the voltage-current relations become? That is, determine r_{ij} or g_{ij} ($i = 1, 2, [j = 1, 2]$) in, respectively,

$$v_1 = r_{11}i_1 + r_{12}i_2 \qquad\qquad i_1 = g_{11}v_1 + g_{12}v_2$$
$$\text{or}$$
$$v_2 = r_{21}i_1 + r_{22}i_2 \qquad\qquad i_2 = g_{21}v_1 + g_{22}v_2$$

where the v_j and i_j ($j = 1, 2$) are the voltages and currents at the gyrator terminal pairs.

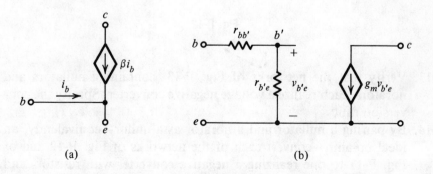

(a)

(b)

Fig. P-11

12. Verify that the networks of Fig. P-12, containing nullators and norators, each realize a current negative converter. Specify the conversion ratio.

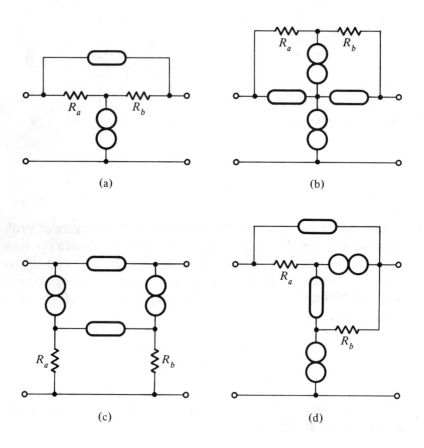

(a)

(b)

(c)

(d)

Fig. P-12

13. Verify that the networks of Fig. P-13, containing nullators and norators, each realize a voltage negative converter. Specify the conversion ratio.

14. By pairing a nullator and a norator as a nullor—equivalently, an ideal op-amp—convert each of the networks of Fig. P-12 and of Fig. P-13 to one realizing a negative converter with resistors and ideal op-amps.

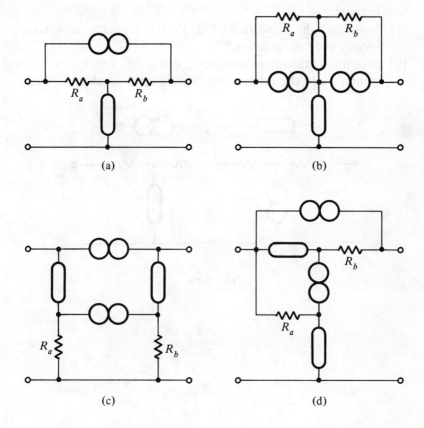

Fig. P-13

15. As necessary, add series connected nullators and norators to the networks of Fig. P-12 and of Fig. P-13 so that in the resulting networks nullators and norators can be paired as common-terminal nullors — equivalently, ideal transistors. Convert each of the resulting networks to one realizing a negative converter with resistors and ideal transistors.

16. A component with two pairs of terminals exhibiting the voltage-current relationships

$$v_1 = n_1 v_2$$

$$i_2 = -n_2 i_1$$

with $n_i > 0$ $(i=1, 2)$ or $n_i < 0$ $(i=1, 2)$ is said to be an active transformer.

(a) Show that the network of Fig. P-16 is an active transformer. Specify the "turns ratios."

(b) Determine equivalent networks, one using resistors and ideal op-amps and the other using resistors and ideal transistors.

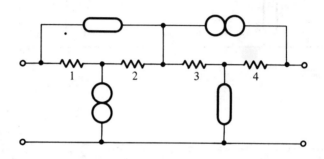

Fig. P-16

PART I
Network Analysis

CHAPTER 2
Linear Graph Theory

As discussed in Chapter 1, the fundamental postulates of network theory are the two Kirchhoff laws and the relationships between the voltages and currents of the components whose interconnection constitutes a network. Kirchhoff's two laws express constraints imposed on the currents and voltages of a network's components by the very arrangement of the components into a structure. *Network topology* is a generic name that refers to all properties arising from the structure or geometry of a network.

The topological properties of a network are independent of the types of components that constitute the network. So it is convenient to replace each component in a network schematic by a simple line segment, thereby not committing oneself to a specific component. The resulting diagram, a linear graph, consists of vertices interconnected by line segments. This correspondence between the schematic and linear graph associated with a network is illustrated in Fig. 1. There is a field of mathematics — linear graph theory — that is concerned with just such structures.

We shall begin a thorough study of network analysis by focusing first on linear graphs and those of their properties that are important in this study. The discussion of linear graphs will not be exhaustive; furthermore, it will be necessary to consider rapidly the definitions of many terms without, perhaps, adequate motivation for their introduction.

2.1 INTRODUCTORY DEFINITIONS

A *linear graph* is defined as a collection of vertices, called *nodes*, and line segments, called *branches*, such that each branch joins two distinct

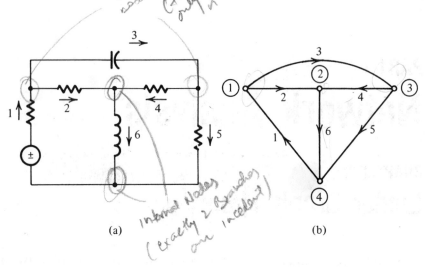

remaining
nodes 2 nodes nodes)
(terminal nodes)
only 1 branch
incident

Internal Nodes
(exactly 2 branches
on incident)

(a)   (b)

Fig. 1   Network: schematic and linear graph

nodes.* It follows immediately that a linear graph, or simply *graph*, may contain a node with no *incident* branch, called an *isolated node*. However, a graph cannot contain a branch without the nodes at which it is incident; the concept of an isolated branch is not viable.

Observe that each branch of the graph in Fig. 1 is oriented by an arrowhead. A linear graph with oriented branches is called an *oriented* (or *directed*) *linear graph*. This concept relates to network analysis as follows: Each component of a network has both a voltage and a current variable, each with its own reference. To relate the orientation (or direction) of the corresponding branch of the graph to these references, we invoke the load reference convention—voltage-reference plus at the tail of the current-reference arrow. Then the branch orientation is assumed to coincide with the component current-reference. Of course, the properties of a graph have nothing to do with network conventions.

A graph composed of a subset of the nodes and branches of another graph is said to be a *subgraph* of that other graph. A subgraph is said to be *proper* if it consists of strictly less than all the branches and nodes of the graph.

A *path* is a subgraph such that: (1) At all but two of its nodes, called *internal nodes*, there are incident exactly two of its branches. (2) At each of its remaining two nodes, called *terminal nodes*, there is incident exactly one of its branches. (3) No proper subgraph of this subgraph,

---

* In some developments of linear graph theory the distinct nodes condition is not invoked.

having the same two terminal nodes, has properties (1) and (2). In the graph of Fig. 1, branches 2, 5, and 6, together with all the nodes, constitute a path; nodes 1 and 3 are the terminal nodes. At first glance property (3) may appear superfluous; thoughtful consideration will show that is not the case. (See Prob. 1.)

A graph is *connected* if there exists at least one path between any two nodes. The graph of Fig. 1 is connected.

A *loop*, sometimes called a *circuit*, is a connected subgraph such that at each of its nodes there are incident exactly two of its branches. Thus, if the terminal nodes of a path did not have to be distinct and were made to coincide, the result, which could be called a *simple closed path*, would be a loop. In the graph of Fig. 1, branches 4, 5, and 6, together with nodes 2, 3, and 4, constitute a loop. Note that a loop can be specified by listing just its branches. If the graph is not a *multigraph* — graph with parallel branches — it can also be specified by listing, in sequence, just its nodes. Thus, in the example, to specify the loop just described it is sufficient to list just the set of branches {4, 5, 6} or the set of nodes {2, 3, 4}.

A *spanning tree* or *complete tree* — herein, and for simplicity, *tree* — is a connected subgraph of a connected graph containing all the nodes of the graph but containing no loops.* When specifying a tree, it is sufficient to list just its branches. In the graph of Fig. 1, branches 2, 4, and 5 constitute a tree. The concept of a tree is a key concept in the theory of graphs. The branches of a tree are called *twigs*; those branches not in a tree are called *links*. The links, together with the nodes to which they are incident, constitute a subgraph which is the *complement* of the tree, or the *cotree*. Note that a tree and corresponding cotree have nodes in common — namely, all those of the cotree — and that the graph is the union of these two subgraphs. (A graph which is the *union* of two graphs is composed of all the nodes and branches of each.) This decomposition of a graph as a tree and cotree — or its branches as twigs and links — is not unique, as a graph generally contains more than one tree. Fig. 2 shows two trees for the graph of Fig. 1. In the first instance branches 4 and 6 are twigs; in the second they are links. Thus, whether a particular branch is a twig or a link cannot be uniquely stated for a graph; such a designation can be made only after a tree has been specified.

---

* The usual mathematical definition of a tree — not necessarily a spanning tree — is: A connected, loop-free subgraph of a graph.

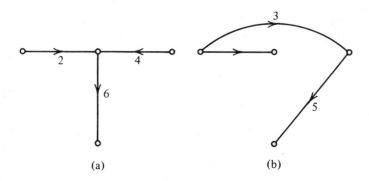

(a)   (b)

Fig. 2   Two trees of a graph

Each of the trees in Fig. 2 has a special structure. In the first, all the branches are incident at a common node; as the tree appears starlike, it is said to be a *star-tree*. In the second, the tree is also a path; since the tree appears as a line between two points, the terminal nodes, it is called a *linear-tree*.

The number of branches in a tree (or the number of twigs in a connected graph) is one less than the number of nodes. This result is easily proved by induction. (See Prob. 2.) For future convenience the number of nodes in a connected graph will be denoted by $n + 1$; then the number of twigs will be n. Furthermore, if b is the number of branches, then the number of links will be $b - n$.

If a graph is not connected, the object corresponding to a tree is a *forest*, which is defined as a union of trees, one for each of the separate parts of the graph. (A *part* is a connected subgraph with the property that the incorporation of any other branch of the graph to create a new subgraph yields an unconnected subgraph.) The number of nodes in a graph of p parts will be denoted $n + p$; it then follows that the number of twigs will be n — just as for a connected (one-part) graph. You should validate this claim. The complement of the forest — links and associated nodes — is referred to as the *coforest*.

2.2   THE INCIDENCE MATRIX

When an oriented graph is given (for example, that in Fig. 1), it is possible to specify precisely which branches are incident at which nodes and their orientations relative to the node. Parenthetically, that is the information needed to give expression to KCL. Conversely, the graph would be completely defined if this information — namely, branch-to-node incidence and orientation data — were available. The most convenient form to give expression to this information is a matrix.

For a graph having $n+p$ nodes and b branches, the *complete incidence matrix* $\mathbf{A}_c = [a_{ij}]$ is an $(n+p) \times b$ matrix whose elements have the following values:

$a_{ij} = 1$ if branch j is incident at node i and oriented away from it;
$a_{ij} = -1$ if branch j is incident at node i and oriented toward it;
$a_{ij} = 0$ if branch j is not incident at node i.

The subscript c on $\mathbf{A}_c$ indicates that the *complete* set of nodes is considered.

For the graph in Fig. 1, the complete incidence matrix is

$$
\mathbf{A}_c =
\begin{array}{c}
\text{Nodes} \\ \downarrow
\end{array}
\begin{array}{c}
\\
1 \\ 2 \\ 3 \\ 4
\end{array}
\overset{\text{Branches} \rightarrow}{
\overset{1 \quad 2 \quad 3 \quad 4 \quad 5 \quad 6}{
\begin{bmatrix}
-1 & 1 & 1 & 0 & 0 & 0 \\
0 & -1 & 0 & -1 & 0 & 1 \\
0 & 0 & -1 & 1 & 1 & 0 \\
1 & 0 & 0 & 0 & -1 & -1
\end{bmatrix}}}.
\tag{1}
$$

In this illustration it is observed that each column contains a single $+1$ and a single -1. This is a general property for any linear graph because each branch is incident at exactly two nodes, and it must perforce be oriented away from one of them and towards the other. Thus, it follows that, if all other rows are added to the last row, the result will be a row of zeros, indicating that the rows are not all linearly independent. At least one of them can be eliminated, since it can be obtained as the negative of the sum of all the others. Thus, the rank of $\mathbf{A}_c$ for a one part $(p = 1)$ graph cannot exceed one less than the number of nodes; that is, $(n+p) - 1 = (n+1) - 1 = n$. For a graph of p parts, the above row-dependency claims apply to each part; hence, the rank of $\mathbf{A}_c$ for a p part graph cannot exceed $(n+p) - p = n$.

The matrix obtained from $\mathbf{A}_c$ by eliminating one row for each part is called the *incidence matrix* and is denoted by $\mathbf{A}$. For emphasis it is sometimes called the *reduced incidence matrix*. It is of order $n \times b$. We shall now discuss the rank of this matrix and how to determine its non-singular submatrices.

For a given graph, select a forest – tree, if the graph is connected. In the incidence matrix arrange the columns so that the first n columns correspond to the twigs and the last $b - n$ columns to the links. In terms of the graph in Fig. 1, let the incidence matrix be obtained from (1) by eliminating the last row. Select the first tree in Fig. 2. Then **A** is to be written as

$$
\mathbf{A} = \begin{array}{c} \text{Node} \\ 1 \\ 2 \\ 3 \end{array}
\begin{array}{ccc cccc}
\overbrace{\begin{array}{ccc} 2 & 4 & 6 \end{array}}^{\text{Twigs}} & \overbrace{\begin{array}{ccc} 1 & 3 & 5 \end{array}}^{\text{Links}} \\
\left[\begin{array}{ccc ccc}
1 & 0 & 0 & -1 & 1 & 0 \\
-1 & -1 & 1 & 0 & 0 & 0 \\
0 & 1 & 0 & 0 & -1 & 1
\end{array}\right]
\end{array} \tag{2}
$$

In general terms, the matrix **A** can be expressed in partitioned form as

$$\mathbf{A} = [\mathbf{A}_t \ \ \mathbf{A}_l], \tag{3}$$

where $\mathbf{A}_t$ is a square matrix of order n whose columns correspond to the twigs and $\mathbf{A}_l$ is a matrix of order $n \times (b - n)$ whose columns correspond to the links.

For the preceding example,

$$
\mathbf{A}_t = \begin{bmatrix}
1 & 0 & 0 \\
-1 & -1 & 1 \\
0 & 1 & 0
\end{bmatrix}.
$$

The determinant of this matrix is found to equal -1, and so the matrix is nonsingular. It therefore follows, for this example, that the incidence matrix is of rank n.

This is a general result. Specifically, the incidence matrix of a p part graph with $n + p$ nodes is of rank n. This result is established by proving: *A submatrix of* **A** *of order* $n \times n$ *whose columns correspond to any set of twigs is nonsingular.* We will give a proof for the case of a con-

[handwritten marginalia: Node 1 & Node 3 / 1st & 3rd row of At / have only one 1 / rest zeroes]

nected ($p = 1$) graph. You should extend the proof to the general case. (See Prob. 3.)

Proof (for $p = 1$): Let $\mathbf{A}$ be partitioned as in (3). The twigs and their associated nodes determine a tree with $n + 1$ nodes, which has $\mathbf{A}_t$ as its incidence matrix. (Keep in mind the fact that the tree is itself a graph with an incidence matrix.) It follows from the properties of a tree that there exists a node — other than the node associated with the row eliminated from $\mathbf{A}_c$ to get $\mathbf{A}$ — at which just one twig is incident. The element of $\mathbf{A}_t$ associated with this node and this twig is ± 1; all other elements associated with this node are 0. Thus, det $\mathbf{A}_t$ is plus or minus the cofactor of this element. The matrix associated with this cofactor is an incidence matrix of a connected subgraph of the tree. This subgraph is a tree with n nodes — one less than in the original tree. After invoking the essential ingredients of the above argument $n - 1$ times, it will be found that det $\mathbf{A}_t$ is plus or minus a cofactor of order 1, which, because it corresponds to a tree with one branch, equals ± 1. Thus, det $\mathbf{A}_t = \pm 1$ and $\mathbf{A}_t$ is nonsingular.

The preceding is a useful result. The converse is also true. That is: *The columns of a nonsingular submatrix of $\mathbf{A}$ of order $n \times n$ correspond to a set of twigs.* The entire proof is left as an exercise. (See Prob. 4.)

By combining these results with the value of det $\mathbf{A}_t$ found in the above proof, it follows that: *The determinant of an order $n \times n$ submatrix of $\mathbf{A}$ is nonzero, equal to ± 1, if and only if the columns of that submatrix correspond to a set of twigs.* With this result, it is possible to deduce a count of the number of forests in a graph — trees, if the graph is connected — since each set of twigs is associated with a forest.

The number of forests by the above result is clearly equal to the number of order $n \times n$ nonsingular submatrices of $\mathbf{A}$. Counting such submatrices would be an exceedingly tedious task if it were necessary to evaluate the determinant of each $n \times n$ submatrix of $\mathbf{A}$ to establish which were nonsingular. Fortunately, this need not be done. The task is simplified by using the Binet-Cauchy theorem [17; p. 9]. According to this theorem

$$\det (\mathbf{AA'}) = \sum_{\substack{\text{all} \\ \text{majors}}} (\text{product of corresponding majors of } \mathbf{A} \text{ and } \mathbf{A'})$$

$$= \sum_{\substack{\text{all} \\ \text{majors}}} (\text{major of } \mathbf{A})^2$$

$$= \text{number of forests} \tag{4}$$

(A major of a rectangular matrix is the determinant of any maximal square submatrix.) The second line follows from the fact that an order $n \times n$ submatrix of the transpose of $\mathbf{A}$ has the same determinant as the corresponding submatrix of $\mathbf{A}$. Since each nonzero major equals ± 1 and since there are as many nonzero majors as forests, the last line follows.

Thus, to find the number of forests in a graph — trees, if the graph is connected — it is required only to evaluate det $(\mathbf{AA'})$. Consider the graph of Fig. 1 and its incidence matrix in (2). The number of trees will be

$$
\det(\mathbf{AA'}) = \det
\begin{bmatrix}
1 & 0 & 0 & -1 & 1 & 0 \\
-1 & -1 & 1 & 0 & 0 & 0 \\
0 & 1 & 0 & 0 & -1 & 1
\end{bmatrix}
\begin{bmatrix}
1 & -1 & 0 \\
0 & -1 & 1 \\
0 & 1 & 0 \\
-1 & 0 & 0 \\
1 & 0 & -1 \\
0 & 0 & 1
\end{bmatrix}
$$

$$
= \det
\begin{bmatrix}
3 & -1 & -1 \\
-1 & 3 & -1 \\
-1 & -1 & 3
\end{bmatrix}
= 16
$$

Given a graph, it is a simple matter to write an incidence matrix. The problem might often be the converse: Given an incidence matrix, draw the graph. In an abstract sense the complete incidence matrix defines the graph. It is one representation of the graph, whereas the drawing — line segments joining vertices — is another representation. However, the incidence matrix, as distinct from the complete incidence matrix, does not by itself define the graph; it must be augmented by some condition, such as: The graph is connected. This is the most likely condition, so it will always be assumed unless some other condition is given. (See Prob. 7.)

The procedure is straightforward. Given $\mathbf{A}$, place on the paper one more node than there are rows in $\mathbf{A}$ and number them according to the rows. Then consider the columns one at a time. There are at most two nonzero elements in each column. Place a branch between the two nodes corresponding to the two rows having nonzero elements in that column. (If there is only one nonzero element, the branch lies between the node corresponding to this row and the extra node.) The orientations will be determined by the signs of the nonzero elements.

To illustrate, let the given incidence matrix be

$$A = \begin{bmatrix} 1 & 1 & 0 & 0 & 0 & 0 & 0 & -1 \\ 0 & -1 & 1 & 1 & 0 & 0 & 0 & 0 \\ 0 & 0 & 0 & -1 & 1 & 1 & 0 & 0 \\ 0 & 0 & 0 & 0 & 0 & -1 & 1 & 1 \end{bmatrix}.$$

From this matrix two apparently differently connected graphs have been drawn and displayed in Fig. 3. The visual differences stem from the fact that initially the nodes were positioned on the paper in different patterns. However, both graphs have the same incidence matrix.

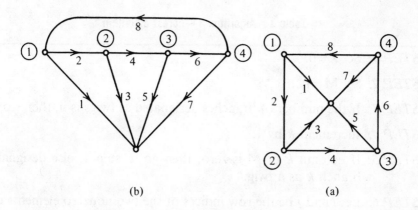

(b)   (a)

Fig. 3   Isomorphic graphs

Visual differences such as in this illustration are not significant. The significant fact is: There is a one-to-one correspondence between nodes and between branches which preserves incidence relationships. Note that branch orientation is not considered in drawing this correspondence. Graphs for which such a correspondence can be established are said to be *isomorphic*, or *topologically* equivalent. It follows that, if two graphs have the same complete incidence matrix — incidence matrix if the graph is connected — then the graphs are isomorphic. Two graphs may be isomorphic under a weaker condition on their complete incidence matrices. (See Prob. 8.)

As the foregoing has made evident, there is a one-to-one relationship between a graph and its complete incidence matrix. It should not be surprising therefore that one of the simplest algorithms to determine a forest of a given graph involves manipulation of that matrix.

The idea behind the algorithm is simple. Start with the original graph (represented by $M = A_c$) and select a twig (the branch corresponding to the first column of M). Suppose that the nodes joined by the selected twig are i and j. If the graph is modified by coalescing these two nodes (i.e., making them one node), and if a tree is found in this modified graph, then this tree, together with the previously selected twig, will be a tree of the original graph. Modifying the original graph is done by an appropriate modification of M. The procedure of selecting a twig and modifying the graph is now repeated for the modified graph. This is continued until the appropriate number of branches has been selected as twigs. The algorithm is given in Table 1.

Table 1   Algorithm 1—Forest algorithm

STEP 1: Set $k = 0$.

STEP 2: Set $M = A_c$.

STEP 3: If the number of branches designated as twigs is n, then stop.

STEP 4: Increment k by 1.

STEP 5: If column k of M is zero, then go to step 4, else designate branch k as a twig.

STEP 6: Let i and j be the row indices of the two nonzero elements of column k.

STEP 7: Add row j of M to row i; then set row j to zero.

STEP 8: Go to step 3.

The key steps in this algorithm are 5 through 7. When at step 5 a column is found to have nonzero elements — there will be just two such elements, a $+1$ and a -1 — the corresponding branch is designated a twig. During the next step, the rows of the two nonzero elements are identified and labeled, i and j. At step 7 matrix $\mathbf{M}$ is modified; this is equivalent to modifying its corresponding graph. The branches formerly incident at either node i or node j become incident at just node i, except that branches incident at both nodes are removed. (Their columns in $\mathbf{M}$ become zero.) In this way observe that branches forming loops with thus far identified twigs are eliminated — that is, are identified as links. Also during this step, node j becomes isolated, as manifested in row j of $\mathbf{M}$ becoming zero. Note that when the algorithm terminates, $\mathbf{M} = 0$; all the nodes will be isolated.

This algorithm does not directly invoke the relationship between a tree and the nonsingularity of its submatrix in the incidence matrix. However, the existence of that relationship suggests that we might be able to modify the algorithm such that $\mathbf{M}$ would be derived from $\mathbf{A}$ rather than $\mathbf{A}_c$ and thereby have, in general, fewer rows than $\mathbf{A}_c$. This is indeed the case as you are asked to show in Prob. 9.

We also want to note that this is not the most efficient algorithm. A "depth-first-search" based algorithm (see Proj. 1) is theoretically more efficient and, for large networks, program realizations of it are more efficient.

2.3   THE LOOP MATRIX

The incidence matrix gives information about the incidences of branches at nodes, but does not explicitly tell anything about the way in which the branches constitute loops, which is the information needed to give expression to KVL. This information can also be given conveniently in matrix form. For this purpose we first endow each loop of a graph with an orientation, which can be specified by an ordered list of its branches and nodes. This order is most easily shown by a curved arrow, as in Fig. 4, where two possibile loops are shown. For these two loops, the ordered lists would be $\{2, ①, 3, ③, 4, ②\}$ and $\{2, ②, 4, ③, 5, ④, 1, ①\}$, where the node labels are circled. To avoid cluttering the diagram, as would most assuredly be the case for a graph with a high degree of connectivity, it might be necessary to avoid the visual presentation — curved arrows — and to provide just the ordered lists. In some cases, as when the graph is not a multigraph, the lists can be somewhat simplified. (See Prob. 10.)

For a graph having b branches, the *complete loop matrix*, sometimes called the *complete circuit matrix*, $\mathbf{B}_c = [b_{ij}]$ is a matrix with b columns and as many rows as the graph has loops. Its elements have the following values:

$b_{ij} = 1$ if branch j is in loop i and their orientations coincide;
$b_{ij} = -1$ if branch j is in loop i and their orientations do not coincide;
$b_{ij} = 0$ if branch j is not in loop i.

The subscript c on $\mathbf{B}_c$ indicates that the complete set of loops is considered.

Unlike the number of rows in the complete incidence matrix (equal to the number of nodes, $n+p$, in the graph), the number of rows in $\mathbf{B}_c$ is not, in general, simply expressible in terms of n, p, and b. (See Prob. 12.) The number must be established by an exhaustive—usually exhausting—search for all the loops. For the graph of Fig. 4 there are seven loops, with the loops and their orientations specified by the following lists of branches (see Prob. 10b):

Loop 1: {2, 3, 4}   Loop 4: {1, 3, 5}

Loop 2: {1, 2, 6}   Loop 5: {1, 2, 4, 5}

Loop 3: {4, 5, 6}   Loop 6: {2, 3, 5, 6}

Loop 7: {1, 3, 4, 6}

The complete loop matrix is

Branches $\rightarrow$

$$
\mathbf{B}_c =
\begin{array}{c}
\text{Loops} \downarrow \\
\begin{array}{c}
1 \\ 2 \\ 3 \\ 4 \\ 5 \\ 6 \\ 7
\end{array}
\end{array}
\begin{array}{cccccc}
1 & 2 & 3 & 4 & 5 & 6 \\
\left[\begin{array}{cccccc}
0 & -1 & 1 & 1 & 0 & 0 \\
1 & 1 & 0 & 0 & 0 & 1 \\
0 & 0 & 0 & -1 & 1 & -1 \\
1 & 0 & 1 & 0 & 1 & 0 \\
1 & 1 & 0 & -1 & 1 & 0 \\
0 & 1 & -1 & 0 & -1 & 1 \\
1 & 0 & 1 & 1 & 0 & 1
\end{array}\right]
\end{array}
$$

The set of all loops in a graph is quite a large set (see Prob. 11) and, in fact, considerably larger than needed. In the case of the above example, rows 4 through 7 are linear combinations of rows 1 through 3. In par-

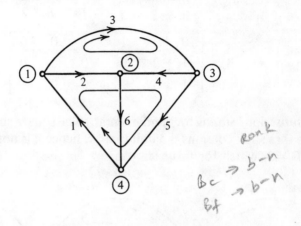

Fig. 4   Two loops of a graph

ticular, row 4 is the sum of rows 1, 2, and 3. (What combinations of rows 1, 2, and 3 yield rows 5, 6, and 7?) Thus, it is to be anticipated that the number of linearly independent rows of $\mathbf{B}_c$, hence, also the rank of $\mathbf{B}_c$, is a relatively small number. This number, as will be shown now by considering a specially defined set of loops, is just $b - n$.

Given a graph, select a forest. Then, one at a time, take the union of a link with the forest. The resulting subgraphs will each contain one loop. In each case, that loop will be characterized by the fact that all but one of its branches are twigs of the chosen forest. Loops formed in this way are called *fundamental loops*, or *f-loops* for short. The orientation of an f-loop is chosen to coincide with that of its defining link. As there are as many f-loops as there are links, this number is $b - n$ in a p part graph of b branches and $n + p$ nodes.

For the example, let the chosen tree be that in Fig. 2(b). (In this case of a connected graph, the forest has but one tree.) The f-loops formed when the links are replaced one at a time are shown in Fig. 5. (Note the orientations.) In writing that portion of the complete loop matrix associated with the f-loops, let the columns be arranged in the same order as for the reduced incidence matrix for the same tree—twigs first, then links. Also, let the order of the loops be the same as the order of the columns of the associated links. For the example, this submatrix of $\mathbf{B}_c$ is

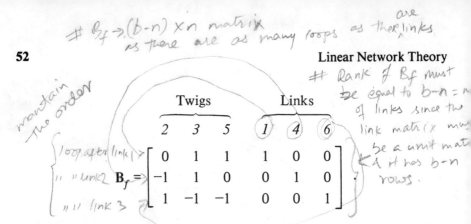

 # $B_f \to (b-n) \times n$ matrix as there are as many loops as there are links

 # maintain The order

 # Rank of B_f must be equal to $b-n = n$ of links since the link matrix must be a unit matrix if it has $b-n$ rows.

	Twigs			Links		
	2	3	5	1	4	6
loop after link 1 →	0	1	1	1	0	0
" " link 2 B_f = →	−1	1	0	0	1	0
" " link 3 →	1	−1	−1	0	0	1

(The subscript f stands for fundamental.) The square submatrix formed by the three link columns is a unit matrix; hence it is nonsingular and of rank $B_f = 3$, which for this example is $b - n$.

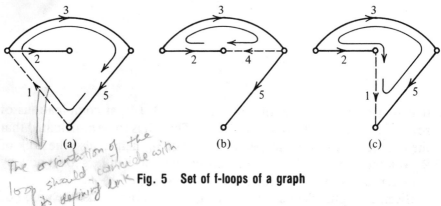

The orientation of the loop should coincide with its defining link

Fig. 5 Set of f-loops of a graph

In general the matrix B_f for an arbitrary graph can, with appropriate ordering of the branches and f-loops, be expressed in partitioned form as

$$B_f = [B_{ft} \ B_{fl}] = [B_{ft} \ U]. \tag{5}$$

The $(b-n) \times (b-n)$ submatrix B_{fl}, whose columns correspond to the links for a particular forest, must be, as indicated, a unit matrix by the very way in which it is formed. Hence, rank $B_f = b - n$.

Since B_f is a submatrix of B_c, it must be that rank $B_c \geqslant b - n$. We shall next show that rank $B_c \leqslant b - n$, and thus that rank $B_c = b - n$. To do this, we shall establish and use a result of considerable importance in its own right.

Given a graph, let the columns of the two matrices A_c and B_c be arranged in the same order. Then it will be true that

$$A_c B_c' = 0 \leftrightarrow B_c A_c' = 0 \tag{6}$$

Of course, the second one will be true if the first one is, since $\mathbf{B}_c\mathbf{A}'_c = (\mathbf{A}_c\mathbf{B}'_c)'$. These relationships are called the *orthogonality relations* and can be proved as follows.

The matrices $\mathbf{A}_c$ and $\mathbf{B}'_c$ will have the following forms:

$$
\mathbf{A}_c =
\begin{array}{c}
\text{Nodes} \\ \downarrow \\[4pt]
1 \\ 2 \\ \cdot \\ \cdot \\ \cdot \\ n+1
\end{array}
\overset{\begin{array}{c}\text{Branches} \to \\[2pt] 1 \quad 2 \ \cdots \ b\end{array}}{\left[\right]}
\qquad
\mathbf{B}'_c =
\begin{array}{c}
\text{Branches} \\ \downarrow \\[4pt]
1 \\ 2 \\ \cdot \\ \cdot \\ \cdot \\ b
\end{array}
\overset{\begin{array}{c}\text{Loops} \to \\[2pt] 1 \quad 2 \ \cdots\end{array}}{\left[\right]}.
$$

Focus attention on any one of the columns of $\mathbf{B}'_c$ and on any one of the rows of $\mathbf{A}_c$; that is, focus attention on a loop and a node. Either the node is on the loop or not. If not, then none of the branches on the loop can be incident at the node. This means that corresponding to any nonzero elements in a column of $\mathbf{B}'_c$ there will be a zero element in the row of $\mathbf{A}_c$; so the product will yield zero. If the node is on the loop, then exactly two of the branches incident at the node will lie on the loop. If these two branches are similarly oriented relative to the node (either both oriented away or both toward), they will be oppositely oriented relative to the loop, and vice versa. In terms of the matrices, if the elements in the row of $\mathbf{A}_c$ corresponding to the two branches are both $+1$ or both -1, the corresponding two elements in the column of $\mathbf{B}'_c$ will be of opposite sign, and vice versa. When the product is formed the result will be zero. The theorem is thus proved. In fact, the result is still true if, instead of $\mathbf{A}_c$ and $\mathbf{B}_c$, we use submatrices of $\mathbf{A}_c$ and $\mathbf{B}_c$ having any number of rows.

With the preceding result it is now possible to determine the rank of $\mathbf{B}_c$ by invoking Sylvester's law of nullity.* According to this law, if the product of two matrices equals zero, the sum of the ranks of the two

---

* Sylvester's law of nullity states that given $\mathbf{P}$ of rank r_P and $\mathbf{Q}$ of rank r_Q, then the rank r_{PQ} of the product matrix $\mathbf{PQ}$ satisfies the following: $r_P + r_Q - n \leqslant r_{PQ} \leqslant \min\{r_P, r_Q\}$, where n is the number of columns of $\mathbf{P}$ (17; vol. I, pp. 65-66).

matrices is not greater than the number of columns of the first matrix in the product. In the present case that number of columns equals the number of branches b of the graph. So, since the rank of a matrix is the same as the rank of its transpose,

$$\text{rank } \mathbf{A}_c + \text{rank } \mathbf{B}_c \leqslant b. \tag{7}$$

The rank of $\mathbf{A}_c$ has already been determined to be n. Hence

$$\text{rank } \mathbf{B}_c \leqslant b - n. \tag{8}$$

Since it was previously established that the rank of $\mathbf{B}_c$ is no less than $b - n$ and it is now found that it can be no greater than $b - n$, then rank $\mathbf{B}_c$ is exactly $b - n$.

Any matrix $\mathbf{B}$ of order $(b - n) \times b$ and rank $b - n$ obtainable from $\mathbf{B}_c$ by deleting rows is called a *loop matrix*. The matrix $\mathbf{B}_f$ is a loop matrix, but, because it corresponds to a very special set of loops, it is called the *fundamental loop matrix*.

Observe that removal of any number of rows from $\mathbf{A}_c$ or from $\mathbf{B}_c$ will not invalidate the orthogonality conditions of (6); so these can be written as

$$\mathbf{AB'} = \mathbf{0} \text{ or } \mathbf{BA'} = \mathbf{0}. \tag{9}$$

2.4 PLANAR GRAPHS

All of the properties of graphs that have been discussed up to this point do not depend on any topological character of a graph. We shall now consider one specific topological structure.

We define a *planar graph* as a graph that can be displayed on a plane in such a way that no two branches cross each other. Fig. 6 shows two graphs having the same number of nodes and branches; the first is planar; the second, nonplanar.

The branches of a planar graph separate a plane into disjoint regions; the branches bounding such a region are called a *mesh*. Specifically, a mesh is a set of branches of a planar graph that enclose no other branch of the graph within the boundary formed by these branches. In Fig. 6(a) the set {1, 2, 3} is a mesh, whereas {1, 2, 4, 5} is not. The outermost set of branches separates the plane into two regions: the finite region in which the remaining branches lie and the infinite region. The infinite region can be looked upon as the interior of this set of branches. It is the complement of the finite region. Hence this set of branches can also be considered a mesh and is called the *outside mesh*. In Fig. 6(a), the outside mesh is {1, 2, 6, 7, 8, 5}. However, when the meshes of a graph are enumerated, the outside mesh is not counted.

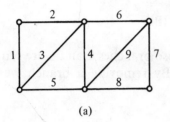
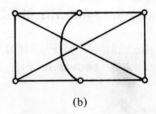

(a)   (b)

Fig. 6   Planar (a) and nonplanar (b) graphs

The set of meshes is a special set of loops in that, as with a set of f-loops, there are $b - n$ of them. Furthermore, the corresponding $(b - n) \times b$ submatrix of $\mathbf{B}_c$, denoted $\mathbf{B}_m$ and called a *mesh matrix*, is of rank $b - n$. You should prove these statements. Now, a question arises as to whether the meshes can be the f-loops for some tree; or, stated differently, is it possible to find a tree, the f-loops corresponding to which are meshes? (This will require that $\mathbf{B}_{mt} = \mathbf{U}$ in the partitioned form $\mathbf{B}_m = [\mathbf{B}_{mt} \ \mathbf{B}_{ml}]$.) To answer this question, note that each f-loop contains a branch—a link—that is in no other f-loop. Hence any branch that is common between two meshes cannot be a link and must be a twig. A tree can surely be found for which the meshes are f-loops if the branches common between meshes form no closed paths. For some planar graphs it will be possible; and for others, not. To illustrate, Fig. 7 shows two

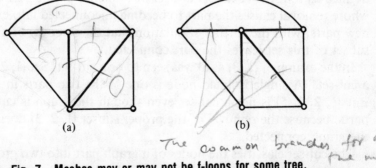

(a)   (b)

Fig. 7   Meshes may or may not be f-loops for some tree.

The common branches for all the meshes should not form a loop if the meshes are to be the f-loops.

very similar planar graphs having the same number of nodes, branches, and meshes. The branches common between meshes are shown darkened. These must be twigs for a tree if the meshes are to be f-loops. However, in the first graph, these branches form a loop, and so the desired result is not possible; whereas it is possible for the second graph.

2.5   CUT-SETS AND THE CUT-SET MATRIX

In the example of Fig. 1(b), suppose branches 1 and 6 are removed. The result is shown in Fig. 8(a). (By removing a branch we mean

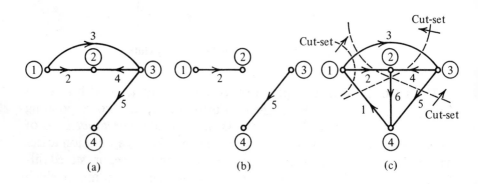

Fig. 8   Removing branches from a graph

deleting it, but leaving intact the nodes at which it is incident.) The graph is still a connected graph. Now if branches 3 and 4 are also removed, the result becomes Fig. 8(b). The graph is now unconnected; it has been "cut" into two parts. This development, which also applies to a part of a multi-part graph, leads to the notion of a cut-set, which is defined as follows: A *cut-set* is a set of branches of one part of a graph whose removal causes the part to become unconnected into exactly two new parts, with the further stipulation that the removal of any proper subset of this set leaves the part connected.

In the example, $\{1, 3, 4, 6\}$ was seen to be a cut-set. Set $\{1, 2, 3\}$ is also a cut-set. (A single isolated node is one of the two parts in this case.) But $\{1, 2, 3, 5\}$ is not a cut-set even though the graph is cut into two parts, because the removal of the proper subset $\{1, 2, 3\}$ does not leave the graph connected.

The cut-set classifies the nodes of a graph part into two groups, each group being in one of the two new parts. Each branch of the cut-set has one of its terminals incident at a node in one group and its other end incident at a node in the other group. A cut-set is oriented by selecting an orientation from one of the two new parts to the other. The orientation can be shown on the graph as in Fig. 8(c). The orientations of the branches in a cut-set will either coincide with the cut-set orientation or they will not.

Just as the incidence matrix described the incidence and the orientations of branches at nodes, so a cut-set matrix can be defined to describe the presence of branches in a cut-set and their orientation relative to that of the cut-set. We next define the *complete cut-set matrix* $\mathbf{Q}_c = [q_{ij}]$, whose rows correspond to cut-sets and whose columns correspond to the branches of a graph. The elements have the following values:

$q_{ij} = 1$ if branch j is in cut-set i, and the orientations coincide;

$q_{ij} = -1$ if branch j is in cut-set i, and the orientations do not coincide;

$q_{ij} = 0$ if branch j is not in cut-set i.

The subscript c indicates that the complete set of cut-sets is considered.

Since removing all branches incident at a node separates this node from the rest of its part of the graph, this set of branches will be a cut-set, provided the rest of the part is not itself separated into more than one part. In the graph shown in Fig. 9, removing the set of branches incident at node 1 will separate this one part graph into three parts, of which the isolated node 1 will be one part. So this set of branches is not a cut-set.

However, the graph shown in Fig. 9 is a peculiar kind of graph, and node 1 is a peculiar node. We define a *hinged graph*, or a *separable*

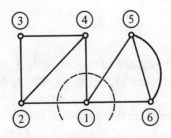

Fig. 9 A hinged, or separable, graph

graph, as a graph in which there is at least one subgraph which has only one node in common with its complement subgraph in the graph. A node having this property is called a *hinge node*, or *separating node*. In a hinged graph the nodes in each hinged part can be grouped, for each hinge node in such a part, into two sets such that every path from a member of one set to a member of the other must pass through the hinge node. In Fig. 9, nodes 2, 3, and 4 form one set, and nodes 5 and 6, the other. If the branches incident at a hinge node are removed, there will be no path from a node in one set to a node in the other. Hence the rest of the part with the hinge node excluded will not be connected; so the set of branches incident at a hinge node will not be a cut-set. For each other node, the set of branches incident there will be a cut-set.

If at a nonhinge node the orientation of the cut-set that consists of all branches incident at the node is chosen to be away from [toward] the node, the complete cut-set matrix will include the row [negative of the row] of the complete incidence matrix corresponding to the node.

For the example of Fig. 1(b), in addition to the cut-sets consisting of the sets of branches incident at each node, there are three other cut-sets: {1, 3, 4, 6}, {2, 3, 5, 6}, and {1, 2, 4, 5}. The complete cut-set matrix $\mathbf{Q}_c$ is then

$$
\begin{array}{c}
\text{Branches} \rightarrow \\
\begin{array}{cccccc}
\text{Cut-sets} & 1 & 2 & 3 & 4 & 5 & 6 \\
\downarrow & & & & & &
\end{array}
\end{array}
$$

$$
\mathbf{Q}_c = \begin{array}{c} 1 \\ 2 \\ 3 \\ 4 \\ 5 \\ 6 \\ 7 \end{array}
\begin{bmatrix}
-1 & 1 & 1 & 0 & 0 & 0 \\
0 & -1 & 0 & -1 & 0 & 1 \\
0 & 0 & -1 & 1 & 1 & 0 \\
1 & 0 & 0 & 0 & -1 & -1 \\
1 & 0 & -1 & 1 & 0 & -1 \\
0 & 1 & 1 & 0 & -1 & -1 \\
-1 & 1 & 0 & 1 & 1 & 0
\end{bmatrix}
$$

where the first four rows are identical with $\mathbf{A}_c$ and the last three rows correspond to the cut-sets {1, 3, 4, 6}, {2, 3, 5, 6}, and {1, 2, 4, 5}, respectively.

At a hinge node the incident branches comprise at least two cut-sets. Therefore, there exists a linear combination of the rows of $\mathbf{Q}_c$ associated with these cut-sets which yields the row of $\mathbf{A}_c$ corresponding to the node. (You should convince yourself of these statements.) Thus, the rows of $\mathbf{A}_c$ can always be obtained as linear combinations of those of

$\mathbf{Q}_c$. It follows that rank $\mathbf{Q}_c \geqslant$ rank $\mathbf{A}_c = n$. This can be established more directly and, in doing so, we will introduce a special set of cut-sets.

Given a graph, select a forest. Then focus on some twig. Removing this twig from its tree — a part of the forest — separates the tree into two parts and, correspondingly, the nodes in the tree into two groups. All the links which join a node in one set to a node in the other, together with the twig in question, constitute a cut-set. We call this a *fundamental cut-set*, or *f-cut-set* for short. For each twig, there will be an f-cut-set, so for a p part graph having $n + p$ nodes (hence, n twigs) there will be n fundamental cut-sets. The orientation of an f-cut-set is chosen to coincide with that of its defining twig.

As an illustration, take the connected graph of Fig. 10. The forest — here a tree — is shown in heavy lines. The f-cut-sets are uniquely deter-

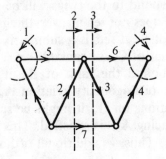

Fig. 10 Example of fundamental cut-sets

mined — one for each twig — and each contains the branches crossing one of the dashed curves in Fig. 10. Let us write that portion of the complete cut-set matrix associated with the f-cut-sets, arranging the columns so that the first n of them correspond to the twigs, in the same order as the associated cut-sets. Thus,

$$
\mathbf{Q}_f =
\begin{array}{c}
\overbrace{}^{\text{Twigs}} \quad \overbrace{}^{\text{Links}} \\
\begin{array}{ccccccc}
1 & 2 & 3 & 4 & 5 & 6 & 7
\end{array} \\
\begin{bmatrix}
1 & 0 & 0 & 0 & -1 & 0 & 0 \\
0 & 1 & 0 & 0 & 1 & 0 & 1 \\
0 & 0 & 1 & 0 & 0 & 1 & 1 \\
0 & 0 & 0 & 1 & 0 & 1 & 0
\end{bmatrix}
\end{array}.
$$

(The subscript f stands for fundamental.) The square submatrix corresponding to the twig columns is seen to be a unit matrix; hence it is nonsingular, and the rank of this cut-set matrix equals 4, the number of twigs.

This is, in fact, a specific illustration of a general result. In the general case let the columns of the matrix $\mathbf{Q}_f$ be arranged for a given forest with the twigs first, then the links, the twigs being in the same order as the cut-sets they define. The matrix can then be partitioned in the form

$$\mathbf{Q}_f = [\mathbf{Q}_{ft} \ \ \mathbf{Q}_{fl}] = [\mathbf{U} \ \ \mathbf{Q}_{fl}]. \tag{10}$$

From the very way in which it is constructed, the $n \times n$ submatrix $\mathbf{Q}_{ft}$ whose columns correspond to the twigs will be a unit matrix. Hence, rank $\mathbf{Q}_f = n$. This still does not tell us everything about the rank of $\mathbf{Q}_c$. But since the matrix of f-cut-sets is a submatrix of $\mathbf{Q}_c$, the rank of $\mathbf{Q}_c$ can be no less than that of $\mathbf{Q}_f$, or rank $\mathbf{Q}_c \geqslant n$.

When seeking to bound the rank of $\mathbf{B}_c$, it became necessary to establish and use the orthogonality relation $\mathbf{A}_c \mathbf{B}_c' = 0$. As $\mathbf{A}_c$ can be derived by row operations on $\mathbf{Q}_c$, it might be suspected that a similar relationship — $\mathbf{Q}_c$ replacing $\mathbf{A}_c$ — is satisfied. This is true, as you should verify. (See Prob. 13.) Thus, as additional orthogonality relations, we have

$$\mathbf{Q}_c \mathbf{B}_c' = 0 \text{ or } \mathbf{B}_c \mathbf{Q}_c' = 0. \tag{11}$$

The rank of $\mathbf{Q}_c$ can now be determined. Using Sylvester's law of nullity and the known rank of $\mathbf{B}_c$, it will follow that rank $\mathbf{Q}_c \leqslant n$. (You should carry out the details.) Since it was previously shown that rank $\mathbf{Q}_c \geqslant n$, it must be that rank $\mathbf{Q}_c$ is exactly equal to n.

Any matrix $\mathbf{Q}$ of order $n \times b$ and rank n obtainable from $\mathbf{Q}_c$ by deleting rows is called a *cut-set matrix*. The matrix $\mathbf{Q}_f$ is a cut-set matrix, but because it corresponds to a very special set of cut-sets, it is called a *fundamental cut-set matrix*.

As removal of any number of rows from $\mathbf{Q}_c$ or $\mathbf{B}_c$ will not invalidate the expressions in (11), the orthogonality relations can be written as

$$\mathbf{QB}' = 0 \text{ or } \mathbf{BQ}' = 0. \tag{12}$$

2.6 RELATIONSHIPS AMONG SUBMATRICES OF A, B AND Q

Let the columns of $\mathbf{A}$, $\mathbf{B}$, and $\mathbf{Q}$ be arranged with the twigs for a given forest first and then the links. These matrices can then be partitioned in the following forms:

$$\mathbf{A} = [\mathbf{A}_t \quad \mathbf{A}_l]$$

$$\mathbf{B} = [\mathbf{B}_t \quad \mathbf{B}_l] \qquad \qquad \mathbf{B}_f = [\mathbf{B}_{ft} \quad \mathbf{U}] \qquad (13)$$

$$\mathbf{Q} = [\mathbf{Q}_t \quad \mathbf{Q}_l] \qquad \qquad \mathbf{Q}_f = [\mathbf{U} \quad \mathbf{Q}_{fl}]$$

where $\mathbf{A}_t$ is square of order n and nonsingular and where $\mathbf{Q}_t$ is square of order n. We shall now show that, with $\mathbf{B}$ partitioned as shown (with $\mathbf{B}_l$ square and of order $b - n$), the submatrix $\mathbf{B}_l$, whose columns are links for the forest, will be nonsingular.

To prove this, use the orthogonality relation (9) to write

$$\mathbf{AB}' = [\mathbf{A}_t \quad \mathbf{A}_l] \begin{bmatrix} \mathbf{B}'_t \\ \mathbf{B}'_l \end{bmatrix} = \mathbf{A}_t \mathbf{B}'_t + \mathbf{A}_l \mathbf{B}'_l = 0. \qquad (14)$$

Since $\mathbf{A}_t$ is nonsingular,

$$\mathbf{B}'_t = -\mathbf{A}_t^{-1}\mathbf{A}_l\mathbf{B}'_l \text{ or } \mathbf{B}_t = -\mathbf{B}_l(\mathbf{A}_t^{-1}\mathbf{A}_l)'. \qquad (15)$$

Finally matrix $\mathbf{B}$ becomes

$$\mathbf{B} = [-\mathbf{B}_l(\mathbf{A}_t^{-1}\mathbf{A}_l)' \quad \mathbf{B}_l] = \mathbf{B}_l[-(\mathbf{A}_t^{-1}\mathbf{A}_l)' \quad \mathbf{U}]. \qquad (16)$$

Now let the same procedure be carried out starting at (14), but this time with the matrix $\mathbf{B}_f$ (of the f-loops for some forest) partitioned as in (13). The details will be left for you to carry out; the result will be

$$\mathbf{B}_f = [-(\mathbf{A}_t^{-1}\mathbf{A}_l)' \quad \mathbf{U}]. \qquad (17)$$

By comparing this with the preceding equation, it follows that

$$\mathbf{B} = \mathbf{B}_l\mathbf{B}_f. \qquad (18a)$$

Since $\mathbf{B}$ and $\mathbf{B}_f$ are both of rank $b - n$, it follows from Sylvester's law of nullity that $\mathbf{B}_l$ is of rank $b - n$ and, hence, nonsingular; the proof is thus complete. Since $\mathbf{B}_l$ is nonsingular, the preceding equation is equivalent to

$$\mathbf{B}_f = \mathbf{B}_i^{-1}\mathbf{B}. \tag{18b}$$

The converse of this result is also true; that is, if the loop-matrix $\mathbf{B}$ is partitioned into two submatrices in the form $\mathbf{B} = [\mathbf{B}_a \ \mathbf{B}_b]$, with $\mathbf{B}_b$ being square of order $b - n$ and nonsingular, the columns of this submatrix will correspond to the links for some forest. The proof is left for you to carry out. (See Prob. 11.)

Additional useful results are obtained by solving (14) for $\mathbf{A}_l$. Since $\mathbf{B}_l$ is nonsingular, we get

$$\mathbf{A}_l = -\mathbf{A}_t\mathbf{B}_t'(\mathbf{B}_l')^{-1} = -\mathbf{A}_t\mathbf{B}_t'(\mathbf{B}_i^{-1})' = -\mathbf{A}_t(\mathbf{B}_i^{-1}\mathbf{B}_t)'. \tag{19}$$

The last step follows because the transpose of a product equals the product of transposes in the reverse order. The preceding step follows because the operations of transpose and inverse are commutative for a nonsingular matrix.

When this is inserted into the partitioned form of the $\mathbf{A}$ matrix, the result will be

$$\mathbf{A} = \mathbf{A}_t[\mathbf{U} \ -(\mathbf{B}_i^{-1}\mathbf{B}_t)']. \tag{20}$$

This should be compared with (16).

Let us now consider the $\mathbf{Q}$ matrix. By a process similar to that which was used to prove that $\mathbf{B}_l$ is nonsingular, it can be shown that $\mathbf{Q}_t$ is nonsingular and, furthermore, that

$$\mathbf{Q} = \mathbf{Q}_t[\mathbf{U} \ -(\mathbf{B}_i^{-1}\mathbf{B}_t)']. \tag{21}$$

(You should provide the details.) In the case of the f-cut-set matrix, the same steps lead to

$$\mathbf{Q}_f = [\mathbf{U} \ -(\mathbf{B}_i^{-1}\mathbf{B}_t)']. \tag{22}$$

Hence, it must also be that

$$\boxed{\mathbf{Q} = \mathbf{Q}_t\mathbf{Q}_f} \to \mathbf{Q}_f = \mathbf{Q}_t^{-1}\mathbf{Q}. \tag{23}$$

Upon comparing (20 and (22), it is clear that

$$A = A_t Q_f \rightarrow Q_f = A_t^{-1} A \quad [A_t \; A_\ell]$$

$$= [A_t A_t^{-1} , \; A_t^{-1} A_\ell) \qquad (24)$$

When **A** is expressed in partitioned form, the last expression becomes

$$Q_f = [U \quad A_t^{-1} A_l]. \qquad (25)$$

Finally, observe that when **B** is replaced by B_f in (22), the result is

$$Q_f = [U \quad -B'_{fl}] \qquad (26)$$

from which it is evident that

$$Q_{fl} = -B'_{ft}. \qquad (27)$$

Thus, Q_f and B_f are related in a computationally simple manner and either is easily evaluated once an incidence matrix and some forest is known.

The preceding results are collected in Table 2 where the matrices across the top are the same as those along the left side. You should provide the missing entries in this table. (See Prob. 14.)

Table 2

	A	B	Q	B_f	Q_f
A	$[A_t \; A_l]$	$B_t[-(A_t \, ^lA_l)' \; U]$		$[-(A_t \, ^lA_l)' \; U]$	$[U \; -A_t \, ^lA_l]$
B	$A_t[U \; -(B_t \, ^lB_l)']$	$[B_t \; B_l]$	$Q_t[U \; -(B_t \, ^lB_l)']$		$[U \; -(B_t \, ^lB_l)']$
Q			$[Q_t \; Q_l]$	$[-Q_t \, ^lQ_l \; U]$	
B_f		$B_f B_f$		$[B_f \; U]$	
Q_f	$A_t Q_f$		$Q_t Q_f$		$[U \; Q_{fl}]$

$$A B_f^T = A_t B_t^T + A_l B_l^T = 0$$

$$B_f = [-(A_t^{-1} A_l)^T \; | \; U]$$

$$A = A_t [U \; | \; -(B_l^{-1} B_t)^T]$$

$$Q_f B_f^T = B_t^T + Q_{fl} B_l^T = 0$$

$$Q_f = A_t^{-1} A$$

$$Q_f = [U \; | \; Q_{fl}] = [U \; | \; -B_{fl}^T]$$

CHAPTER 3
Component Voltage-Current Relations and Kirchhoff's Laws

With the consideration of linear graph theory completed, we may return to the reason for having considered it in the first place. A network is the interconnection of a collection of components, each of which has a voltage and current associated with it. These voltages and currents are constrained by the manner in which the components are interconnected. These structurally imposed constraints—to be made manifest through the Kirchhoff Laws—will require some of the preceding results based on linear graph theory.

3.1 KIRCHHOFF'S CURRENT LAW

Kirchhoff's current law (abbreviated as KCL) states: *At each connection between components in a network, the algebraic sum of the currents leaving the connection is zero.* Expression can be given to these algebraic sums by using the complete node incidence matrix for the oriented linear graph associated with the network. Specifically,

$$\sum_{l=1}^{b} a_{kl} i_l = 0 \quad (k = 1, \ldots, n+p). \tag{1}$$

The matrix form of this set of expressions is

$$\mathbf{A}_c \mathbf{i} = 0, \tag{2}$$

where $\mathbf{i}$ is the vector of component currents: $\mathbf{i} = [i_k]$, $k = 1, 2, 3, \ldots, b$. (Since a branch of a graph can be assigned to each component, this is also the vector of branch currents). As established in the previous section, $\mathbf{A}_c$ is not of full rank. Some rows $-p$ of them — may be deleted without a loss of information. Upon doing so, we get

$$\mathbf{A}\mathbf{i} = \mathbf{0}, \tag{3}$$

which is one of the expressions of KCL.

Let the incidence matrix be partitioned and written as $\mathbf{A} = [\mathbf{A}_t \ \mathbf{A}_l]$ and let $\mathbf{i}$ be similarly partitioned. Thus,

$$\mathbf{i} = \begin{bmatrix} \mathbf{i}_t \\ \mathbf{i}_l \end{bmatrix}, \tag{4}$$

where $\mathbf{i}_t$ is the vector of twig currents and $\mathbf{i}_l$ is the vector of link currents. When these are inserted into the preceding expression for KCL, the result is

$$[\mathbf{A}_t \ \mathbf{A}_l] \begin{bmatrix} \mathbf{i}_t \\ \mathbf{i}_l \end{bmatrix} = \mathbf{A}_t \mathbf{i}_t + \mathbf{A}_l \mathbf{i}_l = \mathbf{0} \tag{5}$$

or, since $\mathbf{A}_t$ is a nonsingular matrix,

$$\mathbf{i}_t = -\mathbf{A}_t^{-1}\mathbf{A}_l \mathbf{i}_l. \tag{6}$$

The message carried by this expression is that, given a forest, there is a linear relationship by which the *twig currents* are determined from the *link currents*. This means that, if the link currents can be determined by some other means, the twig currents become known from (6). Of all the b branch currents, only $b - n$ of them — the link currents — need be determined independently.

The dependence of $\mathbf{i}_t$ on $\mathbf{i}_l$ can be used in (4) to write the current vector as

$$\mathbf{i} = \begin{bmatrix} -\mathbf{A}_t^{-1}\mathbf{A}_l \\ \mathbf{U} \end{bmatrix} \mathbf{i}_l. \tag{7}$$

Now, compare the matrix on the right to the one in (2-17). One is the transpose of the other; hence we may write

$$\mathbf{i} = \mathbf{B}_f' \mathbf{i}_l. \checkmark \tag{8}$$

That is, the vector of all branch currents is obtained as a linear transformation of a smaller set of currents, the link currents. This too is an expression of KCL; we shall refer to this as a *second form expression* of KCL. We say (3) is a *first form expression* of KCL.

A more general second form expression of KCL can be obtained by replacing $\mathbf{B}_f$ in (8) by its equivalent in (2-18b). The result is

$$\mathbf{i} = \underline{\mathbf{B}'\mathbf{B}_l'^{-1}\mathbf{i}_l} = \mathbf{B}'\mathbf{i}_c \tag{9}$$

where

$$\mathbf{i}_c = \mathbf{B}_l'^{-1}\mathbf{i}_l. \tag{10}$$

The elements of $\mathbf{i}_c$ can be thought of as loop currents that circulate on the loops corresponding to the rows of $\mathbf{B}$. They are fictitious because they cannot, in general, be measured. If the loop matrix $\mathbf{B}$ is the mesh matrix $\mathbf{B}_m$, so that $\mathbf{B}_l = \mathbf{B}_{ml}$, then the elements of $\mathbf{i}_c$ can also be referred to as mesh currents and $\mathbf{i}_c$ can be replaced by $\mathbf{i}_m$. Furthermore, $\mathbf{B}_m$ will replace $\mathbf{B}$ in (9). Note that the subscript l is already in use to denote link, so we have chosen c, for *circuit*, the alternate name for loop.

As an illustration of this result, consider the graph in Fig. 1 and the indicated loops. The loop matrix is

Branches →

$$
\mathbf{B} =
\begin{array}{c}
\text{Loops} \\ \downarrow \\ \\ 1 \\ 2 \\ 3 \\ 4
\end{array}
\begin{array}{cccccccc}
1 & 2 & 3 & 4 & 5 & 6 & 7 & 8 \\
\left[\begin{array}{cccccccc}
1 & 0 & 0 & 0 & 1 & 0 & -1 & 0 \\
0 & 1 & 1 & 1 & -1 & 0 & 0 & 0 \\
0 & 0 & 1 & 1 & 0 & -1 & 0 & 0 \\
-1 & -1 & 0 & 0 & 0 & 0 & 0 & 1
\end{array}\right]
\end{array}
$$

and the corresponding second form KCL is

$$
\begin{bmatrix} i_1 \\ i_2 \\ i_3 \\ i_4 \\ i_5 \\ i_6 \\ i_7 \\ i_8 \end{bmatrix}
=
\begin{bmatrix}
1 & 0 & 0 & -1 \\
0 & 1 & 0 & -1 \\
0 & 1 & 1 & 0 \\
0 & 1 & 1 & 0 \\
1 & -1 & 0 & 0 \\
0 & 0 & -1 & 0 \\
-1 & 0 & 0 & 0 \\
0 & 0 & 0 & 1
\end{bmatrix}
\begin{bmatrix} i_{c1} \\ i_{c2} \\ i_{c3} \\ i_{c4} \end{bmatrix}
$$

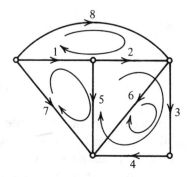

Loops (specified by
ordered branch lists)

1: $\{1, 5, 7\}$
2: $\{2, 3, 4, 5\}$
3: $\{3, 4, 6\}$
4: $\{8, 2, 1\}$

Fig. 1   Example

Note: Loop current i_{c2} cannot be measured — it is fictitious.

Let us now return to the first form of KCL in (3). Since $\mathbf{A}_t^{-1}$ is a non-singular matrix, both sides of (3) can be multiplied by $\mathbf{A}_t^{-1}$ and the result will be equivalent to (3). But $\mathbf{A}_t^{-1}\mathbf{A} = \mathbf{Q}_f$, from (2-24). Hence,

$$\mathbf{Q}_f\mathbf{i} = \mathbf{0}, \tag{11}$$

which is another expression for the first form of KCL.

A somewhat more general expression of this form of KCL is obtained by premultiplying (11) by the nonsingular matrix $\mathbf{Q}_t$ and invoking (2-23). The result is

$$\mathbf{Q}\mathbf{i} = \mathbf{0}. \tag{12}$$

This rather general first form of KCL can be given a physical interpretation. The nonzero elements in each row of $\mathbf{Q}$ correspond to a set of branches which, when removed, separate one part of the network into two pieces. Thus, each element in the product $\mathbf{Q}\mathbf{i}$ is the algebraic sum of currents leaving one such piece. By (12), or its equivalent scalar form,

$$\sum_{l=1}^{b} q_{kl}i_l = 0 \quad (k = 1, \ldots, n), \tag{13}$$

we see that the algebraic sum is zero. (Observe the similarity of [13] and [1].) Just as (1) stems from the demand of the physical world that there can be no charge accumulation at any node, so also (13) corresponds to the demand that there can be no charge accumulation in any piece of the network. A whimsical interpretation is that each such piece of the network is a *super node*; in that case (13) is just KCL at collections of such supernodes.

Both forms of KCL can be generalized by invoking nonsingular transformations. A first form KCL equation may or may not have an obvious physical interpretation and the set of independent variables in a second form KCL may or may not be identifiable currents—fictitious or real. (This topic is explored further in Prob. 15).

3.2 KIRCHHOFF'S VOLTAGE LAW

Kirchhoff's voltage law (abbreviated as KVL) states: *On each closed path in a network, the algebraic sum of the voltages is zero.* This law can be expressed, using the complete loop matrix for the associated graph of the network, as

$$\sum_{l=1}^{b} b_{kl} v_l = 0 \ (k = 1, \ldots) \text{ or } \mathbf{B}_c \mathbf{v} = 0, \tag{14}$$

where $\mathbf{v}$ is the vector of branch voltages $\mathbf{v} = [v_k]$, $k = 1, 2, \ldots, b$. As previously established, $\mathbf{B}_c$ is of rank $b - n$, therefore no information is lost if only $b - n$ linearly independent rows of $\mathbf{B}_c$ are retained. If this is done, we get

$$\mathbf{B}\mathbf{v} = 0, \tag{15}$$

which is a first form expression of KVL.

Let the loop matrix be partitioned and written as $\mathbf{B} = [\mathbf{B}_t \ \mathbf{B}_l]$ and let $\mathbf{v}$ be similarly partitioned. Thus,

$$\mathbf{v} = \begin{bmatrix} \mathbf{v}_t \\ \mathbf{v}_l \end{bmatrix}. \tag{16}$$

where $\mathbf{v}_t$ is the vector of twig voltages and $\mathbf{v}_l$ is the vector of link currents. When these are inserted into the preceding expression for KVL, the result is

$$[\mathbf{B}_t \ \mathbf{B}_l]\begin{bmatrix} \mathbf{v}_t \\ \mathbf{v}_l \end{bmatrix} = \mathbf{B}_t \mathbf{v}_t + \mathbf{B}_l \mathbf{v}_l = 0 \rightarrow \mathbf{v}_l = -\mathbf{B}_l^{-1} \mathbf{B}_t \mathbf{v}_t, \tag{17}$$

since $\mathbf{B}_l$ is a nonsingular matrix.

The message carried by this expression is that, given a forest, there is a linear relationship by which the *link voltages* are determined from the *twig voltages*. If the twig voltages can be determined by some other means, the link voltages become known from (17). Of all the b branch voltages, only n of them — the twig voltages — need be determined independently.

The dependence of $\mathbf{v}_l$ on $\mathbf{v}_t$ can be used in (16) to yield

$$\mathbf{v} = \begin{bmatrix} \mathbf{U} \\ -\mathbf{B}_l^{-1}\mathbf{B}_t \end{bmatrix} \mathbf{v}_t \quad \text{or} \quad \mathbf{v} = \mathbf{Q}_f'\mathbf{v}_t. \qquad (18)$$

(handwritten marginalia: $Q_f = A_t^{-1}A$, $Q_f^T = (A_t^{-1}A)^T = A^T(A_t^{-1})^T$)

The final form results from (2-23). This is an alternative expression of KVL; we shall refer to it as a *second form expression* of KVL. This states that the vector of all branch voltages is obtained as a linear transformation of the vector of a smaller set of voltages, the twig voltages.

Another particular second form expression can be obtained by replacing $\mathbf{Q}_f$ in (18) by its equivalent in (2-24). The result is

$$\mathbf{v} = \mathbf{A}'\mathbf{A}_t'^{-1}\mathbf{v}_t = \mathbf{A}'\mathbf{v}_n, \qquad (19)$$

(handwritten marginalia: node voltages, $A^T(A_t^T)^{-1}$)

where

$$\mathbf{v}_n = \mathbf{A}_t'^{-1}\mathbf{v}_t. \qquad (20)$$

The elements of $\mathbf{v}_n$ can be shown to be measurable voltages. (See Prob. 16.) Each is the voltage of a node relative to that of another node in its part of the network. That other node is called a *reference*, or *datum*, *node*. Each part of a network has a reference node, that associated with one of the eliminated rows of $\mathbf{A}_c$. For reasons which should now be obvious, the elements of $\mathbf{v}_n$ are called *node voltages*. Thus, in addition to twig voltages, node voltages also constitute an independent set of voltages.

A more general second form expression for KVL is obtained when $\mathbf{Q}_f$ in (18) is replaced by its equivalent in (2-18). Thus,

$$\mathbf{v} = \mathbf{Q}'\mathbf{Q}_t'^{-1}\mathbf{v}_t = \mathbf{Q}'\mathbf{v}_c, \qquad (21)$$

where

$$\mathbf{v}_c = \mathbf{Q}_t'^{-1}\mathbf{v}_t. \qquad (22)$$

The transformation matrix giving the vector of all voltages in terms of the vector of a smaller set is the transpose of the cut-set matrix. So we have used the subscript c to designate these voltages. In general, an element of $\mathbf{v}_c$ cannot be identified as a measurable node-pair voltage — voltage between a pair of nodes. Thus, the elements of $\mathbf{v}_c$ are viewed as fictitious voltages. In a sense these fictitious voltages are more fictitious than the fictitious loop currents. If not measurable, the latter can still be identified with something — loops — which in other circumstances might have measurable currents associated with them. In the case of the elements of $\mathbf{v}_c$ no such identity with some graph attribute can be made in general. (This is illustrated by the solution of Exer. 4.)

Both forms of KVL can be generalized by invoking nonsingular transformations. A first form KVL may or may not have an obvious physical interpretation and the set of independent variables in the second form may or may not be measurable voltages. (This topic is explored further in Prob. 17.)

For future reference, the various forms of KCL and KVL are collected and summarized in Table 1.

Table 1 Forms of KCL and KVL

	KCL	KVL
First form	$\mathbf{Ai} = 0$	$\mathbf{B}_m\mathbf{v} = 0$
	$\mathbf{Q}_f\mathbf{i} = 0$	$\mathbf{B}_f\mathbf{v} = 0$
	$\mathbf{Qi} = 0$	$\mathbf{Bv} = 0$
Second form	$\mathbf{i} = \mathbf{B}'_m\mathbf{i}_m$ (mesh)	$\mathbf{v} = \mathbf{A}'\mathbf{v}_n$ (node)
	$\mathbf{i} = \mathbf{B}'_f\mathbf{i}_l$ (link)	$\mathbf{v} = \mathbf{Q}'_f\mathbf{v}_t$ (twig)
	$\mathbf{i} = \mathbf{B}'\mathbf{i}_c$ (loop or circuit)	$\mathbf{v} = \mathbf{Q}'\mathbf{v}_c$ (cut-set)

Note that each of the sets of currents in $\mathbf{i}_m$ (mesh), $\mathbf{i}_l$ (link) and $\mathbf{i}_c$ (circuit) is a *basis set* of $b - n$ independent current variables in terms of which the vector of all currents can be expressed through linear transformations. Similarly, each of the sets of voltages in $\mathbf{v}_n$ (node), $\mathbf{v}_t$ (twig), and $\mathbf{v}_c$ (cut-set) is a *basis set* of n voltage variables in terms of which the vector of all voltages can be expressed through linear transformations.

3.3 COMPONENT CONSTRAINTS

The equations expressing the Kirchhoff laws represent constraints among the voltage and current variables imposed by the network structure alone, quite independent of the specific nature of the components. To complete the picture, we must also specify the constraints among variables imposed by the components themselves. We now turn our attention to this topic.

There is a great deal of flexibility in the manner in which to express the component constraints, even in very simple cases. To illustrate this, consider the case of a 10-ohm resistor connected to a 6-volt battery, as shown in Fig. 2 together with its graph. The component relationships

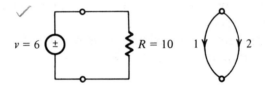

Fig. 2   Illustration

can be written in a number of alternative matrix forms. One possibility, since $v_1 = 6$ and $v_2 = 10i_2$, is

$$\begin{bmatrix} v_1 \\ v_2 \end{bmatrix} = \begin{bmatrix} 0 & 0 \\ 0 & 10 \end{bmatrix} \begin{bmatrix} i_1 \\ i_2 \end{bmatrix} + \begin{bmatrix} 6 \\ 0 \end{bmatrix}$$

But the expression $v_2 = 10i_2$ can just as well be written $i_2 = v_2/10$ or $v_2/10 - i_2 = 0$. Two other possible matrix forms, therefore, are

$$\begin{bmatrix} 1 & 0 \\ 0 & 1/10 \end{bmatrix} \begin{bmatrix} v_1 \\ v_2 \end{bmatrix} = \begin{bmatrix} 0 & 0 \\ 0 & 1 \end{bmatrix} \begin{bmatrix} i_1 \\ i_2 \end{bmatrix} + \begin{bmatrix} 6 \\ 0 \end{bmatrix}$$

$$\begin{bmatrix} 1 & 0 \\ 0 & 1/10 \end{bmatrix} \begin{bmatrix} v_1 \\ v_2 \end{bmatrix} - \begin{bmatrix} 0 & 0 \\ 0 & 1 \end{bmatrix} \begin{bmatrix} i_1 \\ i_2 \end{bmatrix} = \begin{bmatrix} 6 \\ 0 \end{bmatrix}$$

The vector on the right side of the last expression is a voltage source vector; it can be transposed to the left and combined with the voltage vector to yield

$$\begin{bmatrix} 1 & 0 \\ 0 & 1/10 \end{bmatrix} \begin{bmatrix} v_1 - 6 \\ v_2 \end{bmatrix} - \begin{bmatrix} 0 & 0 \\ 0 & 1 \end{bmatrix} \begin{bmatrix} i_1 \\ i_2 \end{bmatrix} = 0$$

With this simple case as background, we shall now introduce a general representation of the branch voltage-current relationships of a network containing components of the types described in Chapter 1. This representation is

$$\mathbf{M}(\mathbf{v} - \mathbf{v}_s) + \mathbf{N}(\mathbf{i} - \mathbf{i}_s) = \mathbf{0}, \tag{23}$$

where $\mathbf{v}$ and $\mathbf{i}$ are vectors of branch voltages and branch currents, respectively and where $\mathbf{v}_s$ and $\mathbf{i}_s$ are vectors of known source functions. In the preceding illustration $\mathbf{M}$ and $\mathbf{N}$ were matrices of constants; in more extensive networks the elements of $\mathbf{M}$ and $\mathbf{N}$ may be more general.

As further illustration of this form, we shall determine such an expression for the network with the schematic and graph shown in Fig. 3.

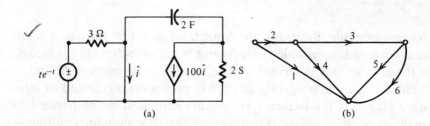

Fig. 3   Network: schematic and graph

Branches 4 and 5 correspond to the controlled source; the independent source is represented by branch 1. The voltage-current relationships of the components impose the following constraints:

$$v_1 = te^{-t} \Rightarrow v_1 - te^{-t} = 0 \qquad v_4 = 0$$

$$v_2 = 3i_2 \Rightarrow v_2 - 3i_2 = 0 \qquad i_5 = 100i_4 \Rightarrow i_5 - 100i_4 = 0$$

$$i_3 = 2\frac{d}{dt}v_3 \Rightarrow i_3 - 2\frac{d}{dt}v_3 = 0 \qquad i_6 = 2v_6 \Rightarrow i_6 - 2v_6 = 0$$

This set of six branch relations can be collected and expressed as a single matrix equation in the form of (23). Thus,

$$
\begin{bmatrix}
1 & 0 & 0 & 0 & 0 & 0 \\
0 & 1 & 0 & 0 & 0 & 0 \\
0 & 0 & -2\dfrac{d}{dt} & 0 & 0 & 0 \\
0 & 0 & 0 & 1 & 0 & 0 \\
0 & 0 & 0 & 0 & 0 & 0 \\
0 & 0 & 0 & 0 & 0 & -2
\end{bmatrix}
\left\{
\begin{bmatrix} v_1 \\ v_2 \\ v_3 \\ v_4 \\ v_5 \\ v_6 \end{bmatrix}
-
\begin{bmatrix} te^{-t} \\ 0 \\ 0 \\ 0 \\ 0 \\ 0 \end{bmatrix}
\right\}
$$

$$
+
\begin{bmatrix}
0 & 0 & 0 & 0 & 0 & 0 \\
0 & -3 & 0 & 0 & 0 & 0 \\
0 & 0 & 1 & 0 & 0 & 0 \\
0 & 0 & 0 & 0 & 0 & 0 \\
0 & 0 & 0 & -100 & 1 & 0 \\
0 & 0 & 0 & 0 & 0 & 1
\end{bmatrix}
\left\{
\begin{bmatrix} i_1 \\ i_2 \\ i_3 \\ i_4 \\ i_5 \\ i_6 \end{bmatrix}
-
\begin{bmatrix} 0 \\ 0 \\ 0 \\ 0 \\ 0 \\ 0 \end{bmatrix}
\right\}
=
\begin{bmatrix} 0 \\ 0 \\ 0 \\ 0 \\ 0 \\ 0 \end{bmatrix}.
$$

As this example illustrates, the branch relation (23) may be a time-domain expression, in which case $\mathbf{M}$ and $\mathbf{N}$ are time-domain operators. For the components described in Chapter 1, the elements of $\mathbf{M}$ and $\mathbf{N}$ can contain the scalar operations of differentiation (d/dt) and of integration $(\int_0^t d\tau)$. If the branch relations are expressed in the frequency-domain — say the Laplace transform of the time-domain relations — then, $\mathbf{M}$ and $\mathbf{N}$ will be matrix-valued functions of the complex frequency variable s. In this latter case we would follow the convention of replacing the lower case symbols for the voltage and current variables by upper case symbols. Thus, (23) would become

$$
\mathbf{M}(\mathbf{V} - \mathbf{V}_s) + \mathbf{N}(\mathbf{I} - \mathbf{I}_s) = \mathbf{0}. \tag{24}
$$

Make a mental note of the fact that $\mathbf{V}_s$ and $\mathbf{I}_s$ are not simply the Laplace transforms of $\mathbf{v}_s$ and $\mathbf{i}_s$. This is due to the fact that initial conditions associated with derivatives must be included in the frequency-domain relation, as the next example will illustrate.

We shall have occasion to deal with both the time-domain and the frequency-domain. As the development proceeds, we would like to avoid writing what amounts to the same expression twice, once with lower case symbols for the time-domain and once with upper case symbols for the frequency-domain. We shall write the equations only once, with lower case symbols; the context (or explicit comment) will make clear whether we mean for this to stand only for the time-domain in this instance, or for both. If we want to limit ourselves in a given development or illustration to the frequency-domain, then we shall use the upper case symbols appropriate to that case.

For the previous example, the branch relations in the frequency domain are

$$V_1 = \frac{1}{(s+1)^2} \qquad\qquad V_4 = 0$$

$$V_2 = 3I_2 \qquad\qquad I_5 = 100I_4$$

$$I_3 = 2sV_3 - 2v_3(0+) \qquad\qquad I_6 = 2V_6$$

These can again be expressed in the form of (24) as

$$
\left\{
\begin{bmatrix}
1 & 0 & 0 & 0 & 0 & 0 \\
0 & 1 & 0 & 0 & 0 & 0 \\
0 & 0 & -2s & 0 & 0 & 0 \\
0 & 0 & 0 & 1 & 0 & 0 \\
0 & 0 & 0 & 0 & 0 & 0 \\
0 & 0 & 0 & 0 & 0 & -2
\end{bmatrix}
\left(
\begin{bmatrix}
V_1 \\ V_2 \\ V_3 \\ V_4 \\ V_5 \\ V_6
\end{bmatrix}
-
\begin{bmatrix}
1/(s+1)^2 \\ 0 \\ 0 \\ 0 \\ 0 \\ 0
\end{bmatrix}
\right)
\right.
$$

$$
\left.
+
\begin{bmatrix}
0 & 0 & 0 & 0 & 0 & 0 \\
0 & -3 & 0 & 0 & 0 & 0 \\
0 & 0 & 1 & 0 & 0 & 0 \\
0 & 0 & 0 & 0 & 0 & 0 \\
0 & 0 & 0 & -100 & 1 & 0 \\
0 & 0 & 0 & 0 & 0 & 1
\end{bmatrix}
\left(
\begin{bmatrix}
I_1 \\ I_2 \\ I_3 \\ I_4 \\ I_5 \\ I_6
\end{bmatrix}
-
\begin{bmatrix}
0 \\ 0 \\ -2v_3(0+) \\ 0 \\ 0 \\ 0
\end{bmatrix}
\right)
\right\}
=
\begin{bmatrix}
0 \\ 0 \\ 0 \\ 0 \\ 0 \\ 0
\end{bmatrix}
$$

The matrices in (23) and (24) are not unique. This was explicitly illustrated by the simple example with which this discussion was introduced. It can also be observed from the fact that if (23) is premultiplied by any nonsingular $b \times b$ matrix of real numbers, the resulting expression is equivalent to (23). This non-uniqueness can be demonstrated on a smaller scale. Consider just branch 2 of the above example. The voltage-current relation could just as well have been written as

$$\alpha V_2 = 3\alpha I_2$$

for any real, non-zero constant α.

3.3.1   Compound Components ✓

In the preceding illustration, the independent source was treated as a component and represented by a branch in the graph, distinct from other branches. It is often convenient to combine sources with other components to get what might be thought of as *compound components*. Such a compound component can be represented by a single branch in the graph. The form of (23) or (24) facilitates this process. Two compound components involving sources are shown in Fig. 4. Because these specific structures are found more often than others, they carry the special designation *general components*.

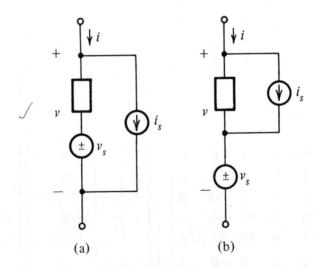

(a)   (b)

Fig. 4   General components

The voltage and current of the non-source component in either case are $v - v_s$ and $i - i_s$. For concreteness, suppose this component is a capacitor C; then the component v-i relation in the time domain is

$$i - i_s = C \frac{d}{dt}(v - v_s),$$

which is the appropriate form for writing (23).

3.3.2 Source Shifts ✓

Given a network, it is almost always possible to obtain an equivalent network in which every independent source is *accompanied by* (some authors say *associated with*) some component other than an independent source. This is done by a process of voltage source shifts or current source shifts to be described below. In the equivalent network, no branch of the network graph corresponds to just an independent source, all such sources being contained in a general component.

Now let us describe these source shifts. Suppose in a given network there is an unaccompanied independent voltage source. Such a source is shown in Fig. 5(a) together with other network components joined at one end of its connections, none of which are independent sources. These components, source included, can be viewed as the model of a multiterminal sub-network which, insofar as the rest of the network is concerned, may be replaced by its equivalent shown in Fig. 5(b). The voltage source has been shifted in the network so that it is no longer unaccompanied. Instead of the four components — 3 nonsource and 1

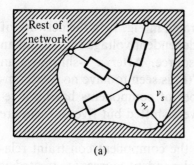 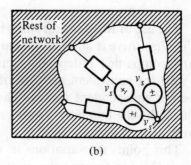

(a)　　　　　　　　　　　　　　　(b)

Fig. 5　Voltage source shift

source—in Fig. 5(a), we now have three general components each of which has a voltage source accompanied by a nonsource component. As far as the rest of the network is concerned, the results of any analysis of the equivalent network in Fig. 5(b) can be applied to the original network. But in determining voltages and currents of components involved in the voltage source shift, care must be exercised. Thus, the voltages of the general branches in Fig. 5(b) are not those of the nonsource branches in the original network; the latter are the former diminished by the voltage of the shifted source.

The voltage source shift, commonly called a *voltage shift* (or *v-shift*), has its counterpart current source shift, known as a *current shift* (or *i-shift*). Equivalence is again between models for a multiterminal subnetwork. The equivalence is illustrated in Fig. 6. You should fill in the details.

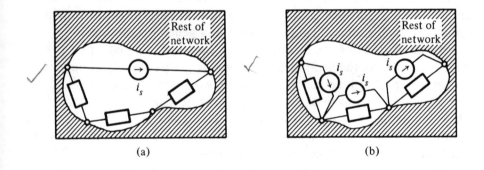

(a)   (b)

Fig. 6 Current source shift

The use of these source shifts is illustrated in Fig. 7. In the network of Fig. 7(a) there is an unaccompanied independent voltage source and an unaccompanied independent current source. After a v-shift and an i-shift the equivalent network of Fig. 7(b) is seen to have no unaccompanied independent source. The number of components has been reduced by the number of sources that were shifted but five of them are now general components.

This points up variations in writing the component constraint relations (23) for a given network. Either independent sources are treated as distinct components or they are not and are combined with accompanying components to form general components. In the latter case, the order of the matrices $\mathbf{M}$ and $\mathbf{N}$ is reduced by the number of sources so treated. Another difference is that in the former case $\mathbf{M}$ will have a row and column of zeros for a current source and $\mathbf{N}$ will for a voltage source. Such rows of zeros will not be present in $\mathbf{M}$ and $\mathbf{N}$ in the latter case.

These points are illustrated in the simple example shown in Fig. 8. If the voltages and currents of the general branches containing R_1 and R_2 are labeled v_a and v_b, respectively, and i_a and i_b, respectively, then the branch constraints in the two cases are

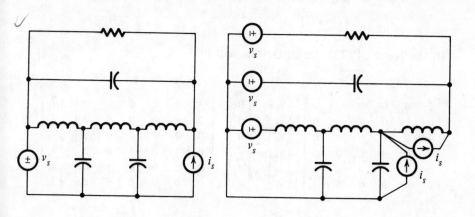

Fig. 7   Illustration: v-shift and i-shift

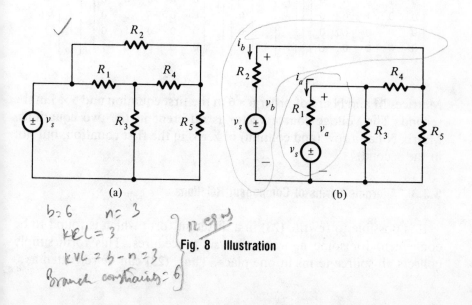

(a)   (b)

Fig. 8   Illustration

(a)   (b)

$$v_1 = R_1 i_1$$ $$v_a - v_s(t) = R_1 i_a$$

$$v_2 = R_2 i_2$$ $$v_b - v_s(t) = R_2 i_b$$

$$v_3 = R_3 i_3$$ $$v_3 = R_3 i_3$$

$$i_4 = G_4 v_4$$ $$i_4 = G_4 v_4$$

$$i_5 = G_5 v_5$$ $$i_5 = G_5 v_5$$

$$v_6 = v_s(t)$$

In the form of (23) the equations will be

$$
\begin{bmatrix}
1 & 0 & 0 & 0 & 0 & 0 \\
0 & 1 & 0 & 0 & 0 & 0 \\
0 & 0 & 1 & 0 & 0 & 0 \\
0 & 0 & 0 & G_4 & 0 & 0 \\
0 & 0 & 0 & 0 & G_5 & 0 \\
0 & 0 & 0 & 0 & 0 & 1
\end{bmatrix}
\left\{
\begin{bmatrix}
v_1 \\ v_2 \\ v_3 \\ v_4 \\ v_5 \\ v_6
\end{bmatrix}
-
\begin{bmatrix}
0 \\ 0 \\ 0 \\ 0 \\ 0 \\ v_s
\end{bmatrix}
\right\}
+
\begin{bmatrix}
-R_1 & 0 & 0 & 0 & 0 & 0 \\
0 & -R_2 & 0 & 0 & 0 & 0 \\
0 & 0 & -R_3 & 0 & 0 & 0 \\
0 & 0 & 0 & -1 & 0 & 0 \\
0 & 0 & 0 & 0 & -1 & 0 \\
0 & 0 & 0 & 0 & 0 & 0
\end{bmatrix}
\begin{bmatrix}
i_1 \\ i_2 \\ i_3 \\ i_4 \\ i_5 \\ i_6
\end{bmatrix}
= 0 .
$$

$$
\begin{bmatrix}
1 & 0 & 0 & 0 & 0 \\
0 & 1 & 0 & 0 & 0 \\
0 & 0 & 1 & 0 & 0 \\
0 & 0 & 0 & G_4 & 0 \\
0 & 0 & 0 & 0 & G_5
\end{bmatrix}
\left\{
\begin{bmatrix}
v_a \\ v_b \\ v_3 \\ v_4 \\ v_5
\end{bmatrix}
-
\begin{bmatrix}
v_s \\ v_s \\ 0 \\ 0 \\ 0
\end{bmatrix}
\right\}
+
\begin{bmatrix}
-R_1 & 0 & 0 & 0 & 0 \\
0 & -R_2 & 0 & 0 & 0 \\
0 & 0 & -R_3 & 0 & 0 \\
0 & 0 & 0 & -1 & 0 \\
0 & 0 & 0 & 0 & -1
\end{bmatrix}
\begin{bmatrix}
i_a \\ i_b \\ i_3 \\ i_4 \\ i_5
\end{bmatrix}
= 0 .
$$

Matrices $\mathbf{M}$ and $\mathbf{N}$ are of order 6×6 in the first equation and 5×5 in the second. The voltage source vector is different in the two equations. Matrix $\mathbf{N}$ has a row (and column) of zeros in the first equation, but not in the second.

3.3.3 Alternate Forms of Component Relations

It is possible to rewrite (23) in a different form which is found to be convenient for some network analysis procedures. This form simply collects all source terms in one place. Thus, (23) can be rewritten as

$$\mathbf{Mv} + \mathbf{Ni} = \mathbf{Mv}_s + \mathbf{Ni}_s = \mathbf{e}, \tag{25}$$

where the source vector $\mathbf{e}$ is defined as

$$\mathbf{e} = \mathbf{Mv}_s + \mathbf{Ni}_s. \tag{26}$$

It is a known function for any given network.

At first sight it may appear that expressing the component relations in the form of (23) or (25) is unnecessarily complicated. However, the full power and general utility will become evident as we examine the various ways of writing network equations in the next chapter, and when we examine adjoint networks in Chapter 9.

The relation in (25) constitutes a set of b equations in the $2b$ current and voltage variables. Kirchhoff's laws introduce another set of b independent equations among the same $2b$ variables. Hence, a network has a unique solution only if all b equations in (25) are independent. A particularly simple form is obtained if the voltage and current vectors are combined into a single vector and the coefficient matrices are catenated. Thus,

$$[\mathbf{M} \ \mathbf{N}]\begin{bmatrix} \mathbf{v} \\ \mathbf{i} \end{bmatrix} = \mathbf{e} \tag{27}$$

When all b of these equations are independent, matrix $[\mathbf{M} \ \mathbf{N}]$ must be of full rank — namely b — and it must have at least one $b \times b$ nonsingular submatrix. We shall hereafter assume that such is the case.

$$AI_B = A_t I_t + A_L I_L = 0 \qquad V_h = [A_t^T]^{-1} V_t$$

$$I_t = -A_t^{-1} A_L I_L =$$

$$I_B = B_f^T I_L = B_f^T C \bar{I}^{-1} = B^T I' \qquad B_f^T C = B^T$$

$$B_f V_B = B_{fL} V_{BL} + B_{ft} V_{Bt} = 0$$

$$V_B = Q_B^T V_t = Q_B^T d V' = Q^T V' \qquad Q_B^T d = Q^T$$

$$V_B = A^T E$$

$$I_M = [B_L^T]^{-1} I_L \qquad V_N = [A_t^T]^{-1} V_t$$

CHAPTER 4
Network Equations

In the preceding chapter, the basic relationships in electrical networks were established. For a network having b components (branches) there are b independent Kirchhoff law relations and b independent component relations. We shall now concern ourselves with the methods by which these relations are combined and the resulting equations solved.

Conceptually, the simplest procedure would be to combine the b Kirchhoff law relations and the b component relations into a set of $2b$ equations. When they are consistent, they can be solved for the $2b$ variables—b currents and b voltages. Although this is a large set of equations, often larger than needed, they are composed simply by matrix catenation. There are methods by which the number of equations to be solved simultaneously can be reduced. But these methods require matrix arithmetic to compose the equations. Each method must obviously use all the basic relations. They differ only in the form of the Kirchhoff laws used and in the order in which all the relations are combined.

These considerations make it clear that there is no one best network analysis method; each one has advantages and disadvantages, as we shall see.

4.1 NODE EQUATIONS

It was observed in the preceding chapter that all branch voltages in a network could be determined in terms of a smaller set, the node voltages. If the node voltages are known, all voltages will become known; then all currents will be determined from the component relations. With these thoughts in mind, the idea is to eliminate all other variables but the node voltages and end up with a set of equations in which these are the only variables.

The beginning point is the branch relations of (3-23), repeated here for convenience.

$$\mathbf{M}(\mathbf{v} - \mathbf{v}_s) + \mathbf{N}(\mathbf{i} - \mathbf{i}_s) = 0. \tag{1}$$

Assume that $\mathbf{N}$ is the negative of a unit matrix or can be made so due to the flexibility in writing component relations; call this assumption the *node assumption*. There might be networks for which this assumption cannot be realized; then node equations cannot be written for the network as it stands. Some of the resulting implications will be examined later.

Putting $\mathbf{N} = -\mathbf{U}$ and using the second form of KVL found in Table 1 to replace $\mathbf{v}$ by $\mathbf{A}'\mathbf{v}_n$, (1) becomes

$$\mathbf{M}\mathbf{A}'\mathbf{v}_n - \mathbf{M}\mathbf{v}_s - \mathbf{i} + \mathbf{i}_s = 0. \tag{2}$$

Each term in this equation dimensionally is a current vector; hence $\mathbf{M}$ is dimensionally an "admittance" operator. It seems appropriate, therefore, to rename it $\mathbf{Y}$. When this is done, and the resulting equation is premultiplied by $\mathbf{A}$, the result is

$$\mathbf{A}\mathbf{Y}\mathbf{A}'\mathbf{v}_n - \mathbf{A}\mathbf{Y}\mathbf{v}_s - \mathbf{A}\mathbf{i} + \mathbf{A}\mathbf{i}_s = 0. \tag{3}$$

But $\mathbf{A}\mathbf{i} = 0$ by KCL; using this and rearranging terms gives

$$\mathbf{A}\mathbf{Y}\mathbf{A}'\mathbf{v}_n = \mathbf{A}(\mathbf{Y}\mathbf{v}_s - \mathbf{i}_s). \tag{4}$$

This is the matrix form of the *node equations* in which the variables are the node voltages. In the time-domain, the elements of $\mathbf{Y}$ include the dynamic operations of differentiation and integration; so (4) is in general an integral-differential equation. It can be solved by analytical or numerical methods. In the frequency-domain, (4) is an algebraic equation in which $\mathbf{Y}$ is the *branch-admittance matrix*, a function of the complex frequency variable s, and the variables are Laplace transforms. (For the sinusoidal steady state, the variables are the corresponding phasors, there are no initial conditions and s has the value $j\omega$.)

The right side of (4) includes all the sources. For compactness, a general source vector is defined as

$$\mathbf{j}_n = \mathbf{A}(\mathbf{Y}\mathbf{v}_s - \mathbf{i}_s) \tag{5}$$

so that (4) can be rewritten as

$$\mathbf{Y}_n \mathbf{v}_n = \mathbf{j}_n, \tag{6}$$

where

$$\mathbf{Y}_n = \mathbf{AYA'} \tag{7}$$

is the *node operator* (or *admittance*) *matrix*. Its elements include dynamic operators in the time-domain and functions of s in the frequency-domain. (We shall not continue such explanatory comments in the subsequent development for similar matrices.)

Equation (6) is a compact form of the node equations. Symbolically, its solution is

$$\mathbf{v}_n = \mathbf{Y}_n^{-1} \mathbf{j}_n. \tag{8}$$

The simplicity of this form masks the substantial effort required to carry out the solution. As stated before, once $\mathbf{v}_n$ is known, every other voltage and all the currents are simply found with no further solving of simultaneous equations.

Now let us briefly consider the implications of the node assumption. If $-\mathbf{N}$ is to be a unit matrix, it cannot have a row of zeros. But the existence of certain components in a network *will* cause such a row of zeros in $-\mathbf{N}$. One such component is an unaccompanied independent voltage source. But this can usually be remedied by combining the voltage source with an accompanying branch, using a v-shift, if necessary. To write node equations, then, voltage sources must always be combined in a general branch. (It is not necessary to go one step further and convert this general branch explicitly into a Norton equivalent.)

A second bothersome component is a voltage-controlled voltage source (VCVS) corresponding to which $-\mathbf{N}$ again would have a row of zeros. Here again it is sometimes possible to combine components into compound components to avoid the row of zeros in $-\mathbf{N}$. We shall not pursue this matter any further here but urge you to examine the basic components in Chapter 1 to see which ones would lead to such difficulties and to consider how they might be augmented to achieve compound components conforming to the node assumption. (See Prob. 29a.)

To illustrate the creation of a set of node equations — we will do so in the frequency-domain and, so, will use capitals for the variables — con-

sider the network schematic in Fig. 1. First, observe that the independent voltage source is accompanied. Next, note that the VCVS together
with the 1 ohm resistor at its input and the 3 Siemen resistor at its output constitute a compound component with suitable voltage-current

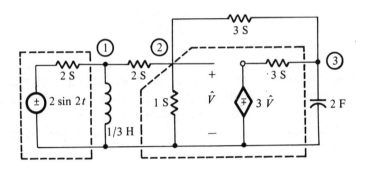

Fig. 1 Network schematic

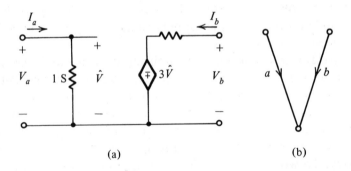

(a)   (b)

Fig. 2 Compound component and graph

constraints. This compound component and its graph are shown in Fig.
2. It is obvious that

$$I_a = V_a$$
$$I_b = 3\{V_b - (-3)V_a\} = 9V_a + 3V_b.$$

Before going on we want to call your attention to the fact that the
augmentation of basic components is a flexible process. In this case, it
would have been sufficient to augment the VCVS with just the 3 Siemen
resistor at its output.

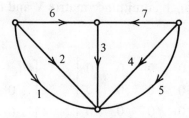

Fig. 3 Network graph

The graph for the network, with one branch for the general component — independent voltage source and 2 Siemen resistor — and two branches for the compound component is shown in Fig. 3. The component-imposed constraints in matrix form are

$$
\begin{bmatrix}
2 & 0 & 0 & 0 & 0 & 0 & 0 \\
0 & 3/s & 0 & 0 & 0 & 0 & 0 \\
0 & 0 & 1 & 0 & 0 & 0 & 0 \\
0 & 0 & 9 & 3 & 0 & 0 & 0 \\
0 & 0 & 0 & 0 & 2s & 0 & 0 \\
0 & 0 & 0 & 0 & 0 & 2 & 0 \\
0 & 0 & 0 & 0 & 0 & 0 & 3
\end{bmatrix}
\left\{
\begin{bmatrix}
V_1 \\ V_2 \\ V_3 \\ V_4 \\ V_5 \\ V_6 \\ V_7
\end{bmatrix}
-
\begin{bmatrix}
2\dfrac{2}{s^2+4} \\ 0 \\ 0 \\ 0 \\ 0 \\ 0 \\ 0
\end{bmatrix}
\right\}
$$

$$
-
\left\{
\begin{bmatrix}
I_1 \\ I_2 \\ I_3 \\ I_4 \\ I_5 \\ I_6 \\ I_7
\end{bmatrix}
-
\begin{bmatrix}
0 \\ \dfrac{1}{s}i_2(0+) \\ 0 \\ 0 \\ -2v_5(0+) \\ 0 \\ 0
\end{bmatrix}
\right\}
=
\begin{bmatrix}
0 \\ 0 \\ 0 \\ 0 \\ 0 \\ 0 \\ 0
\end{bmatrix} .
$$

Clearly $-\mathbf{N}$ is a unit matrix; hence, the node assumption is satisfied. Furthermore, the branch admittance matrix $\mathbf{Y}$ and the vectors $\mathbf{V}_s$ and $\mathbf{I}_s$ are seen to be

$$
\mathbf{Y} = \begin{bmatrix}
2 & 0 & 0 & 0 & 0 & 0 & 0 \\
0 & 3/s & 0 & 0 & 0 & 0 & 0 \\
0 & 0 & 1 & 0 & 0 & 0 & 0 \\
0 & 0 & 9 & 3 & 0 & 0 & 0 \\
0 & 0 & 0 & 0 & 2s & 0 & 0 \\
0 & 0 & 0 & 0 & 0 & 2 & 0 \\
0 & 0 & 0 & 0 & 0 & 0 & 3
\end{bmatrix}, \quad
\mathbf{V}_s = \begin{bmatrix}
4/(s^2+4) \\
0 \\
0 \\
0 \\
0 \\
0 \\
0
\end{bmatrix}, \quad
\mathbf{I}_s = \begin{bmatrix}
0 \\
\dfrac{1}{s} i_2(0+) \\
0 \\
0 \\
-2v_5(0+) \\
0 \\
0
\end{bmatrix}.
$$

The node incidence matrix corresponding to the three labeled nodes is

$$
\begin{array}{c}
\text{Branches} \rightarrow \\
\begin{array}{cccccccc}
\text{Nodes} & 1 & 2 & 3 & 4 & 5 & 6 & 7 \\
\downarrow & & & & & & & \\
\end{array}
\end{array}
$$

$$
\mathbf{A} = \begin{array}{c} 1 \\ 2 \\ 3 \end{array}
\begin{bmatrix}
1 & 1 & 0 & 0 & 0 & 1 & 0 \\
0 & 0 & 1 & 0 & 0 & -1 & -1 \\
0 & 0 & 0 & 1 & 1 & 0 & 1
\end{bmatrix}.
$$

The data now exists to compute the node admittance matrix $\mathbf{Y}_n$. The result is

$$
\mathbf{Y}_n = \mathbf{AYA'} = \begin{bmatrix}
4 + 3/s & -2 & 0 \\
-2 & 6 & -3 \\
0 & 6 & 6 + 2s
\end{bmatrix}.
$$

The excitation vector $\mathbf{J}_n$ is easily evaluated, the result being

$$
\mathbf{J}_n = -\mathbf{AJ}_s + \mathbf{AYV}_s = \begin{bmatrix}
-\dfrac{1}{s} i_2(0+) + \dfrac{8}{s^2+4} \\
0 \\
2v_5(0+)
\end{bmatrix}
$$

Using the $\mathbf{J}_n$ and $\mathbf{Y}_n$ just found as per (5) and (7), the node equations for the network are

$$
\begin{bmatrix}
4 + 3/s & -2 & 0 \\
-2 & 6 & -3 \\
0 & 6 & 6 + 2s
\end{bmatrix}
\begin{bmatrix}
V_{n1} \\
V_{n2} \\
V_{n3}
\end{bmatrix}
=
\begin{bmatrix}
-\dfrac{1}{s} i_2(0+) + \dfrac{8}{s^2 + 4} \\
0 \\
2v_5(0+)
\end{bmatrix}.
$$

For zero initial conditions $-i_2(0+)=0$ and $v_5(0+)=0-$the solution, obtained after premultiplication by

$$
\mathbf{Y}_n^{-1} = \frac{1}{40s^2 + 228s + 162}
\begin{bmatrix}
12s^2 + 54s & 4s^2 + 12s & 6s \\
4s^2 + 12s & 8s^2 + 30s + 18 & 12s + 9 \\
-12s & -24s - 18 & 20s + 18
\end{bmatrix}
$$

is

$$
\begin{bmatrix}
V_1 \\
V_2 \\
V_3
\end{bmatrix}
=
\frac{1}{(s^2 + 4)(40s^2 + 228s + 162)}
\begin{bmatrix}
96s^2 + 432s \\
32s^2 + 96s \\
-96s
\end{bmatrix}.
$$

4.2 CUT-SET EQUATIONS

Another basis set of variables discussed in Chapter 3, in terms of which all other variables could be determined, is the set of cut-set voltages. The preceding development of the node equations can be repeated but instead of using the incidence matrix form of KCL, the cut-set matrix form is used; and instead of premultiplying (2) by $\mathbf{A}$, we premultiply by $\mathbf{Q}$. The result of this process is

$$
\mathbf{Y}_c \mathbf{v}_c = \mathbf{j}_c. \tag{9}
$$

The equations in this set are called the·*cut-set equations* and

$$\mathbf{Y}_c = \mathbf{QYQ}' \tag{10}$$

is the *cut-set operator* (or *admittance*) *matrix* and

$$\mathbf{j}_c = \mathbf{Q}(\mathbf{Yv}_s - \mathbf{i}_s) \tag{11}$$

is a shorthand for a composite source vector. The formal solution of the cut-set equations is

$$\mathbf{v}_c = \mathbf{Y}_c^{-1}\mathbf{j}_c. \tag{12}$$

Clearly, the same assumption about $\mathbf{N}$ must be made in order for (9) to exist; for this reason it might also be called the *cut-set assumption*. Similarly, the discussion about general branches and compound branches is still valid.

When the node (or cut-set) assumption is valid, we say the network has an *admittance representation*. When a fundamental cut-set matrix $\mathbf{Q}_f$ is used, the basis voltage vector $\mathbf{v}_c$ is the twig voltage vector $\mathbf{v}_t$. Also, $\mathbf{j}_c$ and $\mathbf{Y}_c$ become $\mathbf{j}_t$ and $\mathbf{Y}_t$. The equations are then called *twig equations* and $\mathbf{Y}_t$ is the *twig operator* (or *admittance*) *matrix*.

To illustrate the writing of a set of twig equations — let's make it the time-domain this time — consider the previous network with the schematic in Fig. 1 and its graph in Fig. 3. The component-imposed constraints in matrix form are

$$
\left\{
\begin{bmatrix}
2 & 0 & 0 & 0 & 0 & 0 & 0 \\
0 & 3\int_0^t d\tau & 0 & 0 & 0 & 0 & 0 \\
0 & 0 & 1 & 0 & 0 & 0 & 0 \\
0 & 0 & 9 & 3 & 0 & 0 & 0 \\
0 & 0 & 0 & 0 & 2d/dt & 0 & 0 \\
0 & 0 & 0 & 0 & 0 & 2 & 0 \\
0 & 0 & 0 & 0 & 0 & 0 & 3
\end{bmatrix}
\begin{bmatrix}
v_1 \\ v_2 \\ v_3 \\ v_4 \\ v_5 \\ v_6 \\ v_7
\end{bmatrix}
-
\begin{bmatrix}
2\sin 2t \\ 0 \\ 0 \\ 0 \\ 0 \\ 0 \\ 0
\end{bmatrix}
\right\}
$$

$$-\left\{ \begin{bmatrix} i_1 \\ i_2 \\ i_3 \\ i_4 \\ i_5 \\ i_6 \\ i_7 \end{bmatrix} - \begin{bmatrix} 0 \\ i_2(0+) \\ 0 \\ 0 \\ 0 \\ 0 \\ 0 \end{bmatrix} \right\} = \begin{bmatrix} 0 \\ 0 \\ 0 \\ 0 \\ 0 \\ 0 \\ 0 \end{bmatrix}.$$

It is obvious that the cut-set assumption is satisfied. The branch admittance matrix and the source vectors are

$$\mathbf{Y} = \begin{bmatrix} 2 & 0 & 0 & 0 & 0 & 0 & 0 \\ 0 & 3\int_0^t d\tau & 0 & 0 & 0 & 0 & 0 \\ 0 & 0 & 1 & 0 & 0 & 0 & 0 \\ 0 & 0 & 9 & 3 & 0 & 0 & 0 \\ 0 & 0 & 0 & 0 & 2d/dt & 0 & 0 \\ 0 & 0 & 0 & 0 & 0 & 2 & 0 \\ 0 & 0 & 0 & 0 & 0 & 0 & 3 \end{bmatrix}$$

$$\mathbf{v}_s = \begin{bmatrix} 2\sin 2t \\ 0 \\ 0 \\ 0 \\ 0 \\ 0 \\ 0 \end{bmatrix}, \qquad \mathbf{i}_s = \begin{bmatrix} 0 \\ i_2(0+) \\ 0 \\ 0 \\ 0 \\ 0 \\ 0 \end{bmatrix}.$$

Corresponding to the tree consisting of branches 1, 6, and 7, the fundamental cut-set matrix is

$$
\text{Branches} \rightarrow
$$

$$
\text{Cut-sets } \begin{array}{ccccccc} 1 & 2 & 3 & 4 & 5 & 6 & 7 \end{array}
$$

$$
\mathbf{Q}_f = \begin{array}{c} 1 \\ 6 \\ 7 \end{array} \begin{bmatrix} 1 & 1 & 1 & 1 & 1 & 0 & 0 \\ 0 & 0 & -1 & -1 & -1 & 1 & 0 \\ 0 & 0 & 0 & 1 & 1 & 0 & 1 \end{bmatrix}.
$$

We can now evaluate $\mathbf{Y}_t$ as

$$
\mathbf{Y}_t = \mathbf{Q}_f \mathbf{Y} \mathbf{Q}_f' = \begin{bmatrix} 3\int_0^t d\tau + 15 + 2\dfrac{d}{dt} & -13 - 2\dfrac{d}{dt} & 3 + 2\dfrac{d}{dt} \\[3mm] -13 - 2\dfrac{d}{dt} & 15 + 2\dfrac{d}{dt} & -3 - 2\dfrac{d}{dt} \\[3mm] 12 + 2\dfrac{d}{dt} & -12 - 2\dfrac{d}{dt} & 6 + 2\dfrac{d}{dt} \end{bmatrix}
$$

and $\mathbf{j}_t$ as

$$
\mathbf{j}_t = -\mathbf{Q}_f \mathbf{i}_s + \mathbf{Q}_f \mathbf{Y} \mathbf{v}_s = \begin{bmatrix} -i_2(0+) + 4\sin 2t \\ 0 \\ 0 \end{bmatrix}.
$$

After noting that

$$
\mathbf{v}_t = \begin{bmatrix} v_{t1} \\ v_{t2} \\ v_{t3} \end{bmatrix} = \begin{bmatrix} v_1 \\ v_6 \\ v_7 \end{bmatrix},
$$

we may write the twig equations as

$$
\begin{bmatrix} 3\int_0^t d\tau + 15 + 2\dfrac{d}{dt} & -13 - 2\dfrac{d}{dt} & 3 + 2\dfrac{d}{dt} \\[3mm] -13 - 2\dfrac{d}{dt} & 15 + 2\dfrac{d}{dt} & -3 - 2\dfrac{d}{dt} \\[3mm] 12 + 2\dfrac{d}{dt} & -12 - 2\dfrac{d}{dt} & 6 + 2\dfrac{d}{dt} \end{bmatrix} \begin{bmatrix} v_1 \\ v_6 \\ v_7 \end{bmatrix} = \begin{bmatrix} -i_2(0+) + 4\sin 2t \\ 0 \\ 0 \end{bmatrix}.
$$

This is a set of integral-differential equations for the twig voltages. An analytical solution can be obtained by conventional methods. Also, numerical methods will yield an approximate solution at a discrete set of time points with little difficulty.

Before leaving this expression, note that by adding the second equation to the third — which amounts to an elementary row operation on the matrix equation — it becomes obvious that the twig voltages satisfy the following algebraic constraint:

$$v_1 = 3v_6 + 3v_7.$$

If this expression is used to eliminate v_1 from the first two equations, then the result is the smaller set of equations

$$\begin{bmatrix} 9 \int_0^t d\tau + 32 + 4\dfrac{d}{dt} & 9 \int_0^t d\tau + 48 + 8\dfrac{d}{dt} \\ \\ -24 - 4\dfrac{d}{dt} & -42 - 8\dfrac{d}{dt} \end{bmatrix} \begin{bmatrix} v_6 \\ \\ v_7 \end{bmatrix} = \begin{bmatrix} -i_2(0+) + 4\sin 2t \\ \\ 0 \end{bmatrix}.$$

The relationship between the variables in these equations is a dynamic relationship. Thus, although all three of the original cut-set equations are independent, it is not necessary to solve three dynamic equations independently, just two. The third variable is then obtained algebraically from the first two.

4.3   LOOP EQUATIONS

Besides basis variables which are voltages, we saw in Chapter 3 that there are basis variables which are currents. We shall now develop a set of equations in which all variables have been eliminated except a basis set of currents.

The beginning point is again the branch relations in (1). This time assume that $-\mathbf{M}$ is a unit matrix and call it the *loop assumption*. (The implications will be considered later.) Setting $\mathbf{M}$ equal to $-\mathbf{U}$ and using the second form of KCL in Table 1 to replace $\mathbf{i}$ by $\mathbf{B'i}_c$, (1) becomes

$$-\mathbf{v} + \mathbf{v}_s + \mathbf{NB'i}_c - \mathbf{Ni}_s = 0. \tag{13}$$

Dimensionally each term in this equation is a voltage, hence, $\mathbf{N}$ is dimensionally an "impedance." It would be reasonable to rename it $\mathbf{Z}$. When this is done and (13) is premultiplied by $\mathbf{B}$, the result is

$$-\mathbf{Bv} + \mathbf{Bv}_s + \mathbf{BZB'i}_c - \mathbf{BZi}_s = 0. \tag{14}$$

But $\mathbf{Bv} = 0$ by KVL; using this and transposing terms gives

$$\mathbf{BZB'i}_c = \mathbf{B}(\mathbf{Zi}_s - \mathbf{v}_s). \tag{15}$$

This is the matrix form of the *loop equations*; its variables are the loop (or circuit) currents. In the frequency domain, $\mathbf{Z}$ is the *branch impedance matrix*. The right side includes all the sources and can be written in compact form as

$$\mathbf{e}_c = \mathbf{B}(\mathbf{Zi}_s - \mathbf{v}_s). \tag{16}$$

The loop equations can then be written as

$$\mathbf{Z}_c\mathbf{i}_c = \mathbf{e}_c, \tag{17}$$

where

$$\mathbf{Z}_c = \mathbf{BZB'} \tag{18}$$

is an integral-differential operator in the time-domain and a rational matrix function of s in the frequency-domain, called the *loop operator* (or *impedance*) *matrix*.

The formal solution of (17) can be written as:

$$\mathbf{i}_c = \mathbf{Z}_c^{-1}\mathbf{e}_c \tag{19}$$

Note that the variables in (17) are a set of loop currents. The variables could be, more specifically, link currents $\mathbf{i}_l$ for some forest. In that case the $\mathbf{B}$ matrix would be a fundamental loop matrix $\mathbf{B}_f$. After subscript changes for other terms — $\mathbf{Z}_c$ to $\mathbf{Z}_l$ and $\mathbf{e}_c$ to $\mathbf{e}_l$ — the equations are then called the *link equations* and the matrix $\mathbf{Z}_l$ is then called the *link operator* (or *impedance*) *matrix*.

Finally, another variation is possible when the variables are mesh currents $\mathbf{i}_m$ and $\mathbf{B}$ is the mesh matrix $\mathbf{B}_m$. With subscripts changed appropriately, the equations are called the *mesh equations* and $\mathbf{Z}_m$ is the *mesh operator* (or *impedance*) *matrix*.

Now what about the loop assumption? If $-\mathbf{M}$ is to be a unit matrix, it cannot have a row of zeros. This precludes the presence of certain types of components, such as an unaccompanied current source. But it is usually possible—the i-shift if necessary—to ensure that all current sources are accompanied and form part of a general branch. If loop equations are to be written, this must always be done.

A second bothersome component is a current-controlled current source (ICIS) corresponding to which also $-\mathbf{M}$ would have a row of zeros. Here again it is sometimes possible to combine basic components to form compound components to avoid the row of zeros in $-\mathbf{M}$. You should again examine the basic components in Chapter 1 to see which ones would lead to such difficulties and to consider how they might be augmented to form compound components which then conform to the loop assumption. (See Prob. 29b.)

When the loop assumption is valid, we say the network has an *impedance representation*.

To illustrate the creation of a set of time domain mesh equations, consider the network schematic of Fig. 4. The only basic component not conforming to the loop assumption is the negative converter.

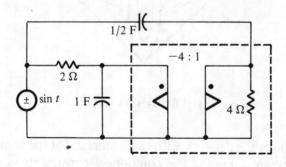

Fig. 4 Network schematic

However, it and the 4 ohm resistor shunting one of its ports become a compound component conforming to the assumption. This compound component and its graph are shown in Fig. 5. It can be easily established (you should do so) that

$$v_a = -16i_a + 4i_b$$
$$v_b = -16i_a + 4i_b$$

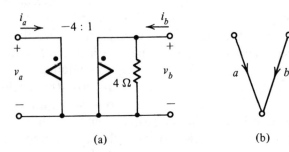

Fig. 5   Compound component and graph

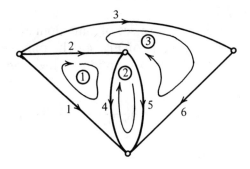

Fig. 6   Network graph

The graph for the network with two branches for the compound component is shown in Fig. 6. The component constraints in matrix form are as follows:

$$
-\left\{
\begin{bmatrix} v_1 \\ v_2 \\ v_3 \\ v_4 \\ v_5 \\ v_6 \end{bmatrix}
-
\begin{bmatrix} \sin t \\ 0 \\ v_3(0+) \\ v_4(0+) \\ 0 \\ 0 \end{bmatrix}
\right\}
+
\begin{bmatrix}
0 & 0 & 0 & 0 & 0 & 0 \\
0 & 2 & 0 & 0 & 0 & 0 \\
0 & 0 & 2\int_0^t d\tau & 0 & 0 & 0 \\
0 & 0 & 0 & \int_0^t d\tau & 0 & 0 \\
0 & 0 & 0 & 0 & -16 & 4 \\
0 & 0 & 0 & 0 & -16 & 4
\end{bmatrix}
\left\{
\begin{bmatrix} i_1 \\ i_2 \\ i_3 \\ i_4 \\ i_5 \\ i_6 \end{bmatrix}
-
\begin{bmatrix} 0 \\ 0 \\ 0 \\ 0 \\ 0 \\ 0 \end{bmatrix}
\right\}
=
\begin{bmatrix} 0 \\ 0 \\ 0 \\ 0 \\ 0 \\ 0 \end{bmatrix}.
$$

As $\mathbf{M}$ is obviously the negative of a unit matrix, the loop assumption is satisfied. In addition the branch impedance matrix $\mathbf{Z}$ and the vectors $\mathbf{v}_s$ and $\mathbf{i}_s$ are seen to be

$$
\mathbf{Z} = \begin{bmatrix}
0 & 0 & 0 & 0 & 0 & 0 \\
0 & 2 & 0 & 0 & 0 & 0 \\
0 & 0 & 2\int_0^t d\tau & 0 & 0 & 0 \\
0 & 0 & 0 & \int_0^t d\tau & 0 & 0 \\
0 & 0 & 0 & 0 & -16 & 4 \\
0 & 0 & 0 & 0 & -16 & 4
\end{bmatrix}
\quad
\mathbf{v}_s = \begin{bmatrix}
\sin t \\
0 \\
v_3(0+) \\
v_4(0+) \\
0 \\
0
\end{bmatrix},
\quad
\mathbf{i}_s = \begin{bmatrix}
0 \\
0 \\
0 \\
0 \\
0 \\
0
\end{bmatrix}.
$$

The mesh matrix for the three identified meshes is

$$
\text{Branches} \rightarrow
$$

$$
\text{Meshes} \downarrow \quad
\mathbf{B}_m = \begin{array}{c} 1 \\ 2 \\ 3 \end{array}
\begin{array}{cccccc}
1 & 2 & 3 & 4 & 5 & 6 \\
\end{array}
\begin{bmatrix}
-1 & 1 & 0 & 1 & 0 & 0 \\
0 & 0 & 0 & -1 & 1 & 0 \\
0 & -1 & 1 & 0 & -1 & 1
\end{bmatrix}.
$$

Upon combining these vectors and matrices as in (18) and (16), we get

$$
\mathbf{Z}_m = \begin{bmatrix}
2 + \int_0^t d\tau & -\int_0^t d\tau & -2 \\
-\int_0^t d\tau & -16 + \int_0^t d\tau & 20 \\
-2 & 0 & 2 + 2\int_0^t d\tau
\end{bmatrix}
$$

and

$$
e_m = \begin{bmatrix} \sin t - v_4(0+) \\ v_4(0+) \\ -v_3(0+) \end{bmatrix}
$$

Therefore, the resulting mesh equations are

$$
\begin{bmatrix} 2 + \int_0^t d\tau & -\int_0^t d\tau & -2 \\ -\int_0^t d\tau & -16 + \int_0^t d\tau & 20 \\ -2 & 0 & 2+2\int_0^t d\tau \end{bmatrix} \begin{bmatrix} i_{m1} \\ i_{m2} \\ i_{m3} \end{bmatrix} = \begin{bmatrix} \sin t - v_4(0+) \\ v_4(0+) \\ -v_3(0+) \end{bmatrix}
$$

It turns out that, as in the previous example, there is an algebraic constraint among the mesh currents. By adding the first equation to the second, that constraint is seen to be

$$
i_{m1} = 8i_{m2} - 9i_{m3} + \frac{1}{2} \sin t.
$$

This expression when substituted in equations 1 and 3 yields

$$
\begin{bmatrix} 16 + 7 \int_0^t d\tau & -20 - 9 \int_0^t d\tau \\ -16 & 20 + 2 \int_0^t d\tau \end{bmatrix} \begin{bmatrix} i_{m2} \\ i_{m3} \end{bmatrix} = \begin{bmatrix} -\frac{1}{2}(1 - \cos t) - v_4(0+) \\ \sin t - v_3(0+) \end{bmatrix}.
$$

The relationship between the variables in these equations is a dynamic relationship. Again we see that, although all three of the original mesh equations are independent, only two dynamic equations need be solved simultaneously. The third loop current is then obtained algebraically in terms of the first two. Further development of this point will be taken up in the section on state equations.

4.4   MIXED-VARIABLE EQUATIONS

Thus far, for networks which have an admittance or an impedance representation, requiring either $-\mathbf{N}$ or $-\mathbf{M}$ in the component relations to be a unit matrix, we have generated a set of equations for either a minimal set of independent voltages (n of them) or for a minimal set of independent currents ($b-n$ of them). However, in doing so we sometimes found the need to precondition some components—basic components into compound components—so as to satisfy the appropriate assumption. This preconditioning is not particularly appropriate to computer-aided analysis in which, by some algorithm, the network equations are composed from basic component models and connection data. The algorithm would be quite complicated were preconditioning needed. (Of course, networks containing the basic components causing difficulty could be excluded from consideration so as to avoid a complex algorithm and, indeed, that is often done.)

These difficulties will disappear if we do not insist on eliminating variables but accept the need to solve simultaneously for both the n voltage variables and the $b-n$ current variables. The necessary b equations for these b variables are obtained as follows without any assumptions about matrices $\mathbf{M}$ and $\mathbf{N}$. The branch relations (3-25) are

$$\mathbf{Mv} + \mathbf{Ni} = \mathbf{e}. \tag{21}$$

Replace $\mathbf{v}$ and $\mathbf{i}$ by their second form KVL and KCL equivalents from Table 3.1. The result is

$$\mathbf{MQ'v}_c + \mathbf{NB'i}_c = \mathbf{e} \tag{22a}$$

or

$$\mathbf{MA'v}_n + \mathbf{NB'i}_c = \mathbf{e}. \tag{22b}$$

By matrix catenation these equations can be expressed as

$$[\mathbf{MQ'} \ \ \mathbf{NB'}] \begin{bmatrix} \mathbf{v}_c \\ \mathbf{i}_c \end{bmatrix} = \mathbf{e}, \tag{23a}$$

or

$$[\mathbf{MA'} \ \ \mathbf{NB'}] \begin{bmatrix} \mathbf{v}_n \\ \mathbf{i}_c \end{bmatrix} = \mathbf{e}. \tag{23b}$$

This is a set of *mixed-variable equations* in a set of basis voltage and basis current variables. Compared with the number of node equations (n) or loop equations ($b-n$), there are b mixed-variable equations. What is involved, in terms of effort to compose the equations, is: (a) setting up a loop matrix and either a cut-set matrix or the incidence matrix; then (b) setting up the **M** and **N** matrices from the component relationships; then (c) carrying out two matrix multiplications. The final step of catenating these matrix products is trivial.

As a frequency-domain example, let us now compose a set of mixed-variable equations for the previous network of Fig. 4. However, we will not this time create a compound component. Using two branches for the negative converter alone, the network graph is shown in Fig. 7. The component constraints in matrix form are

$$
\begin{bmatrix}
1 & 0 & 0 & 0 & 0 & 0 & 0 \\
0 & 1 & 0 & 0 & 0 & 0 & 0 \\
0 & 0 & -\tfrac{1}{2}s & 0 & 0 & 0 & 0 \\
0 & 0 & 0 & -s & 0 & 0 & 0 \\
0 & 0 & 0 & 0 & 1 & -1 & 0 \\
0 & 0 & 0 & 0 & 0 & 0 & 0 \\
0 & 0 & 0 & 0 & 0 & 0 & -1
\end{bmatrix}
\begin{bmatrix}
V_1 \\ V_2 \\ V_3 \\ V_4 \\ V_5 \\ V_6 \\ V_7
\end{bmatrix}
+
\begin{bmatrix}
0 & 0 & 0 & 0 & 0 & 0 & 0 \\
0 & -2 & 0 & 0 & 0 & 0 & 0 \\
0 & 0 & 1 & 0 & 0 & 0 & 0 \\
0 & 0 & 0 & 1 & 0 & 0 & 0 \\
0 & 0 & 0 & 0 & 0 & 0 & 0 \\
0 & 0 & 0 & 0 & 4 & 1 & 0 \\
0 & 0 & 0 & 0 & 0 & 0 & 4
\end{bmatrix}
\begin{bmatrix}
I_1 \\ I_2 \\ I_3 \\ I_4 \\ I_5 \\ I_6 \\ I_7
\end{bmatrix}
=
\begin{bmatrix}
1/s^2 + 1 \\
0 \\
-\tfrac{1}{2}v_3(0+) \\
-v_4(0+) \\
0 \\
0 \\
0
\end{bmatrix}
$$

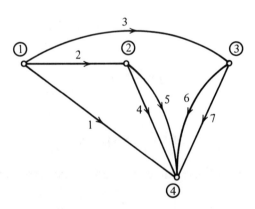

Fig. 7 Network graph

The matrices **M** and **N** (which are of order 7) and the vector **E** are easily identified. The node incidence matrix corresponding to nodes 1 through 3 is

$$\text{Branches} \rightarrow$$

$$A = \begin{matrix} \text{Nodes} \\ \downarrow \\ \\ \\ \end{matrix} \begin{matrix} & 1 & 2 & 3 & 4 & 5 & 6 & 7 \\ \\ 1 \\ 2 \\ 3 \end{matrix} \begin{bmatrix} 1 & 1 & 1 & 0 & 0 & 0 & 0 \\ 0 & -1 & 0 & 1 & 1 & 0 & 0 \\ 0 & 0 & -1 & 0 & 0 & 1 & 1 \end{bmatrix}$$

Corresponding to the set of loops

Loop 1: $\{1, \textcircled{1}, 2, \textcircled{2}, 4, \textcircled{4}\}$

Loop 2: $\{5, \textcircled{4}, 4, \textcircled{2}\}$

Loop 3: $\{5, \textcircled{2}, 2, \textcircled{1}, 3, \textcircled{3}, 6, \textcircled{4}\}$

Loop 4: $\{7, \textcircled{4}, 6, \textcircled{3}\}$

we have the loop matrix

$$\text{Branches} \rightarrow$$

$$B = \begin{matrix} \text{Loops} \\ \downarrow \\ \\ \\ \\ \end{matrix} \begin{matrix} & 1 & 2 & 3 & 4 & 5 & 6 & 7 \\ \\ 1 \\ 2 \\ 3 \\ 4 \end{matrix} \begin{bmatrix} -1 & 1 & 0 & 1 & 0 & 0 & 0 \\ 0 & 0 & 0 & -1 & 1 & 0 & 0 \\ 0 & -1 & 1 & 0 & -1 & 1 & 0 \\ 0 & 0 & 0 & 0 & 0 & -1 & 1 \end{bmatrix}.$$

Next the products $\mathbf{MA'}$ (of order 7×3) and $\mathbf{NB'}$ (of order 7×4) are formed. Finally the result in the form of (23b) is written as follows:

$$\begin{bmatrix} 1 & 0 & 0 & | & 0 & 0 & 0 & 0 \\ 1 & -1 & 0 & | & -2 & 0 & 2 & 0 \\ -\tfrac{1}{2}s & 0 & \tfrac{1}{2}s & | & 0 & 0 & 1 & 0 \\ \hline 0 & -s & 0 & | & 1 & -1 & 0 & 0 \\ 0 & 1 & -1 & | & 0 & 0 & 0 & 0 \\ 0 & 0 & 0 & | & 0 & 4 & -5 & -1 \\ 0 & 0 & -1 & | & 0 & 0 & 0 & 4 \end{bmatrix} \begin{bmatrix} V_{n1} \\ V_{n2} \\ V_{n3} \\ \hline I_{c1} \\ I_{c2} \\ I_{c3} \\ I_{c4} \end{bmatrix} = \begin{bmatrix} 1/(s^2+1) \\ 0 \\ -\tfrac{1}{2}v_3(0+) \\ \hline -v_4(0+) \\ 0 \\ 0 \\ 0 \end{bmatrix}.$$

Whereas there were three loop equations in the previous analysis of the same network (after preconditioning), we find here seven equations to be solved simultaneously. Although this is a larger set of equations, it is easier to compose if computer-aided analysis is to take place.

4.5   STATE EQUATIONS

The analysis procedures described in the preceding pages all culminate in a set of equations (node, loop, mixed variable) which, in the time domain, are integral-differential equations. Each set of equations is of a different order. Furthermore, the number of dynamically independent variables of a given network is not related to the number of equations in these sets. We shall now discuss another analysis procedure resulting in a set of equations, called the state equations, which are differential equations of first order. They can be generally represented in vector form as

$$\frac{d}{dt}\mathbf{x} = \mathbf{f}(\mathbf{x},\mathbf{u}), \qquad (24)$$

where $\mathbf{x}$ is a vector of elements called the *state variables* and $\mathbf{u}$ is a vector of sources.

There are a number of advantages in a state-variable analysis. First, both the setting up of the equations and their solution are easily done on a computer. Secondly, state variable analysis is easily extended to time-varying and nonlinear networks. Furthermore, the order of the vector $\mathbf{x}$ is simply related — equal — to the number of dynamically independent variables in a network.

4.5.1   Order of Complexity

The number of linearly independent equations in (24) is an important parameter for a given network; we call it the *order of complexity*. At the risk of confusion, we shall use the symbol n to represent this quantity. Once (24) has been written for a specific network and n is determined, the order of complexity will become known. But how can the order of complexity be determined short of writing the equations? From a mathematical sense, it is well-known that the general solution of (24) will contain n arbitrary constants. In order to fix these constants and thereby obtain a unique solution, n independent initial conditions must be specified in the network. From a physical point of view, we know that capacitor voltages are constrained by the law of continuity of charge and inductor currents are constrained by the law of continuity of flux linkage. *Initial values* of capacitor voltages and inductor currents thus help determine their respective subsequent values. Hence, the order of complexity will equal the number of *independent* initial conditions that can be specified.

Clearly, the order of complexity cannot exceed the number of capacitors plus inductors, b_{LC}, of a network. Suppose, however, that there is an algebraic constraint relationship among capacitor voltages (or among inductor currents). Then, not all initial capacitor voltages (or all initial inductor currents) can be independently specified and the order of complexity will be less than b_{LC}. In RLC networks, such constraints will be caused by loops consisting only of capacitors and, possibly, voltage sources, C-v_s loops; or by cut-sets consisting only of inductors and, possibly, current sources, L-i_s cut-sets. Such *degeneracies* are illustrated in Fig. 9. Although there are five L's and

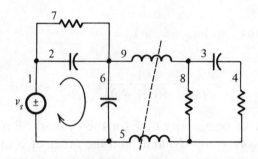

Fig. 9 Network with C-v_s loop and L cut-set

C's, the order of complexity is only 3 because of the constraint equations

$$v_2 + v_6 = v_s$$

$$i_5 + i_9 = 0$$

imposed by the C-v_s loop and the L cut-set.

More generally, when the network includes active and/or non-reciprocal components, constraints among capacitor voltages and inductor currents can arise in other ways besides C-v_s loops and L-i_s cut-sets. For example, there might be a loop formed by capacitors and a controlled voltage source whose controlling variable (voltage or current) is proportional to an independent source voltage or to the voltage of one of the capacitors on the loop. In addition to such topological conditions, constraints might also arise because of specific parameter values. This is illustrated in Fig. 10. The equations accompanying the

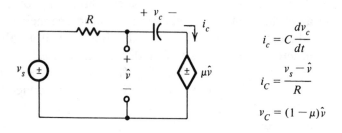

$$i_c = C \frac{dv_c}{dt}$$

$$i_c = \frac{v_s - \hat{v}}{R}$$

$$v_C = (1 - \mu)\hat{v}$$

Fig. 10   Constraint imposed by value of μ

diagram show that, so long as $\mu \neq 1$,

$$\frac{dv_C}{dt} = - \frac{1}{RC(1 - \mu)} v_C + \frac{1}{RC} v_s,$$

giving an order of complexity of 1 for the network. But if $\mu = 1$, then $v_C = 0$; the network is not dynamic and the order of complexity is 0.

The general conclusion for linear, time-invariant networks is that the order of complexity satisfies the inequality relation:

$$0 \leqslant n \leqslant b_{LC} - n_C - n_L, \tag{25}$$

where

b_{LC} = total number of C's and L's
n_C = number of independent C-v_s loops
n_L = number of independent L-i_s cut-sets.

For RLC networks, the equality sign will hold on the right side.

4.5.2   The State Variables

In launching an analysis which is to culminate in a set of state equations, an immediate question arises as to what variables to choose as state variables. Similarly, since any analysis procedure must include the Kirchhoff law equations—which requires forming the cut-set (or incidence) and loop matrices—the question of what branches to choose as twigs and what as links must be answered. We shall subsequently present a powerful algorithmic procedure for deriving state equations which requires no special selection of state variables or of branches as twigs and links; the algorithm simply leads to a set of state equations when they exist. Nevertheless, it is worthwhile to discuss another approach which can be used in the absence of the algorithm (or of a computer to implement it). We shall outline such an approach, but shall not provide an exhaustive, detailed development.

Since the component relationships of capacitors and inductors are dynamic and since the initial conditions that are normally specified are capacitor voltages and inductor currents, it seems reasonable to choose v_C's and i_L's as state variables. The previous discussion of order of complexity should make it clear that not all of these are necessarily independent; algebraic constraints among v_C's or i_L's may cause some of these *excess* variables. Temporarily, suppose that there are no excess variables.

Any analysis procedure must use all the independent Kirchhoff law equations and all the branch relationships. The dynamic components will have their voltage-current relationships expressed as $i_C = C\,dv_C/dt$ or $v_L = L\,di_L/dt$. All other components exclusive of certain general converters are nondynamic—the v-i relations are algebraic. In this respect, controlled sources (as well as gyrators, ideal transformers, etc.) are like ordinary resistors. For this reason, when referring collectively to voltages and currents of nondynamic components, we will use the subscript R.

It was observed in (3-27) that the branch equations of a network can always be written in the form

$$[\mathbf{M} \quad \mathbf{N}] \begin{bmatrix} \mathbf{v} \\ \mathbf{i} \end{bmatrix} = \mathbf{e} \tag{26}$$

and that the matrix $[\mathbf{M} \quad \mathbf{N}]$ will always be of full rank; it will have at least one $b \times b$ nonsingular submatrix. Each row and each column of both $\mathbf{M}$ and $\mathbf{N}$ correspond to a distinct branch. Suppose we consider only the nondynamic branches—not including independent sources. Collecting the corresponding rows and columns of (26), the branch equations of the nondynamic branches can be written

$$0 = [M_R \quad N_R] \begin{bmatrix} v_R \\ i_R \end{bmatrix} = M_R v_R + N_R i_R .$$

$$(27)$$

The matrix $[M_R \ N_R]$ will also be of full rank. In each row of (27) there must be at least one nonzero entry — in either M_R or N_R — and this value can always be made minus one. This is true even of the short-circuits or open-circuits which are the controlling branches of controlled sources. A nonsingular submatrix of $[M_R \ N_R]$ can always be made up by selecting those columns of M_R (say k in number) corresponding to the branches in which the voltage appears with a minus one multiplier and the remaining $b_R - k$ columns from N_R corresponding to those (different) branches in which the current appears with a minus one multiplier. For simplicity, the columns of M_R and N_R can be so ordered that the first k columns and last $b_R - k$ columns, respectively, are the ones which form the nonsingular submatrix.

Now we partition (27) as follows:

$$[M_R \quad N_R] \begin{bmatrix} v_R \\ i_R \end{bmatrix} = [[M_{Ra} \quad M_{Rb}][N_{Ra} \quad N_{Rb}]] \begin{bmatrix} v_{Ra} \\ v_{Rb} \\ i_{Ra} \\ i_{Rb} \end{bmatrix}$$

$$(28)$$

$$= [M_{Ra} \quad N_{Ra}] \begin{bmatrix} v_{Ra} \\ i_{Rb} \end{bmatrix} + [N_{Ra} \quad M_{Rb}] \begin{bmatrix} i_{Ra} \\ v_{Rb} \end{bmatrix} = 0 .$$

In the rearrangement of the last line, the matrix $[M_{Ra} \ N_{Rb}]$ is nonsingular; in fact, it can always be made the negative of a unit matrix. Hence, the nondynamic branch equations can always be written as

$$\begin{bmatrix} v_{Ra} \\ i_{Rb} \end{bmatrix} = [N_{Ra} \quad M_{Rb}] \begin{bmatrix} i_{Ra} \\ v_{Rb} \end{bmatrix}$$

$$(29)$$

Finally, after conformable partitioning of N_{Ra} and M_{Rb}, the following mixed or hybrid form can always be written

$$\begin{bmatrix} \mathbf{v}_{Ra} \\ \mathbf{i}_{Rb} \end{bmatrix} = \begin{bmatrix} \mathbf{H}_{aa} & \mathbf{H}_{ab} \\ \mathbf{H}_{ba} & \mathbf{H}_{bb} \end{bmatrix} \begin{bmatrix} \mathbf{i}_{Ra} \\ \mathbf{v}_{Rb} \end{bmatrix}. \tag{30}$$

So much for the nondynamic branches. The v-i relations of the dynamic branches can be written

$$\mathbf{i}_C = \mathbf{C}\frac{d\mathbf{v}_C}{dt} \tag{31a}$$

$$\mathbf{v}_L = \mathbf{L}\frac{d\mathbf{i}_L}{dt} \tag{31b}$$

In arriving at the desired state equations, all variables but $\mathbf{v}_C$ and $\mathbf{i}_L$ must be eliminated. There are six sets of such variables—$\mathbf{i}_C$, $\mathbf{v}_L$, $\mathbf{v}_{Ra}$, $\mathbf{v}_{Rb}$, $\mathbf{i}_{Ra}$ and $\mathbf{i}_{Rb}$—so we must have six sets of independent equations. Two sets are obtained from (30); the others must come from KCL and KVL. Suppose we could find independent KCL equations so as to be able to write $\mathbf{i}_C$ in terms of $\mathbf{i}_{Rb}$ (and source quantities) and we could find independent KVL equations so as to write $\mathbf{v}_L$ in terms of $\mathbf{v}_{Ra}$ (and source quantities). These would eliminate $\mathbf{i}_C$ and $\mathbf{v}_L$. If we now can find independent KCL equations relating $\mathbf{i}_{Ra}$ to $\mathbf{i}_{Rb}$, and independent KVL equations relating $\mathbf{v}_{Rb}$ to $\mathbf{v}_{Ra}$, the elimination of the remaining undesired variables could be carried to completion. There seems to be something haphazard in this development; in the next section we shall discuss a systematic method for determining the categories of variables "a" and "b."

Let us illustrate the procedure with an example. The object is to write a set of state equations for the network shown with its corresponding graph in Fig. 11.

The dynamic v-i equations are

$$i_2 = C_2\frac{dv_2}{dt}$$

$$v_8 = L_8\frac{di_8}{dt}$$

A KCL equation written at node 2 solved for i_2 and a KVL equation written around the loop $\{1, 3, 6, 4, 8\}$ solved for v_8 can be used to eliminate i_2 and v_8 from the preceding expressions, leading to

$$C_2 \frac{dv_2}{dt} = i_2 = \begin{bmatrix} -1 & -1 \end{bmatrix} \begin{bmatrix} i_5 \\ i_7 \end{bmatrix} - i_9$$

$$L_8 \frac{di_8}{dt} = v_8 = \begin{bmatrix} -1 & -1 & -1 \end{bmatrix} \begin{bmatrix} v_3 \\ v_4 \\ v_6 \end{bmatrix} + v_1$$

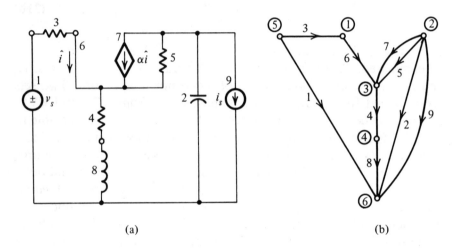

(a)   (b)

Fig. 11   Illustrative example

These give us the clue as to which variables we wish to fall in the two groups "a" and "b": 3, 4, and 6 belong to "a" while 5 and 7 belong to "b."

The nondynamic branch equations can now be written, with the appropriate ordering of the variables; thus,

$$\begin{bmatrix} -1 & 0 & 0 & 0 & 0 \\ 0 & -1 & 0 & 0 & 0 \\ 0 & 0 & -1 & 0 & 0 \\ 0 & 0 & 0 & G_5 & 0 \\ 0 & 0 & 0 & 0 & 0 \end{bmatrix} \begin{bmatrix} v_3 \\ v_4 \\ v_6 \\ v_5 \\ v_7 \end{bmatrix} + \begin{bmatrix} R_3 & 0 & 0 & 0 & 0 \\ 0 & R_4 & 0 & 0 & 0 \\ 0 & 0 & 0 & 0 & 0 \\ 0 & 0 & 0 & -1 & 0 \\ 0 & 0 & \alpha & 0 & -1 \end{bmatrix} \begin{bmatrix} i_3 \\ i_4 \\ i_6 \\ i_5 \\ i_7 \end{bmatrix} = \begin{bmatrix} 0 \\ 0 \\ 0 \\ 0 \\ 0 \end{bmatrix}.$$

These can be rewritten in the form of (30) as

$$
\begin{bmatrix} v_3 \\ v_4 \\ v_6 \\ \hline i_5 \\ i_7 \end{bmatrix} = \begin{bmatrix} R_3 & 0 & 0 & 0 & 0 \\ 0 & R_4 & 0 & 0 & 0 \\ 0 & 0 & 0 & 0 & 0 \\ \hline 0 & 0 & 0 & G_5 & 0 \\ 0 & 0 & \alpha & 0 & 0 \end{bmatrix} \begin{bmatrix} i_3 \\ i_4 \\ i_6 \\ \hline v_5 \\ v_7 \end{bmatrix}
$$

The submatrices in (30) are identified by the partitions. There now remains the task of writing KCL equations involving the two current vectors and KVL equations involving the two voltage vectors. Appropriate linear combinations of KCL equations at nodes ①, ④, and ③, and KVL equations around loops {5, 2, 1, 3, 6} and {7, 2, 1, 3, 6} yield

$$
\begin{bmatrix} i_3 \\ i_4 \\ i_6 \end{bmatrix} = \begin{bmatrix} -1 & -1 \\ 0 & 0 \\ -1 & -1 \end{bmatrix} \begin{bmatrix} i_5 \\ i_7 \end{bmatrix} + \begin{bmatrix} 1 \\ 1 \\ 1 \end{bmatrix} i_8,
$$

$$
\begin{bmatrix} v_5 \\ v_7 \end{bmatrix} = \begin{bmatrix} 1 & 0 & 1 \\ 1 & 0 & 1 \end{bmatrix} \begin{bmatrix} v_3 \\ v_4 \\ v_6 \end{bmatrix} + \begin{bmatrix} 1 \\ 1 \end{bmatrix} v_2 - \begin{bmatrix} 1 \\ 1 \end{bmatrix} v_1.
$$

The preceding four sets of equations can be solved for the four nondynamic current and voltage vectors. These can then be inserted into the expressions for $C_2 dv_2/dt$ and $L_8 di_8/dt$ and culminate in the following:

$$
\begin{bmatrix} C_2 \dfrac{dv_2}{dt} \\ L_8 \dfrac{di_8}{dt} \end{bmatrix} = \frac{1}{\Delta} \begin{bmatrix} -G_5 & -(R_3 G_5 + \alpha) \\ R_3 G_5 & -(R_3 + R_4 \Delta) \end{bmatrix} \begin{bmatrix} v_2 \\ i_8 \end{bmatrix} + \frac{1}{\Delta} \begin{bmatrix} G_5 \\ 1+\alpha \end{bmatrix} v_s + \begin{bmatrix} -1 \\ 0 \end{bmatrix} i_s,
$$

where $\Delta = 1 + \alpha + R_3 G_5$.

These are a pair of first-order differential equations in the capacitor voltage and inductor current. They constitute state equations.

4.5.3 Approach Using a Normal Forest

The success of carrying out the procedure discussed above depended on two sets of nondynamic voltages and currents being the same; namely, those that are related to i_C's and v_L's through KCL and KVL and those that are obtained from the partitioning of the nondynamic v-i equations leading to (30). Furthermore, the KCL and KVL relations on the currents and voltages of the nondynamic component variables had to be introduced. A systematic procedure is needed in order to carry out the scheme whenever it is possible. We shall now outline such a scheme.

In the preceding approach there was no need for choosing a forest and specifying the kinds of branches that were twigs. The procedure we shall now outline starts from the selection of a forest. From a topological perspective, twig voltages constitute a basis — all other voltages can be determined from them. The nature of independent voltage sources is such that they should be twigs. (If there is a loop of such sources, this will require that at least one be a link. But in this situation, the network will be inconsistent, unless the voltage source voltages satisfy KVL, which means they aren't really independent sources.) Similarly, current sources should be links. (If there is a cut-set of such sources, this will require that at least one be a twig. But in this case, also, the network is inconsistent unless the source currents satisfy KCL, which means they aren't really independent sources.) In the algorithmic procedure to be introduced later, voltage source links and current source twigs can be handled easily. But for the present purpose, we shall assume that the following conditions are satisfied:

1. There are no loops consisting of only independent voltage sources.
2. There are no cut-sets consisting of only independent current sources.

Then, all of the voltage sources will be chosen as twigs and none of the current sources.

Subject to all voltage sources being twigs and no current sources being twigs, we define a *normal forest* as one containing a maximal number of capacitors and a minimal number of inductors.

The selection of a normal forest is not unique. If there are no KVL-induced algebraic constraints among capacitor voltages, then all capacitors will be twigs in a normal forest (by definition); if there are, the selection of capacitor twigs is not unique. Similarly, if there are no KCL-induced algebraic constraints among inductor currents, no inductors will be twigs; if such constraints exist, at least one inductor will be a twig and its selection is not generally unique. Special consideration must be given to the branches representing controlled sources. In any controlled source, the controlling branch is either a short-circuit or an open-circuit. The short-circuit is specified by $v = 0$; this is like an independent voltage source whose voltage equals zero. Similarly, the open-circuit is specified by $i = 0$, like an independent current source whose value is zero. From these considerations, it seems that branches that are short circuits should be chosen as twigs and those that are open-circuits as links. Similarly, controlled branches of controlled voltage sources should be chosen as twigs and those of controlled current sources, as links.*

Based on these preliminaries, the twigs and links in the normal forest are ordered in accordance with the following scheme:

Twigs	Links
1. Voltage sources	5. Capacitor links
2. Capacitor twigs	6. Nondynamic links
3. Nondynamic twigs	7. Inductor links
4. Inductor twigs	8. Current sources

(Keep in mind that both branches of a controlled source are included among nondynamic components.) The current and voltage vectors can now be partitioned in a corresponding order, thus

$$\mathbf{v} = \begin{bmatrix} \mathbf{v}_t \\ \mathbf{v}_\ell \end{bmatrix} \Rightarrow \mathbf{v}_t = \begin{bmatrix} \mathbf{v}_E \\ \mathbf{v}_{Ct} \\ \mathbf{v}_{Rt} \\ \mathbf{v}_{Lt} \end{bmatrix} \text{ and } \mathbf{v}_\ell = \begin{bmatrix} \mathbf{v}_{C\ell} \\ \mathbf{v}_{R\ell} \\ \mathbf{v}_{L\ell} \\ \mathbf{v}_J \end{bmatrix} \tag{32a}**$$

---

* These choices are not always possible if degeneracies are introduced by the controlled sources. Subsequent discussion will illustrate this point.

** For practical reasons, two symbols were used for the subscript standing for *link*; for example, a link voltage vector is given in some places as $\mathbf{v}_\ell$ and in others as $\mathbf{v}_l$. We hope this will not cause confusion.

$$i = \begin{bmatrix} i_t \\ i_\ell \end{bmatrix} \Rightarrow i_t = \begin{bmatrix} i_E \\ i_{Ct} \\ i_{Rt} \\ i_{Lt} \end{bmatrix} \text{ and } i_\ell = \begin{bmatrix} i_{C\ell} \\ i_{R\ell} \\ i_{L\ell} \\ i_J \end{bmatrix} \tag{32b}$$

Next we turn to KCL and KVL; the second form expressions derivable from Table 3.1 are

$$i_t = -Q_\ell i_\ell, \tag{33a}$$

$$v_\ell = Q'_\ell v_t, \tag{33b}$$

where the usual partitioning of the fundamental loop and cut-set matrices are $B_f = [B_t \ U]$ and $Q_f = [U \ Q_\ell]$ and where $B_t = -Q'_\ell$. (For simplicity, the subscript f has been omitted from Q_{fl} and B_{ft}.)

If the preceding partitions of the v and i vectors are to be used here, then Q_ℓ must also be partitioned accordingly into four rows and four columns. Arranging the rows and columns in the order decided upon, Q_ℓ becomes partitioned as follows:

$$
Q_\ell = \begin{array}{c} \\ \\ \text{Twigs} \\ \downarrow \end{array}
\overset{\text{Links} \rightarrow}{
\begin{bmatrix}
Q_{EC} & Q_{ER} & Q_{EL} & Q_{EJ} \\
Q_{CC} & Q_{CR} & Q_{CL} & Q_{CJ} \\
0 & Q_{RR} & Q_{RL} & Q_{RJ} \\
0 & 0 & Q_{LL} & Q_{LJ}
\end{bmatrix}
} \tag{34}
$$

Three of the entries in Q_ℓ are identically zero. (Some others might be zero and any might be null in specific cases.) This can be explained as follows. If there is a capacitor link, it will be by virtue of a loop consisting of capacitors and, possibly, voltage sources. Since there will be no nondynamic branches or inductors in such a loop, the column corresponding to a capacitor link cannot have a nonzero entry in the rows corresponding to R and L twigs; that is, the entries in the first column, third and fourth rows must be zero. Similarly, if there is an inductor twig, it is by virtue of a cut-set of inductors and, possibly, current sources. Since there can be no nondynamic branches or capacitors in such a cut-set, the row corresponding to inductor twigs cannot have nonzero entries in the columns corresponding to C and R links.

When $\mathbf{Q}_t$ in (34) and the partitioned vectors from (32) are inserted into (33), and the indicated operations carried out, a set of eight equations will result. Two of these, one giving the vector of currents of voltage sources, $\mathbf{i}_E$, and the other the vector of voltages of current sources, $\mathbf{v}_J$, are needed only to find these variables once everything else has been determined. We shall not consider them any further. The remaining sets can be written out and then regrouped as follows:

$$\begin{bmatrix} \mathbf{i}_{Rt} \\ \mathbf{v}_{R\ell} \end{bmatrix} = \begin{bmatrix} 0 & -\mathbf{Q}_{RR} \\ \mathbf{Q}'_{RR} & 0 \end{bmatrix} \begin{bmatrix} \mathbf{v}_{Rt} \\ \mathbf{i}_{R\ell} \end{bmatrix} + \begin{bmatrix} 0 & -\mathbf{Q}_{RL} \\ \mathbf{Q}'_{CR} & 0 \end{bmatrix} \begin{bmatrix} \mathbf{v}_{Ct} \\ \mathbf{i}_{L\ell} \end{bmatrix} + \begin{bmatrix} 0 & -\mathbf{Q}_{RJ} \\ \mathbf{Q}'_{ER} & 0 \end{bmatrix} \begin{bmatrix} \mathbf{v}_E \\ \mathbf{i}_J \end{bmatrix} \tag{35}$$

$$\mathbf{i}_{Lt} = -\mathbf{Q}_{LL}\mathbf{i}_{L\ell} - \mathbf{Q}_{LJ}\mathbf{i}_J \tag{36a}$$

$$\mathbf{v}_{C\ell} = \mathbf{Q}'_{EC}\mathbf{v}_E + \mathbf{Q}'_{CC}\mathbf{v}_{Ct} \tag{36b}$$

$$[\mathbf{U} \quad \mathbf{Q}_{CC}] \begin{bmatrix} \mathbf{i}_{Ct} \\ \mathbf{i}_{C\ell} \end{bmatrix} = -\mathbf{Q}_{CR}\mathbf{i}_{R\ell} - \mathbf{Q}_{CL}\mathbf{i}_{L\ell} - \mathbf{Q}_{CJ}\mathbf{i}_J \tag{37a}$$

$$[\mathbf{U} \quad -\mathbf{Q}'_{LL}] \begin{bmatrix} \mathbf{v}_{L\ell} \\ \mathbf{v}_{Lt} \end{bmatrix} = \mathbf{Q}'_{EL}\mathbf{v}_E + \mathbf{Q}'_{CL}\mathbf{v}_{Ct} + \mathbf{Q}'_{RL}\mathbf{v}_{Rt} \tag{37b}$$

Two other equations come from the branch equations of the nondynamic branches, as in (30). Now, however, the sets "a" and "b" refer to twigs and links, or the converse. More specifically, one or the other of the following might be written

$$\begin{bmatrix} \mathbf{v}_{Rt} \\ \mathbf{i}_{R\ell} \end{bmatrix} = \begin{bmatrix} \mathbf{H}_{tt} & \mathbf{H}_{t\ell} \\ \mathbf{H}_{\ell t} & \mathbf{H}_{\ell\ell} \end{bmatrix} \begin{bmatrix} \mathbf{i}_{Rt} \\ \mathbf{v}_{R\ell} \end{bmatrix} \tag{38a}$$

or

$$\begin{bmatrix} \mathbf{i}_{Rt} \\ \mathbf{v}_{R\ell} \end{bmatrix} = \begin{bmatrix} \mathbf{G}_{tt} & \mathbf{G}_{t\ell} \\ \mathbf{G}_{\ell t} & \mathbf{G}_{\ell\ell} \end{bmatrix} \begin{bmatrix} \mathbf{v}_{Rt} \\ \mathbf{i}_{R\ell} \end{bmatrix} . \tag{38b}$$

If the procedure being developed is to work, it must be possible so to choose the nondynamic twigs and links that a branch representation such as one of these is possible. It may not always be possible, in which case the method will fail.

Finally, consider the dynamic branch relations

$$\begin{bmatrix} i_{Ct} \\ i_{C\ell} \end{bmatrix} = \frac{d}{dt} \begin{bmatrix} C_t & 0 \\ 0 & C_\ell \end{bmatrix} \begin{bmatrix} v_{Ct} \\ v_{C\ell} \end{bmatrix} = \frac{d}{dt} \begin{bmatrix} C_t & 0 \\ 0 & C_\ell \end{bmatrix} \left\{ \begin{bmatrix} U \\ Q'_{CC} \end{bmatrix} v_{Ct} + \begin{bmatrix} 0 \\ Q'_{EC} \end{bmatrix} v_E \right\} \quad (39a)$$

$$\begin{bmatrix} v_{L\ell} \\ v_{Lt} \end{bmatrix} = \frac{d}{dt} \begin{bmatrix} L_{\ell\ell} & L_{\ell t} \\ L_{t\ell} & L_{tt} \end{bmatrix} \begin{bmatrix} i_{L\ell} \\ i_{Lt} \end{bmatrix} = \frac{d}{dt} \begin{bmatrix} L_{\ell\ell} & L_{\ell t} \\ L_{t\ell} & L_{tt} \end{bmatrix} \left\{ \begin{bmatrix} U \\ -Q_{LL} \end{bmatrix} i_{L\ell} + \begin{bmatrix} 0 \\ -Q_{LJ} \end{bmatrix} i_J \right\} \quad (39b)$$

The right sides are obtained by substituting for v_{Ct} and i_{Lt} from (36). If these expressions are substituted into (37) the result becomes

$$\mathscr{C} \frac{d}{dt} v_{Ct} = -Q_{CR} i_{Rt} - Q_{CL} i_{Lt} - Q_{CJ} i_J - \hat{\mathscr{C}} \frac{dv_E}{dt} \quad (40a)$$

$$\mathscr{L} \frac{d}{dt} i_{Lt} = Q'_{CL} v_{Ct} + Q'_{RL} v_{Rt} + Q'_{EL} v_E + \hat{\mathscr{L}} \frac{di_J}{dt} \quad (40b)$$

where

$$\mathscr{C} = C_t + Q_{cc} C_t Q'_{cc} \quad (41a)$$

$$\mathscr{L} = L_{tt} - L_{tt} Q_{LL} - Q'_{LL} L_{tt} + Q'_{LL} L_{tt} Q_{LL} \quad (41b)$$

and

$$\hat{\mathscr{C}} = Q_{cc} C_t Q'_{EC} \quad (41c)$$

$$\hat{\mathscr{L}} = (L_{tt} - Q'_{LL} L_{tt}) Q_{LJ} \quad (41d)$$

Now all the equations are before us. Observe that the two sets of equations represented by (38a) or (38b) and those in (35) must be solved for the vectors v_{Rt} and i_{Rt}. (A solution may not exist, in which case the procedure again fails.)

We shall partially carry out these steps of elimination. Suppose the nondynamic branch representation in (38a) is possible. Then, this expression is inserted into (35) and the result rewritten as

$$
\begin{bmatrix} U+Q_{RR}H_{\ell t} & Q_{RR}H_{\ell\ell} \\ Q'_{RR}H_{tt} & U-Q'_{RR}H_{t\ell} \end{bmatrix} \begin{bmatrix} i_{Rt} \\ v_{R\ell} \end{bmatrix} = \begin{bmatrix} 0 & -Q_{RL} \\ Q'_{CR} & 0 \end{bmatrix} \begin{bmatrix} v_{Ct} \\ i_{L\ell} \end{bmatrix} + \begin{bmatrix} 0 & Q_{RJ} \\ Q'_{ER} & 0 \end{bmatrix} \begin{bmatrix} v_E \\ i_J \end{bmatrix}. \quad (42)
$$

In order to proceed to a solution it must be possible to invert the matrix on the left; this is where the process can fail. If the inversion is possible, the vector $[i_{Rt} \ v_{R\ell}]'$ is obtained in terms of state variables and source variables only. When this is substituted back into (38a), the desired value of v_{Rt} and i_{Rt} are determined and then inserted into (40). The result is the state equations.

Alternatively, suppose the nondynamic branch representation (38b) is possible. When this expansion is combined with (35), the result can be rewritten as

$$
\begin{bmatrix} G_{tt} & G_{t\ell}+Q_{RR} \\ G_{\ell t}-Q'_{RR} & G_{\ell\ell} \end{bmatrix} \begin{bmatrix} v_{Rt} \\ i_{R\ell} \end{bmatrix} = \begin{bmatrix} 0 & -Q_{RL} \\ Q'_{CR} & 0 \end{bmatrix} \begin{bmatrix} v_{Ct} \\ i_{L\ell} \end{bmatrix} + \begin{bmatrix} 0 & Q_{RJ} \\ Q'_{ER} & 0 \end{bmatrix} \begin{bmatrix} v_E \\ i_J \end{bmatrix}. \quad (43)
$$

Again, success depends on the invertability of the matrix on the left. This time, if the inversion is possible, the vector $[v_{Rt} \ i_{Rt}]'$ is obtained directly without the need to insert back into (38b). Both in this respect — and in the simplicity of the matrix to be inverted in (43) compared with that in (42) — the present case requires less effort than the previous one.

When the state equations are obtained in either of the two cases, they can be written in the following form.

$$
\begin{bmatrix} \mathscr{C} & 0 \\ 0 & \mathscr{L} \end{bmatrix} \frac{d}{dt} \begin{bmatrix} v_{Ct} \\ i_{L\ell} \end{bmatrix} = \begin{bmatrix} -\mathscr{Y} & \mathscr{H} \\ \mathscr{G} & -\mathscr{Z} \end{bmatrix} \begin{bmatrix} v_{Ct} \\ i_{L\ell} \end{bmatrix} + \begin{bmatrix} -\hat{\mathscr{Y}} & \hat{\mathscr{H}} \\ \hat{\mathscr{G}} & -\hat{\mathscr{Z}} \end{bmatrix} \begin{bmatrix} v_E \\ i_J \end{bmatrix} + \begin{bmatrix} \hat{\mathscr{C}} & 0 \\ 0 & \hat{\mathscr{L}} \end{bmatrix} \frac{d}{dt} \begin{bmatrix} v_E \\ i_J \end{bmatrix}. \quad (44)
$$

The notation for the submatrices on the right is intended to be mnemonic. After multiplying by the inverse of the matrix on the left, and letting $x = [v_{Ct} \ i_{Lt}]'$,

$$\frac{d}{dt}\mathbf{x} = \mathbf{A}\mathbf{x} + \mathbf{B}_0\mathbf{e} + \mathbf{B}_1\frac{d\mathbf{e}}{dt}. \tag{45}$$

Note that from the definition of $\mathscr{C}$, the derivative dv_E/dt is present only when $\mathbf{Q}_{EC}$ is nonzero; that is, only when there is at least one capacitor loop that includes a voltage source. Similarly, di_J/dt is present only when there exists at least one inductor cut-set that includes a current source.

To illustrate the procedure, let us again find the state equations for the network in Fig. 11. The normal tree will contain the voltage source, the capacitor, and the short-circuit branch of the controlled source. It cannot contain the inductor, the current source and the controlled branch of the controlled current source. That leaves nondynamic branches 3, 4, and 5, of which two must be twigs. Branches 3 and 5 cannot both be twigs—there would then be a loop of twigs—so the only two choices are {3,4} or {4,5}. If we choose the latter, the graph will take the form shown in Fig. 12.

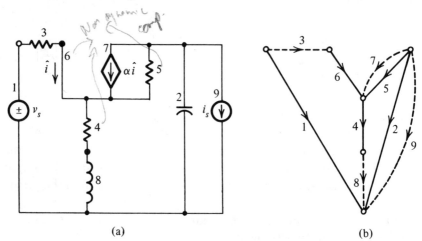

(a)   (b)

Fig. 12   Illustrative example repeated

The various subvectors can now be identified from the graph. Thus,

$$\mathbf{v}_{Rt} = \begin{bmatrix} v_4 \\ v_5 \\ v_6 \end{bmatrix}, \quad \mathbf{i}_{Rt} = \begin{bmatrix} i_4 \\ i_5 \\ i_6 \end{bmatrix}, \quad \mathbf{v}_{R\ell} = \begin{bmatrix} v_3 \\ v_7 \end{bmatrix}, \quad \mathbf{i}_{R\ell} = \begin{bmatrix} i_3 \\ i_7 \end{bmatrix}$$

The nondynamic branch relations are now written as

$$
\begin{bmatrix} -U & 0 \\ & \begin{bmatrix} G_3 & 0 \\ 0 & 0 \end{bmatrix} \\ 0 & \end{bmatrix}
\begin{bmatrix} v_4 \\ v_5 \\ v_6 \\ \hline v_3 \\ v_7 \end{bmatrix}
+
\begin{bmatrix} \begin{bmatrix} R_4 & 0 & 0 \\ 0 & R_5 & 0 \\ 0 & 0 & 0 \end{bmatrix} & 0 \\ \begin{bmatrix} 0 & 0 & 0 \\ 0 & 0 & \alpha \end{bmatrix} & -U \end{bmatrix}
\begin{bmatrix} i_4 \\ i_5 \\ i_6 \\ \hline i_3 \\ i_7 \end{bmatrix}
= 0 .
$$

The KCL equations for fundamental cut-sets defined by nondynamic twigs and the KVL equations for fundamental loops defined by nondynamic links corresponding to (35) can now be written directly from the graph. Thus,

$$
\begin{bmatrix} i_4 \\ i_5 \\ i_6 \end{bmatrix} = - \begin{bmatrix} 0 & 0 \\ 1 & 1 \\ -1 & 0 \end{bmatrix} \begin{bmatrix} i_3 \\ i_7 \end{bmatrix} - \begin{bmatrix} -1 \\ -1 \\ 0 \end{bmatrix} i_8 ,
$$

$$
\begin{bmatrix} v_3 \\ v_7 \end{bmatrix} = \begin{bmatrix} 0 & 0 & -1 \\ 0 & 1 & 0 \end{bmatrix} \begin{bmatrix} v_4 \\ v_5 \\ v_6 \end{bmatrix} + \begin{bmatrix} -1 \\ 0 \end{bmatrix} v_2 + \begin{bmatrix} 1 \\ 0 \end{bmatrix} v_1
$$

When these are combined with the preceding nondynamic branch equations, the solution yields

$$
\begin{bmatrix} i_3 \\ i_7 \end{bmatrix} = \frac{1}{\Delta'} \begin{bmatrix} -G_3 & G_3 R_5 \\ -\alpha G_3 & \alpha G_3 R_5 \end{bmatrix} \begin{bmatrix} v_2 \\ i_8 \end{bmatrix} + \frac{1}{\Delta'} \begin{bmatrix} G_3 \\ \alpha G_3 \end{bmatrix} v_1 ,
$$

$$
\begin{bmatrix} v_4 \\ v_5 \\ v_6 \end{bmatrix} = \frac{1}{\Delta'} \begin{bmatrix} 0 & R+\Delta' \\ R_5 G_3 (1+\alpha) & R_5 \\ 0 & 0 \end{bmatrix} \begin{bmatrix} v_2 \\ i_8 \end{bmatrix} + \frac{1}{\Delta'} \begin{bmatrix} 0 \\ -R_5 G_3 (1 + \alpha) \\ 0 \end{bmatrix} v_1 .
$$

where $\Delta' = 1 + G_3 R_5 (1 + \alpha)$. The KCL and KVL equations corresponding to (37) each include one scalar equation in this case. They are

$$[i_2] = -[-1 \quad 0] \begin{bmatrix} i_3 \\ i_7 \end{bmatrix} - [i_8] - [i_9] \; ,$$

$$[v_8] = [-1 \quad -1 \quad 0] \begin{bmatrix} v_4 \\ v_5 \\ v_6 \end{bmatrix} + [v_2] \; .$$

When the solutions for the vectors from the preceding equations are substituted here, and these are inserted into the dynamic branch equations, the result with v_1 replaced by v_s and i_9 replaced by i_s becomes

$$\begin{bmatrix} \dfrac{dv_2}{dt} \\[3ex] \dfrac{di_8}{dt} \end{bmatrix} = \dfrac{1}{\Delta'} \begin{bmatrix} \dfrac{-G_3}{C_2} & \dfrac{-(1+\alpha G_3 R_5)}{C_2} \\[3ex] \dfrac{1}{L_8} & \dfrac{-(R_5 + R_4\Delta')}{L_8} \end{bmatrix} \begin{bmatrix} v_2 \\[3ex] i_8 \end{bmatrix} + \dfrac{1}{\Delta'} \begin{bmatrix} \dfrac{G_3}{C_2} \\[3ex] -R_5 G_3(1+\alpha) \\ L_8 \end{bmatrix} v_s + \begin{bmatrix} \dfrac{-1}{C_2} \\[3ex] 0 \end{bmatrix} i_s \; .$$

You should compare this with the state equations obtained earlier for the same network and show that they are the same.

4.5.4 Algorithm for Generating State Equations

Besides the normal forest method for obtaining state equations for a network discussed above, a number of other procedures also exist. As in the preceding method, some of these procedures impose restrictions on the kinds of networks that can be handled. We shall now present a completely general algorithmic approach which places no restrictions on the network to be treated. We make no initial decision as to the selection of state variables or of a forest. It will become apparent later how the details are modified in the event the network falls in specific categories.

The beginning point of the analysis is the set of mixed-variable equations in the time domain, repeated here for convenience,

$$[MQ' \quad NB'] \begin{bmatrix} v_c \\ i_c \end{bmatrix} = e \; . \tag{46}$$

These equations already incorporate the Kirchhoff laws and the branch relationships. We shall assume that the voltage-current constraints of the dynamic components (capacitors and inductors — including coupled inductors) are expressed in differential form. (No integrals.) This is in no way restrictive. It is possible to collect the derivative operators together in the coefficient matrix of (46) and to write them separately from the algebraic terms. Thus,

$$[\mathbf{MQ'} \ \ \mathbf{NB'}] = \mathbf{P}^0 \frac{d}{dt} - \mathbf{A}^0, \tag{47}$$

where $\mathbf{P}^0$ and $\mathbf{A}^0$ are matrices of constants. The superscripts are included to indicate that these are initial values in the iterative procedure to be discussed.

Recall also that the source vector $\mathbf{e}$ is given by

$$\mathbf{e} = \mathbf{M}\mathbf{v}_s + \mathbf{N}\mathbf{i}_s = [\mathbf{M} \quad \mathbf{N}] \begin{bmatrix} \mathbf{v}_s \\ \mathbf{i}_s \end{bmatrix}. \tag{48}$$

The source vector on the right has $2b$ elements. In any given network, only some of the elements of $\mathbf{v}_s$ and $\mathbf{i}_s$ are nonzero. Let $\mathbf{u}$ be a vector whose elements are nonzero elements of $\mathbf{v}_s$ and $\mathbf{i}_s$; these are the inputs to the network, so $\mathbf{u}$ is called the *input* vector. Retaining only the nonzero elements of $\mathbf{v}_s$ and $\mathbf{i}_s$, $\mathbf{e}$ in (48) can be expressed in terms of $\mathbf{u}$ as

$$\mathbf{e} = \mathbf{B}^0\mathbf{u}. \tag{49}$$

When (47) and (49) are inserted in (46), the result is

$$\mathbf{P}^0 \frac{d}{dt}\mathbf{x}_0 - \mathbf{A}^0\mathbf{x}_0 - \mathbf{B}^0\mathbf{u} = \mathbf{0}, \tag{50}$$

where

$$\mathbf{x}_0 = \begin{bmatrix} \mathbf{v}_c \\ \mathbf{i}_c \end{bmatrix} \tag{51}$$

is the vector of *all* the variables in the mixed-variable equations, the number of which is b, the number of branches in the network. It is highly unlikely that all b equations in b unknowns in (50) are dynamically independent, meaning that $\mathbf{P}^0$ is singular and implying that the number of equations in this set can be reduced by eliminating some of the variables through manipulations that are merely algebraic. The algorithm to be presented carries out this elimination process systematically when no more variables can be eliminated algebraically. We might think of (50) as the "initial state equations."

In a given problem, the desired *output variables* may or may not include some of the state variables. In this respect, state variables are auxiliary variables; the desired output variables must be determined from the state variables, once the latter have been determined. Recall that any branch voltage or current can be obtained purely algebraically (through Kirchhoff's laws) from $\mathbf{v}_c$ and $\mathbf{i}_c$. The vector of all branch voltages and currents includes any conceivable output variable. By catenating the second form KCL and KVL expressions from Table 3.1 this vector can be expressed in terms of $\mathbf{x}_0$ as follows:

$$\begin{bmatrix} \mathbf{v} \\ \mathbf{i} \end{bmatrix} = \begin{bmatrix} \mathbf{Q}' & 0 \\ 0 & \mathbf{B}' \end{bmatrix} \begin{bmatrix} \mathbf{v}_c \\ \mathbf{i}_c \end{bmatrix} = \begin{bmatrix} \mathbf{Q}' & 0 \\ 0 & \mathbf{B}' \end{bmatrix} \mathbf{x}_0 \qquad (52)$$

Any desired output vector, $\mathbf{w}$, is simply a vector whose elements are those specific elements of $\mathbf{v}$ and $\mathbf{i}$ which are desired as outputs. Collecting the corresponding rows from (52), the output vector can be written as

$$\mathbf{w} = \mathbf{C}^0 \mathbf{x}_0. \qquad (53)$$

This is the "initial output equation."

In accordance with the procedure we are developing, we shall combine (50) and (53) into a single matrix equation by catenation. Thus,

$$\begin{bmatrix} \mathbf{U} & 0 & -\mathbf{C}^0 & 0 \\ 0 & \mathbf{P}^0 & -\mathbf{A}^0 & -\mathbf{B}_0^0 \end{bmatrix} \begin{bmatrix} \mathbf{w} \\ \dot{\mathbf{x}}_0 \\ \mathbf{x}_0 \\ \mathbf{u} \end{bmatrix} = \begin{bmatrix} 0 \\ 0 \end{bmatrix} \qquad (54)$$

where we have adopted the dot notation, $\dot{\mathbf{x}}_0 = d\mathbf{x}_0/dt$, to indicate differentiation. This equation is the first in a finite sequence of such equations to be generated by application of an iterative algorithm to be described below. The jth equation of this sequence will be

$$\begin{bmatrix} U & 0 & -C^j & -D_0^j & -D_1^j \ldots -D_{j-1}^j & 0 \\ 0 & P^j & -A^j & -B_0^j & -B_1^j \ldots -B_{j-1}^j & -B_j^j \end{bmatrix} \begin{bmatrix} w \\ \dot{x}_j \\ x_j \\ u \\ u^{(1)} \\ \vdots \\ u^{(j-1)} \\ u^{(j)} \end{bmatrix} = \begin{bmatrix} 0 \\ 0 \end{bmatrix} \quad (55)$$

Note: $u^{(k)}$ denotes the kth derivative of u with respect to time, and the matrix superscripts, used here for notational convenience, are indices, not exponents.

The sequence of equations terminates — stops — when, following a row echelon reduction for some value of j — denote it by s for "stop" — the rank of P^j equals its row order; that is, when $P^j = P^s$ is of full rank. Let ν denote the rank of P^s. Let us express the final equation in this sequence as

$$\begin{bmatrix} U & 0 & -C^s & -D_0 & -D_1 \ldots -D_{s-1} & 0 \\ 0 & P^s & -A^s & -B_0 & -B_1 \ldots -B_{s-1} & -B_s \end{bmatrix} \begin{bmatrix} w \\ \dot{x}_s \\ x_s \\ u^{(1)} \\ \vdots \\ u^{(s-1)} \\ u^{(s)} \end{bmatrix} = \begin{bmatrix} 0 \\ 0 \end{bmatrix}. \quad (56)$$

The superscript s on the submatrices indicates that the sequence has stopped and the coefficient matrix is in row echelon form. For notational simplicity, the superscripts have been omitted from the submatrices B_i and D_i.

When the indicated matrix multiplications are carried out in (56), the second and first rows, respectively, become

$$\mathbf{P}^s\dot{\mathbf{x}}_s - \mathbf{A}^s\mathbf{x}_s - \sum_{i=0}^{s} \mathbf{B}_i\mathbf{u}^{(i)} = \mathbf{0} \tag{57}$$

$$\mathbf{w} - \mathbf{C}^s\mathbf{x}_s - \sum_{i=0}^{s-1} \mathbf{D}_i\mathbf{u}^{(i)} = \mathbf{0} \tag{58}$$

These constitute a form of the state and output equations. However, the state equations are not yet in *normal* form. The final task is to carry out a transformation which will achieve this result.

Since the coefficient matrix of (56) is in row echelon form and since the rank and row order of $\mathbf{P}^s$ are equal (of value ν), it must be that the columns of $\mathbf{P}^s$ include those of a unit matrix. Thus, there must exist a nonsingular permutation matrix $\mathbf{T}$ such that

$$\mathbf{P}^s\mathbf{T} = [\mathbf{U} \ \hat{\mathbf{P}}]. \tag{59}$$

Now the term $\mathbf{P}^s\dot{\mathbf{x}}_s$ in (57) can be written as $\mathbf{P}^s\mathbf{T}\mathbf{T}^{-1}\dot{\mathbf{x}}_s$. The first two factors have already been written in partitioned form in (50). The product of the last two factors constitutes an ordering of the state variables, which can be partitioned as

$$\mathbf{T}^{-1}\dot{\mathbf{x}}_s = \begin{bmatrix} \dot{\mathbf{x}} \\ \dot{\hat{\mathbf{x}}} \end{bmatrix}, \tag{60}$$

where the first vector, $\dot{\mathbf{x}}$, in the partition is of order ν.

The other products in (57) and (58) — $\mathbf{A}^s\mathbf{x}_s$ and $\mathbf{C}^s\mathbf{x}_s$ — can be treated in a similar way. Thus, let us define

$$\mathbf{A}^s\mathbf{T} = [\mathbf{A} \ \hat{\mathbf{A}}], \tag{61a}$$

$$\mathbf{C}^s\mathbf{T} = [\mathbf{C} \ \hat{\mathbf{C}}], \tag{61b}$$

where the partition in each case is between columns ν and $\nu + 1$. (Thus, $\mathbf{A}$ is a square matrix since the row order of $\mathbf{A}^s$ is also ν.)

Using the last four equations (together with the undifferentiated equivalent of [60]), the corresponding products in (57) and (58) can be rewritten as

$$\mathbf{P}^s\dot{\mathbf{x}}_s = \mathbf{P}^s\mathbf{T}\mathbf{T}^{-1}\dot{\mathbf{x}}_s = [\mathbf{U} \ \hat{\mathbf{P}}]\begin{bmatrix} \dot{\mathbf{x}} \\ \dot{\hat{\mathbf{x}}} \end{bmatrix} = \dot{\mathbf{x}} + \hat{\mathbf{P}}\dot{\hat{\mathbf{x}}}, \tag{62a}$$

$$\mathbf{A}^s\mathbf{x}_s = \mathbf{A}\mathbf{x} + \hat{\mathbf{A}}\hat{\mathbf{x}}, \tag{62b}$$

$$\mathbf{C}^s\mathbf{x}_s = \mathbf{C}\mathbf{x} + \hat{\mathbf{C}}\hat{\mathbf{x}}. \tag{62c}$$

Finally, substituting these into (57) and (58), the result is

$$\dot{\mathbf{x}} = \mathbf{A}\mathbf{x} + \sum_{i=0}^{s} \mathbf{B}_i\mathbf{u}^{(i)} + \hat{\mathbf{A}}\hat{\mathbf{x}} - \hat{\mathbf{P}}\dot{\hat{\mathbf{x}}}, \tag{63}$$

$$\mathbf{w} = \mathbf{C}\mathbf{x} + \sum_{i=0}^{s-1} \mathbf{D}_i\mathbf{u}^{(i)} + \hat{\mathbf{C}}\hat{\mathbf{x}}. \tag{64}$$

The first of these constitutes the state equations in normal form. It is a first order vector differential equation for the state vector x which is of order ν. The second constitutes the output equations.

In addition to the state and input vectors, there appears a vector $\hat{\mathbf{x}}$ and its derivative in the state equations. We shall later explore the issues surrounding the appearance of these terms but note that the vector $\hat{\mathbf{x}}$ is completely arbitrary.

In the preceding, we have given the outline of a procedure for constructing the state and output equations for a given network. A key ingredient in this process is the algorithm for generating the sequence of equations (55). That algorithm is given in Table 1.*

The major steps in the algorithm are steps 2 and 7. We met a process similar to Step 7 in the examples of cut-set equations and loop equations treated earlier. In each case, there was an algebraic constraint on the variables which led to a reduced set of dynamic equations. That's what happens in the present case also.

In Step 6, algebraic constraints among source terms are catenated to those determined previously. When the algorithm reaches its stop condition, the collection of such constraints may be expressed as

$$\sum_{i=0}^{s} \mathbf{K}_i\mathbf{u}^{(i)} = \mathbf{0}. \tag{65}$$

---

* The state equations algorithm developed and presented herein is due to A. Dervisoglu and C. A. Desoer in "Degenerate networks and minimal differential equations," *IEEE Transactions on Circuits and Systems*, vol. CAS-22, 1976, pp. 769-775.

If we let

$$\mathbf{K} = \sum_{i=0}^{s} \mathbf{K}_i \frac{d^i}{dt^i},$$ (66)

then the previous result can be expressed as

$$\mathbf{K}\mathbf{u} = 0.$$ (67)

We will give these constraints further consideration later.

Table 1   Algorithm 1—State Equations Algorithm

STEP 1: Set $j = 0$.

STEP 2: Reduce to row-echelon form the coefficient matrix of (54) when $j = 0$ and of the reduced equations from Step 7 when $j > 0$, so as to obtain (55).

STEP 3: Set the rank of $\mathbf{P}^j$ equal to ν_j and set the row order of $\mathbf{P}^j$ equal to μ_j.

STEP 4: If $\nu_j = \mu_j$, then stop.

STEP 5: If among the reduced equations there are some trivial "zero equals zero" equations, remove them. (Any such equations will lie in the last rows of [55]. The existence of such equations will mean the network has no unique solution since there will be fewer equations than unknowns.)

STEP 6: If there are corresponding rows of zeros in $\mathbf{P}^j$ and $\mathbf{A}^j$ but not in all the $\mathbf{B}_i^j$'s, there will be algebraic constraints among the source terms. Catenate them to those determined at Step 6 in earlier iterations for smaller values of j.

STEP 7: If there are rows of zeros in $\mathbf{P}^j$ but not in corresponding rows of $\mathbf{A}^j$ (and also possibly the $\mathbf{B}_i^j$'s), there will be algebraic constraints on the elements of $\mathbf{x}_j$ (which may also involve the source terms). Use these constraints to eliminate, by back substitution, as many elements of $\dot{\mathbf{x}}_j$ and $\mathbf{x}_j$ from the equations as possible. Note: The back substitution will, in general, introduce elements of $\mathbf{u}^{(j+1)}$ into the equations.

STEP 8: Increment j by one.

STEP 9: Go to Step 2.

4.5.5 Example

As an illustration of this method of achieving a set of state equations, consider the network illustrated in Fig. 13. The branch relations in matrix form are

$$
\begin{bmatrix}
1 & 0 & 0 & 0 & 0 & 0 & 0 & 0 \\
0 & 1 & 0 & 0 & 0 & 0 & 0 & 0 \\
0 & 0 & -2d/dt & 0 & 0 & 0 & 0 & 0 \\
0 & 0 & 0 & -2d/dt & 0 & 0 & 0 & 0 \\
0 & 0 & 0 & 0 & -2 & 0 & 0 & 0 \\
0 & 0 & 0 & 0 & 0 & -d/dt & 0 & 0 \\
0 & 0 & 0 & 0 & 0 & 0 & 1 & 0 \\
0 & 0 & 0 & 0 & 0 & 0 & 0 & 1
\end{bmatrix}
\left\{
\begin{bmatrix}
v_1 \\ v_2 \\ v_3 \\ v_4 \\ v_5 \\ v_6 \\ v_7 \\ v_8
\end{bmatrix}
-
\begin{bmatrix}
e_1 \\ e_2 \\ 0 \\ 0 \\ 0 \\ 0 \\ 0 \\ 0
\end{bmatrix}
\right\}
$$

$$
+
\begin{bmatrix}
0 & 0 & 0 & 0 & 0 & 0 & 0 & 0 \\
0 & 0 & 0 & 0 & 0 & 0 & 0 & 0 \\
0 & 0 & 1 & 0 & 0 & 0 & 0 & 0 \\
0 & 0 & 0 & 1 & 0 & 0 & 0 & 0 \\
0 & 0 & 0 & 0 & 1 & 0 & 0 & 0 \\
0 & 0 & 0 & 0 & 0 & 1 & 0 & 0 \\
0 & 0 & 0 & 0 & 0 & 0 & -1 & 0 \\
0 & 0 & 0 & 0 & 0 & 0 & 0 & -1
\end{bmatrix}
\left\{
\begin{bmatrix}
i_1 \\ i_2 \\ i_3 \\ i_4 \\ i_5 \\ i_6 \\ i_7 \\ i_8
\end{bmatrix}
-
\begin{bmatrix}
0 \\ 0 \\ 0 \\ 0 \\ 0 \\ 0 \\ 0 \\ 0
\end{bmatrix}
\right\}
=
\begin{bmatrix}
0 \\ 0 \\ 0 \\ 0 \\ 0 \\ 0 \\ 0 \\ 0
\end{bmatrix} .
$$

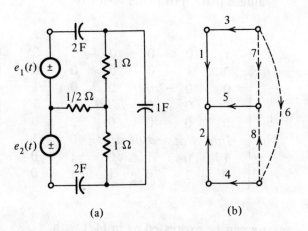

(a)   (b)

Fig. 13   Network schematic and graph

Clearly, it is not necessary to use fundamental loop and fundamental cut-set matrices, much less those associated with the same forest, to write the mixed-variable equation (46). However, it is, in general, convenient to do so. For the tree consisting of branches 1, 2, 3, 4, and 5 the fundamental cut-set and fundamental loop matrices are

$$
\mathbf{Q}_f =
\begin{array}{c}
\\
\text{Twigs} \\
\downarrow
\end{array}
\begin{array}{c}
\text{Branches} \rightarrow \\
\begin{array}{ccccccccc}
 & 1 & 2 & 3 & 4 & 5 & 6 & 7 & 8 \\
1 & \left[\begin{array}{c}1\end{array}\right. & 0 & 0 & 0 & 0 & 1 & 1 & 0 \\
2 & 0 & 1 & 0 & 0 & 0 & -1 & 0 & 1 \\
3 & 0 & 0 & 1 & 0 & 0 & 1 & 1 & 0 \\
4 & 0 & 0 & 0 & 1 & 0 & -1 & 0 & 1 \\
5 & 0 & 0 & 0 & 0 & 1 & 0 & -1 & -1 \left.\right]
\end{array}
\end{array}
$$

and

$$
\mathbf{B}_f =
\begin{array}{c}
\\
\text{Links} \\
\downarrow
\end{array}
\begin{array}{c}
\text{Branches} \rightarrow \\
\begin{array}{ccccccccc}
 & 1 & 2 & 3 & 4 & 5 & 6 & 7 & 8 \\
6 & \left[\begin{array}{c}-1\end{array}\right. & 1 & -1 & 1 & 0 & 1 & 0 & 0 \\
7 & -1 & 0 & -1 & 0 & 1 & 0 & 1 & 0 \\
8 & 0 & -1 & 0 & -1 & 1 & 0 & 0 & 1 \left.\right]
\end{array}
\end{array}
$$

aluate $[\mathbf{MQ}_f'\quad \mathbf{NB}_f']$; the result is

$$
[\mathbf{MQ}_f'\quad \mathbf{NB}_f'] =
\begin{bmatrix}
1 & 0 & 0 & 0 & 0 & 0 & 0 & 0 \\
1 & 1 & 0 & 0 & 0 & 0 & 0 & 0 \\
0 & 0 & -2d/dt & 0 & 0 & -1 & -1 & 0 \\
0 & 0 & 0 & -2d/dt & 0 & 1 & 0 & -1 \\
0 & 0 & 0 & 0 & -2 & 0 & 1 & 1 \\
-d/dt & d/dt & -d/dt & d/dt & 0 & 1 & 0 & 0 \\
1 & 0 & 1 & 0 & -1 & 0 & -1 & 0 \\
0 & 1 & 0 & 1 & -1 & 0 & 0 & -1
\end{bmatrix}.
$$

Now, this matrix can be expressed as in (47) with

$$\mathbf{P}^0 = \begin{bmatrix} 0 & 0 & 0 & 0 & 0 & 0 & 0 & 0 \\ 0 & 0 & 0 & 0 & 0 & 0 & 0 & 0 \\ 0 & 0 & -2 & 0 & 0 & 0 & 0 & 0 \\ 0 & 0 & 0 & -2 & 0 & 0 & 0 & 0 \\ 0 & 0 & 0 & 0 & 0 & 0 & 0 & 0 \\ -1 & 1 & -1 & 1 & 0 & 0 & 0 & 0 \\ 0 & 0 & 0 & 0 & 0 & 0 & 0 & 0 \\ 0 & 0 & 0 & 0 & 0 & 0 & 0 & 0 \end{bmatrix}$$

and

$$-\mathbf{A}^0 = \begin{bmatrix} 1 & 0 & 0 & 0 & 0 & 0 & 0 & 0 \\ 0 & 1 & 0 & 0 & 0 & 0 & 0 & 0 \\ 0 & 0 & 0 & 0 & 0 & -1 & -1 & 0 \\ 0 & 0 & 0 & 0 & 0 & 1 & 0 & -1 \\ 0 & 0 & 0 & 0 & -2 & 0 & 1 & 1 \\ 0 & 0 & 0 & 0 & 0 & 1 & 0 & 0 \\ 1 & 0 & 1 & 0 & -1 & 0 & -1 & 0 \\ 0 & 1 & 0 & 1 & -1 & 0 & 0 & -1 \end{bmatrix}$$

An examination of the branch relations discloses the expression for the source vector $\mathbf{e}$. From it we extract the input vector $\mathbf{u}$ and matrix $\mathbf{B}^0$ to use in (49). Thus,

$$\mathbf{u} = \begin{bmatrix} e_1 \\ \\ e_2 \end{bmatrix} \qquad \text{and} \qquad \mathbf{B}^0 = \begin{bmatrix} 1 & 0 \\ 0 & 1 \\ 0 & 0 \\ 0 & 0 \\ 0 & 0 \\ 0 & 0 \\ 0 & 0 \\ 0 & 0 \end{bmatrix}.$$

Let us choose v_6 and i_5 as outputs. That is, the output vector is $\mathbf{w} = [v_6 \; i_5]'$. Then, after composing (52) for this network, the matrix $\mathbf{C}^0$ of (53) is seen to be

$$\mathbf{C}^0 = \begin{bmatrix} 1 & -1 & 1 & -1 & 0 & 0 & 0 & 0 \\ 0 & 0 & 0 & 0 & 0 & 0 & 1 & 1 \end{bmatrix}.$$

The "initial" equations (54) can now be composed. They are

$$
\left[\begin{array}{cc|cccccccc|cccccccc|cc}
1 & 0 & 0 & 0 & 0 & 0 & 0 & 0 & 0 & 0 & -1 & 1 & -1 & 1 & 0 & 0 & 0 & 0 & 0 & 0 \\
0 & 1 & 0 & 0 & 0 & 0 & 0 & 0 & 0 & 0 & 0 & 0 & 0 & 0 & 0 & 0 & -1 & -1 & 0 & 0 \\
\hline
0 & 0 & 0 & 0 & 0 & 0 & 0 & 0 & 0 & 0 & 1 & 0 & 0 & 0 & 0 & 0 & 0 & 0 & -1 & 0 \\
0 & 0 & 0 & 0 & 0 & 0 & 0 & 0 & 0 & 0 & 0 & 1 & 0 & 0 & 0 & 0 & 0 & 0 & 0 & -1 \\
0 & 0 & 0 & 0 & -2 & 0 & 0 & 0 & 0 & 0 & 0 & 0 & 0 & 0 & 0 & -1 & -1 & 0 & 0 & 0 \\
0 & 0 & 0 & 0 & 0 & -2 & 0 & 0 & 0 & 0 & 0 & 0 & 0 & 0 & 0 & 1 & 0 & -1 & 0 & 0 \\
0 & 0 & 0 & 0 & 0 & 0 & 0 & 0 & 0 & 0 & 0 & 0 & 0 & 0 & -2 & 0 & 1 & 1 & 0 & 0 \\
0 & 0 & -1 & 1 & -1 & 1 & 0 & 0 & 0 & 0 & 0 & 0 & 0 & 0 & 0 & 1 & 0 & 0 & 0 & 0 \\
0 & 0 & 0 & 0 & 0 & 0 & 0 & 0 & 0 & 0 & 1 & 0 & 1 & 0 & -1 & 0 & -1 & 0 & 0 & 0 \\
0 & 0 & 0 & 0 & 0 & 0 & 0 & 0 & 0 & 0 & 0 & 1 & 0 & 1 & -1 & 0 & 0 & -1 & 0 & 0
\end{array}\right]
\begin{bmatrix}
v_6 \\ i_5 \\ \hline v_1 \\ v_2 \\ v_3 \\ v_4 \\ v_5 \\ i_6 \\ i_7 \\ i_8 \\ \hline v_1 \\ v_2 \\ v_3 \\ v_4 \\ v_5 \\ i_6 \\ i_7 \\ i_8 \\ \hline e_1 \\ e_2
\end{bmatrix}
=
\begin{bmatrix}
0 \\ 0 \\ 0 \\ 0 \\ 0 \\ 0 \\ 0 \\ 0 \\ 0 \\ 0
\end{bmatrix}
$$

Until this point we have been composing matrices using the Kirchhoff equations and branch relationships in the network in appropriate combinations. The next step is the algorithm. The row echelon reduction in step 2 with $j=0$ yields the following set of equations equivalent to (55) when $j=0$:

$$
\left[\begin{array}{cc|cccccccc|cccccccc|cc}
1 & 0 & & & & & & & & & 0 & 0 & 0 & 0 & 0 & 0 & -1 & 1 & 0 & 0 \\
0 & 1 & & & \bigcirc & & & & & & 0 & 0 & 0 & 0 & 0 & 0 & -1 & -1 & 0 & 0 \\
\hline
 & & 1 & -1 & 0 & 0 & 0 & 0 & 0 & 0 & 0 & 0 & 0 & 0 & 0 & -2 & -\tfrac{1}{2} & \tfrac{1}{2} & 0 & 0 \\
 & & 0 & 0 & 1 & 0 & 0 & 0 & 0 & 0 & 0 & 0 & 0 & 0 & 0 & \tfrac{1}{2} & \tfrac{1}{2} & 0 & 0 & 0 \\
 & & 0 & 0 & 0 & 1 & 0 & 0 & 0 & 0 & 0 & 0 & 0 & 0 & 0 & -\tfrac{1}{2} & 0 & \tfrac{1}{2} & 0 & 0 \\
 \bigcirc & & 0 & 0 & 0 & 0 & 0 & 0 & 0 & 0 & 1 & 0 & 0 & 0 & 0 & 0 & 0 & 0 & -1 & 0 \\
 & & 0 & 0 & 0 & 0 & 0 & 0 & 0 & 0 & 0 & 1 & 0 & 0 & 0 & 0 & 0 & 0 & 0 & -1 \\
 & & 0 & 0 & 0 & 0 & 0 & 0 & 0 & 0 & 0 & 0 & 1 & 0 & 0 & 0 & -\tfrac{1}{2} & -\tfrac{1}{2} & 1 & 0 \\
 & & 0 & 0 & 0 & 0 & 0 & 0 & 0 & 0 & 0 & 0 & 0 & 1 & 0 & 0 & -\tfrac{1}{2} & \tfrac{3}{2} & 0 & 1 \\
 & & 0 & 0 & 0 & 0 & 0 & 0 & 0 & 0 & 0 & 0 & 0 & 0 & 1 & 0 & -\tfrac{1}{2} & -\tfrac{1}{2} & 0 & 0
\end{array}\right]
\begin{bmatrix}
v_6 \\ i_5 \\ \hline v_1 \\ v_2 \\ v_3 \\ v_4 \\ v_5 \\ i_6 \\ i_7 \\ i_8 \\ \hline v_1 \\ v_2 \\ v_3 \\ v_4 \\ v_5 \\ i_6 \\ i_7 \\ i_8 \\ \hline e_1 \\ e_2
\end{bmatrix}
=
\begin{bmatrix}
0 \\ 0 \\ 0 \\ 0 \\ 0 \\ 0 \\ 0 \\ 0 \\ 0 \\ 0
\end{bmatrix}
$$

Since the row order (μ_0) of $\mathbf{P}^0$ is 8 and its rank (ν_0) is 3, we must reach step 5 of the algorithm. There are no "zero equals zero" equations and no algebraic constraints among source terms so we reach step 7. The last 5 rows of $\mathbf{P}^0$ are zero. Corresponding to these rows, the following algebraic constraints occur:

$$
\begin{bmatrix}
1 & 0 & 0 & 0 & 0 & 0 & 0 & 0 & -1 & 0 \\
0 & 1 & 0 & 0 & 0 & 0 & 0 & 0 & 0 & -1 \\
0 & 0 & 1 & 0 & 0 & 0 & -\tfrac{3}{2} & -\tfrac{1}{2} & 1 & 0 \\
0 & 0 & 0 & 1 & 0 & 0 & -\tfrac{1}{2} & -\tfrac{3}{2} & 0 & 1 \\
0 & 0 & 0 & 0 & 1 & 0 & -\tfrac{1}{2} & -\tfrac{1}{2} & 0 & 0
\end{bmatrix}
\begin{bmatrix}
v_1 \\ v_2 \\ v_3 \\ v_4 \\ v_5 \\ i_6 \\ i_7 \\ i_8 \\ e_1 \\ e_2
\end{bmatrix}
=
\begin{bmatrix}
0 \\ 0 \\ 0 \\ 0 \\ 0
\end{bmatrix} .
$$

We shall use this to express v_1 through v_5 in terms of i_6, i_7, i_8, e_1, and e_2. The back-substitution removes v_1 through v_5 from the equations and leaves us with

$$
\begin{bmatrix}
1 & 0 & & & 0 & -1 & 1 & & & \\
0 & 1 & & & 0 & -1 & -1 & & & \\
& & 0 & 0 & 0 & -2 & -\tfrac{1}{2} & \tfrac{1}{2} & & 1 & -1 \\
& & 0 & \tfrac{3}{2} & \tfrac{1}{2} & \tfrac{1}{2} & \tfrac{1}{2} & 0 & & -1 & 0 \\
& & 0 & \tfrac{1}{2} & \tfrac{3}{2} & -\tfrac{1}{2} & 0 & \tfrac{1}{2} & & 0 & -1
\end{bmatrix}
\begin{bmatrix}
v_6 \\ i_5 \\ i_6 \\ i_7 \\ i_8 \\ i_6 \\ i_7 \\ i_8 \\ e_1 \\ e_2 \\ e_1^{(1)} \\ e_2^{(1)}
\end{bmatrix}
=
\begin{bmatrix}
0 \\ 0 \\ 0 \\ 0 \\ 0
\end{bmatrix} .
$$

One cycle has now been completed. After setting $j = 1$, we are again ready to carry out a row echelon reduction in step 2 of the next cycle. This reduction converts the preceding equation to the following for (55) when $j = 1$:

$$
\left[
\begin{array}{cc|c|cc|c|c}
1 & 0 & & 0 & -1 & 1 & \\
0 & 1 & \bigcirc & 0 & -1 & -1 & \bigcirc \\
\hline
 & & 0\ 1\ 0 & 0 & \frac{1}{4} & 0 & -\frac{1}{2}\ \ 0 \\
\bigcirc & & 0\ 0\ 1 & 0 & 0 & \frac{1}{4} & \bigcirc\ \ 0\ \ -\frac{1}{2} \\
 & & 0\ 0\ 0 & 1 & \frac{1}{4} & -\frac{1}{4} & -\frac{1}{2}\ \ \frac{1}{2}
\end{array}
\right]
\left[
\begin{array}{c}
v_6 \\ i_5 \\ \hline i_6 \\ i_7 \\ i_8 \\ \hline i_6 \\ i_7 \\ i_8 \\ \hline e_1 \\ e_2 \\ e_1^{(1)} \\ e_2^{(1)}
\end{array}
\right]
=
\left[
\begin{array}{c}
0 \\ 0 \\ 0 \\ 0 \\ 0
\end{array}
\right].
$$

By inspection the rank and row order of $\mathbf{P}^1$ are seen to be $\nu_1 = 2$ and $\mu_1 = 3$. So we pass to step 5. Again there are no trivial equations and no constraints among source times. So we reach step 7. There is one algebraic constraint among the variables; it yields the following expression for i_6:

$$
[i_6] = [-\tfrac{1}{4} \quad \tfrac{1}{4}]
\left[
\begin{array}{c}
i_7 \\ i_8
\end{array}
\right]
+ [\tfrac{1}{2} \quad -\tfrac{1}{2}]
\left[
\begin{array}{c}
e_1^{(1)} \\ e_2^{(1)}
\end{array}
\right].
$$

The back-substitution to remove i_6 from the equations leaves us with

$$
\left[
\begin{array}{cc|c|cc|c|c|c}
1 & 0 & & -1 & 1 & & & \\
0 & 1 & \bigcirc & -1 & -1 & \bigcirc & \bigcirc & \bigcirc \\
\hline
 & & 1\ 0 & \frac{1}{4} & 0 & & -\frac{1}{2}\ \ 0 & \\
\bigcirc & & 0\ 1 & 0 & \frac{1}{4} & \bigcirc & 0\ \ -\frac{1}{2} & \bigcirc
\end{array}
\right]
\left[
\begin{array}{c}
v_6 \\ i_5 \\ \hline i_7 \\ i_8 \\ \hline i_7 \\ i_8 \\ \hline e_1 \\ e_2 \\ \hline e_1^{(1)} \\ e_2^{(1)} \\ \hline e_1^{(2)} \\ e_2^{(2)}
\end{array}
\right]
=
\left[
\begin{array}{c}
0 \\ 0 \\ 0 \\ 0
\end{array}
\right].
$$

After j is set to 2 at step 6, the algorithm returns to step 2 and immediately passes to step 3, as the above coefficient matrix is already in row echelon form. At this point $v_2 = 2$ and $\mu_2 = 2$; therefore, the algorithm has reached its stop instruction. The above equations correspond to (56) — equivalently, (55) with $j = s = 2$.

In the two passes through step 6, no algebraic constraints on the source terms were generated. Thus, for this example, the matrix $\mathbf{K}$ of (67) is null — it does not exist.

The value of v ($= v_s$) is 2. Thus, the state vector will be of order 2. Note from the final equations that $\mathbf{P}^2$ is a unit matrix, so the matrix $\mathbf{T}$ in (59), (61a), and (61b) is a unit matrix; hence, matrices $\hat{\mathbf{P}}$, $\hat{\mathbf{A}}$ and $\hat{\mathbf{C}}$ do not exist in this example and the terms containing these matrices in (63) and (64) do not appear.

Rewriting the final equation leads to the following state equations and the associated output equations:

$$\frac{d}{dt}\begin{bmatrix} i_7 \\ i_8 \end{bmatrix} = \begin{bmatrix} -\tfrac{1}{4} & 0 \\ 0 & -\tfrac{1}{4} \end{bmatrix} \begin{bmatrix} i_7 \\ i_8 \end{bmatrix} + \begin{bmatrix} \tfrac{1}{2} & 0 \\ 0 & \tfrac{1}{2} \end{bmatrix} \frac{d}{dt} \begin{bmatrix} e_1 \\ e_2 \end{bmatrix}$$

$$\begin{bmatrix} v_6 \\ i_5 \end{bmatrix} = \begin{bmatrix} 1 & -1 \\ 1 & 1 \end{bmatrix} \begin{bmatrix} i_7 \\ i_8 \end{bmatrix} .$$

In this example, the elements of the state vector are, surprisingly, the nondynamic component currents i_7 and i_8. This is not a desirable situation. The voltage-current relationship of non-dynamic components are algebraic, not dynamic; hence, their currents do not seem to be natural choices for the elements of the state vector. Furthermore, the initial conditions for i_7 and i_8 must be derived from those of the capacitors, which are the elements in this network exhibiting a dynamic voltage-current relationship. You should verify that

$$\begin{bmatrix} i_7(0) \\ i_8(0) \end{bmatrix} = \begin{bmatrix} \tfrac{1}{4}\{3e_1(0) - e_2(0) + 3v_3(0) - v_4(0)\} \\ \tfrac{1}{4}\{-e_1(0) + 3e_2(0) - v_3(0) + 3v_4(0)\} \end{bmatrix} .$$

For this simple example, there is very little work to evaluate these initial values. However, that ease is not to be expected generally if non-dynamic component variables appear as state vector elements. For this reason, if for no other, it is desirable to require the elements of the state vector to be dynamic component variables — capacitor voltages and inductor currents. This will be the case if some modifications are made in the procedure for developing the state equation. We shall now discuss such modifications.

4.5.6 The State Variables Using a Proper Forest

When writing the mixed variable equations (46) no restrictions were placed in choosing a forest for the purpose of determining the cut-set matrix $\mathbf{Q}$ and the loop matrix $\mathbf{B}$. Since we wish to concentrate attention on specific components (the dynamic ones) we should place some restrictions on how a forest is chosen. We define a *proper forest* as a forest having a maximum number of capacitor branches and a minimum number of inductor branches. (The *proper coforest* will have a maximum number of inductor branches and a minimum number of capacitor branches.) The only circumstance that would make the "maximum number of capacitors" less than all the capacitors would be the existence of an all-capacitor loop, not including voltage sources. Similarly, the only way there would be any inductors in the proper forest would be the existence of an all-inductor cut-set, not including current sources. The difference between a proper forest and the previously-defined normal forest is that the latter may have fewer capacitors (or more inductors) because of C-v_s loops (or L-i_s cut-sets).

An algorithm had previously been presented in Chapter 3 for generating a forest for a network. This algorithm can be modified by ordering the branches in such a way that first priority is given to capacitors and last priority to inductors in twig selection. An algorithm for generating a proper forest is given in Table 2

With the proper forest chosen, the $\mathbf{Q}$ and $\mathbf{B}$ matrices used in the preceding development of the state equations will be those corresponding to fundamental cut-sets and fundamental loops, respectively. Then, in (46) and (52), the voltage vector $\mathbf{v}_c$ will become $\mathbf{v}_t$ and the current vector $\mathbf{i}_c$ will become $\mathbf{i}_t$. The only change to be made in Algorithm 1 is to replace step 1 by the change shown in Table 3.

From the definition of a proper forest and from the choice of variables $\mathbf{v}_t$ and $\mathbf{i}_l$ for $\mathbf{v}_c$ and $\mathbf{i}_c$ in (46) and (52), $\mathbf{x}_0$ contains a maximum number of dynamic component variables. (See Prob. 31.) The reorder-

ing of step 1b in Table 3 guarantees that the row echelon reduction of
step 2 in Algorithm 1 will always result in a preference for removal of
algebraic component variables. Furthermore, any removed dynamic
component variables will have been expressed in terms of other dynamic
component variables and source terms. You should show that, as the
ultimate consequence, all the elements of $\mathbf{x}$ must be dynamic component variables—capacitor voltages and inductor currents. (See Prob.
32.)

For the network of the example any normal tree would contain the
three capacitor branches—branches 3, 4, and 6. To observe the effect of
the modified step 1, you should select a normal tree and repeat the

Table 2   Algorithm 2—Proper Forest Algorithm

STEP 1: Set $l = 0$.

STEP 2: Let $\mathbf{k}$ be a list of branches, labeled 1 through b and ordered as
follows: capacitor branch labels are first in the list and induc-
tor branch labels are last in the list.

STEP 3: Set $\mathbf{M} = \mathbf{A}_c$.

STEP 4: If the number of branches designated as twigs is n, then stop.

STEP 5: Increment l by 1.

STEP 6: If column k_l of $\mathbf{M}$ is zero, then go to Step 5, else designate
branch k_l as a twig.

STEP 7: Let i and j be the row indices of the two nonzero elements of
column k_l.

STEP 8: Add row j of $\mathbf{M}$ to row i; then set row j to zero.

STEP 9: Go to Step 4.

Table 3   Change in Algorithm 1, the State Equations Algorithm

STEP 1a: Set $j = 0$.

STEP 1b: Reorder the rows of $\mathbf{x}_0$ such that capacitor voltages and inductor currents—which are elements of $\mathbf{v}_t$ and $\mathbf{i}_l$, respectively, and hence of $\mathbf{x}_0$—appear last. Reorder the columns of
$\mathbf{P}^0$, $\mathbf{A}^0$, and $\mathbf{C}^0$ correspondingly.

derivation of the state and output equations with the modified algorithm, where at step 1b the reordering makes v_6, v_3, and v_4, in that order, the last elements of $\mathbf{x}_0$ and verify that the equations become

$$\frac{d}{dt}\begin{bmatrix} v_3 \\ v_4 \end{bmatrix} = \begin{bmatrix} -\frac{1}{4} & 0 \\ 0 & -\frac{1}{4} \end{bmatrix}\begin{bmatrix} v_3 \\ v_4 \end{bmatrix} + \begin{bmatrix} -\frac{1}{4} & 0 \\ 0 & -\frac{1}{4} \end{bmatrix}\begin{bmatrix} e_1 \\ e_2 \end{bmatrix} + \begin{bmatrix} -\frac{1}{4} & \frac{1}{4} \\ \frac{1}{4} & -\frac{1}{4} \end{bmatrix}\frac{d}{dt}\begin{bmatrix} e_1 \\ e_2 \end{bmatrix},$$

$$\begin{bmatrix} v_6 \\ i_5 \end{bmatrix} = \begin{bmatrix} 1 & -1 \\ \frac{1}{2} & \frac{1}{2} \end{bmatrix}\begin{bmatrix} v_3 \\ v_4 \end{bmatrix} + \begin{bmatrix} 1 & -1 \\ \frac{1}{2} & \frac{1}{2} \end{bmatrix}\begin{bmatrix} e_1 \\ e_2 \end{bmatrix}.$$

4.5.6 General Observations

A few general comments will help in appreciating how the generating algorithm for state equations handles anomalous situations. Choosing a normal forest guarantees that the number of capacitor twigs cannot exceed the number of capacitors n_C reduced by the number of independent all-capacitor loops. Similarly, it reduces the number of inductor links to n_L less the number of independent all-inductor cut-sets. But the order of complexity is not necessarily equal to the number of capacitor twigs plus inductor links. It may be reduced from this number by virtue of the existence of loops consisting of capacitors *and* voltage sources and the existence of cut-sets consisting of inductors *and* current sources. In the case of C-v_s loops, all the capacitors on the loop are twigs and at least one of the voltage sources is a link. Step 7 of the algorithm leads to a constraint among capacitor twig voltages and the voltage source terms. For each such constraint, a capacitor voltage is eliminated from the initial selection of state variables and the order of complexity is thereby reduced.

In the case of the L-i_s cut-sets, all the inductors in the cut-set are links and at least one of the current sources is a twig. Step 7 of the algorithm leads to a constraint among inductor currents and the current source terms. For each such constraint an inductor current is eliminated from the initial selection of state variables and the order of complexity is again reduced.

But the presence of C-v_s loops and L-i_s cut-sets is not the only circumstance that will reduce the order of complexity; the presence of such components as controlled sources may also do the same thing, as illustrated earlier in Fig. 10. (Additional illustrations of component-induced reductions in the order of complexity are to be found in Exercise 21.)

Furthermore, such components can also introduce other anomalies besides reducing the order of complexity.

Consider, for example, the network of Fig. 14. The state equation can be written as

$$\frac{dv}{dt} = -\frac{1}{RC}v + \frac{r}{RC}\hat{i},$$

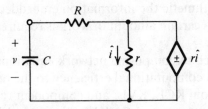

Fig. 14   Degenerate network

where $\hat{i}$ is completely arbitrary. The arbitrary current $\hat{i}$ appears because the controlled source sustains whatever voltage appears across the resistor r, independent of its value. Such a network would have no intrinsic value since its response to just the initial conditions of the dynamic variables would not be unique; we say it is *degenerate*. Nevertheless, an analysis procedure must allow for such networks if it is to be universally applicable.

The algebraic constraints on the source terms extracted at step 5 and expressed in (67) arise because of such pathological network conditions as loops of independent voltage sources and cut-sets of independent current sources. Since such pathological conditions do not arise in well-designed networks of practical value, networks with such conditions are also said to be degenerate. Thus if $\mathbf{K}$ of (67) is not null, the network is degenerate.

To summarize, a network is said to be degenerate if $\hat{\mathbf{P}}$ or $\hat{\mathbf{A}}$ in (63), or $\hat{\mathbf{C}}$ in (64), or $\mathbf{K}$ in (67) is other than null. Further illustrations of degenerate networks are to be found in Exercises 20 and 21.

4.6 TABLEAU EQUATIONS

In the preceding sections of this chapter we have presented a number of network analysis procedures. Each of them ends in a set of equations of different order: n for the node equations, $b - n$ for the loop equations, b for the mixed-variable equations, and the order of complexity for the state equations. Each procedure is based on the same fundamental relationships: component equations and topological equations expressing Kirchhoff's laws.

Given a network — or tabulations of the component parameter values and their connection data — the incident matrix $\mathbf{A}$, the parameter matrices $\mathbf{M}$ and $\mathbf{N}$, and the source vectors $\mathbf{v}_s$ and $\mathbf{i}_s$ are easily composed. But carrying out any one of the preceding analysis procedures and obtaining the corresponding sets of equations requires transforming through matrix arithmetic the information embedded in these matrices and vectors. Thus a certain amount of work is required just to set up the equations.

Another approach to composing network equations is possible which is often superior in computational efficiency to the preceding methods. It too must start from KCL, KVL, and component relations. For KCL, we shall use the first form and for KVL, the second form. From Table 3.1, these are

$$\mathbf{Ai} = 0, \tag{68a}$$

$$\mathbf{v} = \mathbf{A}'\mathbf{v}_n. \tag{68b}$$

We shall write the component equations as

$$\mathbf{Mv} + \mathbf{Ni} = \mathbf{e}. \tag{69}$$

Without any matrix arithmetic, these can be catenated and written as

$$\begin{bmatrix} 0 & \mathbf{A} & 0 \\ \mathbf{A}' & 0 & -\mathbf{U} \\ 0 & \mathbf{N} & \mathbf{M} \end{bmatrix} \begin{bmatrix} \mathbf{v}_n \\ \mathbf{i} \\ \mathbf{v} \end{bmatrix} = \begin{bmatrix} 0 \\ 0 \\ \mathbf{e} \end{bmatrix}. \tag{70}$$

This single matrix equation includes all the basic relationships from which all the other analysis procedures have been derived. It could be the beginning point of the procedure to be discussed but we shall deal with a variation which separates the dynamic from the nondynamic components in (69).

Specifically, for the dynamic variables we shall write the component relations in the form

$$q_k = C_k v_k \quad \text{and} \quad \lambda_j = L_j i_j \tag{71a}$$

with

$$i_k = \frac{dq_k}{dt} \quad \text{and} \quad v_j = \frac{d\lambda_j}{dt}. \tag{71b}$$

where q_k is the kth capacitor charge and λ_j is the jth inductor flux. Let $\mathbf{x}$ be the vector of capacitor charges and inductor fluxes. Then, the replacement of (69) will be

$$\hat{\mathbf{M}}v + \hat{\mathbf{N}}i + \hat{\mathbf{P}}\mathbf{x} = \mathbf{e}. \tag{72}$$

The elements of all the matrices in this expression are constants; there are no derivative operators. We have introduced b_{LC} additional variables in (72), as many as the total of all capacitors and inductors in the network, and we must have that many additional equations. And we do, in (71b); when written in matrix form, these become

$$\mathbf{K}_i i + \mathbf{K}_v v - \frac{d}{dt}\mathbf{x} = \mathbf{0}. \tag{73}$$

The nonzero entries in $\mathbf{K}_i$ and $\mathbf{K}_v$ correspond only to dynamic branches. Matrix $[\mathbf{K}_i \ \mathbf{K}_v]$ is column equivalent to the matrix $[\mathbf{U} \ \mathbf{0}]$ of the same order. Finally, instead of using the branch relations in the form of (69), we use the equivalent (72) and (73). When these are catenated with KCL and KVL in (68), the result will be

$$\begin{array}{cccc} & n & b & b & b_{LC} \end{array}$$
$$\begin{array}{c} n \\ b \\ b \\ b_{LC} \end{array} \begin{bmatrix} 0 & A & 0 & 0 \\ A' & 0 & -U & 0 \\ 0 & \hat{N} & \hat{M} & \hat{P} \\ 0 & K_i & K_v & -U\dfrac{d}{dt} \end{bmatrix} \begin{bmatrix} v_n \\ i \\ v \\ x \end{bmatrix} = \begin{bmatrix} 0 \\ 0 \\ e \\ 0 \end{bmatrix}. \tag{74a}$$

(For clarity, the row and column orders of the submatrices have been indicated.) Because we shall discuss computational solutions of this equation, it is useful to show the frequency-domain form; it is

$$\begin{bmatrix} 0 & A & 0 & 0 \\ A' & 0 & -U & 0 \\ 0 & \hat{N} & \hat{M} & \hat{P} \\ 0 & K_i & K_v & -Us \end{bmatrix} \begin{bmatrix} V_n \\ I \\ V \\ X \end{bmatrix} = \begin{bmatrix} 0 \\ 0 \\ E \\ -x(0) \end{bmatrix}. \tag{74b}$$

These equations, in either domain, are a tableau of all the known variable constraints associated with the network and are called *tableau equations*. The coefficient matrix is known as the *tableau matrix*.*

4.6.1 Solution of the Tableau Equations

Note that the number of equations and of variables is $2b + n + b_{LC}$, a large number indeed, much larger than for the other formulation methods. When the equations are solved, the solution will give not only all branch voltages and currents but also the node voltages and all capacitor charges and inductor fluxes. Clearly, this is overkill and there must be some justification for doing it. The justification lies not just in the ease of setting up the equations but also in the ease of obtaining a numerical solution by means of a computer, often with greater computational efficiency than setting up and solving the far fewer equations resulting from other formulation methods.

We shall illustrate these comments by devoting some attention, though not exhaustive, to the solution process. (This was not done explicitly for other formuatlion methods but solution procedures are involved in Progs. 5-6 and Projs. 11-12. See also Progs. 3-4 and Projs. 2-10.)

In the time-domain, a numerical solution is sought at a discrete set of time values t_m ($m = 0, 1, \dots$) with $t_{m+1} > t_m$. For simplicity we shall use a superscript m on a variable to indicate that the variable is evaluated at t_m. Since time is no longer continuous, the time derivative can only be approximated; hence, some error will be introduced. A simple approximation for a derivative comes from its basic definition; the so-called backward Euler formula can be written as

$$\dot{x}^m \approx \frac{x^m - x^{m-1}}{t_m - t_{m-1}} = \frac{1}{t_m - t_{m-1}} x^m - \left\{ \frac{1}{t_m - t_{m-1}} x^{m-1} \right\}. \qquad (75a)$$

Another approximation to the derivative is the trapezoidal formula

$$\dot{x}^m \approx 2\frac{x^m - x^{m-1}}{t_m - t_{m-1}} - \dot{x}^{m-1} = \frac{2}{t_m - t_{m-1}} x^m - \left\{ \frac{2}{t_m - t_{m-1}} x^{m-1} - \dot{x}^{m-1} \right\} \qquad (75b)$$

---

* The tableau equations, as a method for network analysis, were first proposed by G. D. Hachtel, R. K. Brayton, and F. G. Gustavson in "The sparse tableau approach to network analysis and design," *IEEE Transactions on Circuit Theory*, vol. CT-18, 1971, pp. 101-113.

These and other similar approximations (see Proj. 12) can be written in the following general form

$$\dot{\mathbf{x}}^m \approx \gamma_m \mathbf{x}^m - \phi(\mathbf{x}^{m-1}, \ldots, \mathbf{x}^{m-k}, \dot{\mathbf{x}}^{m-1}, \ldots, \dot{\mathbf{x}}^{m-k}) \qquad (76)$$

$$= \gamma_m \mathbf{x}^m - \phi^m.$$

If this approximation is used to replace the derivative at t_m in the tableau equations, it becomes

$$\begin{bmatrix} 0 & \mathbf{A} & 0 & 0 \\ \mathbf{A}' & 0 & -\mathbf{U} & 0 \\ 0 & \hat{\mathbf{N}} & \hat{\mathbf{M}} & \hat{\mathbf{P}} \\ 0 & \mathbf{K}_i & \mathbf{K}_v & -\gamma_m \mathbf{U} \end{bmatrix} \begin{bmatrix} \mathbf{v}_n^m \\ \mathbf{i}^m \\ \mathbf{v}^m \\ \mathbf{x}^m \end{bmatrix} = \begin{bmatrix} 0 \\ 0 \\ \mathbf{e}^m \\ -\phi^m \end{bmatrix} \qquad (77)$$

These are a set of $2b + n + b_{LC}$ algebraic equations with real coefficients, which can be solved, formally at least, by finding the inverse of the tableau matrix.

In the frequency-domain, a numerical solution is usually sought for discrete values of frequency. For this case, the variables in the frequency-domain tableau equations (74b) are interpreted as phasors (which are complex numbers) representing sinusoids, the initial values are set equal to zero, and s is set to $j\omega_m$ $(m = 0, 1, \ldots)$ with $\omega_{m+1} > \omega_m$. In number and form, the frequency-domain tableau equations are exactly like the time-domain equations in (77) except that the real quantity γ_m is replaced by the imaginary one $j\omega_m$ and ϕ^m is replaced by the zero vector $\mathbf{0}$. In subsequent steps in the computation, the entries in the corresponding matrices will thus generally be complex in the frequency-domain.

The solution of the tableau equations can be achieved efficiently because of the nature of the tableau matrix of (77). It has very few nonzero elements, usually not more than about three per row. For large networks — hundreds and even thousands of branches — the percentage of nonzero elements is usually very small — fractions of a percent. Because addition and multiplication operations in which zero is one of the operands are wasteful operations, it is imperative to avoid zero adds and zero multiplies when solving the tableau equations. Furthermore, it is a waste of storage space to retain zero elements. It is sufficient to retain just the nonzero elements of the tableau matrix together with their row and column indices. A matrix which has only a small percentage of

nonzero elements is said to be a *sparse matrix* and the techniques invoked to solve the associated equations without the type of waste cited
are known as *sparse matrix techniques.* Several of the projects for this
chapter (see Projs. 5 through 9) will introduce some of the basic concepts in working with sparse matrices.

There are various methods by which to achieve a solution of the
tableau equations. Gauss elimination, or one of its variants, plays a key
role amongst the direct (that is, non-iterative) methods. In the elimination phase of Gauss elimination, a pivot element must be selected at
each stage. It must be selected so as to maintain numerical accuracy
while using finite precision arithmetic. In addition its selection should
reflect concern for limiting the amount of *fill-in,* a term used to label
growth in the percentage of nonzero elements as the elimination proceeds from its first through its last stage. Because of the need to recon-
cile these and other criteria, there is need for a pivot selection strategy.
The strategy reflects the degree to which each criterion is compromised.
In computer-aided analysis the strategy chosen also reflects machine
factors such as storage capacity, arithmetic and logic operations rates,
and arithmetic precision. Several of the projects (see Projs. 3 through 6)
require consideration of pivot selection strategies.

4.6.2 Example of the Tableau Equations

To illustrate the results above, consider the network shown in Fig. 15.

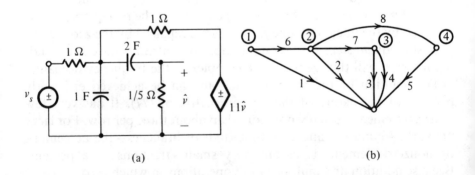

(a)   (b)

Fig. 15   Network: schematic and graph

A set of branch relations in the form of (72) is

$$
\begin{bmatrix}
1 & 0 & 0 & 0 & 0 & 0 & 0 & 0 \\
0 & 1 & 0 & 0 & 0 & 0 & 0 & 0 \\
0 & 0 & 5 & 0 & 0 & 0 & 0 & 0 \\
0 & 0 & 0 & 0 & 0 & 0 & 0 & 0 \\
0 & 0 & 0 & 11 & -1 & 0 & 0 & 0 \\
0 & 0 & 0 & 0 & 0 & 1 & 0 & 0 \\
0 & 0 & 0 & 0 & 0 & 0 & 2 & 0 \\
0 & 0 & 0 & 0 & 0 & 0 & 0 & -1
\end{bmatrix}
\begin{bmatrix} v_1 \\ v_2 \\ v_3 \\ v_4 \\ v_5 \\ v_6 \\ v_7 \\ v_8 \end{bmatrix}
+
\begin{bmatrix}
0 & 0 & 0 & 0 & 0 & 0 & 0 & 0 \\
0 & 0 & 0 & 0 & 0 & 0 & 0 & 0 \\
0 & 0 & -1 & 0 & 0 & 0 & 0 & 0 \\
0 & 0 & 0 & 1 & 0 & 0 & 0 & 0 \\
0 & 0 & 0 & 0 & 0 & 0 & 0 & 0 \\
0 & 0 & 0 & 0 & 0 & -1 & 0 & 0 \\
0 & 0 & 0 & 0 & 0 & 0 & 0 & 0 \\
0 & 0 & 0 & 0 & 0 & 0 & 0 & 1
\end{bmatrix}
\begin{bmatrix} i_1 \\ i_2 \\ i_3 \\ i_4 \\ i_5 \\ i_6 \\ i_7 \\ i_8 \end{bmatrix}
+
\begin{bmatrix}
0 & 0 \\
-1 & 0 \\
0 & 0 \\
0 & 0 \\
0 & 0 \\
0 & 0 \\
0 & -1 \\
0 & 0
\end{bmatrix}
\begin{bmatrix} q_2 \\ q_7 \end{bmatrix}
=
\begin{bmatrix} v_s \\ 0 \\ 0 \\ 0 \\ 0 \\ 0 \\ 0 \\ 0 \end{bmatrix} .
$$

Note: Branches 4 and 5 correspond to the VCVS. The supplemental branch relations in the form of (73) are

$$
\begin{bmatrix}
0 & 0 & 0 & 0 & 0 & 0 & 0 & 0 \\
0 & 0 & 0 & 0 & 0 & 0 & 0 & 0
\end{bmatrix}
\begin{bmatrix} v_1 \\ v_2 \\ v_3 \\ v_4 \\ v_5 \\ v_6 \\ v_7 \\ v_8 \end{bmatrix}
+
\begin{bmatrix}
0 & 1 & 0 & 0 & 0 & 0 & 0 & 0 \\
0 & 0 & 0 & 0 & 0 & 0 & 0 & 1 \\
\end{bmatrix}
\begin{bmatrix} i_1 \\ i_2 \\ i_3 \\ i_4 \\ i_5 \\ i_6 \\ i_7 \\ i_8 \end{bmatrix}
- \frac{d}{dt}
\begin{bmatrix} q_2 \\ q_7 \end{bmatrix}
=
\begin{bmatrix} 0 \\ 0 \end{bmatrix} .
$$

The incidence matrix for the designated nodes 1 through 4 is

$$
\mathbf{A} =
\begin{bmatrix}
1 & 0 & 0 & 0 & 0 & 1 & 0 & 0 \\
0 & 1 & 0 & 0 & 0 & -1 & 1 & 1 \\
0 & 0 & 1 & 1 & 0 & 0 & -1 & 0 \\
0 & 0 & 0 & 0 & 1 & 0 & 0 & -1
\end{bmatrix} .
$$

Lastly, let us assume that the numerical integration is to proceed with a fixed step-size of $0.01 - t_m = 0.01m$ $(m = 0, 1, 2, \ldots)$ — using the backward Euler formula as in (75a) which, in this case, becomes

$$
\begin{bmatrix} q_2(t_m) \\ q_7(t_m) \end{bmatrix}
\approx 100
\begin{bmatrix} q_2^m \\ q_7^m \end{bmatrix}
- 100
\begin{bmatrix} q_2^{m-1} \\ q_7^{m-1} \end{bmatrix}
$$

The tableau equations in the form of (77) are easily composed by catenation. The result is

$$
\begin{bmatrix} \; \cdots \; \end{bmatrix}
\begin{bmatrix}
v_{n1}^m \\
v_{n2}^m \\
v_{n3}^m \\
v_{n4}^m \\
i_1^m \\
i_2^m \\
i_3^m \\
i_4^m \\
i_5^m \\
i_6^m \\
i_7^m \\
i_8^m \\
v_1^m \\
v_2^m \\
v_3^m \\
v_4^m \\
v_5^m \\
v_6^m \\
v_7^m \\
v_8^m \\
q_2^m \\
q_7^m
\end{bmatrix}
=
\begin{bmatrix}
v_s^m \\
0 \\
0 \\
0 \\
0 \\
0 \\
0 \\
-100\,q_2^{m-1} \\
-100\,q_7^{m-1}
\end{bmatrix}
$$

Take note that in this network of just eight branches, the percentage of nonzero elements in the tableau matrix is a little less than ten percent. Let us see how this affects the number of arithmetic operations through the first several steps in the elimination phase of a Gauss elimination. For this elimination process we will adhere to the following pivot strategy: In the tableau matrix, column-by-column, choose the pivot from a row which (a) contains no previously selected pivot and (b) has a minimum number of elements; the pivot subject to (a) and (b) should be of maximum magnitude. (Of course, if it should happen that there is no pivot in a column, because all the column elements are zero, then the tableau matrix is singular and the network would be degenerate.)

Suppose the capacitors have zero initial charge and $v_s(t) = 1$ — a unit step. Then at the first time step, $m = 1$, the right hand side of the tableau equations will have $v_s^1 = 1$, $q_2^0 = 0$, and $q_7^0 = 0$. For the tableau equations at this time step, the first pivot is the $(5,1)$ element. In the elimination phase of a regular Gauss elimination we would then augment the tableau matrix by the right hand side of the tableau equations and then add to the (i,j)th element, $i \neq 5$ and $j \neq 1$, the negative of the product of element $(5,j)$ and of element $(i,1)$ divided by the pivot $(5,1)$. This would require 21 divides, 462 multiplies, and 462 adds. If zero-multiplies and zero-adds are bypassed, only 1 divide and 1 multiply are needed.

At the end of the first elimination step very few changes have occurred in the tableau equations. The submatrices in the block $(2,1)$ and $(2,3)$ positions in the tableau matrix have each had a single element changed: The 1 originally in the $(6,1)$ position of the first has become 0 and the 0 originally in the $(6,1)$ position of the second has become 1. There were at the start 48 nonzero elements in the tableau matrix and this number has not changed — the fill-in was zero.

The second pivot is the $(6,2)$ element. To complete the elimination step in this case requires 3 divides and 3 multiplies — compared with 20 divides, 420 multiplies and 420 adds for nonsparse techniques. Again only the submatrices in block positions $(2,1)$ and $(2,3)$ in the tableau matrix change. This time the nonzero elements in the last 3 rows of the second column in the first submatrix are changed to 0; and the 0 elements in the last three rows of the second column of the second submatrix are changed to $- 1$, 1, and 1, respectively. Again the number of nonzero elements remains the same — no fill-in has occurred.

Now either of the elements $(7,3)$ or $(8,3)$ satisfies the pivot strategy; we will use the former. After the third elimination step, again only the same two submatrices have changed. They have become

$$\begin{bmatrix} 1 & 0 & 0 & 0 \\ 0 & 1 & 0 & 0 \\ 0 & 0 & 1 & 0 \\ 0 & 0 & \boxed{0} & 0 \\ \boxed{0} & 0 & 0 & 1 \\ 0 & \boxed{0} & 0 & 0 \\ 0 & \boxed{0} & \boxed{0} & 0 \\ 0 & \boxed{0} & 0 & -1 \end{bmatrix}, \quad \begin{bmatrix} -1 & 0 & 0 & 0 & 0 & 0 & 0 & 0 \\ 0 & -1 & 0 & 0 & 0 & 0 & 0 & 0 \\ 0 & 0 & -1 & 0 & 0 & 0 & 0 & 0 \\ 0 & 0 & \boxed{1} & -1 & 0 & 0 & 0 & 0 \\ 0 & 0 & 0 & 0 & -1 & 0 & 0 & 0 \\ \boxed{1} & \boxed{-1} & 0 & 0 & 0 & -1 & 0 & 0 \\ 0 & \boxed{1}\boxed{-1} & 0 & 0 & 0 & -1 & 0 \\ 0 & \boxed{1} & 0 & 0 & 0 & 0 & 0 & -1 \end{bmatrix}.$$

The elements that have changed since the first step have been enclosed in squares. Compared to non-sparse techniques which would require 19 divides, 380 multiplies and 380 adds, only 2 divides and 2 multiplies were needed. At this point the tableau matrix fill-in remains zero.

We shall not continue with the details of this example, but give the final form of the tableau equations at the end of the Gauss elimination:

$$\left[\begin{array}{cccc|cccccccc|cccccccc|cc}
 & & & & 1 & 0 & 0 & 0 & 0 & 1 & 0 & 0 & 0 & 0 & 0 & 0 & 0 & 0 & 0 & 0 & 0 & 0 \\
 & \bigcirc & & & 0 & 0 & 0 & 0 & 0 & 0 & 0 & 0 & 0 & 0 & 0 & 0 & 0 & 0 & 0 & 1 & 101 & 100 \\
 & & & & 0 & 0 & 0 & 0 & 0 & 0 & -1 & 0 & 0 & 0 & 5 & 0 & 0 & 0 & 0 & 0 & 0 & 0 \\
 & & & & 0 & 0 & 0 & 0 & 1 & 0 & 0 & -1 & 0 & 0 & 0 & 0 & 0 & 0 & 0 & 0 & 0 & 0 \\ \hline
1 & 0 & 0 & 0 & & & & & & & & & -1 & 0 & 0 & 0 & 0 & 0 & 0 & 0 & 0 & 0 \\
0 & 1 & 0 & 0 & & & & & & & & & 0 & -1 & 0 & 0 & 0 & 0 & 0 & 0 & 0 & 0 \\
0 & 0 & 1 & 0 & & & & & & & & & 0 & 0 & -1 & 0 & 0 & 0 & 0 & 0 & 0 & 0 \\
0 & 0 & 0 & 0 & & & \bigcirc & & & & & & 0 & 0 & 1 & -1 & 0 & 0 & 0 & 0 & 0 & 0 \\
0 & 0 & 0 & 1 & & & & & & & & & 0 & 0 & 0 & 0 & -1 & 0 & 0 & 0 & 0 & 0 \\
0 & 0 & 0 & 0 & & & & & & & & & 0 & -1 & 0 & 0 & 0 & -1 & 0 & 0 & 0 & 0 \\
0 & 0 & 0 & 0 & & & & & & & & & 0 & 0 & 0 & 0 & 0 & 0 & 0 & 0 & 1 & -20.5 \\
0 & 0 & 0 & 0 & & & & & & & & & 0 & 0 & 0 & 0 & 0 & 0 & 0 & 0 & 0 & 1.97\times10^3 \\ \hline
 & & & & 0 & 0 & 0 & 0 & 0 & 0 & 0 & 0 & 1 & 0 & 0 & 0 & 0 & 0 & 0 & 0 & 0 & 0 \\
 & & & & 0 & 0 & 0 & 0 & 0 & 0 & 0 & 0 & 0 & 0 & 0 & 0 & 0 & -1 & 0 & 0 & -1 & 0 \\
 & & & & 0 & 0 & -1 & 0 & 0 & 0 & 0 & 0 & 0 & 0 & 5 & 0 & 0 & 0 & 0 & 0 & 0 & 0 \\
 & & & & 0 & 0 & 0 & 1 & 0 & 0 & 0 & 0 & 0 & 0 & 0 & 0 & 0 & 0 & 0 & 0 & 0 & 0 \\
 & \bigcirc & & & 0 & 0 & 0 & 0 & 0 & 0 & 0 & 0 & 0 & 0 & 0 & 11 & -1 & 0 & 0 & 0 & 0 & 0 \\
 & & & & 0 & 0 & 0 & 0 & 0 & -1 & 0 & 0 & 0 & 0 & 0 & 0 & 0 & 1 & 0 & 0 & 0 & 0 \\
 & & & & 0 & 0 & 0 & 0 & 0 & 0 & 0 & 0 & 0 & 0 & 0 & 0 & 0 & 0 & 2 & 0 & 0 & -1 \\
 & & & & 0 & 0 & 0 & 0 & 0 & 0 & 0 & 1 & 0 & 0 & 0 & 0 & 0 & 0 & 0 & -1 & 0 & 0 \\ \hline
 & & & & 0 & 1 & 0 & 0 & 0 & 0 & 0 & 0 & 0 & 0 & 0 & 0 & 0 & 0 & 0 & 0 & -100 & 0 \\
 & \bigcirc & & & 0 & 0 & 0 & 0 & 0 & 0 & 0 & 0 & 0 & 0 & 0 & 0 & .455 & 0 & 0 & 0 & 0 & -100
\end{array}\right]
\begin{bmatrix} v_{n1}^1 \\ v_{n2}^1 \\ v_{n3}^1 \\ v_{n4}^1 \\ i_1^1 \\ i_2^1 \\ i_3^1 \\ i_4^1 \\ i_5^1 \\ i_6^1 \\ i_7^1 \\ i_8^1 \\ v_1^1 \\ v_2^1 \\ v_3^1 \\ i_4^1 \\ i_5^1 \\ i_6^1 \\ i_7^1 \\ i_8^1 \\ q_2^1 \\ q_7^1 \end{bmatrix} = \begin{bmatrix} 0 \\ 1 \\ 0 \\ 0 \\ 0 \\ 0 \\ 0 \\ 0 \\ 0 \\ 0 \\ -1 \\ 0 \\ 1 \\ 1 \\ -1 \\ 0 \\ 0 \\ 0 \\ 0 \\ 0 \\ 0 \\ 0 \end{bmatrix}$$

The number of operations compared to those in a regular Gauss elimination step are summarized in Table 4.

In the back substitution phase of the Gauss elimination, the unknown network variables are evaluated from the bottom up, that is, starting with the last equation from the elimination phase, as

$$1.97 \times 10^3 q_7^1 = 1.00 \to q_7^1 = 1.00 \div 1.97 \times 10^3 = 0.507 \times 10^3$$

$$1.00 q_2^1 - 2.05 q_7^1 = 0.000 \to q_2^1 = [0.000 + 20.5 \times 0.508 \times 10^{-3}] \div 1.00 = 10.4 \times 10^{-3}$$

.

.

.

Upon completion of the back substitution phase — with but 22 divides, 20 multiplies, and 4 adds — the result is

Table 4   Elimination Phase Statistics

| Step | Regular Elimination | | | Sparse Elimination | | | |
	Divides	Multiplies	Adds	Divides	Multiplies	Adds	Fill-in
1	21	462	462	1	1	0	0
2	20	420	420	3	3	0	0
3	19	380	380	2	2	0	0
4	18	342	342	1	1	0	0
5	17	306	306	0	0	0	0
6	16	272	272	1	1	0	0
7	15	240	240	1	1	0	0
8	14	210	210	1	0	0	−1
9	13	182	182	0	0	0	0
10	12	156	156	1	1	0	0
11	11	132	132	1	1	0	0
12	10	110	110	1	1	0	0
13	9	90	90	1	1	0	−1
14	8	72	72	3	6	0	0
15	7	64	64	3	3	0	0
16	6	42	42	3	3	0	0
17	5	30	30	3	3	0	0
18	4	20	20	3	6	3	−1
19	3	12	12	1	1	1	−1
20	2	6	6	1	3	2	−1
21	1	2	2	1	1	1	−1
Total	231	3,542	3,542	32	39	7	−6

$$
\begin{bmatrix}
v_{n1}^1 \\
v_{n2}^1 \\
v_{n3}^1 \\
v_{n4}^1 \\
\hline
i_1^1 \\
i_2^1 \\
i_3^1 \\
i_4^1 \\
i_5^1 \\
i_6^1 \\
i_7^1 \\
i_8^1 \\
\hline
v_1^1 \\
v_2^1 \\
v_3^1 \\
v_4^1 \\
v_5^1 \\
v_6^1 \\
v_7^1 \\
v_8^1 \\
\hline
q_2^1 \\
q_7^1
\end{bmatrix}
=
\begin{bmatrix}
1.00 \\
0.0104 \\
0.0101 \\
0.112 \\
\hline
-0.990 \\
1.04 \\
0.0507 \\
0.000 \\
-0.101 \\
0.990 \\
0.0507 \\
-0.101 \\
\hline
1.00 \\
0.0104 \\
0.0101 \\
0.0101 \\
0.112 \\
0.990 \\
0.000254 \\
-0.104 \\
\hline
0.0104 \\
0.000507
\end{bmatrix} .
$$

A regular back substitution phase would have required 22 divides, 231 multiplies and 231 adds.

It is strongly evident that sparse Gaussian elimination brought about a substantial saving in the number of arithmetic operations for this problem. However, the real comparison to be made is that between sparse elimination applied to the tableau equations and composition of and regular elimination applied to some other set of network equations, such as the node equations. An operations count for the node equations indicates that 10 divides, 634 multiplies, and 666 adds are needed at each time step.

Clearly the saving in arithmetic operations using the tableau equations would be significant. However, the saving could be made even greater if, in addition to eliminating multiplication by 0, we were to suppress multiplication and division by ± 1 — taking the result as simply the value, or the sign reversed value, of the other operand, respectively. Looking back at the illustrated first three steps of the elimination phase shows that no divides or multiplies would have been needed under these conditions. In fact, for the entire elimination phase the number of operations would decrease to just 7 divides, 9 multiplies, and 7 adds. The back substitution phase would diminish to 4 divides, 7 multiplies, and 4 adds.

$$ZI_L = B_g(-E_S + Z_B I_S) \; ; \quad Z = s B_L L_B B_L^T + B_R R_B B_R^T + B_C \frac{S_B}{s}$$

$$YV_t = -Q[-Y_B E_S + I_S]$$

$$Y = \frac{1}{s} Q_r \Gamma_B Q_r^T + Q_G G_B Q_G^T + s Q_C C_B Q_C^T$$

$$Y[v - V_S] - [I - I_S] = 0$$

$$Y_n = A Y A^T$$

$$J_n = -A J_S + A Y V_S$$

Question Set: Part I

EXERCISES

1. In each of the graphs of Fig. E-1 determine the number of forests.

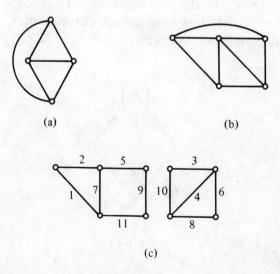

(a)

(b)

(c)

2. In the graph of Fig. E-1(c) branches {2,3,4,5,7,8,11} form a forest. Using this forest, write $\mathbf{A}$, $\mathbf{B}_f$, and $\mathbf{Q}_f$, partitioned as follows: $\mathbf{A} = [\mathbf{A}_t \ \mathbf{A}_l]$, $\mathbf{Q}_f = [\mathbf{U} \ \mathbf{Q}_{fl}]$, and $\mathbf{B}_f = [\mathbf{B}_{ft} \ \mathbf{U}]$. Verify that $-\mathbf{B}'_{ft} = \mathbf{Q}_{fl} = \mathbf{A}_t^{-1}\mathbf{A}_l$.

3. In Fig. E-3 the following loops exist:

   Loop 1: {a,e,g,b}   Loop 3: {a,d,f,j,h,b}

   Loop 2: {d,c,g,f}   Loop 4: {e,c,h,j}

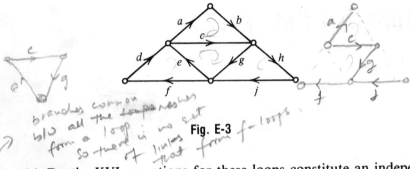

Fig. E-3

(a) Do the KVL equations for these loops constitute an independent set?

(b) Either (1) find a set of links that form f-loops that are meshes of the graph or (2) prove that there is no such set.

4. Consider the graph and three indicated cut-sets in Fig. E-4. Determine $\mathbf{Q}$. Then, for the tree consisting of branches 1, 2, and 3, evaluate $\mathbf{Q}_t'^{-1}$ and show that not all elements of v_c in (3-22) are measurable node-pair voltages.

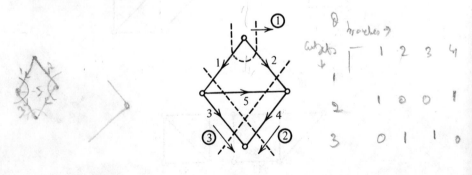

Fig. E-4

5. A connected graph has five nodes and seven branches. The reduced incidence matrix for this graph is given as

$$\mathbf{A} = \begin{bmatrix} 1 & 1 & 0 & 0 & 0 & 0 & 1 \\ -1 & -1 & 1 & 0 & 0 & 0 & 0 \\ 0 & 0 & -1 & 1 & 0 & 0 & 0 \\ 0 & 0 & 0 & -1 & -1 & -1 & 0 \end{bmatrix}$$

(a) It is claimed that branches $\{1,3,4,5\}$ constitute a tree. Without drawing the graph, verify the truth of this claim.

(b) For this tree write the matrix of f-loops, $\mathbf{B}_f$ (again, without drawing a graph).

(c) For the same tree determine the matrix of f-cut-sets, $\mathbf{Q}_f$. (No graphs, please.)

(d) Determine the number of trees in the graph.

(e) Draw the graph and verify the preceding results.

6. Repeat Exer. 5 for the following incidence matrices and the specified branches.

$$\mathbf{A} = \begin{bmatrix} 0 & 0 & 1 & 1 & 1 & 0 & -1 \\ 0 & 1 & 0 & 0 & -1 & 1 & 1 \\ -1 & 0 & -1 & 0 & 0 & -1 & 0 \end{bmatrix}, \text{Branches} : \left\{2,3,4\right\}$$

$$\mathbf{A} = \begin{bmatrix} 0 & 0 & -1 & 1 & 1 & 0 & 0 & -1 \\ 0 & 1 & 0 & 0 & 0 & 1 & 0 & 1 \\ 0 & -1 & 0 & 0 & 0 & 0 & -1 & 0 \\ -1 & 0 & 0 & -1 & 0 & 0 & 1 & 0 \end{bmatrix}, \text{Branches} : \left\{1,3,5,6\right\}$$

7. For the graph in Fig. E-7, let $\mathbf{B}_m$ be the mesh matrix.

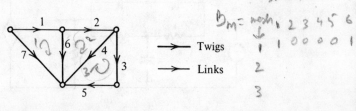

Fig. E-7

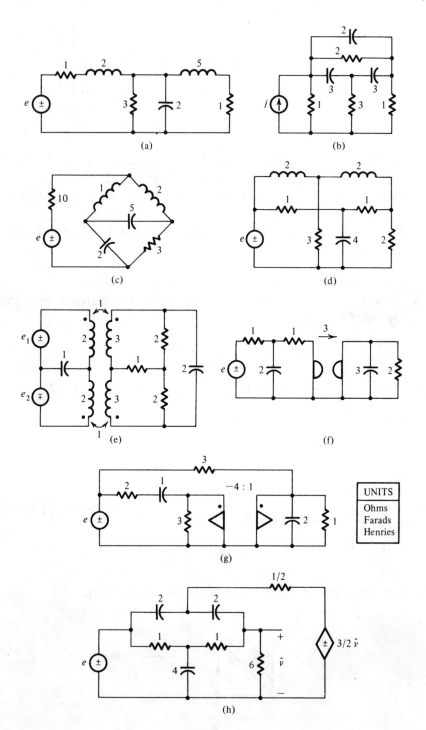

(a)

(b)

(c)

(d)

(e)

(f)

(g)

UNITS

Ohms
Farads
Henries

(h)

Fig. E-9

(a) Form $\mathbf{B}'_m(\mathbf{B}^{-1}_{ml})'$ and verify that the branch currents are correctly given in terms of the link currents for the tree shown.

(b) For the same tree determine $\mathbf{B}_f$ directly and verify that $\mathbf{B}_f = (\mathbf{B}^{-1}_{ml})\mathbf{B}_m$.

8. For the network illustrated in Fig. 4.1, determine the time-domain node equations. Then, Laplace transform them; the result should be the same as the one derived on p. 89.

9. For the networks of Fig. E-9 choose the lowest node(s) as datum(s) and write a set of node equations in the (a) time-domain and (b) frequency-domain.

10. For the networks of Fig. E-9 choose a forest and write a set of twig equations in the (a) time-domain and (b) frequency-domain.

11. For the networks in Fig. E-9: (a) Write mesh equations in the time-domain. (For which of these networks do the meshes constitute f-loops for some forest?) (b) Choose some forest — different from that of part (a) — and write link equations in the frequency-domain.

12. For the network in Fig. E-12: (a) Write a set of node equations in the frequency-domain using a convenient node for datum. (b) Write a set of link equations in the frequency-domain for the tree shown.

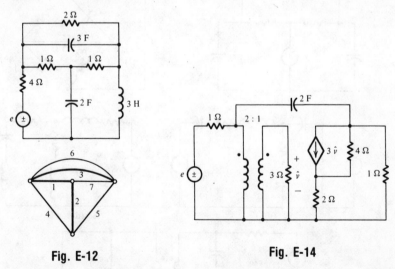

Fig. E-12   Fig. E-14

13. For the networks of Fig. E-9 choose some forest and write mixed-variable equations in the (a) time-domain and (b) frequency-domain.

14. For the network in Fig. E-14 set up in matrix form (a) node equations in the time-domain and (b) mixed-variable equations in the frequency-domain.

15. For the network of Fig. E-15 set up (a) node equations in the frequency-domain and (b) mixed-variable equations in the time-domain. (Use the small-signal transistor model given.)

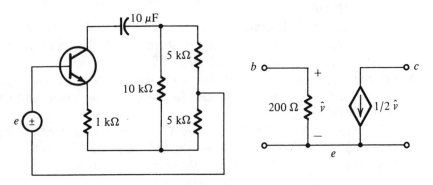

Fig. E-15

16. For each of the networks in (a) Fig. E-16 and (b) Fig. E-17, draw at least one proper forest.

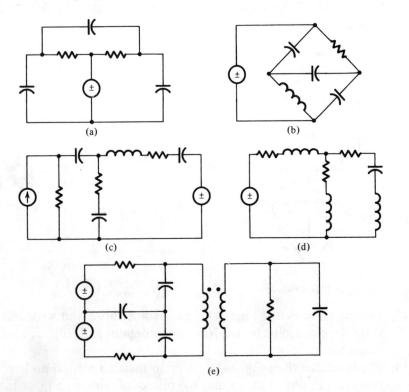

Fig. E-16

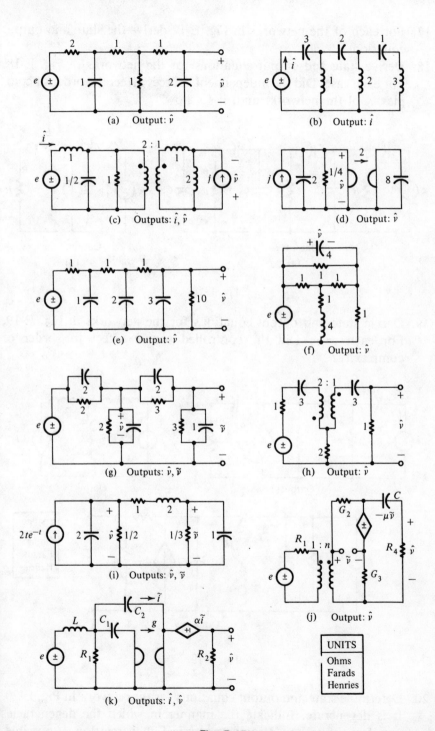

Fig. E-17

17. For each of the networks in Fig. E-17 derive the state and output equations.

18. Derive state and output equations for the networks in Fig. E-18. For each case: Did the independent sources affect the order of complexity of the networks and, if so, how?

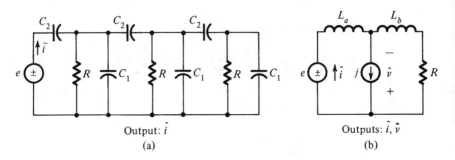

Output: $\hat{i}$ Outputs: $\hat{i}, \hat{v}$

(a)   (b)

Fig. E-18

19. Derive state and output equations for the networks in Fig. E-19. For each case: Did the controlled source affect the order of complexity?

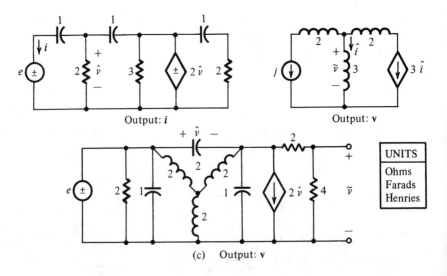

Output: i Output: v

(c)   Output: v

UNITS
Ohms
Farads
Henries

Fig. E-19

20. Determine state and output equations for the network in Fig. E-20. It is degenerate. Indicate the manner in which the degeneracies manifest themselves. Provide a physical interpretation, if possible.

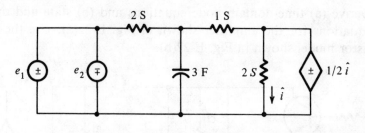

Fig. E-20

21. Consider the network in Fig. E-21. Determine the state and output equations for:

   (a) $k_1 = 1$, $k_2 = 1$, $k_3 = 1$
   (b) $k_1 = 2$, $k_2 = 1$, $k_3 = 4$
   (c) $k_1 = 1$, $k_2 = 2$, $k_3 = 5$
   (d) $k_1 = 3$, $k_2 = 2$, $k_3 = 5$

Discuss the observable decrease in the order of complexity and the simultaneous increase in the actual number — not just the bound (s on p. 123) on that number — of source derivatives appearing in the state equations as the controlled sources are changed in going from case (a) to case (c). The network under the conditions of case (d) is degenerate. In what ways is it degenerate? If possible, give a physical interpretation for the degeneracies.

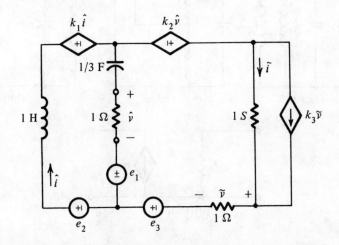

Fig. E-21

22. Derive (a) time-domain node equations and (b) state and output equations for the amplifier shown in Fig. E-22(a). Use the transistor model shown in Fig. E-22(b).

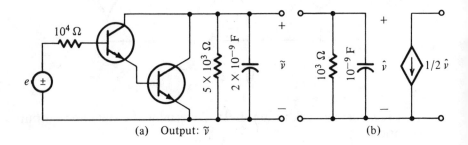

(a)　Output: $\tilde{v}$　　　　　　　　　　　　　　　　　　(b)

Fig. E-22

23. Determine (a) time-domain node equations and (b) state and output equations for each of the oscillator networks shown in Figs. E-23(a) through E-23(b) by using the transistor model shown in Fig. E-23(d).

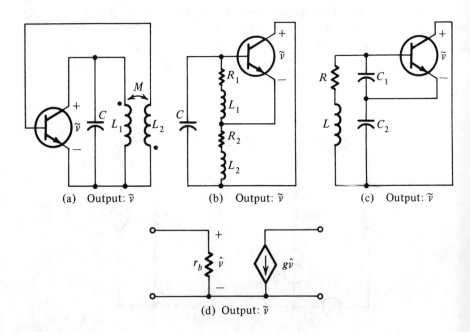

(a)　Output: $\tilde{v}$　　　(b)　Output: $\tilde{v}$　　　(c)　Output: $\tilde{v}$

(d)　Output: $\tilde{v}$

Fig. E-23

24. Derive (a) time-domain twig equations and (b) state and output equations for the network shown in Fig. E-24. Use the transistor model shown in Fig. E-22(b).

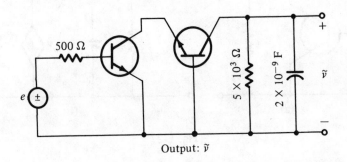

Fig. E-24

25. Derive (a) time-domain mesh equations and (b) state and output equations for the network in Fig. E-25. For the transistor use the model shown in Fig. E-23(d). The response variables are the voltages across all the inductors.

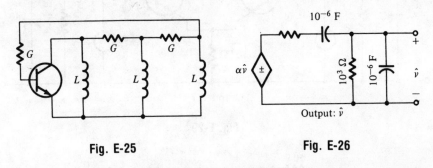

Fig. E-25   Fig. E-26

26. The network shown in Fig. E-26 is a simple RC oscillator circuit. Determine (a) time-domain link equations and (b) state and output equations and indicate for what value of α there will be two conjugate imaginary eigenvalues of $\mathbf{A}$. Note: It is for that value of α that the response is a sinusoid.

27. Derive the (a) time-domain mixed-variable equations and (b) state and output equations for the single-stage amplifier shown in Fig. E-27(a). Use the hybrid-pi equivalent circuit for the transistor, as shown in Fig. E-27(b). The voltage $\tilde{v}$ is the network response.

28. Derive (a) time-domain and (b) frequency-domain tableau equations for the networks of Fig. E-17.

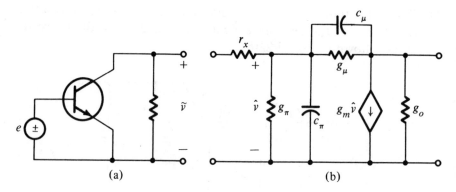

Fig. E-27

29. Derive (a) state and output equations and (b) time-domain tableau equations for the differential amplifier network shown in Fig. E-29. Use the transistor mode shown in Fig. E-22(b).

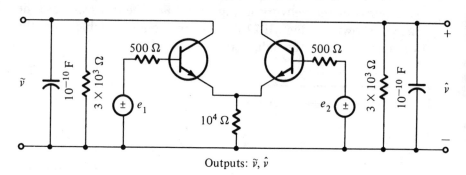

Outputs: $\tilde{v}$, $\hat{v}$

Fig. E-29

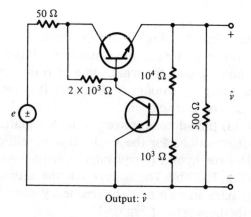

Output: $\hat{v}$

Fig. E-30

30. Derive (a) state and output equations and (b) time-domain tableau equations for the network shown in Fig. E-30 using the transistor model shown in Fig. E-22(b).

PROBLEMS

1. Display a graph which satisfies properties 1 and 2 of a path but which is not a path.
2. Prove that the number of branches in a tree is one less than the number of its nodes.
3. Extend the proof given on page 45 so that it is valid for all positive integers p—not just $p = 1$.
4. Prove that any set of n branches in a graph that contains no loops is a forest.
5. Prove that the columns of an nth order nonsingular submatrix of $\mathbf{A}$ correspond to a set of twigs.
6. The incidence matrix of a graph can be partitioned as $\mathbf{A} = [\mathbf{A}_t\ \mathbf{A}_l]$, where the columns of $\mathbf{A}_t$ correspond to twigs and the columns of $\mathbf{A}_l$ correspond to links for a given forest. The submatrix $\mathbf{A}_t$ is non-singular; in some cases it will be a unit matrix. What must be the structure of the forest for which $\mathbf{A}_t = \mathbf{U}$? Prove and illustrate with an example.
7. (a) Write the complete incidence matrices for the two graphs in Fig. P-7.
   (b) Derive the incidence matrix for graph (a) by deleting the rows corresponding to nodes 1 and 3. Derive two incidence matrices for graph (b), one by deleting the row corresponding to node 4 and the other by deleting the row corresponding to node 6. (These nodes are datum nodes.)
   (c) Draw the graph associated with each incidence matrix when augmented, in turn, by each of the following conditions: (i) The graph is connected. (ii) Datum nodes of the graph are not hinge-nodes. Discuss the results.

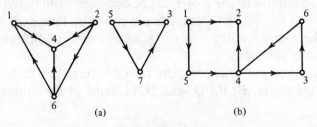

(a)　　　　　　　　　　　　　(b)

Fig. P-7

8. Let $\mathbf{A}_c$ be the complete incidence matrix of an oriented graph. Let $\mathbf{M}_c$ be derived by replacing -1 elements of $\mathbf{A}_c$ by 1. Then, $\mathbf{M}_c$ is the complete incidence matrix of the associated unoriented graph. Discuss and illustrate the claim: Two graphs are isomorphic if and only if there exist permutation matrices $\mathbf{P}$ and $\mathbf{Q}$ such that $\mathbf{P}\mathbf{M}_{c1}\mathbf{Q} = \mathbf{M}_{c2}$, where $\mathbf{M}_{c1}$ and $\mathbf{M}_{c2}$ are complete incidence matrices of the unoriented graphs. Note: A permutation matrix is square and has exactly one nonzero element—value 1—in each row and column.

9. In algorithm 2.1—the Forest Algorithm—replace Step 2 by the following:

Step 2a: Set $\mathbf{M} = \mathbf{A}$.

Step 2b: Augment $\mathbf{M}$ by one row such that the sum of the elements in each column of $\mathbf{M}$ is zero.

Show when $p > 1$ that this modified algorithm will designate a set of twigs comprising a forest.

10. (a) If a loop contains more than two branches, show that its orientation can be specified by an ordered list of its branch labels.

    (b) If a graph is not a multigraph, show that an oriented loop can be specified by an ordered list of its branch labels or its node labels.

11. Let $\mathbf{B}$ be a loop matrix that is of order $(b - n) \times b$ and of maximum rank, equal to $b - n$. Furthermore, let $\mathbf{B}_l$ be a $(b - n)$th order nonsingular submatrix of $\mathbf{B}$. Prove that the columns of $\mathbf{B}_l$ correspond to the links for some coforest of the graph.

12. Consider a connected graph, not a multigraph, which is maximally connected; that is, a graph with a single branch joining every pair of nodes. Determine the number of loops in this graph.

13. Prove the orthogonality relations (2-11). Hint: First show that a cut-set and loop must have an even number of branches in common. Then show that any pair of branches similarly [oppositely] oriented relative to the loop must be oppositely [similarly] oriented relative to the cut-set. Complete the proof by then demonstrating that the corresponding row of $\mathbf{Q}_c$ and column of $\mathbf{B}_c$ must have a zero inner product.

14. To the extent possible, complete the table on page 63, showing expressions for $\mathbf{A}$, $\mathbf{B}$, $\mathbf{B}_f$, $\mathbf{Q}$, and $\mathbf{Q}_f$ in terms of the submatrices of each.

15. (a) Let $\mathbf{M}$ be any $n \times n$ nonsingular matrix. Show that

$$\hat{\mathbf{Q}}\mathbf{i} = \mathbf{0},$$

where $\hat{\mathbf{Q}} = \mathbf{MQ}$, is a valid first form KCL expression.

(b) Let $\mathbf{N}$ be any $(b-n) \times (b-n)$ nonsingular matrix. Show that

$$\mathbf{i} = \hat{\mathbf{B}}'\mathbf{i}_f,$$

where $\hat{\mathbf{B}} = \mathbf{NB}$ and $\mathbf{i}_f = \mathbf{N}'^{-1}\mathbf{i}_f$, is a valid second form KCL expression.

(c) Let G be the graph of a given network and let T be another graph—a tree graph—with the same set of nodes. Suppose $[\mathbf{T}\ \mathbf{A}]$ is the node incidence matrix for the graph $T \cup G$, with the columns of $\mathbf{T}$ corresponding to the branches of T. Show that there exists an $\mathbf{M}$ such that $\hat{\mathbf{Q}} = \mathbf{T}^{-1}\mathbf{A}$. In this case give a physical interpretation of $\hat{\mathbf{Q}}\mathbf{i} = \mathbf{0}$.

16. Prove that the elements of $\mathbf{v}_n$ in (3-20) are the node voltages relative to a datum node.

17. (a) Let $\mathbf{N}$ be any $(b-n) \times (b-n)$ nonsingular matrix. Show that

$$\hat{\mathbf{B}}\mathbf{v} = \mathbf{0},$$

where $\hat{\mathbf{B}} = \mathbf{NB}$, is a valid first form KVL expression.

(b) Let $\mathbf{M}$ be any $n \times n$ nonsingular matrix. Show that

$$\mathbf{v} = \hat{\mathbf{Q}}'\mathbf{v}_{\hat{c}},$$

where $\hat{\mathbf{Q}} = \mathbf{MQ}$ and $\mathbf{v}_{\hat{c}} = \mathbf{M}'^{-1}\mathbf{v}_c$, is a valid second form KVL expression.

(c) Determine $\hat{\mathbf{Q}}$ as in Prob. 15(c). In this case identify the elements of $\mathbf{v}_{\hat{c}}$. Hint: They will be measurable.

18. Prove this statement: In a linear graph every cut-set has an even number of branches in common with every loop.

19. Define a *path matrix* $\mathbf{P} = |p_{ij}|$ of a forest as follows:

$p_{ij} = +1$ [alternatively, -1] if branch j is in the (unique) directed path in a tree of the forest from node i to the datum node of that tree and its orientation agrees [alternatively, disagrees] with that of the path, and $p_{ij} = 0$ otherwise.

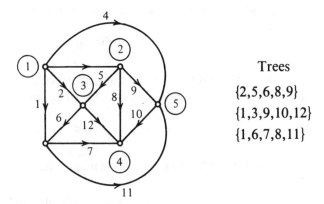

Trees

$\{2,5,6,8,9\}$

$\{1,3,9,10,12\}$

$\{1,6,7,8,11\}$

Fig. P-19

The path matrix **P** is a square matrix whose rows correspond to paths from the corresponding nodes to a datum node and whose columns correspond to branches. For example, the nonzero entries in, say the third column, specify the paths on which branch 3 lies, and the nonzero entries in, say the fourth row, specify the branches that lie on the path from node 4 to datum. Write the path matrix for each of the indicated forests, here trees, in the graph of Fig. P-19.

20. When forming $\mathbf{B}_f$ or $\mathbf{Q}_f$ from the incidence matrix, it is necessary to find the inverse of $\mathbf{A}_t$. A simple method of doing this is required. Prove that $\mathbf{A}_t^{-1} = \mathbf{P}'$, where **P** is the path matrix of the forest whose branches are the columns of $\mathbf{A}_t$.

21. Let $\mathbf{A} = [\mathbf{A}_t \ \mathbf{A}_l]$, where $\mathbf{A}_t$ is nonsingular. Prove that the nonzero elements in each row of $\mathbf{A}_t^{-1}$ must have the same sign.

22. Use the result of Prob. 20 to find $\mathbf{A}_t^{-1}$ for the trees of Fig. P-19. Verify by evaluation of $\mathbf{A}_t\mathbf{P}'$. For each case verify the result of Prob. 21.

23. (a) Two branches are in parallel in a graph. Determine the relationship of the columns corresponding to these two branches in the $\mathbf{Q}_f$ matrix.

    (b) Repeat if the two branches are in series.

24. Let $\mathbf{Q}_f = [\mathbf{U} \ \mathbf{Q}_l]$. Suppose a column of $\mathbf{Q}_l$, say the jth, has a single nonzero entry, and this is in the kth row. What can you say about the structure of the graph as it relates to branches j and k?

25. Prove that a graph contains at least one loop if two or more branches are incident at each node.

26. For a p-part planar graph of b branches and $n + p$ nodes show that the **B** matrix of the meshes is of rank $b - n$. This will mean that the mesh currents will be an adequate basis for expressing all branch currents.

27. Let a branch t of a graph be a twig in some forest. The f-cut-set determined by t contains a set of links $l_1, l_2, \ldots$ for that forest. Each of these links defines an f-loop. Show that every one of the f-loops formed by these links contains twig t.

28. It is possible for two f-loops of a graph for a given forest to have twigs and nodes in common. Prove that it is possible for two f-loops to have two nodes in common only if the path in the forest between the nodes is common to the two loops.

29. (a) Indicate which of the three- or four-terminal components considered in Chapter 1 conform to the node (or cut-set) assumption. For those that do not, indicate in what way they might be augmented by two-terminal components to create a compound component satisfying the assumption.

    (b) Repeat part (a) for the loop, rather than the node, assumption.

30. In the development of the node equations the same node incidence matrix was used to express KVL (3-19) and KCL (3-3). It was not necessary to do so; however, there is an advantage in doing so. Prove: If a network is composed of reciprocal components, then $\mathbf{Y}_n$ of (4-7) is symmetric.

31. The following statement is made on page 132: $\mathbf{x}_o$ contains a maximum of dynamic component variables. Prove that statement.

32. Prove the following statement made on page 133: All the elements of $\mathbf{x}$ must be dynamic component variables — capacitor voltages and inductor currents.

33. Consider a network with a designated normal forest. Show that capacitor link voltages [inductor twig currents] can be expressed algebraically in terms of capacitor twig voltages [inductor link currents].

34. Consider a network having capacitors as the only dynamic components and assume that the branch relations can be written such that $\mathbf{N} = -\mathbf{U}$. Suppose twig equations are determined using a normal forest to establish the cut-set matrix and suppose the twigs are ordered such that $\mathbf{v}_t$ can be partitioned as

$$\mathbf{v}_t = \begin{bmatrix} \mathbf{v}_c \\ \mathbf{v}_r \end{bmatrix}, \quad .$$

where $\mathbf{v}_c$ is the vector of capacitor twig voltages. Show that the twig equations can be alternatively expressed as

$$\begin{bmatrix} \mathbf{C} & \mathbf{0} \\ \mathbf{0} & \mathbf{0} \end{bmatrix} \frac{d}{dt} \begin{bmatrix} \mathbf{v}_c \\ \mathbf{v}_r \end{bmatrix} + \begin{bmatrix} \mathbf{G}_{cc} & \mathbf{G}_{cr} \\ \mathbf{G}_{rc} & \mathbf{G}_{rr} \end{bmatrix} \begin{bmatrix} \mathbf{v}_c \\ \mathbf{v}_r \end{bmatrix} = \begin{bmatrix} \mathbf{j}_c \\ \mathbf{j}_r \end{bmatrix} .$$

Assume $\mathbf{C}$ and $\mathbf{G}_{rr}$ are nonsingular; then verify that

$$\dot{\mathbf{v}}_c = -\mathbf{C}^{-1}[\mathbf{G}_{cc} - \mathbf{G}_{cr}\mathbf{G}_{rr}^{-1}\mathbf{G}_{rc}]\mathbf{v}_c + \mathbf{C}^{-1}[\mathbf{j}_c - \mathbf{G}_{rr}\mathbf{j}_r] ,$$

is a state equation for the network. Illustrate this procedure for determining a state equation by doing so for the networks of Fig. E-17(a) and Fig. E-17(g).

35. Establish the dual result to that of Prob. 34 for a network having inductors as the only dynamic components. Illustrate the resulting procedure for finding a state equation.

36. A network is degenerate whenever there exists a network variable which is not uniquely determined by the Kirchhoff laws and the component constraints. The degeneracy is made manifest by a failure of some set of network equations to exhibit a unique solution. The latter would be true if (a) a node-admittance matrix, (b) a cut-set-admittance matrix, (c) a loop impedance matrix, (d) a mixed-variable coefficient matrix, or (e) a tableau matrix were of less than full rank — that is, singular. The network of Fig. P-36 is potentially degenerate. Determine conditions among its parameters which will make the node-admittance matrix singular. Note: A v-shift will be needed to write node equations. Show that the other matrices (b) through (e), are of less than full rank under these conditions.

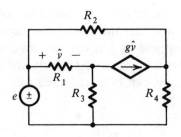

Fig. P-36

37. Consider the network depicted in Fig. P-37 in which, contrary to the pre-conditions given in Chapter 3 for a v-shift, one of the non-source components is joined to both source connections — parallels the source. Why is a v-shift to realize general components not acceptable? Also give the dual result with respect to the i-shift.

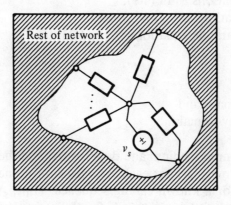

Fig. P-37

38. The network of Fig. P-38 is degenerate. Which of conditions (a) through (e) in Prob. 36 detect that fact. (You may find the results of Prob. 37 helpful.)

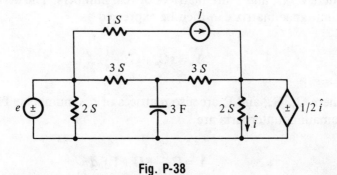

Fig. P-38

PROGRAMS

1. Write a subroutine which realizes algorithm 2.1 or that algorithm as modified in Prob. 9.
2. Write a subroutine which realizes algorithm 4.2.

3. Consider a, possibly disconnected, network. Assume a subroutine to determine a forest (see Prog. 1) and a subroutine to invert a matrix (see Appendix A) are available. Write programs to create the

   (a) node equations as in (4-6),
   (b) twig equations as in (4-9),
   (c) link equations as in (4-17), and
   (d) mixed-variable equations as in (4-23)

   in the

   (i) time-domain and
   (ii) frequency-domain.

   Specify the input medium and data format and the output medium and data format. Use for each assumed subroutine a fictitious, but reasonable, or a known calling sequence. Hint: An array such as the branch admittance matrix Y for the components of Chapter 1 can be expressed as

$$Y = sC + G + \frac{1}{s}\Gamma,$$

   where C, G, and Γ are matrices of real numbers. The derived node admittance matrix can then be expressed as

$$Y_n = sC_n + G_n + \frac{1}{s}\Gamma_n,$$

   where C_n, G_n, and Γ_n are also matrices of real numbers. Their time-domain counterparts are

$$Y = C\frac{d}{dt} + G + \Gamma \int_0^t d\tau$$

   and

$$Y_n = C_n\frac{d}{dt} + G_n + \Gamma_n \int_0^t d\tau.$$

   Similar statements hold with respect to the matrices encountered in the other analysis methods.

4. Consider a, possibly disconnected, network. Assume a subroutine to determine a normal forest (see Prog. 2) and a subroutine to reduce a matrix to row echelon form (see Appendix A) are available. Write a program, incorporating a realization of algorithm 4.1 as modified in Table 4.3, to create the state and output equations (4-63) and (4-64) and the source constraint equations (4-65). Specify the input medium and data format and the output medium and data format. Use for each assumed subroutine a fictitious, but reasonable, or a known calling sequence.

5. Just as derivatives can be replaced by the approximation (4-75) when seeking a numerical solution of the time-domain tableau equations, they can be replaced by the same approximation when seeking a numerical solution of the time-domain

   (a) node equations as in (4-6),
   (b) twig equations as in (4-9),
   (c) link equations as in (4-17),
   (d) mixed-variable equations as in (4-23), and
   (e) state and output equations as in (4-63) and (4-64).

   In addition, integrals (in cases [a] through [d]) can be similarly approximated; thus,

   $$\int_0^{t_m} \mathbf{x}(\tau)d\tau \approx \delta_m \mathbf{x}^m + \psi(\mathbf{x}^{m-1}, \ldots, \mathbf{x}^0).$$

   (You should show that with these approximations the resulting equations are algebraic equations for the approximate value of the vector of

   (a) node voltages $\mathbf{v}_n^m$,
   (b) twig voltages $\mathbf{v}_r^m$,
   (c) link currents $\mathbf{i}_l^m$,
   (d) twig voltages and link currents $[\mathbf{v}_r^{m'} \ \mathbf{i}_l^{m'}]'$, and
   (e) state variables $\mathbf{x}^m$

   at time t_m [$m = 0, 1, 2, \ldots$].) Assume the availability of programs — here to be thought of as subroutines — to create the several sets of time-domain equations. (See Progs. 3 and 4.) Assume also the availability of a matrix inversion subroutine. (See Appendix A.) Write programs to create and solve these several sets of equations. Output data should be in an easy to use format. In a short report on these programs discuss the rationale for the format adopted. For the derivative approximation use the trapezoidal rule (for derivatives)

$$\dot{\mathbf{x}}(t)\big|_{t=t_m} \approx \frac{2}{h}\mathbf{x}^m - \left\{ \frac{2}{h}\mathbf{x}^{m-1} + \dot{\mathbf{x}}^{m-1} \right\}$$

and for the integral approximation use the trapezoidal rule (for integrals)

$$\int_0^{t_m} \mathbf{x}(\tau)d\tau \approx \frac{h}{2}\mathbf{x}^m + \left\{ h\mathbf{x}^{m-1} + \ldots + h\mathbf{x}^1 + \frac{h}{2}\mathbf{x}^0 \right\}.$$

6. The sinusoidal steady-state numerical solution of the

   (a) node equations as in (4-6),
   (b) twig equations as in (4-9),
   (c) link equations as in (4-17), and
   (d) mixed-variable equations as in (4-23)

corresponds to solving their frequency-domain counterparts under zero initial conditions for a discrete set of values of s on the imaginary axis $- s = j\omega_m$ $(m = 0, 1, 2, \ldots)$. (You should validate this statement.) Assume the availability of programs — here to be thought of as subroutines — to create the several sets of frequency-domain equations. (See Prog. 3.) Assume, also, the availability of a matrix inversion subroutine. (See Appendix A.) Write programs to create and solve these several sets of equations. Output data should be in an easy to use format. In a short report on these programs discuss the rationale for the format adopted.

PROJECTS

1. Read

    R. Tarjan, "Depth-first search and linear graph algorithms," *SIAM Journal on Computing*, vol. 1, 1972, pp. 146-160.

The depth-first search algorithm by which to determine a forest is developed in this paper. Compare this algorithm to algorithm 2.1 with respect to numbers of arithmetic and logic operations. Next read

L. K. Chen, B. S. Ting, and A. Sangiovanni-Vincentelli, "An edge-oriented adjacency list for undirected graphs," *International Journal on Circuit Theory and Applications*, vol. 7, 1979, pp. 55-63.

The edge-oriented adjacency list for data storage is developed in this paper. Compare this method, with respect to numbers of words of computer storage, to that used in the description of the depth-first search algorithm.

2. The algorithmic method of formulating state and output equations of the text is ideally suited to program realization. It is not particularly well suited to "by-hand" formulation of these equations. There are two well developed methods more appropriate to by-hand formulation:

   (a) the topological method and
   (b) the multiport method.

   (The former is the basis for the widely distributed network analysis program SCEPTRE.) A description of these methods is to be found in

N. Balabanian and T. A. Bickart, *Electrical Network Theory*, John Wiley and Sons, New York, chap. 4 (secs. 5-6).

   A description of the topological method restricted to RLCM networks is to be found in

L. O. Chua and P.-M. Lin, *Computer-Aided Analysis of Electronic Circuits*, Prentice-Hall, Englewood Cliffs, New Jersey, 1975, chap. 8 (sec. 2).

   Prepare a brief report on these methods. Be certain to include any restrictive assumptions — there are some — which must be observed in using these methods. Illustrate the methods by determining state and output equations for several of the networks of Fig. E-17 by each method.

3. Read

C.-W. Ho, A. E. Ruehli, and P. A. Brennan, "The modified nodal nodal analysis to network analysis," *IEEE Transactions on Circuits and Systems*, vol. CAS-22, 1975, pp. 504-509.

Then develop a flowchart for a program to create and solve the modified nodal equations described in this paper. Prepare a short report in which you describe the rationale followed in designing the flowchart.

4. Read

> G. D. Hachtel, R. K. Brayton, and F. G. Gustavson, "The sparse tableau approach to network analysis and design," *IEEE Transactions on Circuit Theory*, vol. CT-18, 1971, pp. 101-113.

and

> W. T. Weeks, *et al.*, "Algorithms for ASTAP—a network analysis program," *IEEE Transactions on Circuit Theory*, vol. CT-20, 1973, pp. 628-634.

The first paper is the original paper on tableau equations. The second describes ASTAP, the first major network analysis program based on the tableau equations. Prepare a short report on this—tableau equations based network analysis, theory and realization—and any related material you choose to read.

5. Read

> R. P. Tewarson, *Sparse Matrices*, Academic Press, New York, 1973, chaps. 1-2.

Then write a subroutine for some sparse matrix storage scheme which creates an elimination form inverse of a matrix. Adopt a pivot strategy which establishes an upper bound on the local fill-in and which limits round-off error by placing a lower bound on the pivot magnitude. You should consider using row and column scaling to precondition the matrix before performing the Gauss elimination. In addition you are to prepare flowcharts for programs to compose and solve the

(a) time-domain and
(b) frequency-domain

tableau equations which incorporate this subroutine. For the derivative approximation of (4-74) use the backward Euler formula

$$\dot{x}(t)\big|_{t=t_m} \approx \frac{1}{h}x^m - \left\{\frac{1}{h}x^{m-1}\right\},$$

where h is the time-step $t_m - t_{m-1}$. Prepare a short report in which you describe the rationale followed in designing the subroutine and flowchart. Include test results which illustrate the subroutine's performance.

6. Read

> M. Nakhla, K. Singhal, and J. Vlach, "An optimal pivoting order for the solution of sparse systems of equations," *IEEE Transactions on Circuits and Systems*, vol. CAS-21, 1974, pp. 222-225.

and

> R. P. Tewarson, *Sparse Matrices*, Academic Press, New York, 1973, chap. 1.

Then carry out the task of Proj. 5 for an LU factorization, rather than an elimination form inverse, of a matrix. The pivot strategy adopted should be that proposed in the above paper.

7. Read

> R. P. Tewarson, *Sparse Matrices*, Academic Press, New York, 1973, chaps 1, 2 (secs. 1-3), and 5.

Then carry out the task of Proj. 5 for an LU factorization of a matrix, using the Crout method, rather than an elimination form inverse of a matrix. Next read

> F. G. Gustavson, W. Liniger, and R. Willoughby, "Symbolic generation of an optimal Crout algorithm for sparse systems of linear equations," *Journal ACM*, vol. 17, 1970, pp. 87-109.

In your report comment on the algorithm of this paper vis-a-vis that realized by your subroutine.

8. Read

> R. P. Tewarson, *Sparse Matrices*, Academic Press, New York, 1973, chaps. 1, 2 (secs. 1-3), and 5.

Then carry out the task of Proj. 5 for a product form inverse, rather than an elimination form inverse, of a matrix using Gauss-Jordan, rather than Gauss, elimination.

9. Read

R. P. Tewarson, *Sparse Matrices*, Academic Press, New York, chaps. 1, 2 (secs. 1-3), and 5.

Then write a subroutine for some sparse matrix storage scheme which creates the row echelon form of a matrix. Adopt a pivot strategy which establishes an upper bound on the local fill-in and which limits round-off error by placing a lower bound on the pivot magnitude. Note: Only partial pivoting can be used in creating the row echelon form of a matrix. The implications of this fact should be discussed in your report. You should consider using row and column scaling to precondition the matrix before performing the Gauss-Jordan elimination. In addition you are to prepare a flowchart for a program to compose state and output equations, which incorporates this subroutine. Prepare a short report in which you describe the rationale followed in designing the subroutine. Include test results which illustrate the subroutine's performance.

10. Read

A. Sangiovanni-Vincentelli, L.-K. Chen, and L. O. Chua, "An efficient heuristic cluster algorithm for tearing large scale networks," *IEEE Transactions on Circuits and Systems*, vol. CAS-24, 1977, pp. 709-717.

This paper describes a procedure for branch and node ordering which leads to node equations exhibiting a special block structure. Write a short report on node-tearing nodal analysis which includes an algorithm for realizing these specially structured node equations. Then read

R. P. Tewarson, *Sparse Matrices*, Academic Press, New York, 1973, chaps. 2 (secs. 1-3) and 3 (secs. 9-10)

and, possibly,

J. R. Bunch, "Block methods for solving sparse linear systems," *Sparse Matrix Computations*, J. R. Bunch and D. J. Rose, eds., Academic Press, New York, 1976, pp. 39-58.

Other sources, cited in these two, might be of value in the next part of this project. Include in your report a description — including algorithm — of a solution method for these specially structured node equations.

11. The state equations of (4-63) can be solved analytically in the time-domain and, after Laplace transforming them, in the frequency-domain. Matrix function theory is needed. Read

    N. Balabanian and T. A. Bickart, *Electrical Network Theory*, John Wiley and Sons, New York, 1969, chap. 4 (secs. 3-4)

or

    C. T. Chen, *Introduction to Linear System Theory*, Holt, Rinehart, and Winston, New York, 1970, chap. 4

or

    L. O. Chua and P.-M. Lin, *Computer-Aided Analysis of Electronic Circuits*, Prentice-Hall, Englewood Cliffs, New Jersey, 1975, chap. 9 (secs. 1, 5).

Prepare a report on analytic solution methods. Illustrate these methods by solving several sets of state equations.

12. Networks with many components tend to be stiff, a property characterized by natural modes with significantly different real parts. Stiff networks require special procedures to efficiently achieve a numerical solution in the time-domain. Prepare a report on such procedures based upon multistep numerical integration formulas. You may, if you wish, focus on those multistep formulas known as the backward differentiation formulas. For simplicity assume you are seeking to solve the state equations numerically. You will find sufficient material in the following sources, but depending on your inclination, you may supplement them by material obtained by citations from and to these.

    C. W. Gear, *Numerical Initial Value Problems in Ordinary Differential Equations*, Prentice-Hall, Englewood Cliffs, New Jersey, 1971, chaps. 1, 7-11.

    R. K. Brayton, F. G. Gustavson, and G. D. Hachtel, "A new efficient algorithm for solving differential-algebraic systems using implicit backward differentiation formulas," *Proceedings IEEE*, vol. 60, 1972, pp. 98-108.

13. Read

N. B. G. Rabbat, A. L. Sangiovanni-Vincentelli, and H. Y. Hsieh, "A multilevel Newton algorithm with macromodeling and latency for the analysis of large-scale nonlinear circuits in the time domain," *IEEE Transactions on Circuits and Systems*, vol. CAS-26, 1979, pp. 733-741.

Then prepare a report on the concept of latency in the analysis of very large linear—not nonlinear, as considered by the authors— networks.

PART II
Network Properties

CHAPTER 5
Multiterminal and Multiport Representations

In the last chapter we described a number of systematic methods for applying the fundamental laws of network theory to obtain sets of simultaneous equations: node, cut-set, loop, mixed-variable, state, and tableau equations. Of course, these formal procedures are not necessarily the simplest to use for all problems. In many problems involving networks of only moderate structural complexity, mere inspection, Thévenin's theorem, or other shortcuts may doubtless provide answers more easily than setting up and solving, say, the mixed-variable equations. The value of these systematic procedures lies in their generality and in our ability to utilize computers in setting them up and solving them.

The equations to which these systematic methods lead are differential or integrodifferential. Classical methods — analytic and numeric — for solving such equations can be employed, but often solutions will be obtained by the Laplace transform. With this in mind, the formulation was often carried out in Laplace-transformed form.

Assuming that a network and the Laplace-transformed equations describing its behavior are available, we now turn to the solution of these equations and the determination of the network functions in terms of which the network behavior is described.

5.1 DRIVING-POINT AND TRANSFER FUNCTIONS

Given a linear, time-invariant network, excited by any number of independent voltage and current sources, and with arbitrary initial capacitor voltages and inductor currents (which can also be represented as independent sources) a set of node, cut-set, or loop equations can be written. The network may be nonpassive and nonreciprocal. In matrix form these equations will all be similar. Thus,

$$\mathbf{Y}_n(s)\mathbf{V}_n(s) = \mathbf{J}_n(s) \qquad \text{(node)} \tag{1a}$$

$$\mathbf{Y}_c(s)\mathbf{V}_c(s) = \mathbf{J}_c(s) \qquad \text{(cut-set)} \tag{1b}$$

$$\mathbf{Z}_c(s)\mathbf{I}_c(s) = \mathbf{E}_c(s) \qquad \text{(loop)} \tag{1c}$$

The right-hand sides are the contributions of the sources, including the initial-condition equivalent sources; for example, $\mathbf{J}_n = [J_i]$, where J_i is the sum of current sources, including Norton equivalents of accompanied voltage sources, connected at node i, with due regard for the orientations.

The symbolic solution of these equations can be written easily and is obtained by multiplying each equation by the inverse of the corresponding coefficient matrix. Thus,

$$\mathbf{V}_n(s) = \mathbf{Y}_n^{-1}\mathbf{J}_n(s) \tag{2a}$$

$$\mathbf{V}_c(s) = \mathbf{Y}_c^{-1}\mathbf{J}_c(s) \tag{2b}$$

$$\mathbf{I}_c(s) = \mathbf{Z}_c^{-1}\mathbf{E}_c(s) \tag{2c}$$

Each of these has the same form. For purposes of illustration the first one will be shown in expanded form. Thus,

$$\begin{bmatrix} V_1 \\ V_2 \\ \vdots \\ V_m \end{bmatrix} = \begin{bmatrix} \dfrac{\Delta_{11}}{\Delta} & \dfrac{\Delta_{21}}{\Delta} & \cdots & \dfrac{\Delta_{m1}}{\Delta} \\ \dfrac{\Delta_{12}}{\Delta} & \dfrac{\Delta_{22}}{\Delta} & \cdots & \dfrac{\Delta_{m2}}{\Delta} \\ \vdots & \vdots & & \vdots \\ \dfrac{\Delta_{1m}}{\Delta} & \dfrac{\Delta_{2m}}{\Delta} & \cdots & \dfrac{\Delta_{mm}}{\Delta} \end{bmatrix} \begin{bmatrix} J_1 \\ J_2 \\ \vdots \\ J_m \end{bmatrix} ,$$

where Δ is the determinant of the node admittance matrix and Δ_{jk} is its (j,k)th cofactor. The expression for just one of the node voltages, say V_k, is

$$V_k = \frac{\Delta_{1k}}{\Delta}J_1 + \frac{\Delta_{2k}}{\Delta}J_2 + \ldots + \frac{\Delta_{mk}}{\Delta}J_m. \qquad (4)$$

This gives the transform of a node voltage as a linear combination of the equivalent sources. The J's are not in general the actual sources. As an example, consider the network in Fig. 1 and suppose that any initial conditions are zero. The **J**-matrix will be

$$\mathbf{J} = \begin{bmatrix} J_1 \\ J_2 \\ J_3 \end{bmatrix} = \begin{bmatrix} I_{g2} + Y_1 V_{g1} \\ -I_{g2} + I_{g3} \\ -Y_1 V_{g1} \end{bmatrix}.$$

When the appropriate expressions in terms of actual sources are substituted for the J's, it is clear that (4) can be arranged to give V_k as a linear combination of the actual sources. Thus for Fig. 1 the expression for V_k would become

$$V_k = \left(\frac{\Delta_{1k} - \Delta_{3k}}{\Delta}\right) Y_1 V_{g1} + \left(\frac{\Delta_{1k} - \Delta_{2k}}{\Delta}\right) I_{g2} + \left(\frac{\Delta_{2k}}{\Delta}\right) I_{g3}. \qquad (5)$$

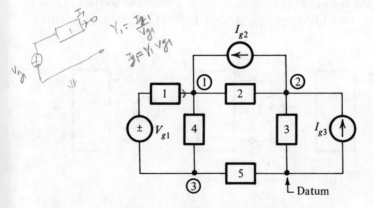

Fig. 1   Illustration for equivalent sources

As a general statement, it can be said that any response transform can be written as a linear combination of excitation (or input) transforms.

The coefficients of this linear combination are themselves linear combinations of various functions of s. These functions are, or are proportional to, ratios of two determinants, the denominator one being the determinant of $\mathbf{Y}_n$, $\mathbf{Y}_c$, or $\mathbf{Z}_c$ and the numerator one being some cofactor of these matrices; for example, in (5) the denominator determinant is det Y_n, and the coefficient of $\mathbf{I}_{g2}$ is the difference between two such ratios of determinants.

Once the functions relating some response transform (whether voltage or current) to some excitation transform (again, voltage or current) are known, then the response to any given excitation can be determined. Thus in (5) knowledge of the quantities in parentheses is enough to determine the response V_k for any given values of V_{g1}, I_{g2}, and I_{g3}.

We shall define the general term *network function* as the ratio of a response transform to an excitation transform. Both the response and the excitation may be either voltage or current. If the response and excitation refer to the same terminals (in which case one must be a voltage, the other a current), then the function is called a *driving-point function*, either *impedance* or *admittance*. If the excitation and response refer to different terminals, then the function is a *transfer function*.

5.1.1 Driving-Point Functions

To be more specific, consider Fig. 2(a) in which attention is focused on one pair of terminals to which external connections can be made. We assume that the network: (1) contains no independent sources, (2) is initially relaxed, and (3) does not present a short or open circuit to the terminals.

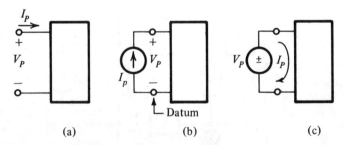

(a)   (b)   (c)

Fig. 2   Driving-point functions

By the "driving-point impedance" and the "driving-point admittance" of a network at a pair of terminals we mean

$$Z(s) = \frac{V_P(s)}{I_P(s)} \text{ and } Y(s) = \frac{I_P(s)}{V_P(s)} = \frac{1}{Z(s)}, \tag{6}$$

where V_P and I_P are the transforms of the terminal voltage and current with references as shown in Fig. 2. In making this definition nothing is said about how the terminals are excited or what is connected to them. The implication is that it makes no difference, which is true by the assumption that the network does not appear to be short or open at the terminals. The conditions of no independent sources and zero initial conditions are essential to the definition. Clearly, if the network contains independent sources or initial conditions, then Z or Y can take on different values, depending on what is connected at the terminals; thus it will not be an invariant characteristic of the network itself.

Another factor to be noted is that no assumption has been made about the nature of the time functions $v_P(t)$ and $i_P(t)$. Whatever they may be, the definition of Z or Y involves the ratio of their Laplace transforms.

Now let us turn to an evaluation of Z and Y for a network and let us initially assume that the network contains no *nonpassive, nonreciprocal components*. Since it makes no difference, suppose the network is excited with a current source, as in Fig. 2(b). Let us write a set of node equations. We choose one of the two external terminals as the datum node in order that the source appear in only one of the node equations. We order the remaining nodes starting with the other external node as number one. Under these circumstances the solution for the first node voltage, V_P, can be obtained from (4), in which only J_1 is nonzero and its value is I_P. Hence for the impedance we find

$$Z(s) = \frac{V_P(s)}{I_P(s)} = \frac{\Delta_{11}(s)}{\Delta(s)}\bigg|_y, \tag{7}$$

where Z is the *driving-point impedance* at the terminals of the network. The notation $|_y$ has been used to indicate that the determinants are those of the node equations.

A dual formula for the driving-point admittance Y can be obtained, quite evidently, by considering that the network is excited by a voltage source as in Fig. 2(c); a set of loop equations is then written. The loops are chosen such that the voltage source appears only in the first loop; thus V_P will appear in only the first of the loop equations. The solution for the loop equations will be just like (3), except that the sources will be the equivalent voltage sources E_k (of which all but the first will be zero in this case and this one will equal V_P) and the variables will be the loop currents. Solving for the first loop current, I_P, then gives

$$Y(s) = \frac{I_P(s)}{V_P(s)} = \frac{\Delta_{11}(s)}{\Delta(s)}\bigg|_z, \tag{8}$$

where Y is the *driving point admittance* and the notation $|_z$ indicates that the determinants are those of the loop impedance matrix.

Expressions (7) and (8) are useful for calculating Z and Y, but it should be remembered that they apply when there are no controlled sources or other such components. They may also apply in specific cases when controlled sources are present, but not always.

As an illustration of a simple case in which (8) does not apply when a controlled source is present, consider the network shown in Fig. 3(a).

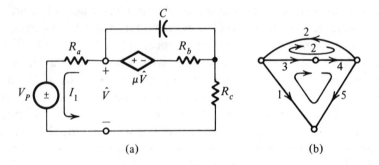

(a)   (b)

Fig. 3   Amplifier network

Since the voltage-controlled voltage source has no impedance representation (i.e., it does not satisfy the loop assumption), let us express the controlling voltage $\hat{V}$ in terms of some branch current; from Fig. 3(a) one possibility is $\hat{V} = -R_a I_1 - V_P$. This act replaces the old controlling branch by the general branch—branch 1 in the graph of Fig. 3(b)— composed of the independent voltage source V_P and the resistor R_a. The controlled branch voltage (branch 3 in the graph) is $V_3 = \mu\hat{V} = -\mu R_a I_1 - \mu V_P$. This is an impedance representation of the branch, with μV_P being simply an independent accompanying source that will appear in the voltage source vector. The loop matrix **B**, the branch impedance matrix **Z**, and the voltage source vector $\mathbf{V}_s$ can be written as follows:

$V_1 = R_a I_1 + V_P \Rightarrow R_a I_1 - (V_1 - V_P) = 0$

$$Z = \begin{bmatrix} R_a & 0 & 0 & 0 & 0 \\ 0 & \dfrac{1}{sC} & 0 & 0 & 0 \\ -\mu R_a & 0 & 0 & 0 & 0 \\ 0 & 0 & 0 & R_b & 0 \\ 0 & 0 & 0 & 0 & R_c \end{bmatrix}, \quad V_s = \begin{bmatrix} V_P \\ 0 \\ -\mu V_P \\ 0 \\ 0 \end{bmatrix}, \quad B = \begin{bmatrix} -1 & 0 & 1 & 1 & 1 \\ 0 & -1 & -1 & -1 & 0 \end{bmatrix}.$$

The loop equations $(BZB I_c = -BV_s)$ now become:

Zc $ec = +B(Z i_s - V_s) = -B V_s$ since $i_s = 0$

$$\begin{bmatrix} (1+\mu)R_a + R_b + R_c & -R_b \\ -\mu R_a - R_b & R_b + \dfrac{1}{sC} \end{bmatrix} \begin{bmatrix} I_{c1} \\ I_{c2} \end{bmatrix} = \begin{bmatrix} V_P + \mu V_P \\ -\mu V_P \end{bmatrix}$$

The driving-point admittance is I_{c1}/V_P, since $I_P = I_{c1}$. This can be found by solving the loop equations for I_{c1}. The result is:

$$Y = \frac{I_{c1}}{V_P} = \frac{\Delta_{11} + \mu(\Delta_{11} - \Delta_{21})}{\Delta}.$$

$$\begin{bmatrix} I_{c1} \\ I_{c2} \end{bmatrix} = \begin{bmatrix} \dfrac{\Delta_{11}}{\Delta} & \dfrac{\Delta_{12}}{\Delta} \\ \dfrac{\Delta_{21}}{\Delta} & \dfrac{\Delta_{22}}{\Delta} \end{bmatrix} \begin{bmatrix} V_P + \mu V_P \\ -\mu V_P \end{bmatrix}$$

Thus, even though we were careful to choose only one loop through the exciting source, the source voltage V_P appears in both loop equations, and the final result differs from (8). It may be concluded that one should not rely on special formulas such as (7) and (8) when calculating a network function, but should go to definitions such as (6).

5.1.2 Transfer Functions

When the excitation and response are at different terminals, the network function is defined to be a transfer function. Let the response be the voltage or current of some branch. We can focus attention on the branch by drawing it separately as in Fig. 4. For the notion of transfer function to be meaningful, we continue to assume that there are no internal independent sources and the network is initially relaxed. In Fig. 4(a), four different transfer functions can be defined with either $V_L(s)$ or $I_L(s)$ as the response and either $V_P(s)$ or $I_P(s)$ as the excitation. Assuming the network does not present an open circuit to the terminals at which

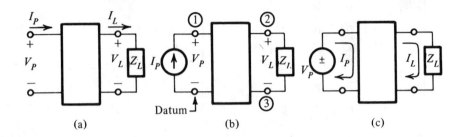

Fig. 4   Transfer functions

the excitation is applied, let us use a current source as the excitation, as shown in Fig. 4(b), and write node equations. The solutions for the node voltages are given by (4). The only thing left to settle is: What are the sources? Even though there is only one actual source, this may appear in more than one node equation if the network contains controlled sources. Hence, let us temporarily assume there are no controlled sources. Then all the J's in (4) are zero except J_1 which equals I_P. The result will be

$$V_P(s) = V_{n1} = \frac{\Delta_{11}}{\Delta}\bigg|_y I_P(s),$$

$$V_L(s) = V_{n2} - V_{n3} = \frac{\Delta_{12} - \Delta_{13}}{\Delta}\bigg|_y I_P(s).$$

From these, and from the fact that $I_L = Y_L V_L$, each of the transfer functions V_L/V_P, V_L/I_P, I_L/V_P, and I_L/I_P can be obtained. In a similar manner, when a voltage source is applied, as shown in Fig. 4(c), the loop equations may be written. The resulting expressions from both the node and loop equations will be

Transfer impedance

$$\frac{V_L(s)}{I_P(s)} = \frac{\Delta_{12} - \Delta_{13}}{\Delta}\bigg|_y = Z_L \frac{\Delta_{12}}{\Delta_{11}}\bigg|_z, \tag{9a}$$

Transfer admittance

$$\frac{I_L(s)}{V_P(s)} = Y_L \frac{\Delta_{12} - \Delta_{13}}{\Delta_{11}}\bigg|_y = \frac{\Delta_{12}}{\Delta}\bigg|_z, \tag{9b}$$

Voltage gain, or *transfer voltage ratio*

$$\frac{V_L(s)}{V_P(s)} = \frac{\Delta_{12} - \Delta_{13}}{\Delta_{11}}\bigg|_y = Z_L \frac{\Delta_{12}}{\Delta}\bigg|_z, \tag{9c}$$

Current gain, or *transfer current ratio*

$$\frac{I_L(s)}{I_P(s)} = Y_L \frac{\Delta_{12} - \Delta_{13}}{\Delta}\bigg|_y = \frac{\Delta_{12}}{\Delta_{11}}\bigg|_z. \tag{9d}$$

Let us emphasize:

1. These formulas are valid in the absence of controlled sources and other nonpassive, nonreciprocal devices. (When controlled sources are present, these particular formulas may or may not apply. Nevertheless, the transfer functions will still be linear combinations of similar ratios of determinants and cofactors.)
2. The transfer impedance is not the reciprocal of the transfer admittance.
3. The references of voltage and current must be as shown in Fig. 4.

5.2 MULTITERMINAL AND MULTIPORT NETWORKS

In our study of electric networks up to this point we have assumed that the internal structure of the network is available and that an analysis is to be carried out for the purpose of determining the currents and voltages anywhere in the network. However, very often there is no interest in all the branch voltages and currents. Interest is limited to only a number of these; namely, those corresponding to terminals to which external connections to the network are to be made. As far as the outside world is concerned, the details of the internal structure of a network are not important; it is only important to know the relationships among the voltages and currents at the external terminals. The external behavior of the network is completely determined once these relationships are known.

Consider the network shown in Fig. 5(a), having six terminals to which external connections can be made. Exactly how should the voltage and current variables be defined? Consider Fig. 5(b). Should the voltages be defined so that each terminal voltage is referred to some arbitrary datum (or ground), such as V_2? Should they be defined as the voltages between pairs of terminals, such as V_{12}, or V_{46}? Should the cur-

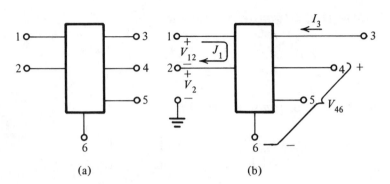

(a)   (b)

Fig. 5   Six-terminal network

rents be the terminal currents, such as I_3, or should they be like the loop current J_1 shown entering one terminal and leaving another? In fact, each of these may be useful for different purposes, as we shall observe.

In many applications external connections are made to the terminals of the network only in pairs. Each pair of terminals, or *terminal-pair*, represents an entrance to, and exit from, a network and is quite descriptively called a *port*. The six-terminal network of Fig. 5 is shown as a *three-port* in Fig. 6(a) and as a *five-port* in Fig. 6(b). Note that no other external connections are to be made except at the ports shown; for example, in Fig. 6(a) no connection is to be made between terminals 1 and 3 or 1 and 5. Connections must be so made that the same current enters one terminal of the port as leaves the network through the second terminal of the port. The port voltages are the voltages between the pairs of terminals that constitute the port.

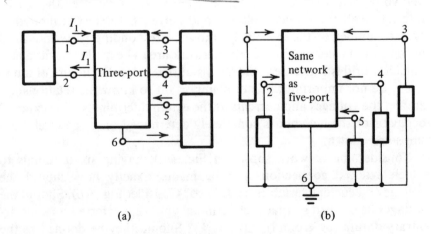

(a)   (b)

Fig. 6   Six-terminal network connected (a) as a three-port and (b) as a five-port

There is a basic difference (besides the number of ports) between the two types of multiport networks shown in Fig. 6. In Fig. 6(b), one of the terminals of each port is common to all the ports. The port voltages are therefore the same as the terminal voltages of all but one terminal, relative to this last one. Such a network is called a *common-terminal*, or *grounded*, multiport. In the first network in Fig. 6 there is no such identified common ground.

It is possible that connections may be required to a multiterminal network besides the terminal-pair kind. In such a case a port description is not appropriate. An alternative means of description, which is necessary in this case, will be discussed in the last section.

5.3 TWO-PORT NETWORKS

At this point it is possible to proceed by treating the general multiport network and discussing sets of equations relating the port variables. After doing this, the results could be applied to the special case of a two-port. An alternative approach is to treat the simplest multiport (namely, the two-port) first. This might be done because of the importance of the two-port in its own right, and because treating the simplest case first can lead to insights into the general case that will not be obvious without experience with the simplest case. We shall take this second approach.

A two-port network is illustrated in Fig. 7. Because of the application of two-ports as transmission networks, one of the ports — normally the port labelled 1 — is called the *input*; the other, port 2, is called the *output*. The port variables are two port currents and two port voltages, with the standard references shown in Fig. 7. (In some of the literature the reference for I_2 is taken opposite to our reference. When comparing any formulas with those in other publications, verify the references of the port variables.) External networks that may be connected at the input and output are called the *terminations*. We shall deal throughout with the transformed variables and shall assume the two-port to be initially relaxed and to contain no independent sources.

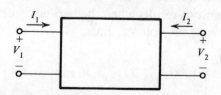

Fig. 7 Two-port network

The discussion that follows may appear somewhat unmotivated, since in restricting ourselves to analysis we have lost much of the motivation for finding various ways of describing the behavior of two-port networks. The need for these various schemes arises from the demands made by the many applications of two-ports. A method of description that is convenient for a power system, say, may be less so for a filter network, and may be completely unsuited for a transistor amplifier. For this reason we shall describe many alternative ways of describing two-port behavior.

In the problem of synthesizing a network for a specific application, it is often very convenient to break down a complicated problem into several parts. The pieces of the overall network are designed separately and then put together in a manner consistent with the original decomposition. In order to carry out this procedure it is necessary to know how the description of the behavior of the overall network is related to the behavior of the constituent parts. For this reason we shall spend some time on the problem of interconnecting two-ports.

Many of the results obtained in this section require a considerable amount of algebraic manipulation that is quite straightforward. We shall not attempt to carry through all the steps, but shall merely outline the desired procedure, leaving to you the task of filling in the omitted steps.

5.3.1 Impedance and Admittance Matrices

To describe the relationships among the port voltages and currents of a linear multiport requires as many linear equations as there are ports. Thus, for a two-port, two linear equations are required among the four variables. However, which two variables are considered "independent" and which "dependent" is a matter of choice and convenience in a given application. To return briefly to the general case, in an n-port, there will be $2n$ voltage and current variables. The number of ways in which these $2n$ variables can be arranged in two groups of n each equals the number of ways in which $2n$ things can be taken n at a time; namely, $(2n)!/(n!)^2$. For a two-port this number is six.

One set of equations results when the two-port currents are expressed in terms of the two-port voltage; thus,

$$
\begin{bmatrix} I_1(s) \\ I_2(s) \end{bmatrix} = \begin{bmatrix} y_{11} & y_{12} \\ y_{21} & y_{22} \end{bmatrix} \begin{bmatrix} V_1(s) \\ V_2(s) \end{bmatrix}.
\tag{10}
$$

It is a simple matter to obtain interpretations for the elements of this matrix by letting each of the voltages be zero in turn. It follows from the equation that

$$y_{11}(s) = \frac{I_1(s)}{V_1(s)}\bigg|_{V_2=0} , \qquad y_{12}(s) = \frac{I_1(s)}{V_2(s)}\bigg|_{V_1=0} , \qquad (11)$$

$$y_{21}(s) = \frac{I_2(s)}{V_1(s)}\bigg|_{V_2=0} , \qquad y_{22}(s) = \frac{I_2(s)}{V_2(s)}\bigg|_{V_1=0} .$$

Dimensionally, each parameter is an admittance. Setting a port voltage to zero means short-circuiting the port. Hence the y's (for which the lower case letter y will be reserved) are called the *(short-circuit) admittance parameters—y-parameters* for short. The matrix of y's is designated **Y** and is called the *admittance matrix*. The terms y_{11} and y_{22} are the driving-point admittances at the two ports, and y_{21} and y_{12} are transfer admittances. In particular, y_{21} is the *forward* transfer admittance—that is, the ratio of a current response in port 2 to a voltage excitation in port 1—and y_{12} is the *reverse* transfer admittance.

A second set of relationships can be written as expressing the port voltages in terms of the port currents as

$$\begin{bmatrix} V_1(s) \\ V_2(s) \end{bmatrix} = \begin{bmatrix} z_{11} & z_{12} \\ z_{21} & z_{22} \end{bmatrix} \begin{bmatrix} I_1(s) \\ I_2(s) \end{bmatrix} . \qquad (12)$$

This time interpretations are obtained by letting each current be zero in turn. Then,

$$z_{11}(s) = \frac{V_1(s)}{I_1(s)}\bigg|_{I_2=0} , \qquad z_{12}(s) = \frac{V_1(s)}{I_2(s)}\bigg|_{I_1=0} , \qquad (13)$$

$$z_{21}(s) = \frac{V_2(s)}{I_1(s)}\bigg|_{I_2=0} , \qquad z_{22}(s) = \frac{V_2(s)}{I_2(s)}\bigg|_{I_1=0} .$$

Dimensionally, each parameter is an impedance. Setting a port current equal to zero means open-circuiting the port. Hence the z's (for which the lower case letter z will be reserved) are called the *(open-circuit) impedance parameters—z-parameters* for short. The matrix of z's is designated **Z** and is called the *impedance matrix*. The elements z_{11} and z_{22} are the driving-point impedances at the two ports, and z_{21} and z_{12} are the transfer impedances; z_{21} is the *forward* transfer impedance, and z_{12} is the *reverse* transfer impedance.

It should be clear from (10) and (12) that the **Y** and **Z** matrices are inverses of each other; that is,

$$\mathbf{Y} = \begin{bmatrix} y_{11} & y_{12} \\ y_{21} & y_{22} \end{bmatrix} = \mathbf{Z}^{-1} = \frac{1}{\det \mathbf{Z}} \begin{bmatrix} z_{22} & -z_{12} \\ -z_{21} & z_{11} \end{bmatrix}. \tag{14}$$

From this it follows that

$$\det \mathbf{Y} = \frac{1}{\det \mathbf{Z}}. \tag{15}$$

Demonstration of this is left as an exercise.

The results developed so far apply whether the network is passive or active, reciprocal or nonreciprocal. Now consider the two transfer functions y_{21} and y_{12}. If the network is reciprocal, according to the definition in Chapter 1, they will be equal. So also will z_{12} and z_{21}; that is, for a reciprocal network

$$y_{12} = y_{21} \text{ and } z_{12} = z_{21}, \tag{16}$$

which means that both **Y** and **Z** are symmetrical for reciprocal networks.

5.3.2 Hybrid Matrices

The z and y representations are two of the ways in which the relationships among the port variables can be expressed. They express the two voltages in terms of the two currents, and vice versa. Two other sets of equations can be obtained by expressing a current and voltage from opposite ports in terms of the other voltage and current. Thus,

$$\begin{bmatrix} V_1 \\ I_2 \end{bmatrix} = \begin{bmatrix} h_{11} & h_{12} \\ h_{21} & h_{22} \end{bmatrix} \begin{bmatrix} I_1 \\ V_2 \end{bmatrix} \tag{17}$$

and

$$\begin{bmatrix} I_1 \\ V_2 \end{bmatrix} = \begin{bmatrix} g_{11} & g_{12} \\ g_{21} & g_{22} \end{bmatrix} \begin{bmatrix} V_1 \\ I_2 \end{bmatrix} \tag{18}$$

The interpretations of these parameters can be easily determined from the preceding equations to be the following:

$$h_{11} = \frac{V_1(s)}{I_1(s)}\bigg|_{V_2=0}, \qquad h_{12} = \frac{V_1(s)}{V_2(s)}\bigg|_{I_1=0},$$

$$h_{21} = \frac{I_2(s)}{I_1(s)}\bigg|_{V_2=0}, \qquad h_{22} = \frac{I_2(s)}{V_2(s)}\bigg|_{I_1=0}, \qquad (19)$$

$$g_{11} = \frac{I_1(s)}{V_1(s)}\bigg|_{I_2=0}, \qquad g_{12} = \frac{I_1(s)}{I_2(s)}\bigg|_{V_1=0},$$

$$g_{21} = \frac{V_2(s)}{V_1(s)}\bigg|_{I_2=0}, \qquad g_{22} = \frac{V_2(s)}{I_2(s)}\bigg|_{V_1=0}.$$

Thus we see that the elements of the **H** and **G** matrices are interpreted under a mixed set of terminal conditions, some of them under open-circuit and some under short-circuit conditions. They are called the *hybrid h-* and *hybrid g-parameters*. From these interpretatons we see that h_{11} and g_{22} are impedances, whereas h_{22} and g_{11} are admittances. They are related to the z's and y's by

$$h_{11} = \frac{1}{y_{11}}, \qquad g_{11} = \frac{1}{z_{11}}$$

$$\qquad\qquad\qquad\qquad\qquad\qquad (20)$$

$$h_{22} = \frac{1}{z_{22}}, \qquad g_{22} = \frac{1}{y_{22}}.$$

The transfer g's and h's are dimensionless. The quantity h_{21} is the *forward (short-circuit) current gain*, and g_{12} is the *reverse (short-circuit) current gain*. The other two are voltage ratios: g_{21} is the *forward (open-circuit) voltage gain* and h_{12} is the *reverse (open-circuit) voltage gain*.

By direct computation we find the following relations among the transfer parameters:

$$h_{12} = \frac{-z_{12}}{z_{21}} h_{21}, \qquad\qquad\qquad (21a)$$

$$g_{12} = \frac{-y_{12}}{y_{21}} g_{21}. \qquad\qquad\qquad (21b)$$

In the special case of reciprocal networks these expressions simplify to $h_{12} = -h_{21}$ and $g_{12} = -g_{21}$. In words this means that for reciprocal networks, the open-circuit voltage gain for transmission in one direction through the two-port equals the negative of the short-circuit current gain for transmission in the opposite direction.

Just as $\mathbf{Z}$ and $\mathbf{Y}$ are each the other's inverse, so also $\mathbf{H}$ and $\mathbf{G}$ are each the other's inverse. Thus,

$$\mathbf{G}(s) = \mathbf{H}^{-1}(s) \quad \text{and} \quad \det \mathbf{G} = \frac{1}{\det \mathbf{H}}. \tag{22}$$

You should verify this.

5.3.3 Chain Matrix

The remaining two sets of equations relating the port variables express the voltage and current at one port in terms of the voltage and current at the other. Historically, in the analysis of transmission lines, these were the first sets used. One of these is

$$\begin{bmatrix} V_1(s) \\ I_1(s) \end{bmatrix} = \begin{bmatrix} A & B \\ C & D \end{bmatrix} \begin{bmatrix} V_2(s) \\ -I_2(s) \end{bmatrix}. \tag{23}$$

The matrix is called the *chain*, or *ABCD*, matrix. The first name comes from the fact that this is the natural representation to use in a cascade, or chain, connection typical of a transmission system. Note the negative sign in $-I_2$, which is a consequence of the choice of reference for I_2.

In the preceding, we used the historical symbols for these parameters rather than using, say a_{ij} with i and j equal 1 and 2, to make the system of notation uniform with the previous parameters. We are also not introducing further notation to define the inverse parameters obtained by inverting (23), simply to avoid further proliferation of symbols.

The determinant of the chain matrix can be computed in terms of the z's or the y's. It is found to be

$$\det \begin{bmatrix} A & B \\ C & D \end{bmatrix} = AD - BC = \frac{z_{12}}{z_{21}} = \frac{y_{12}}{y_{21}}, \tag{24}$$

For reciprocal two-ports, this determinant equals 1.

The preceding discussion is rather detailed and can become tedious if one loses sight of the objective of developing methods of representing the external behavior of two-ports by giving various relationships among the port voltages and currents. Each of these sets of relationships finds useful applications. For future reference we shall tabulate the interrelationships among the various parameters. The result is given in Table 1. Note that these relationships are valid for a general nonreciprocal two-port.

Table 1

	Impedance Parameters	Admittance Parameters	Chain Parameters		Hybrid h-Parameters	Hybrid g-Parameters
z	$z_{11}\quad z_{12}$	$\dfrac{y_{22}}{\lvert y\rvert}\quad \dfrac{-y_{12}}{\lvert y\rvert}$	$\dfrac{A}{C}$	$\dfrac{AD-BC}{C}$	$\dfrac{\lvert h\rvert}{h_{22}}\quad \dfrac{h_{12}}{h_{22}}$	$\dfrac{1}{g_{11}}\quad \dfrac{-g_{21}}{g_{11}}$
	$z_{21}\quad z_{22}$	$\dfrac{-y_{21}}{\lvert y\rvert}\quad \dfrac{y_{11}}{\lvert y\rvert}$	$\dfrac{1}{C}$	$\dfrac{D}{C}$	$\dfrac{-h_{21}}{h_{22}}\quad \dfrac{1}{h_{22}}$	$\dfrac{g_{21}}{g_{11}}\quad \dfrac{\lvert g\rvert}{g_{11}}$
y	$\dfrac{z_{22}}{\lvert z\rvert}\quad \dfrac{-z_{12}}{\lvert z\rvert}$	$y_{11}\quad y_{12}$	$\dfrac{D}{B}$	$\dfrac{-(AD-BC)}{B}$	$\dfrac{1}{h_{11}}\quad \dfrac{-h_{12}}{h_{11}}$	$\dfrac{\lvert g\rvert}{g_{22}}\quad \dfrac{g_{12}}{g_{22}}$
	$\dfrac{-z_{21}}{\lvert z\rvert}\quad \dfrac{z_{11}}{\lvert z\rvert}$	$y_{21}\quad y_{22}$	$\dfrac{-1}{B}$	$\dfrac{A}{B}$	$\dfrac{h_{21}}{h_{11}}\quad \dfrac{\lvert h\rvert}{h_{11}}$	$\dfrac{-g_{21}}{g_{22}}\quad \dfrac{1}{g_{22}}$
$ABCD$	$\dfrac{z_{11}}{z_{21}}\quad \dfrac{\lvert z\rvert}{z_{21}}$	$\dfrac{-y_{22}}{y_{21}}\quad \dfrac{-1}{y_{21}}$	A	B	$\dfrac{-\lvert h\rvert}{h_{21}}\quad \dfrac{-h_{11}}{h_{21}}$	$\dfrac{1}{g_{21}}\quad \dfrac{g_{22}}{g_{21}}$
	$\dfrac{1}{z_{21}}\quad \dfrac{z_{22}}{z_{21}}$	$\dfrac{-\lvert y\rvert}{y_{21}}\quad \dfrac{-y_{11}}{y_{21}}$	C	D	$\dfrac{-h_{22}}{h_{21}}\quad \dfrac{-1}{h_{21}}$	$\dfrac{g_{11}}{g_{21}}\quad \dfrac{\lvert g\rvert}{g_{21}}$
h	$\dfrac{\lvert z\rvert}{z_{22}}\quad \dfrac{z_{12}}{z_{22}}$	$\dfrac{1}{y_{11}}\quad \dfrac{-y_{12}}{y_{11}}$	$\dfrac{B}{D}$	$\dfrac{AD-BC}{D}$	$h_{11}\quad h_{12}$	$\dfrac{g_{22}}{\lvert g\rvert}\quad \dfrac{-g_{12}}{\lvert g\rvert}$
	$\dfrac{-z_{21}}{z_{22}}\quad \dfrac{1}{z_{22}}$	$\dfrac{y_{21}}{y_{11}}\quad \dfrac{\lvert y\rvert}{y_{11}}$	$\dfrac{-1}{D}$	$\dfrac{C}{D}$	$h_{21}\quad h_{22}$	$\dfrac{-g_{21}}{\lvert g\rvert}\quad \dfrac{g_{11}}{\lvert g\rvert}$
g	$\dfrac{1}{z_{11}}\quad \dfrac{-z_{12}}{z_{11}}$	$\dfrac{\lvert y\rvert}{y_{22}}\quad \dfrac{y_{12}}{y_{22}}$	$\dfrac{C}{A}$	$\dfrac{-(AD-BC)}{A}$	$\dfrac{h_{22}}{\lvert h\rvert}\quad \dfrac{-h_{12}}{\lvert h\rvert}$	$g_{11}\quad g_{12}$
	$\dfrac{z_{21}}{z_{11}}\quad \dfrac{\lvert z\rvert}{z_{11}}$	$\dfrac{-y_{21}}{y_{22}}\quad \dfrac{1}{y_{22}}$	$\dfrac{1}{A}$	$\dfrac{B}{A}$	$\dfrac{-h_{21}}{\lvert h\rvert}\quad \dfrac{h_{11}}{\lvert h\rvert}$	$g_{21}\quad g_{22}$

5.3.4 Transmission Zeros

There is an important observation that can be made concerning the locations of the zeros of the various transfer functions. This can be seen most readily, perhaps, by looking at one of the columns in Table 1; for example, the column in which all parameters are expressed in terms of the y-parameters. We see that

$$z_{21} = \frac{-y_{21}}{y_{11}y_{22} - y_{12}y_{21}}, \tag{25a}$$

$$h_{21} = \frac{y_{21}}{y_{11}}, \tag{25b}$$

$$g_{21} = \frac{-y_{21}}{y_{22}}. \tag{25c}$$

Except for possible cancellations, all of these transfer functions will have the same zeros. We use the generic term *transmission zero* to refer to a value of s for which there is a transfer-function zero, without having to specify which transfer function—whether current gain, transfer admittance, or any other.

5.3.5 Computation of Two-Port Parameters

For a given two-port, the parameters in any one of the sets can be determined by the application of appropriate sources at the ports and the evaluation of the resulting responses at those ports. To determine the hybrid-h parameters, as an example, a current source is applied at port 1 and a voltage source at port 2. An analysis is then carried out to find the responses V_1 and I_2 and the result put in the form of (17). It is sometimes simpler, however, to determine one parameter at a time by the use of expressions like those in (19).

As an illustrative example of the computation of two-port parameters, consider the network shown in Fig. 8. Let us compute the y-parameters for this network. The simplest procedure is to use the interpretations in (11). If the output terminals are short-circuited, the resulting network will take the form shown in Fig. 9. As far as the input

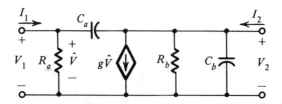

Fig. 8   Example for calculating two-port parameters

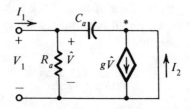

Fig. 9   Network with output terminals shorted

terminals are concerned, the controlled source has no effect. Hence y_{11} is the admittance of the parallel combination of R_a and C_a:

$$y_{11}(s) = \frac{1}{R_a} + sC_a.$$

To find y_{21}, assume that a voltage source with transform V_1 is applied at the input terminals. By applying Kirchhoff's current law at the node labeled * in Fig. 9, we find that $I_2 = gV_1 - sC_aV_1$. Hence, y_{21} becomes

$$y_{21} = \frac{I_2}{V_1}\bigg|_{V_2=0} = g - sC_a.$$

Now short-circuit the input port of the original network and assume that the output port is excited by a voltage source. The result will take the form in Fig. 10. The dependent source does not appear, since $\hat{V} = V_1$

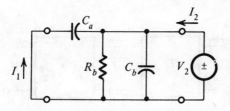

Fig. 10   **Network with input terminals shorted**

is zero and, hence, the dependent source current is also zero. It is now a simple matter to compute y_{22} and y_{12}:

$$y_{22} = \frac{I_2}{V_2}\bigg|_{V_1=0} = s(C_a + C_b) + \frac{1}{R_b},$$

$$y_{12} = \frac{I_1}{V_2}\bigg|_{V_1=0} = -sC_a.$$

We see that y_{12} is different from y_{21}, as it should be, because of the presence of the controlled source.

If the y-parameters are known, any of the other sets of parameters can be computed by using Table 1. Note that, even under the conditions that C_a and C_b are zero and R_a infinite, the y-parameters exist; but the z-parameters do not $-z_{11}$, z_{22}, and z_{21} become infinite.

5.4 INTERCONNECTION OF TWO-PORT NETWORKS

A given two-port network having some degree of complexity can often be viewed as being composed of simpler two-port networks whose ports are interconnected in certain ways. Conversely, a two-port network that is to be designed can often be constructed as an interconnection of simple two-port structures used as building blocks. From the designer's standpoint it is much easier to design simple blocks and to interconnect them than to design a complex network in one piece.

5.4.1 Cascade Connection

There are a number of ways in which two-ports can be interconnected. In the simplest interconnection of a pair of two-ports, called the *cascade*, or *chain*, *connection*, one port of each network is involved. A pair of two-ports is said to be connected *in cascade* if the output port of one is the input port of the second as shown in Fig. 11.

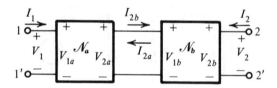

Fig. 11   Cascade connection of two-ports

From an analysis viewpoint, our interest in the problem of "interconnection" is to study how the parameters of the overall network are related to the parameters of the individual building blocks. The tandem combination is most conveniently studied by means of the *ABCD*-parameters. From the references in the figure we see that

$$\begin{bmatrix} V_1 \\ I_1 \end{bmatrix} = \begin{bmatrix} V_{1a} \\ I_{1a} \end{bmatrix}, \quad \begin{bmatrix} V_{2a} \\ -I_{2a} \end{bmatrix} = \begin{bmatrix} V_{1b} \\ I_{1b} \end{bmatrix}, \quad \begin{bmatrix} V_{2b} \\ -I_{2b} \end{bmatrix} = \begin{bmatrix} V_2 \\ -I_2 \end{bmatrix} .$$

Hence, using the *ABCD* system of equations of the network N_b, we can write

$$\begin{bmatrix} V_{2a} \\ -I_{2a} \end{bmatrix} = \begin{bmatrix} V_{1b} \\ I_{1b} \end{bmatrix} = \begin{bmatrix} A_b & B_b \\ C_b & D_b \end{bmatrix} \begin{bmatrix} V_2 \\ -I_2 \end{bmatrix}.$$

Furthermore, if we write the $ABCD$ system of equations for the network N_a and then substitute from the last equation, we get

$$\begin{bmatrix} V_1 \\ I_1 \end{bmatrix} = \begin{bmatrix} A_a & B_a \\ C_a & D_a \end{bmatrix} \begin{bmatrix} V_{2a} \\ -I_{2a} \end{bmatrix} = \begin{bmatrix} A_a & B_a \\ C_a & D_a \end{bmatrix} \begin{bmatrix} A_b & B_b \\ C_b & D_b \end{bmatrix} \begin{bmatrix} V_2 \\ -I_2 \end{bmatrix}.$$

Thus, *the ABCD-matrix of two-ports in cascade is equal to the product of the ABCD matrices of the individual networks*; that is,

$$\begin{bmatrix} A & B \\ C & D \end{bmatrix} = \begin{bmatrix} A_a & B_a \\ C_a & D_a \end{bmatrix} \begin{bmatrix} A_b & B_b \\ C_b & D_b \end{bmatrix}. \tag{26}$$

Once the relationships between the parameters of the overall two-port and those of the components are known for any one set of parameters, it is merely algebraic computation to get the relationships for any other set; for example, the impedance parameters of the overall two-port can be found in terms of those for each of the two cascaded ones by first expressing the z-parameters in terms of the $ABCD$-parameters for the overall network, then using (26), and finally expressing the $ABCD$-parameters for each network in the cascade in terms of their corresponding z-parameters. The result will be

$$\begin{bmatrix} z_{11} & z_{12} \\ z_{21} & z_{22} \end{bmatrix} = \begin{bmatrix} z_{11a} - \dfrac{z_{12a}z_{21a}}{z_{22a} + z_{11b}} & \dfrac{z_{12a}z_{12b}}{z_{22a} + z_{11b}} \\[4mm] \dfrac{z_{21a}z_{21b}}{z_{22a} + z_{11b}} & z_{22b} - \dfrac{z_{12b}z_{21b}}{z_{22a} + z_{11b}} \end{bmatrix}. \tag{27}$$

The details of this computation are left to you.

A word of caution is necessary. When it is desired to determine some specific parameter of an overall two-port in terms of the parameters of the components in the interconnection, it may be simpler to use a direct analysis, rather than first to find the most natural set of parameters and then use Table 1 to find the desired one. As an example, suppose it is desired to find the expression for z_{21} in Fig. 11. The term z_{21} is the ratio of open-circuit output voltage to input current: $z_{21} = V_2/I_1$. Suppose a current source I_1 is applied; then, with reference to the output terminals of N_a, let the network be replaced by its Thévenin equivalent. The result is shown in Fig. 12. Now, by definition, $z_{21b} = V_2/I_{1b}$ with the output

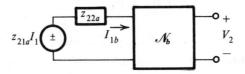

Fig. 12   Replacement of network N_a by its Thévenin equivalent

terminals open. But I_{1b} can easily be found from the network in Fig. 12 to be

$$I_{1b} = \frac{z_{21a}I_1}{z_{22a} + z_{11b}}.$$

Hence,

$$z_{21b} = \frac{V_2}{I_{1b}} = \frac{V_2}{\dfrac{z_{21a}I_1}{z_{22a} + z_{11b}}} = \left(\frac{z_{22a} + z_{11b}}{z_{21a}} \right) \frac{V_2}{I_1}.$$

Finally,

$$z_{21} = \frac{V_2}{I_1} = \frac{z_{21a}z_{21b}}{z_{22a} + z_{11b}},$$

which agrees with (27) but requires less effort to find.

An important feature of cascaded two-ports is observed from the expressions for the transfer impedances in (27). The zeros of z_{21} are the zeros of z_{21a} and z_{21b}. (A similar relationship holds for z_{12}.) Thus the transmission zeros of the overall cascade consist of the transmission zeros of each of the constituent two-ports. This is the basis of some important methods of network synthesis. It permits individual two-ports to be designed to achieve certain transmission zeros before they are connected together. It also permits independent adjustment and tuning of elements within each two-port to achieve a desired null without influencing the adjustment of the other cascaded two-ports.

5.4.2 Parallel and Series Connections

Now let us turn to other interconnections of two-ports, which, unlike the cascade connection, involve both ports. Two possibilities that immediately come to mind are parallel and series connections. *A pair of two-ports is said to be connected in parallel if corresponding (input and output) ports are connected in parallel*, as in Fig. 13(a). In the parallel

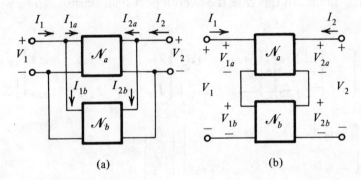

(a)   (b)

Fig. 13 Parallel and series connections of two-ports

connection the input and output voltages of the component two-ports are forced to be the same, whereas the overall port currents equal the sums of the corresponding component port currents. This statement assumes that the port relationships of the individual two-ports are not altered when the connection is made. Conditions to ensure this are discussed subsequently. In this case the overall port relationship can be written as

$$
\begin{bmatrix} I_1 \\ I_2 \end{bmatrix} = \begin{bmatrix} I_{1a} \\ I_{2a} \end{bmatrix} + \begin{bmatrix} I_{1b} \\ I_{2b} \end{bmatrix} = \begin{bmatrix} y_{11a} & y_{12a} \\ y_{21a} & y_{22a} \end{bmatrix} \begin{bmatrix} V_{1a} \\ V_{2a} \end{bmatrix} + \begin{bmatrix} y_{11b} & y_{12b} \\ y_{21b} & y_{22b} \end{bmatrix} \begin{bmatrix} V_{1b} \\ V_{2b} \end{bmatrix}
$$

$$
= \begin{bmatrix} y_{11a} + y_{11b} & y_{12a} + y_{12b} \\ y_{21a} + y_{21b} & y_{22a} + y_{22b} \end{bmatrix} \begin{bmatrix} V_1 \\ V_2 \end{bmatrix}. \tag{28}
$$

That is, *The admittance matrix of two-ports connected in parallel equals the sum of the admittance matrices of the constituent two-ports*:

$$Y = Y_a + Y_b. \tag{29}$$

The dual of the parallel connection is the series connection. *A pair of two-ports is connected in series if corresponding ports (input and output) are connected in series*, as shown in Fig. 13(b). In this connection the input and output port currents are forced to be the same, whereas the overall port voltages equal the sums of the corresponding port voltages of the individual two-ports. Again, it is assumed that the port relationships of the individual two-ports are not altered when the connection is made. In this case the overall port relationship can be written as

$$\begin{bmatrix} V_1 \\ V_2 \end{bmatrix} = \begin{bmatrix} V_{1a} \\ V_{2a} \end{bmatrix} + \begin{bmatrix} V_{1b} \\ V_{2b} \end{bmatrix} = \begin{bmatrix} z_{11a} & z_{12a} \\ z_{21a} & z_{22a} \end{bmatrix} \begin{bmatrix} I_{1a} \\ I_{2a} \end{bmatrix} + \begin{bmatrix} z_{11b} & z_{12b} \\ z_{21b} & z_{22b} \end{bmatrix} \begin{bmatrix} I_{1b} \\ I_{2b} \end{bmatrix}$$

$$= \begin{bmatrix} z_{11a} + z_{11b} & z_{12a} + z_{12b} \\ z_{21a} + z_{21b} & z_{22a} + z_{22b} \end{bmatrix} \begin{bmatrix} I_1 \\ I_2 \end{bmatrix}. \tag{30}$$

That is, *the impedance matrix of two-ports connected in series equals the sum of the impedance matrices of the constituent two-ports*:

$$Z = Z_a + Z_b. \tag{31}$$

Of these two — parallel and series connections — the parallel connection is more useful and finds wider application in synthesis. One reason for this is the practical one that permits two common-terminal (grounded) two-ports to be connected in parallel, the result being a common-terminal two-port. An example of this is the *parallel-ladders network* (of which the twin-tee null network is a special case) shown in Fig. 14.

On the other hand, the series connection of two common-terminal two-ports is not a common-terminal two-port unless one of them is a tee network. Consider two grounded two-ports connected in series, as in Fig. 15(a). It is clear that this is inadmissible, since the ground terminal of n_a will short out parts of n_b, thus violating the condition that the individual two-ports be unaltered by the interconnection. The situation is

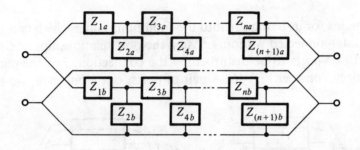

Fig. 14   Parallel-ladders network

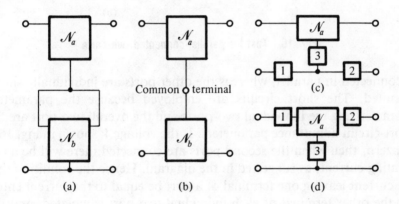

Fig. 15   Series connection of common-terminal two-ports

remedied by making the common terminals of both two-ports common to each other, as in Fig. 15(b). In this case the resulting two-port is not a common-terminal one. If one of the component two-ports is a tee, the series connection takes the form shown in Fig. 15(c). This can be trivially retructured, as in Fig. 15(d), as a common-terminal two-port. That the last two networks have the same $\mathbf{Z}$ matrix is left for you to demonstrate.

Variations of the series and parallel types of interconnections are possible by connecting the ports in series at one end and in parallel at the other. These are referred to as the *series-parallel* and *parallel-series* connections. As one might surmise, it is the *h*- and *g*-matrices of the individual two-ports that are added to give the overall *h*- and *g*-matrices, respectively. This also is left as an exercise. (See Prob. 4.)

5.4.3   Permissibility of Interconnection

It remains for us to inquire into the conditions under which two-ports can be interconnected without causing the port relationships of the individual two-ports to be disturbed by the connection. For the parallel connection, consider Fig. 16. A pair of ports, one from each two-port,

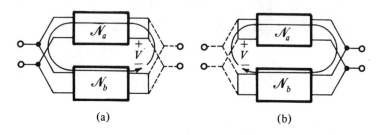

(a)   (b)

Fig. 16   Test for parallel-connected two-ports

is connected in parallel, whereas the other ports are individually short-circuited. The short circuits are employed because the parameters characterizing the individual two-ports and the overall two-port are the short-circuit admittance parameters. If the voltage V shown in Fig. 16 is nonzero, then when the second ports are connected there will be a circulating current, as suggested in the diagram. Hence the condition that the current leaving one terminal of a port be equal to the current entering the other terminal of each individual two-port is violated, and the port relationships of the individual two-ports are altered.

For the case of the series connection, consider Fig. 17. A pair of ports, one from each two-port, is connected in series, whereas the other ports are left open. The open circuits are employed because the

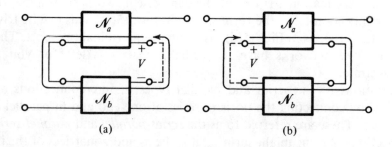

(a)   (b)

Fig. 17   Test for series-connected two-ports

parameters characterizing the individual two-ports and the overall two-port are the open-circuit impedance parameters. If the voltage V is nonzero, then when the second ports are connected in series there will be a circulating current, as suggested in the diagram. Again, the port relationships of the individual two-ports will be modified by the connection, and hence the addition of impedance matrices will not be valid.

Obvious modifications of these tests apply to the series-parallel and parallel-series connections. The preceding discussion of the conditions under which the overall parameters for interconnected two-ports can be obtained by adding the component two-port parameters has been in rather skeletal form. We leave to you the task of supplying details.

When it is discovered that a particular interconnection cannot be made because circulating currents will be introduced, there is a way of stopping such currents and thus permitting the connection to be made. The approach is simply to put an isolating ideal transformer of 1:1 turns ratio at one of the ports, as illustrated in Fig. 18 for the case of the parallel connection.

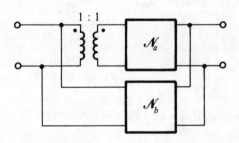

Fig. 18   Isolating transformer to permit interconnection

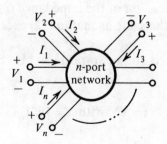

Fig. 19   Multiport network

5.5 MULTIPORT NETWORKS

The preceding section has dealt with two-port networks in considerable detail. Let us now turn our attention to networks having more
than two ports. The ideas discussed in the last section apply also to
multiports with obvious extensions.

Consider the n-port network shown in Fig. 19. The external behavior
of this network is completely described by giving the relationships
among the port voltages and currents. One such relationship expresses
all the port voltages in terms of the port currents. Thus,

$$
\begin{bmatrix} V_1 \\ V_2 \\ \vdots \\ V_n \end{bmatrix} = \begin{bmatrix} z_{11} & z_{12} & \cdots & z_{1n} \\ z_{21} & z_{22} & \cdots & z_{2n} \\ \vdots & \vdots & & \vdots \\ z_{n1} & z_{n2} & \cdots & z_{nn} \end{bmatrix} \begin{bmatrix} I_1 \\ I_2 \\ \vdots \\ I_n \end{bmatrix}, \tag{32a}
$$

or

$$
\mathbf{V} = \mathbf{Z}\mathbf{I}. \tag{32b}
$$

By direct observation, it is seen that the elements of $\mathbf{Z}$ can be interpreted
as

$$
z_{jk} = \frac{V_j}{I_k} \bigg|_{\substack{\text{all other} \\ \text{currents} = 0}}, \tag{33}
$$

which is simply the extension of the impedance representation of a two-
port. The matrix $\mathbf{Z}$ is the same as that in (12) except that it is of order n
rather than 2.

The admittance matrix for a two-port can also be directly extended to
an n-port. Thus,

$$
\mathbf{I} = \mathbf{Y}\mathbf{V} \quad \text{with} \quad \mathbf{Y} = [y_{jk}], \tag{34}
$$

where

$$
y_{jk} = \frac{I_j}{V_k} \bigg|_{\substack{\text{all other} \\ \text{voltages} = 0}}. \tag{35}
$$

If we now think of extending the hybrid representations of a two-port, we encounter some problems. In a hybrid representation the variables are mixed voltage and current. For a network of more than two ports, how are the "independent and "dependent" variables to be chosen? In a three-port network, for example, the following three choices can be made:

$$
\begin{bmatrix} V_1 \\ V_2 \\ I_3 \end{bmatrix} = \mathbf{M}_1 \begin{bmatrix} I_1 \\ I_2 \\ V_3 \end{bmatrix}, \quad \begin{bmatrix} V_1 \\ I_2 \\ V_3 \end{bmatrix} = \mathbf{M}_2 \begin{bmatrix} I_1 \\ V_2 \\ I_3 \end{bmatrix}, \quad \begin{bmatrix} I_1 \\ V_2 \\ I_3 \end{bmatrix} = \dot{\mathbf{M}}_3 \begin{bmatrix} V_1 \\ I_2 \\ I_3 \end{bmatrix},
$$

as well as their inverses. In these choices each vector contains exactly one variable from each port. It would also be possible to make such selections as

$$
\begin{bmatrix} V_1 \\ V_2 \\ I_2 \end{bmatrix} = \mathbf{M}_4 \begin{bmatrix} I_1 \\ I_3 \\ V_3 \end{bmatrix},
$$

where each vector contains both the current and voltage of one particular port. The former category is like the hybrid h and hybrid g representations of a two-port. The latter has some of the features of the chain-matrix representation. It is clearly not very productive to pursue this topic of possible representations in the general case.

Just as in the case of two-ports, it is possible to interconnect multiports. Two multiports are said to be connected in parallel if their ports are connected in parallel in pairs. It is not necessary for the two multiports to have the same number of ports. The ports are connected in parallel in pairs until we run out of ports. It does not matter whether we run out for both networks at the same time or earlier for one network. Similarly, two multiports are said to be connected in series if their ports are connected in series in pairs. Again, the two multiports need not have the same number of ports.

As in the case of two-ports, the overall y-matrix for two n-ports connected in parallel equals the sum of the y-matrices of the individual

n-ports. Similarly, the overall z-matrix of two n-ports connected in series equals the sum of the z-matrices of the individual n-ports. This assumes, of course, that the interconnection does not alter the parameters of the individual n-ports. A question for you to consider is: What are the overall y- and z-matrices, when the networks have a different number of ports? (See Prob. 6.)

5.6 THE INDEFINITE ADMITTANCE MATRIX

The port description of networks is useful when external connections are to be made to the network terminals taken in pairs. However, the terminals of a network need not be paired into ports. In such a case it would be useful to have a description of the external behavior as a multiterminal network rather than as a multiport network. In this section we shall introduce such a description.

Let us return to Fig. 6. The six-terminal network shown there is viewed as a common-terminal five-port by defining the voltages of five of the terminals with reference to the voltage of the sixth one as a datum. For any such common-terminal multiport, suppose instead that the datum for voltage is taken as an arbitrary point external to the network, as shown for an n-terminal network in Fig. 20. We assume that the network is connected, implying that none of the terminals is isolated from the rest of the network.

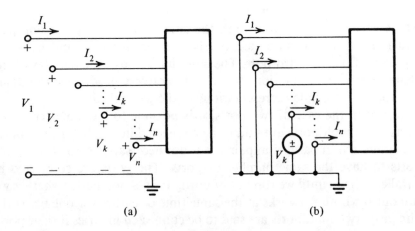

(a)   (b)

Fig. 20   Definition of terminal variables

The currents are not port currents but terminal currents. Clearly, they satisfy Kirchhoff's current law, so that

$$\sum_{k=1}^{n} I_k(s) = 0.$$

Since the network is linear, currents can be expressed as a linear combination of the terminal voltages to yield

$$
\begin{bmatrix} I_1 \\ I_2 \\ \vdots \\ I_n \end{bmatrix}
=
\begin{bmatrix}
y_{11} & y_{12} & \cdots & y_{1n} \\
y_{21} & y_{22} & \cdots & y_{2n} \\
\vdots & \vdots & & \vdots \\
y_{n1} & y_{n2} & \cdots & y_{nn}
\end{bmatrix}
\begin{bmatrix} V_1 \\ V_2 \\ \vdots \\ V_n \end{bmatrix}.
\tag{36}
$$

The elements of the coefficient matrix of this equation are, dimensionally, admittance. They are, in fact, short-circuit admittances. Figure 20(b) shows all terminals but one grounded to the arbitrary datum; to the kth terminal is connected a voltage source. Each of the terminal currents can now be found. It follows immediately that the elements of the matrix are

$$
y_{jk} = \frac{I_j}{V_k} \bigg|_{\substack{\text{all other terminals} \\ \text{grounded to datum}}}.
\tag{37}
$$

They are almost like the y-parameters of a multiport. We shall examine the relationship below.

The coefficient matrix in (36) is called the *indefinite admittance matrix* and is designated $\mathbf{Y}_i$. A number of the properties of this matrix will now be established.

First, suppose the scalar equations represented by the matrix equation (36) are all added. By Kirchhoff's current law that sum must be zero, as the sum of the currents is zero. Hence, the sum of the right sides will be

$$
(y_{11} + y_{21} + \ldots + y_{n1})V_1 + (y_{12} + y_{22} + \ldots + y_{n2})V_2 + \ldots
$$
$$
+ (y_{1n} + y_{2n} + \ldots + y_{nn})V_n = 0.
$$

Note that the quantity within each pair of parentheses is the sum of the elements in a column of $\mathbf{Y}_i$. Now the terminal voltages are all independent. Suppose all terminals but one, say the kth one, are short-circuited. This expression then reduces to

$$(y_{1k} + y_{2k} + \ldots + y_{nk})V_k = 0.$$

Since $V_k \neq 0$, this means the sum of elements in each column of the indefinite admittance matrix equals zero. Thus the rows are not all independent and $\mathbf{Y}_i$ is a singular matrix.

What is true of the rows is also true of the columns. This can be shown as follows. Suppose all terminals are left open but the kth, and to the kth terminal is applied a voltage source V_k. Assuming, as we did, that none of the terminals is isolated, the voltages of all other terminals will also equal V_k. All terminal currents will be zero—all but I_k, obviously, because the terminals are open, and I_k because of Kirchhoff's current law. With all the voltages equal in (36), the jth current can be written as

$$I_j = (y_{j1} + y_{j2} + \ldots + y_{jn})V_k = 0.$$

Since $V_k \neq 0$, the sum of elements in each row of $\mathbf{Y}_i$ equals zero. Hence, the columns are not all independent.

5.6.1 Conversions to Common-Terminal Multiports

To make a common-terminal n-port out of a network with $n + 1$ terminals is simple once the indefinite admittance matrix is known. If the terminal that is to be common to the n-ports, say terminal $n + 1$, is taken as the arbitrary datum, its voltage will be zero. Hence the last column of $\mathbf{Y}_i$ in (36) can be removed, since its elements are the coefficients of this zero voltage. Also, the current at this terminal is redundant, by Kirchhoff's current law, and hence the last row of $\mathbf{Y}_i$ can also be removed. Thus, to make one of terminals of a network the common terminal of a grounded n-port, simply delete the row and column of the indefinite admittance matrix corresponding to that terminal.

The converse operation permits the formation of the indefinite admittance matrix from the admittance matrix of a grounded n-port. First, given the admittance matrix of a common-terminal n-port, add to the matrix another row, each of whose elements is the negative sum of all elements in the corresponding column. Then add another column, each of whose elements is the negative of the sum of all elements in the corresponding row.

Let us illustrate this process with the common-terminal two-port shown in Fig. 21(a). The port voltages that would normally be labeled V_1 and V_2 are labeled V_{ac} and V_{bc} to emphasize the two terminals of each port. In Fig. 21(b) the voltage datum is taken as a point other than one

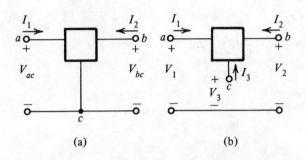

(a)   (b)

Fig. 21   Grounded two-port represented as three-terminal network

of the terminals. Let us first write the two-port admittance equations and then replace V_{ac} by $V_1 - V_3$ and V_{bc} by $V_2 - V_3$; thus,

$$I_1 = y_{11}V_{ac} + y_{12}V_{bc} = y_{11}(V_1 - V_3) + y_{12}(V_2 - V_3),$$
$$I_2 = y_{21}V_{ac} + y_{22}V_{bc} = y_{21}(V_1 - V_3) + y_{22}(V_2 - V_3).$$

By Kirchhoff's current law, I_3 in Fig. 21(b) equals $-(I_1 + I_2)$. When this equation is added to the previous two the result becomes

$$I_1 = y_{11}V_1 + y_{12}V_2 - (y_{11} + y_{12})V_3,$$
$$I_2 = y_{21}V_1 + y_{22}V_2 - (y_{21} + y_{22})V_3,$$
$$I_3 = -(y_{11} + y_{21})V_1 - (y_{12} + y_{22})V_2 + (y_{11} + y_{12} + y_{21} + y_{22})V_3.$$

The coefficient matrix of these equations is $\mathbf{Y}_i$. Notice how it could have been formed immediately from the original $\mathbf{Y}$ matrix by the process of adding a row and column, using the zero-sum property of rows and columns.

The preceding discussion provides a method for taking the $\mathbf{Y}$ matrix of a common-terminal multiport with a specific terminal as the common one and from it easily writing the $\mathbf{Y}$ matrix of the common-terminal multiport with any other terminal taken as the common terminal. This is especially useful in obtaining, say the common-base representation of a transistor from the common-emitter representation.

To illustrate the approach, consider the transistor and transistor model shown in Fig. 22. The impedance matrix of this transistor as a common-base two-port is easily shown to be

$$
\mathbf{Z}_b = \begin{bmatrix} r_b + r_e & r_b \\ r_b + \alpha r_c & r_b + r_c \end{bmatrix} \begin{matrix} e \\ c \end{matrix} \Rightarrow \quad \mathbf{Y}_b = \frac{1}{\Delta} \begin{bmatrix} r_b + r_c & -r_b \\ -r_b - \alpha r_c & r_b + r_e \end{bmatrix} \begin{matrix} e \\ c \end{matrix} \quad ,
$$

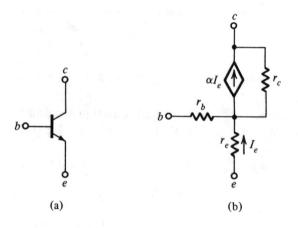

(a)   (b)

Fig. 22   Transistor with model

with $\Delta = r_b r_e + r_e r_c + (1 - \alpha) r_b r_c$. The admittance matrix is obtained by inversion of $\mathbf{Z}_b$. (The letters at the top and the right identify the columns and the rows with specific terminals.) From this the indefinite admittance matrix is immediately written as

$$
\mathbf{Y}_i = \frac{1}{\Delta} \begin{bmatrix} r_b + r_c & -r_b & -r_c \\ -r_b - \alpha r_c & r_b + r_e & -r_e + \alpha r_c \\ -(1 - \alpha) r_c & -r_e & r_e + (1 - \alpha) r_c \end{bmatrix} \begin{matrix} e \\ c \\ b \end{matrix} \quad .
$$

Now, to find the admittance matrix of the grounded-emitter configuration, all that is necessary is to delete the row and column corresponding to the emitter terminal, which is the first one. Of course, it should be ensured that the order of the remaining rows and columns correspond to the desired order of input and output—in this case base and collector. This requires an interchange of rows and columns. Thus,

$$
\mathbf{Y}_{sc\ e} = \frac{1}{\Delta}
\begin{array}{cc}
\quad b & \quad c \\
\left[
\begin{array}{cc}
r_e + (1 - \alpha)r_c & -r_e \\[1em]
-r_e + \alpha r_c & r_b + r_e
\end{array}
\right]
&
\begin{array}{c}
b \\[1em]
c
\end{array}
\end{array}.
$$

Once the indefinite admittance matrix of a multiterminal network is at hand, the results of further manipulations on the network easily show up as changes in the $\mathbf{Y}_i$ matrix. Some of these will now be discussed.

5.6.2 Connecting Two Terminals Together

Suppose two terminals of an n-terminal network are connected together into a single external terminal. The two external currents are replaced by one, equal to the sum of the original two. The two voltages are now identical. Hence the $\mathbf{Y}_i$ matrix of the resulting $(n-1)$ terminal network is obtained by adding the two corresponding rows and the two corresponding columns of the original $\mathbf{Y}_i$ matrix. These sums replace the original two rows and the original columns, respectively. The extension to more than two terminals is obvious.

5.6.3 Suppressing Terminals

Suppose one of the terminals is to be made an internal terminal to which external connections are not to be made. This procedure is called *suppressing a terminal*. The current at that terminal, say the nth one, will be zero. The equation for $I_n = 0$ can be solved for V_n (assuming $y_{nn} \neq 0$) and the result substituted into the remaining equations. This will eliminate V_n and will leave $n - 1$ equations in $n - 1$ voltages.

This process can be extended in matrix form to more than one terminal in the following manner. With $\mathbf{I} = \mathbf{Y}_i \mathbf{V}$, partition the matrices as

$$
\left[
\begin{array}{c}
\mathbf{I}_a \\[1em]
\mathbf{I}_b
\end{array}
\right]
=
\left[
\begin{array}{cc}
\mathbf{Y}_{11} & \mathbf{Y}_{12} \\[1em]
\mathbf{Y}_{21} & \mathbf{Y}_{22}
\end{array}
\right]
\left[
\begin{array}{c}
\mathbf{V}_a \\[1em]
\mathbf{V}_b
\end{array}
\right],
$$

or

$$\mathbf{I}_a = \mathbf{Y}_{11}\mathbf{V}_a + \mathbf{Y}_{12}\mathbf{V}_b,$$
$$\mathbf{I}_b = \mathbf{Y}_{21}\mathbf{V}_a + \mathbf{Y}_{22}\mathbf{V}_b, \tag{38}$$

where $\mathbf{I}_b$ and $\mathbf{V}_b$ correspond to the terminals that are to be suppressed; that is, vector $\mathbf{I}_b = \mathbf{0}$. From the second equation solve for $\mathbf{V}_b$ and substitute into the first equation. The result will be

$$\mathbf{V}_b = - \mathbf{Y}_{22}^{-1}\mathbf{Y}_{21}\mathbf{V}_a,$$
$$\mathbf{I}_a = (\mathbf{Y}_{11} - \mathbf{Y}_{12}\mathbf{Y}_{22}^{-1}\mathbf{Y}_{21})\mathbf{V}_a. \tag{39}$$

The new indefinite admittance matrix is

$$\mathbf{Y}_{i(new)} = \mathbf{Y}_{11} - \mathbf{Y}_{12}\mathbf{Y}_{22}^{-1}\mathbf{Y}_{21}. \tag{40}$$

The existence of the new indefinite admittance matrix depends on the nonsingularity of $\mathbf{Y}_{22}$. But this is similar to the requirement $y_{nn} \neq 0$ in the scalar case considered previously.

5.6.4 Networks in Parallel

The indefinite admittance matrix of two networks connected in parallel equals the sum of the $\mathbf{Y}_i$ matrices of each. By "connected in parallel" we mean that each terminal of one network is connected to a terminal of the other and both have a common datum for voltage. It is not necessary that the two networks have the same number of terminals. If they do not, then the $\mathbf{Y}_i$ matrix of the network having the fewer terminals is augmented by rows and columns of zeros. In particular, a simple two-terminal branch connected across two terminals of a multi-terminal network can be considered to be connected in parallel with it. Note that the indefinite admittance matrix of a branch having admittance Y is

$$\mathbf{Y}_i \text{ (of a single branch)} = \begin{bmatrix} Y & -Y \\ -Y & Y \end{bmatrix}.$$

The appropriate row/column subscripts to be used correspond to the terminals of the multiterminal network to which this branch is to be connected.

5.6.5 Cofactors of the Determinant of Y_i

A very interesting property of the determinant of the indefinite admittance matrix results from the fact that the sum of the elements in each row or column equals zero. Suppose det Y_i is expanded along the jth row. The result would be

$$\det \mathbf{Y}_i = y_{j1}\Delta_{j1} + y_{j2}\Delta_{j2} + \ldots + y_{jn}\Delta_{jn},$$

where Δ_{jk} is the (j,k)th cofactor of det $\mathbf{Y}_i$. Because the elements of the jth row sum to zero, we can write one of the elements as the negative sum of all the others. Thus,

$$y_{j1} = -(y_{j2} + y_{j3} + \ldots + y_{jn}).$$

When this is inserted into the preceding equation and terms are collected, the result becomes

$$\det \mathbf{Y}_i = y_{j2}(\Delta_{j2} - \Delta_{j1}) + y_{j3}(\Delta_{j3} - \Delta_{j1}) + \ldots + y_{jn}(\Delta_{jn} - \Delta_{j1}) = 0.$$

The determinant equals zero because $\mathbf{Y}_i$ is singular. Furthermore, it is zero no matter what the values of the elements y_{jk} might be. Hence the last equations can be satisfied only if each of the parenthetical terms is zero; that is,

$$\Delta_{jk} = \Delta_{j1}.$$

This means all cofactors of elements of any row are equal.

The same procedure, starting with an expansion of det $\mathbf{Y}_i$ along a column, will yield a similar result concerning the equality of cofactors of elements of any column. Since each row and column has a common element, the cofactor of this element equals all cofactors of that row and column. The conclusion is that *all (first) cofactors of the indefinite admittance matrix are equal*. This property has led to the name *equicofactor* matrix for $\mathbf{Y}_i$.

5.6.6 Example

Let us now illustrate with an example how the indefinite admittance matrix can be used for certain network calculations. Consider the common terminal two-port network shown in Fig. 23(a). It is desired to find the admittance matrix of this network. We shall do this by (1) finding the indefinite admittance matrix of the four-terminal network in Fig. 23(b), (2) adding to it that of the single branch, (3) suppressing terminal 3, and finally (4) making terminal 4 the datum.

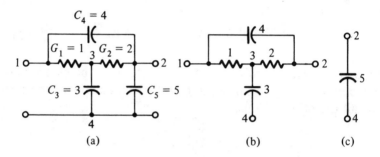

Fig. 23   Finding short-circuit admittances by using $\mathbf{Y}_i$

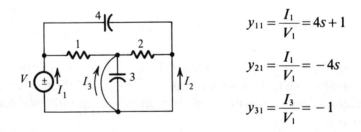

$$y_{11} = \frac{I_1}{V_1} = 4s + 1$$

$$y_{21} = \frac{I_1}{V_1} = -4s$$

$$y_{31} = \frac{I_3}{V_1} = -1$$

Fig. 24   Calculating $\mathbf{Y}$ for the three-port

To find $\mathbf{Y}_i$ in Fig. 23(b), we shall first treat that network as a common-terminal three-port with terminal 4 as datum. The y-parameters of this three-port can be found from the definitions; for example, apply a voltage to the left-hand port and short-circuit the other two, as in Fig. 24. Three of the y-parameters are easily found from the diagram and are shown there. The remaining y's are found in a similar way, with the result

$$Y = \begin{bmatrix} 4s + 1 & -4s & -1 \\ -4s & 4s + 2 & -2 \\ -1 & -2 & 3s + 3 \end{bmatrix}.$$

The indefinite admittance matrix is easily found by adding a row and a column whose elements are determined by the zero-sum property of rows and columns. To this is added the $\mathbf{Y}_i$ matrix of branch 5. Since it is connected between terminals 2 and 4, its nonzero elements appear in those two rows and columns. The overall $\mathbf{Y}_i$ matrix is

$$\mathbf{Y}_i = \begin{bmatrix} 4s + 1 & -4s & -1 & 0 \\ -4s & 4s + 2 & -2 & 0 \\ -1 & -2 & 3s + 3 & -3s \\ 0 & 0 & -3s & 3s \end{bmatrix} + \begin{bmatrix} 0 & 0 & 0 & 0 \\ 0 & 5s & 0 & -5s \\ 0 & 0 & 0 & 0 \\ 0 & -5s & 0 & 5s \end{bmatrix}$$

$$= \begin{bmatrix} 4s + 1 & -4s & -1 & 0 \\ -4s & 9s + 2 & -2 & -5s \\ -1 & -2 & 3s + 3 & -3s \\ 0 & -5s & -3s & 8s \end{bmatrix}.$$

The next step is to suppress terminal 3. For this purpose we interchange rows and columns 3 and 4 in order to make 3 the last one. Then we partition, in order to identify the submatrices in (38), as follows:

$$\mathbf{Y}_i = \left[\begin{array}{ccc|c} 4s + 1 & -4s & 0 & -1 \\ -4s & 9s + 2 & -5s & -2 \\ 0 & -5s & 8s & -3s \\ \hline -1 & -2 & -3s & 3s + 3 \end{array} \right] = \begin{bmatrix} \mathbf{Y}_{11} & \mathbf{Y}_{12} \\ \mathbf{Y}_{21} & \mathbf{Y}_{22} \end{bmatrix}$$

Then

$$
\mathbf{Y}_{12}\,\mathbf{Y}_{22}^{-1}\,\mathbf{Y}_{21} = \begin{bmatrix} -1 \\ -2 \\ -3s \end{bmatrix} [\frac{1}{3s+3}]\,[-1 \quad -2 \quad -3s] = \frac{1}{3s+1} \begin{bmatrix} 1 & 2 & 3s \\ 2 & 4 & 6s \\ 3s & 6s & 9s^2 \end{bmatrix}
$$

The new indefinite admittance matrix with terminal 3 suppressed, using (40), is

$$
\mathbf{Y}_{i\ new} = \begin{bmatrix} 4s+1 & -4s & 0 \\ -4s & 9s+2 & -5s \\ 0 & -5s & 8s \end{bmatrix} - \frac{1}{3s+3} \begin{bmatrix} 1 & 2 & 3s \\ 2 & 4 & 6s \\ 3s & 6s & 9s^2 \end{bmatrix}
$$

$$
= \begin{bmatrix} 4s+1-\dfrac{1}{3s+3} & -(4s+\dfrac{2}{3s+3}) & \dfrac{-3s}{3s+3} \\[3mm] -(4s+\dfrac{2}{3s+3}) & 9s+2-\dfrac{4}{3s+3} & -(5s+\dfrac{6s}{3s+3}) \\[3mm] \dfrac{-3}{3s+3} & -(5s+\dfrac{6s}{3s+3}) & 8s-\dfrac{9s^2}{3s+3} \end{bmatrix} .
$$

Finally, terminal 4 is made the common terminal by deleting the last row and column. The desired y-matrix of the two-port is

$$
\mathbf{Y}_{sc} = \begin{bmatrix} 4s+1-\dfrac{1}{3s+3} & -(4s+\dfrac{2}{3s+3}) \\[3mm] -(4s+\dfrac{2}{3s+3}) & 9s+2-\dfrac{4}{3s+3} \end{bmatrix} .
$$

It may appear that a conventional approach would have required less work. It is true that more steps are involved here, but each step is almost trivial; many of them are simply written by inspection. Also, the last row and column of $\mathbf{Y}_{i(new)}$ need not be calculated since it will be deleted subsequently; it is done here only for completeness.

$$z_{11} = \frac{Z_a Z_b \left(n^2 + 1 \big| n^2 \right)}{Z_a + Z_b \left(n^2 + 1/n^2 \right)}$$

$$z_{12} = z_{21} = \frac{Z_a Z_b \left(1/n \right)}{Z_a + Z_b \left(n^2 + 1/n^2 \right)}$$

$$z_{22} = \frac{Z_a + Z_b n^2 \left(Z_a + Z_b \right)}{Z_b \left(n^2 + 1 \right) + Z_a n^2}$$

series — parallel

parallel — series

$H = H_a + H_b$

inverse.

$$\begin{array}{cc} A\ B \\ C\ D \end{array} = \begin{array}{cc} 1\ z \\ 0\ 1 \end{array}$$

$$\begin{array}{cc} A\ B \\ C\ D \end{array} = \begin{array}{cc} 1\ 0 \\ y\ 1 \end{array}$$

$$Y_i = Y_{rr} - Y_{rs}\, Y_{ss}^{-1}\, Y_{sr}$$

$$Y_{un} = \frac{1}{Z_{11}}$$

$$Z = Z_{22}$$

$$Y = Y_{11}$$

$$Z = \frac{1}{Y_{11}}$$

$$\begin{bmatrix} 1 & 0 \\ \frac{1}{sL} & 1 \end{bmatrix}$$

$$\begin{bmatrix} -1 & 0 \\ -\frac{1}{sL} & -1 \end{bmatrix}$$

$$\begin{array}{c|c} rr & rs \\ \hline sr & ss \end{array}$$

$$\begin{bmatrix} 1+n & 0 \\ 0 & \frac{1}{1+n} \end{bmatrix}$$

$$\frac{L_{22}}{L_{22} - L_{12}}$$

$$B =$$

$$\frac{1}{s(L_{22} - L_{12})}$$

$$C =$$

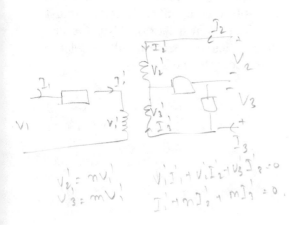

$$V_2' = nV_1'$$
$$V_3' = mV_1'$$

$$V_1'I_1' + V_1'I_2 + V_3'I_3' = 0$$
$$I_1' + nI_2' + mI_3' = 0.$$

$$Y_{11} = 1/Z_{11} \qquad Y_{12} = Y_{21} = \frac{1}{(m \cdot n)Z_1}$$

$$Y_{13} = Y_{31} = \frac{1}{(n \cdot m)Z_1}$$

$$Y_{22} = \frac{Z_1 m^2 + Z_2}{Z_1 Z_2 (n \cdot m)^2}$$

$$Y_{23} = Y_{32} = -\frac{Z_2 + nmZ_1}{Z_1 Z_2 (n \cdot m)^2}$$

$$Y_{33} = \frac{1}{Z_3} \cdot \frac{Z_2 + n^2 Z_1}{Z_1 Z_2 (n \cdot m)^2}$$

CHAPTER 6
Scattering Parameters

The properties and behavior of multiport networks can be described in terms of *impedance*, *admittance*, or *hybrid matrices*, as discussed in Chapter 5. These matrices are defined in terms of open-circuit port voltages and/or short-circuit port currents. In actuality a multiport may not be operating under open- or short-circuit conditions at any of its ports. Nevertheless, such open- and short-circuit parameters can be used to describe adequately the operation of a multiport under any terminating condition. Of course, some networks may not have a z-matrix representation, some may not have a y-matrix representation, and some (such as an ideal transformer) may have neither.

It would be of value to have another representation of a multiport network, one that described network operation with port-loading conditions other than open- or short-circuit. If a set of parameters is defined with some finite loading at each port, this set should be more convenient to use when describing transmission (of power) from a physical generator (with internal impedance) at one port to some loads at the other ports. The scattering parameters are such a set.

Scattering parameters originated in the theory of transmission lines. They are of particular value in microwave network theory where the concept of power is much more important than the concepts of voltage and current; in fact, the latter become somewhat artificial. Scattering parameters should be defined in such a way, then, that the quantities of interest in power transmission take on very simple expressions.

In the development here we shall freely use concepts and labels such as incidence and reflection from transmission-line theory, purely for motivational purposes. The resulting mathematical expressions, however, do not depend for their validity on such interpretation. We shall start by treating the simpler one-port network before graduating to two-ports and multiports.

6.1 THE SCATTERING RELATIONS OF A ONE-PORT

We begin by considering the situation shown in Fig. 1. A one-port network is shown terminating a voltage source in series with an impedance $z(s)$, which can be considered as the Thévenin equivalent of another network, a source network, to which Z is connected as a load. The lower case letter z stands for the *source impedance*. If it is real, the situation will be as shown in Fig. 1(b). The one-port will absorb power from the source network. Optimal matching will occur when $Z(s) = z(-s)$, in which case maximum power is transferred. [When $s = j\omega$, $z(-s)$ becomes $z(-j\omega) = z(\overline{j\omega}) = \overline{z}(j\omega)$. Thus $Z(s) = z(-s)$ reduces to $Z(j\omega) = \overline{z}(j\omega)$, which is the usual form for maximum power transfer.]

When z is real (equal to r), matching will occur when $Z = r$. Using the terminology of wave propagation, we say that if the one-port is matched to the source (network), there will be no reflection at the terminals.

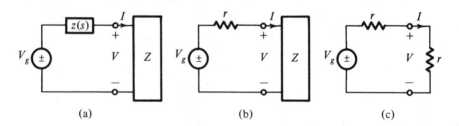

(a)   (b)   (c)

Fig. 1   A one-port network terminating a second one represented by its Thévenin equivalent

Under unmatched conditions the voltage transform V at the terminals is pictured as having contributions from the "incident wave" arriving from the left and the "reflected wave" coming back from the one-port. A similar case obtains for the current transform I. Thus we can write

$$V = V_i + V_r, \qquad\qquad I = I_i - I_r, \qquad (1)$$

where the subscripts i and r refer to "incident" and "reflected," respectively. The negative sign in the second equation is a result of the reference chosen for the reflected current, namely, opposite to that of I and I_i. Suppose we think of a real quantity r as the "characteristic impedance" of the transmission system to the left of the one-port terminals. Then the incident and reflected quantities are related by

$$\frac{V_i}{I_i} = \frac{V_r}{I_r} = r, \tag{2}$$

which are well-known relations for a transmission line. By using this result, (1) can be inverted to give

$$V_i = \tfrac{1}{2}(V + rI), \qquad\qquad I_i = \tfrac{1}{2}(gV + I), \tag{3a}$$

$$V_r = \tfrac{1}{2}(V - rI), \qquad\qquad I_r = \tfrac{1}{2}(gV - I), \tag{3b}$$

where $g = 1/r$.

It is now possible to define a *voltage reflection coefficient* ϱ as the ratio between reflected and incident voltage transforms, and a *current reflection coefficient* as the ratio between reflected and incident current transforms. Thus, using (3) for the incident and reflected variables, we get

$$\varrho = \frac{V_r}{V_i} = \frac{V - rI}{V + rI} = \frac{Z - r}{Z + r} = \frac{Z/r - 1}{Z/r + 1} = \frac{gZ - 1}{gZ + 1} = \frac{gV - I}{gV + I} = \frac{I_r}{I_i}. \tag{4}$$

Some of the steps in this sequence used $V = ZI$.

Just as the impedance Z can characterize the behavior of the one-port network, so also the reflection coefficient can characterize it completely. There is a one-to-one correspondence between Z and ϱ given by the bilinear transformation $\varrho = (Z - r)(Z + r)^{-1}$. We observe that the current and voltage reflection coefficients are the same. It must be emphasized, however, that this is true only for the case under consideration; namely, a real source impedance. In the general case the two reflection coefficients are different.

The wave-propagation concepts that were used in the preceding discussion are artificial in the case of lumped networks. Nevertheless, it is possible to regard (3) as formal definitions of the variables V_i, V_r and I_i, I_r without attaching any interpretive significance to these quantities that reflect their intuitive origin. In the development we used r as the characteristic impedance. However, this idea is not necessary in the definitions expressed by (3) or (4); r is simply an arbitrary real positive number that has the dimensions of impedance.

It is, in fact, possible to introduce the incident and reflected voltages in an alternative way. Consider again the one-port in Fig. 1; it is characterized by the two variables V and I. Instead of these, a linear combination of these variables can be used as an equally adequate set. Thus the transformation

$$V_i = a_{11} V + a_{12} I,$$
$$V_r = a_{21} V + a_{22} I \tag{5}$$

defines two new variables V_i and V_r in terms of the old ones, V and I. The coefficients of the transformation should be chosen in such a way that the new variables become convenient to use. The choice $a_{11} = a_{21} = \frac{1}{2}$ and $a_{12} = -a_{22} = r/2$ will make (5) reduce to (3). Other choices could lead to additional formulations, which may or may not be useful for different applications.

It is possible to interpret the incident and reflected variables by reference to the situation shown in Fig. 1(c), in which the one-port is matched to the real source impedance. In this case $V = rI$. Hence, from (3a) we find that

$$V_i = V \text{ and } I_i = I \text{ when matched.} \tag{6}$$

This tells us that when the one-port is matched to its terminations, the voltage at the port is V_i and the current is I_i. Furthermore, under matched conditions, (3b) tells us that $V_r = 0$ and $I_r = 0$; and from Fig. 1(c) we observe that

$$V_i = \frac{1}{2} V_g. \tag{7}$$

From (4) we see that, under matched conditions, the reflection coefficient is zero.

When the one-port is not matched, V_r and ϱ are not zero. In fact, (1) can be written as

$$V_r = V - V_i, \tag{8a}$$

$$I_r = I_i - I; \tag{8b}$$

that is, the reflected voltage V_r is a measure of the deviation of the one-port voltage under actual operation, from its value when matched. Similarly, I_r is a measure of the deviation of the current under actual operation, from its value when matched. Note the slight asymmetry, in that one deviation is positive and the other negative.

6.1.1 Normalized Variables

The preceding discussion has been carried out by using two pairs of variables: the incident and reflected voltages, and the incident and reflected currents. Since these quantities are proportional in pairs, from (2), it should be sufficient to talk about one incident variable and one reflected variable. However, rather than select either the voltage or current, we use normalized variables related to both.

The *normalized* incident and reflected variables are defined as follows:

$$a(s) = \sqrt{r} I_i(s) = \frac{V_i(s)}{\sqrt{r}}, \tag{9a}$$

$$b(s) = \sqrt{r} I_r(s) = \frac{V_r(s)}{\sqrt{r}}. \tag{9b}$$

We refer to a and b as the *scattering variables*.

By using (3), these new variables can be expressed in terms of the voltage and current as

$$a = \tfrac{1}{2}(r^{-1/2}V + r^{1/2}I),$$
$$b = \tfrac{1}{2}(r^{-1/2}V - r^{1/2}I). \tag{10}$$

The square root of r appearing on the right of these expressions is disconcerting. It could be eliminated by defining normalized voltage and current, as follows:

$$V_n = r^{-1/2}V, \tag{11a}$$

$$I_n = r^{1/2}I. \tag{11b}$$

Then the scattering variables become

$$a = \tfrac{1}{2}(V_n + I_n), \tag{12a}$$

$$b = \tfrac{1}{2}(V_n - I_n). \tag{12b}$$

A glance at (4) with (9) shows that the reflection coefficient is in all cases the ratio of a reflected variable — V_r, I_r, or b — to an incident variable — V_i, I_i, or a, respectively — irrespective of the value of the normalizing resistance. Thus,

$$\varrho = \frac{V_r}{V_i} = \frac{I_r}{I_i} = \frac{b}{a}. \tag{13a}$$

Furthermore, by incorporating (12) it follows that

$$\varrho = \frac{Z_n - 1}{Z_n + 1} = \frac{Z - r}{Z + r}, \tag{13b}$$

where $Z_n = Z/r$ is the normalized impedance and $1 = r/r$ is the normalized source impedance. Thus, all impedances — network and source — have been normalized. Now, using the word normalize to mean both network and source, we can state: *The reflection coefficient is invariant to normalization.*

Conversely, the normalized voltage, current, and impedance can be expressed in terms of the scattering variables and the reflection coefficient by inverting (12) and (13). Thus,

$$V_n = a + b \tag{14a}$$

$$I_n = a - b \tag{14b}$$

$$Z_n = \frac{1 + \varrho}{1 - \varrho} = (1 + \varrho)(1 - \varrho)^{-1}. \tag{14c}$$

The normalizing quantity, r, is a real parameter and for that reason the term normalization is often qualified as real normalization. The considerably more complicated case of complex normalization is left to you as a project. (See Proj. 2.)

6.1.2 Augmented Network

The normalization just carried out can be interpreted by reference to the network shown in Fig. 2. The normalized value of the source resistance is 1. The ideal transformer of turns ratio $1:\sqrt{r}$ gives the appropriate equations relating the actual voltage and current on its secondary side to the normalized voltage and current on the primary side. The original one-port in cascade with the ideal transformer can be called the normalized one-port network. When the original one-port is matched to r, this is equivalent to the normalized one-port being matched to unity. Because of its normalizing function, r is called the *normalizing number*, or the *reference resistance*. In the event that the normalizing number is unity, the resulting 1:1 ideal transformer in Fig. 2 need not be included.

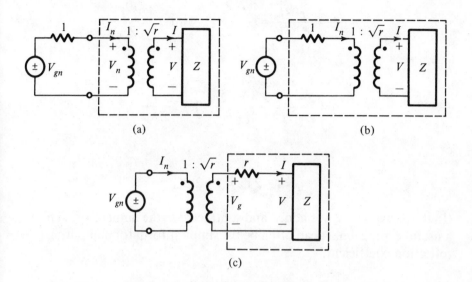

Fig. 2 (a) Normalized network; (b) augmented normalized network;
(c) normalized augmented network

From the normalized network it is clear that when the one-port is matched, the input impedance at the transformer primary is a unity resistance. Hence $I_n = V_n$; from (12), this means $a = I_n = V_n$ and $b = 0$. That is, under matched conditions, the incident scattering variable equals the normalized current and the normalized voltage, and the reflected scattering variable is zero. Furthermore, with the normalized source voltage defined as $V_{gn} = r^{-1/2} V_g$, we see that the relationship of V_g to V_i given in (7) implies that

$$a = \frac{1}{2} V_{gn}. \tag{15}$$

We can go one more step and include the series unity resistance with the normalized network, as illustrated in Fig. 2(b). The result is then called the (series) *augmented normalized network*. Of course, it is possible to think of the original network as being augmented by the series resistance r, without reference to normalization. This augmented network appears in the *normalized augmented network* displayed in Fig. 2(c). As you can show, the normalized augmented network is equivalent at its port to the augmented normalized network in Fig. 2(b).

The reflection coefficient of the original network can be expressed in terms of the input admittance Y_a of the augmented network or Y_{an} of the augmented normalized network. It is clear from Fig. 2 that we can write

$$Y_{an} = \frac{I_n}{V_{gn}} = \frac{r^{1/2}I}{r^{-1/2}V_g} = r\frac{I}{V_g} = rY_a, \text{ with } Y_a = \frac{1}{Z+r}.$$

Then

$$\varrho = \frac{Z-r}{Z+r} = \frac{Z+r-2r}{Z+r} = 1 - 2\frac{r}{Z+r}$$

or

$$\varrho = 1 - 2Y_{an} = 1 - 2rY_a. \tag{16}$$

(In the derivation, r was added and subtracted in the numerator.) This is a useful expression. It can often be the simplest form for computing the reflection coefficient.

6.1.3   Reflection Coefficient for Time-Invariant, Passive, Reciprocal Network

The analytic properties of $\varrho(s)$ for a time-invariant, passive, reciprocal network can be obtained by reference to (13b). For such a network, $Z_n(s)$ is a positive real function of s. (If you are not familiar with positive real functions, also bounded real functions, then you should skip this subsection until you study Chapter 11.) Now, a positive real $Z_n(s)$ maps the $j\omega$-axis of the s-plane into the closed right half Z_n-plane. Equation 13b is a bilinear transformation. The bilinear transformation maps the closed right half of the Z_n-plane into the interior or boundary of the ϱ-plane unit disk. Hence, when $s = j\omega$, the corresponding point lies inside or on the boundary of the ϱ-plane unit disk. Thus,

$$|\varrho(j\omega)| \leq 1. \tag{17}$$

As for the poles of $\varrho(s)$, they are given by the zeros of $Z_n(s) + 1$. They cannot lie in the closed right half-plane since this would require Re $Z_n(s) = -1$ for a point in the closed right half-plane, which is impossible for a positive real function. Hence $\varrho(s)$ is regular in the closed right half-plane.

We see that the positive real condition on the impedance of a one-port can be translated into equivalent conditions on the reflection coefficient — in summary: (1) $\varrho(s)$ is real when s is real, (2) $\varrho(s)$ is regular in the closed right half-plane, and (3) $|\varrho(j\omega)| \leq 1$ for all ω. The above discussion has shown that *for a time-invariant, passive, reciprocal network the reflection coefficient is a bounded real function.*

6.1.4 Power Relations

We have seen that the scattering variables have special significance in describing the power transfer from a source to a load. We shall here discuss the power relation in the network of Fig. 1 in terms of the scattering variables. Let us assume sinusoidal steady-state conditions. The complex power delivered to the one-port is $W = V(j\omega)\bar{I}(j\omega)$. What happens to this expression if the voltage and current are normalized as in (11)? With the stipulation that r is a positive real number, the answer is: nothing. When the normalization is inserted, we still have

$$W = V_n(j\omega)\bar{I}_n(j\omega). \tag{18}$$

We can now use (14) to express this result in terms of the scattering variables. From this derived expression the real power will be

$$P = \text{Re } W = \text{Re } (a+b)(\overline{a-b}) = |a(j\omega)|^2 - |b(j\omega)|^2$$
$$= |a(j\omega)|^2(1 - |\varrho(j\omega)|^2). \tag{19}$$

The last step follows from $\varrho = b/a$.

A number of observations can be made from here. The magnitude square of both a and b has the dimension of power. Thus, *the dimensions of the scattering variables are the square root of power*, (voltage $\times$ current)$^{1/2}$. We can think of the net power delivered to the one-port as being made up of the power in the incident wave, $P_i = |a|^2$, less the power returned to the source by the reflected wave, $P_r = |b|^2$; thus, $P = P_i - P_r$. Of course, under matched conditions there is no reflection. The power delivered under these conditions is the maximum available power, say P_m, from the source in series with resistance r. This maximum available power is easily found from Fig. 1(c) to be

$$P_m = \frac{|V_g|^2}{4r} = \frac{|r^{-1/2}V_g|^2}{4} = \frac{|V_{gn}|^2}{4} = |a|^2. \tag{20}$$

The last step follows from (15). With this fact, (19) can be rewritten as

$$\frac{P}{P_m} = 1 - |\varrho(j\omega)|^2. \tag{21}$$

This is an extremely important result. The right side specifies the fraction of the maximum available power that is actually delivered to the one-port. If there is no reflection ($\varrho = 0$), this ratio is unity.

For a passive one-port, the power delivered cannot exceed the maximum available; that is, $P/P_m \leqslant 1$. Hence,

$$|\varrho(j\omega)| \leqslant 1 \text{ (for a passive one-port).} \qquad (22)$$

6.2 MULTIPORT SCATTERING RELATIONS

As discussed in the last section, the scattering parameters are particularly useful in the description of power transfer. The simplest of such situations is the transfer of power from a source with an internal impedance to a load, which we have already discussed. More typical is the transfer from a source to a load through a coupling network $\mathcal{N}$, as shown in Fig. 3. The two-port network $\mathcal{N}$ may be a filter or an equalizer matching network. The load may be passive, either real or complex, or it may be active (e.g., a suitably biased tunnel diode). More generally, the coupling network is a multiport with transmission of power from one or more ports to one or more other ports.

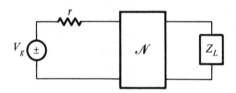

Fig. 3   Two-port filter or matching network

We shall deal in detail with the situation shown in Fig. 4(a), where each port is terminated with a positive real resistance and a source. A special case is the two-port shown in Fig. 4(b). The development is simply a generalization of the one-port case except that scalar relationships will now be replaced by vector relationships. We shall treat the general n-port case but will illustrate the details with the two-port for ease of visualization.

To begin, we define the vector variables

$$\mathbf{V} = \begin{bmatrix} V_1 \\ V_2 \\ . \\ . \\ V_k \end{bmatrix}, \quad \mathbf{I} = \begin{bmatrix} I_1 \\ I_2 \\ . \\ . \\ I_k \end{bmatrix}, \quad \mathbf{V}_g = \begin{bmatrix} V_{g1} \\ V_{g2} \\ . \\ . \\ V_{gk} \end{bmatrix} \qquad (23)$$

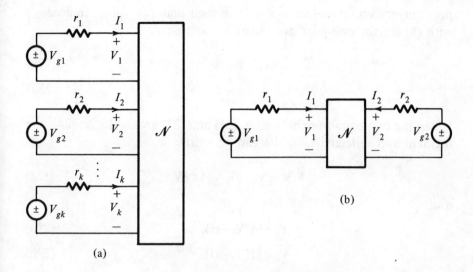

Fig. 4 **Multiports with real normalizing numbers**

and the diagonal matrix $\mathbf{r} = \text{diag}\,[r_i]$, $i = 1, 2, \ldots, k$. The matrix $\mathbf{r}$ is non-singular and positive definite, since all the r_i's are assumed to be positive real. From Fig. 4 we can write

$$\mathbf{V}_g = \mathbf{V} + \mathbf{r}\mathbf{I} = (\mathbf{Z} + \mathbf{r})\mathbf{I}, \tag{24}$$

where $\mathbf{Z}$ is the impedance matrix of multiport $\mathcal{N}$. Suppose now that at each of the ports the multiport is matched to the source resistance. This means the ratio V_j/I_j is to equal the resistance r_j at the jth port. In matrix form this becomes $\mathbf{V} = \mathbf{r}\mathbf{I}$, or $\mathbf{Z} = \mathbf{r}$ when the multiport is matched. By analogy with the one-port case, we introduce the *incident-voltage vector* $\mathbf{V}_i$ and the *incident-current vector* $\mathbf{I}_i$ as equal to the port-voltage vector and the port-current vector, respectively, when the ports are all matched; that is

$$\mathbf{V}_i = \mathbf{V} \text{ and } \mathbf{I}_i = \mathbf{I}, \text{ when matched}, \tag{25}$$

and

$$\mathbf{V}_i = \mathbf{r}\mathbf{I}_i. \tag{26}$$

Similarly, we introduce the *reflected-voltage vector* $\mathbf{V}_r$ and the *reflected-current* vector $\mathbf{I}_r$, as the deviation of the port-voltage vector and the port-current vector, respectively, from their matched value. In analogy with (8) for the one-port case, they are written as

$$V_r = V - V_i, \tag{27a}$$

$$I_r = I_i - I. \tag{27b}$$

When the two pairs of equations in (25) and (27) are used with (24), the incident and reflected variables can be written as

$$V_i = \tfrac{1}{2}V_g, \quad I_i = \tfrac{1}{2}r^{-1}V_g \tag{28}$$

and

$$V_i = \tfrac{1}{2}(V + rI), \tag{29a}$$

$$V_r = \tfrac{1}{2}(V - rI), \tag{29b}$$

$$I_i = \tfrac{1}{2}r^{-1}(V + rI), \tag{29c}$$

$$I_r = \tfrac{1}{2}r^{-1}(V - rI). \tag{29d}$$

These expressions should be compared with (7) and (3) for the one-port.

6.2.1 The Scattering Matrix

For the one-port a reflection coefficient was defined relating reflected to incident voltage and another one relating reflected to incident current. These two turned out to have the same value and to be invariant to normalization. In the multiport case the relationship of reflected to incident variables is a vector relationship. We define two such relationships — one for the voltages and one for the currents — as follows:

$$I_r = S_I I_i, \tag{30a}$$

$$V_r = S_V V_i, \tag{30b}$$

where S_I is the *current-scattering matrix* and S_V is the *voltage-scattering matrix*. These matrices can be expressed in terms of Z and the terminating impedances by using (29) for the incident and reflected variables, and by using $V = ZI$. The details will be left to you; the result is as follows:

$$S_I = r^{-1}(Z - r)(Z + r)^{-1}r = (Z + r)^{-1}(Z - r), \tag{31a}$$

$$S_V = (Z - r)(Z + r)^{-1} = r(Z + r)^{-1}(Z - r)r^{-1}. \tag{31b}$$

Study these expressions carefully, note how S_I is relatively simple when $(Z+r)^{-1}$ premultiplies $(Z-r)$, and how S_V is relatively simple when it postmultiplies $(Z-r)$.

What is $(Z+r)$? It is, in fact, the impedance matrix of the augmented network; that is, the multiport in Fig. 4, which includes the series resistance at each port as part of the multiport. The inverse, $(Z+r)^{-1}$, is the admittance matrix of the augmented multiport, which we shall label Y_a. In terms of Y_a, the two reflection coefficients are found from (31), after some manipulation, to be

$$S_I = U - 2Y_a r, \tag{32a}$$

$$S_V = U - 2r Y_a. \tag{32b}$$

The only difference in these two expressions is that in one case r postmultiplies Y_a and in the other case it premultiplies Y_a. Each of these equations can be solved for Y_a. When these two expressions for Y_a are equated, a relationship between S_I and S_V is found; it is

$$S_I r^{-1} = r^{-1} S_V \tag{33a}$$

or, equivalently,

$$r S_I = S_V r. \tag{33b}$$

We seem to be at an impasse; the matrix r or r^{-1} seems to crop up and spoil things. Perhaps normalization will help. Look back at (9) to see how the incident and reflected voltages and currents were normalized. Suppose we carry out a similar normalization, but in matrix form. To normalize currents, we multiply by the matrix $r^{1/2}$; and to normalize voltages, we multiply by $r^{-1/2}$, where

$$r^{1/2} = \text{diag}\ \{r_i^{1/2}\}. \tag{34}$$

is a real diagonal matrix, each diagonal entry of which is the positive square root of the corresponding entry of the matrix r. To see what will happen, let us multiply both sides of (30a) by $r^{1/2}$ and both sides of (30b) by $r^{-1/2}$. Then

$$r^{1/2} I_r = r^{1/2} S_I (r^{-1/2} r^{1/2}) I_i = (r^{1/2} S_I r^{-1/2})(r^{1/2} I_i), \tag{35a}$$

$$r^{-1/2} V_r = r^{-1/2} S_V (r^{1/2} r^{-1/2}) V_i = (r^{-1/2} S_V r^{1/2})(r^{-1/2} V_i) \tag{35b}$$

The two normalized vectors on the right sides of these expressions ($\mathbf{r}^{1/2}\mathbf{I}_i$ and $\mathbf{r}^{-1/2}\mathbf{V}_i$) are equal, in view of (26). Furthermore, by premultiplying and postmultiplying both sides of (33a) by $\mathbf{r}^{1/2}$, we find that

$$\mathbf{r}^{1/2}\mathbf{S}_I\mathbf{r}^{-1/2} = \mathbf{r}^{-1/2}\mathbf{S}_V\mathbf{r}^{1/2} = \mathbf{S}, \tag{36}$$

where the matrix $\mathbf{S}$ is introduced for convenience. Hence, the two right sides in (35) are the same; so it follows that the two normalized variables on the left side of (35) are also equal.

With the preceding discussion as justification, we now define the *normalized vector scattering variables* as

$$\mathbf{a} = \mathbf{r}^{1/2}\mathbf{I}_i = \mathbf{r}^{-1/2}\mathbf{V}_i, \tag{37a}$$

$$\mathbf{b} = \mathbf{r}^{1/2}\mathbf{I}_r = \mathbf{r}^{-1/2}\mathbf{V}_r. \tag{37b}$$

These *scattering variables* are related by the *scattering matrix* $\mathbf{S}$, itself related by (36) to the current- and voltage-scattering matrices, by

$$\mathbf{b} = \mathbf{S}\mathbf{a}. \tag{38}$$

This matrix equation is a scattering representation of a multiport. In many respects, it is a superior way of describing the operation of a multiport as compared to an impedance or admittance representation.

6.2.2 Relationship to Impedance and Admittance Matrices

The relationship between this scattering matrix and the matrices $\mathbf{Z}$ and $\mathbf{Y}_a$ can be found by appropriately pre- and postmultiplying (32) and (31) by $\mathbf{r}^{1/2}$ and $\mathbf{r}^{-1/2}$ consistent with (36). If we define

$$\mathbf{Y}_{an} = \mathbf{r}^{1/2}\mathbf{Y}_a\mathbf{r}^{1/2}, \tag{38a}$$

$$\mathbf{Z}_n = \mathbf{r}^{-1/2}\mathbf{Z}\mathbf{r}^{-1/2}, \tag{39b}$$

$$\mathbf{Y}_n = \mathbf{r}^{1/2}\mathbf{Y}\mathbf{r}^{1/2}, \tag{39c}$$

where $\mathbf{Y}$, the admittance matrix of the multiport, is $\mathbf{Z}^{-1}$, then

$$\mathbf{S} = \mathbf{U} - 2(\mathbf{Z}_n + \mathbf{U})^{-1} = \mathbf{U} - 2\mathbf{Y}_{an}, \tag{40}$$

$$\begin{aligned}\mathbf{S} &= (\mathbf{Z}_n - \mathbf{U})(\mathbf{Z}_n + \mathbf{U})^{-1} = (\mathbf{Z}_n + \mathbf{U})^{-1}(\mathbf{Z}_n - \mathbf{U}) \\ &= (\mathbf{U} - \mathbf{Y}_n)(\mathbf{U} + \mathbf{Y}_n)^{-1} = (\mathbf{U} + \mathbf{Y}_n)^{-1}(\mathbf{U} - \mathbf{Y}_n).\end{aligned} \tag{41}$$

We leave the details for you to work out. Compare (40) with (16), which is the corresponding scalar result for a one-port.

The relationship between $\mathbf{S}$ and $\mathbf{Y}_{an}$ points up an important property that is not evident from the manner in which it was obtained. Because of the series resistances in the augmented network, this (augmented) network may have an admittance matrix even though the original multiport has neither an impedance nor an admittance matrix. This, fortunately, will be true for any passive network. Thus an advantage of *scattering parameters*, as we call the elements of the scattering matrix, is that they exist for all passive networks, even those for which impedance or admittance parameters do not exist.

An illustration is provided by the ideal transformer shown in Fig. 5. Actually, what is shown is the augmented network for unity reference resistances at both ports. The ideal transformer has neither an impedance nor an admittance matrix. Nevertheless, the augmented network has an admittance representation. The admittance matrix of the augmented network can be calculated directly, and then (40) will give the scattering matrix. The details are left to you; the result will be

$$
\mathbf{Y}_{an} = \begin{bmatrix} \dfrac{1}{n^2+1} & \dfrac{-n}{n^2+1} \\[3mm] \dfrac{-n}{n^2+1} & \dfrac{n^2}{n^2+1} \end{bmatrix}, \quad \mathbf{S} = \begin{bmatrix} \dfrac{n^2-1}{n^2+1} & \dfrac{2n}{n^2+1} \\[3mm] \dfrac{2n}{n^2+1} & -\dfrac{n^2-1}{n^2+1} \end{bmatrix}
$$

This reduces to an especially simple scattering matrix for a turns ratio of $n=1$.

Note that S_{22} is the negative of S_{11}. Two-ports that satisfy the condition $S_{22} = -S_{11}$ are said to be *antimetric*, in contrast to *symmetric* two-ports, for which $S_{22} = S_{11}$. (See Prob. 15.)

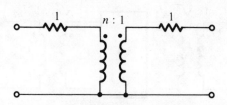

Fig. 5 Ideal transformer

6.2.3   Normalization and the Augmented Multiport

The normalized scattering variables **a** and **b** can be expressed in terms of voltages and currents (rather than incident and reflected variables) by applying the normalization to (29). Defining the normalized voltage and current as $\mathbf{V}_n = \mathbf{r}^{-1/2}\mathbf{V}$ and $\mathbf{I}_n = \mathbf{r}^{1/2}\mathbf{I}$, these equations and their inverses take the relatively simple forms

$$\mathbf{a} = \tfrac{1}{2}(\mathbf{V}_n + \mathbf{I}_n), \qquad\qquad \mathbf{V}_n = \mathbf{a} + \mathbf{b},$$
$$\mathbf{b} = \tfrac{1}{2}(\mathbf{V}_n - \mathbf{I}_n), \qquad\qquad \mathbf{I}_n = \mathbf{a} - \mathbf{b}. \tag{42}$$

Comparing these with (12) and (14) shows that the expressions for the multiport scattering variables are identical with those for the one-port, except that they are vector expressions in the present case.

Finally, note that the two expressions in (28) relating incident-voltage and incident-current to $\mathbf{V}_g$, reduce to a single equation under normalization:

$$\mathbf{a} = \tfrac{1}{2}\mathbf{V}_{gn}. \tag{43}$$

The normalization again can be interpreted by appending ideal transformers to the ports. This is illustrated for the two-port in Fig. 6. The turns ratio of the transformers are $1:\sqrt{r_1}$ and $1:\sqrt{r_2}$. They provide the appropriate equations relating the actual voltages and currents to

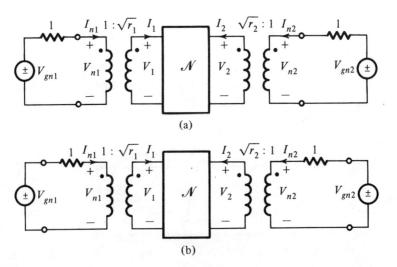

(a)

(b)

Fig. 6   Normalized and augmented normalized two-port

the normalized values. The total network, including the ideal transformers, is called the normalized network. Even though the reference
resistances at the ports may be different, the matched condition corresponds to an input resistance of unity at each port. If we include a
series unit resistance at each port, the resulting overall network is the
augmented normalized network, as shown in Fig. 6(b). We could of
course create its port equivalent, the normalized augmented network,
by adding series resistances r_1 and r_2 at the ports of $\mathcal{N}$ and then follow
by appending the ideal transformers.

How are the port normalizing numbers r_j chosen? In the ideal-
transformer example, for instance, what caused us to choose unity normalizing numbers for both ports? The answer to these questions is,
simply, convenience. If a network will actually operate with certain terminating resistances, it would clearly be convenient, and would simplify
the resulting expressions, if these resistances were chosen as the normalizing numbers. In other cases choice of some parameter in the network as the normalizing number leads to simplification. Consider, for
example, the gyrator shown in Fig. 7. It has an impedance representation, as given in the figure, containing the gyration resistance r. If the
port normalizing numbers, r_1 and r_2, for both ports are chosen equal to
r, the matrix $\mathbf{Z}_n$ can be written very simply. Equation 40 then leads to
the scattering matrix. Thus,

$$\mathbf{Z} = \begin{bmatrix} 0 & \dfrac{-r}{\sqrt{r_1 r_2}} \\[2mm] \dfrac{r}{\sqrt{r_1 r_2}} & 0 \end{bmatrix} = \begin{bmatrix} 0 & -1 \\ 1 & 0 \end{bmatrix},$$

$$\mathbf{S} = \mathbf{U} - 2(\mathbf{U} + \mathbf{Z}_n)^{-1} = \begin{bmatrix} 1 & 0 \\ 0 & 1 \end{bmatrix} - 2 \begin{bmatrix} 1 & -1 \\ 1 & 1 \end{bmatrix}^{-1} = \begin{bmatrix} 0 & -1 \\ 1 & 0 \end{bmatrix}.$$

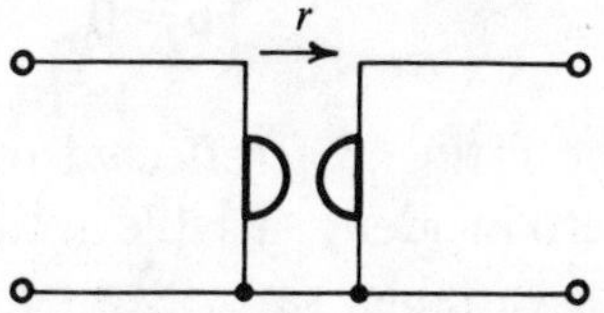

$$\mathbf{Z} = \begin{bmatrix} 0 & -r \\ r & 0 \end{bmatrix}$$

Fig. 7   Gyrator

6.3   THE SCATTERING MATRIX AND POWER TRANSFER

The preceding discussion provides means for finding the scattering parameters of a multiport from either its impedance or admittance matrix – or the admittance matrix of the augmented normalized network. But the scattering parameters appear in the relationships between incident and reflected scattering variables. We shall now consider in greater detail what these relationships are. For simplicity we shall treat the two-port, for which the equations are

$$b_1 = S_{11}a_1 + S_{12}a_2, \tag{44a}$$

$$b_2 = S_{21}a_1 + S_{22}a_2. \tag{44b}$$

We shall assume arbitrary loading of the two-port, with signals possibly applied to each port, as shown in Fig. 8.

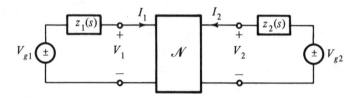

Fig. 8   Two-port with arbitrary loading

6.3.1   Interpretation of Scattering Parameters

By (44) the scattering parameters can be interpreted as follows:

$$S_{11} = \left. \frac{b_1}{a_1} \right|_{a_2=0}, \qquad S_{12} = \left. \frac{b_1}{a_2} \right|_{a_1=0},$$

$$S_{21} = \left. \frac{b_2}{a_1} \right|_{a_2=0}, \qquad S_{22} = \left. \frac{b_2}{a_2} \right|_{a_1=0}. \tag{45}$$

We see that each parameter is the ratio of a reflected to an incident variable, under the condition of zero incident variable at the other port. What does it mean for an incident variable, say a_2, to be zero? This is easily answered by reference to (42) or, equivalently, (29), which relate scattering variables to voltages and currents. Thus $a_2 = 0$ means $V_{n2} = -I_{n2}$, or $V_2 = -r_2 I_2$. Now look at Fig. 8. The condition $V_2 = -r_2 I_2$

means that port 2 is terminated in r_2 (rather than in impedance z_2) and that there is no voltage source; that is, port 2 is *match-terminated*. Furthermore, if there is no incident variable and $V_2 = -r_2 I_2$, (29b) shows that the reflected voltage is the total voltage at the port ($V_{r2} = V_2$) and (29d) shows that the reflected current is the total current ($I_{r2} = I_2$). Similar meanings attach to the condition $a_1 = 0$.

Thus the scattering parameters of a two-port are defined as the ratio of a reflected to an incident variable when the other incident variable is zero — meaning, when the other port is match-terminated. More specifically, consider S_{11}. This is the ratio of reflected to incident variables at port 1 (b_1/a_1) when port 2 is match-terminated. Let us now substitute into b_1/a_1 the scalar equation for port 1 resulting from (42). Then,

$$S_{11} = \frac{b_1}{a_1} = \frac{V_{n1} - I_{n1}}{V_{n1} + I_{n1}} = \frac{Z_{n1} - 1}{Z_{n1} + 1} = \frac{Z_1 - r_1}{Z_1 + r_1}, \tag{46}$$

where Z_{n1} is the normalized input impedance at port 1. Comparing this with (13), which gives the reflection coefficient for a one-port, we see that S_{11} *is the reflection coefficient at port 1 when the other port is match-terminated.* A similar conclusion is reached about S_{22}.

Now look at the off-diagonal terms, specifically S_{21}. When $a_2 = 0$, as we have already mentioned, $b_2 = V_{n2}$, or $V_{r2} = V_2$. Furthermore, $a_1 = V_{gn1}/2$, from (43). Hence,

$$S_{21} = \frac{b_2}{a_1} \bigg|_{a_2 = 0} = \frac{V_{n2}}{V_{gn1}/2} = 2\sqrt{\frac{r_1}{r_2}} \frac{V_2}{V_{g1}}. \tag{47}$$

Thus S_{21} is seen to be proportional to a voltage gain, a *forward* voltage gain. A further clarification is given in terms of Fig. 9. Here the two-port has been replaced by an ideal transformer of such turns ratio that the resistance r_2 becomes matched to r_1. (The resistance looking into the transformer primary is r_1.) The output voltage under this condition is

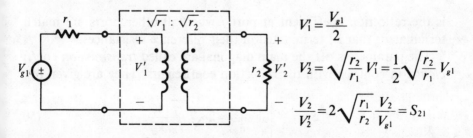

Fig. 9   Transducer voltage ratio

called V_2'. Now if we take the ratio of the actual output voltage V_2 to V_2', the result is called the *forward transducer voltage ratio*. The calculation given in the figure shows this quantity to be the same as the right-hand side of (47). Hence, S_{21} is the forward transducer voltage ratio. When the source is matched as in Fig. 9, it will deliver to the network at its terminals (namely, the primary side of the transformer) the maximum available power. This is seen to be $P_{m1} = |V_{g1}|^2/4r_1$.

Now return to the original setup. The power transferred to the load with network $\mathcal{N}$ in place, when it is matched and when the port 2 voltage is V_2, will be $P_2 = |V_2|^2/r_2$. Hence the magnitude squared of S_{21} in (47) will be

$$|S_{21}(j\omega)|^2 = 4\frac{r_1}{r_2}\frac{|V_2(j\omega)^2|}{|V_{g1}(j\omega)^2|} = \frac{P_2}{P_{m1}} = G(\omega^2). \qquad (48)$$

Thus the magnitude squared of S_{21}, which is often called the (*forward*) *transducer power gain*, $G(\omega^2)$, is simply the ratio of actual load power to the maximum power available from the generator when both ports are matched. (The argument is written ω^2 because G is an even function of frequency.) A completely similar discussion can be carried out for S_{12}, the *reverse transducer voltage ratio*.

A slight manipulation of (48) leads to $|S_{21}|^2 = |V_{n2}|^2/|V_{gn1}/2|^2$. This is, in fact, the transducer power gain for the normalized network. The conclusion is that the transducer power gain is unchanged by normalization.

Without detailed exposition, it should be clear that the scattering parameters for a multiport an be interpreted in a similar fashion. The parameters on the main diagonal of $\mathbf{S}$ will be *reflection coefficients*. Thus,

$$S_{jj} = \frac{b_j}{a_j}\bigg|_{\substack{\text{all other}\\a\text{'s}=0}} = \frac{Z_j - r_j}{Z_j + r_j} \qquad (49)$$

is the reflection coefficient at port j when all other ports are match-terminated; that is, terminated in their reference resistances.

The parameters off the main diagonal are called *transmission coefficients*, in contrast with the reflection coefficients. They are given by

$$S_{ij} = \frac{b_i}{a_j}\bigg|_{\substack{\text{all other}\\a\text{'s}=0}} = 2\sqrt{\frac{r_j}{r_i}}\frac{V_i}{V_{gj}}. \qquad (50)$$

Following an analysis like that leading to (49), we find the magnitude squared of a transmission coefficient to be the ratio of (1) the load power at one port to (2) the maximum available power from a source at another port when all ports are match-terminated. Thus,

$$|S_{ij}|^2 = \frac{4r_j}{r_i} \frac{|V_i|^2}{|V_{gj}|^2} = \frac{P_i}{P_{mj}}. \tag{51}$$

6.3.2 Example

As an illustration, consider the network of Fig. 10. A three-port is formed with a gyrator between ports 1 and 2 (oriented towards port 2) by making an extra port, as shown. (The gyrator symbol shown is mentioned in Exer. 9.) The objective is to find the scattering matrix of the

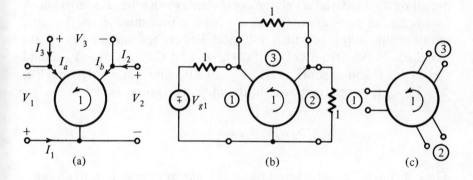

Fig. 10 Gyrator as three-port circulator

three-port and to interpret its elements. Let the gyration resistance be taken as unity. This is equivalent to choosing the normalizing numbers at each of the ports as equal to the gyration resistance. Then, the gyrator relationship is

$$\begin{bmatrix} -V_1 \\ V_2 \end{bmatrix} = \begin{bmatrix} 0 & -1 \\ 1 & 0 \end{bmatrix} \begin{bmatrix} I_a \\ I_b \end{bmatrix}.$$

But $I_a = -I_1 + I_3$, $I_b = I_2 - I_3$, and $V_3 = -V_1 - V_2$, as observed from Fig. 10. From these we get

$$
\begin{bmatrix} V_1 \\ V_2 \\ V_3 \end{bmatrix} = \begin{bmatrix} 0 & i & -i \\ -1 & 0 & 1 \\ 1 & -1 & 0 \end{bmatrix} \begin{bmatrix} I_1 \\ I_2 \\ I_3 \end{bmatrix}
$$

The coefficient matrix here is $\mathbf{Z}_n$. The scattering matrix can now be computed from (41). The result is

$$
\mathbf{S} = \begin{bmatrix} 0 & 0 & 1 \\ -1 & 0 & 0 \\ 0 & -1 & 0 \end{bmatrix} \quad \text{or} \quad \begin{matrix} b_1 = -a_3, \\ b_2 = -a_1, \\ b_3 = -a_2 \end{matrix} \tag{52}
$$

This is a very interesting result. Note first that the diagonal elements are all zero. Hence the reflection coefficients at all ports are zero, which means all the ports are matched. As for the transmission coefficients, consider Fig. 10(b), in which only port 1 is excited and all 3 ports are matched. Hence, from (28) and (37), we find that $a_1 = V_{i1} = V_{g1}/2$ and $a_2 = a_3 = 0$, and from (52), $b_1 = b_3 = 0$ and $b_2 = -V_{g1}/2$. But $b_2 = V_{r2} = V_2$; hence the power in the matched load at port 2 is

$$
P_2 = |V_2|^2 = \frac{|V_{g1}|^2}{4} = P_{m1}.
$$

The conclusion is that when a signal is incident at port 1, with all ports match-terminated, none is reflected ($b_1 = 0$) and none is transmitted to port 3 ($b_3 = 0$) — all of it is transmitted, without loss, to port 2, the power there being the maximum available from the source at port 1.

Similar conclusions follow from (52) for the other transmissions; namely, that a signal incident at port 2 is all transmitted to port 3, and a signal incident at port 3 is all transmitted to port 1. In each case, because of the minus sign in, for example, $b_2 = -a_1$, there is a reversal in voltage phase, but the power transmitted is not affected.

The three-port in Fig. 10 seems to have a cyclic power-transmission property. Power entering one port is transmitted to an adjacent port in a cyclic order, as shown by the circular arrow. A multiport device having this property is called a *circulator*, the symbol for which is shown in Fig. 10(c) for a three-port. For our circulator in Fig. 10, the cyclic order is 123. Clearly, a circulator of the opposite cyclic order, 132, is also possible. Its scattering matrix must clearly be of the form

$$S = \begin{bmatrix} 0 & S_{12} & 0 \\ 0 & 0 & S_{23} \\ S_{31} & 0 & 0 \end{bmatrix} ,$$

with $|S_{13}| = |S_{21}| = |S_{32}| = 1$. If realized by a gyrator reversed in orientation from that in Fig. 10, then each of the nonzero parameters will equal -1. However, at a single frequeny the angles of the nonzero parameters can have any values without influencing the power transmission pattern — port 1 to port 3, etc. That is, each of the nonzero transmission coefficients, in general, can be an all-pass function — a function of unit magnitude and any angle.

The particularly happy way in which the scattering parameters are related to power transmission and reflection gives a further, though belated, justification for the normalization that we carried out in (37). It was done there for the purpose of arriving at a single scattering matrix rather than the two based on current and voltage. These simple interpretations of the scattering parameters in terms of power transmission and reflection would not have been possible had we continued to deal with the current and the voltage scattering matrices.

6.4 PROPERTIES OF THE SCATTERING MATRIX

Since the scattering parameters have meanings intimately connected with power, the processes of power transmission are quite conveniently expressed in terms of scattering parameters. Assume a multiport with arbitrary terminating impedances in series with voltage sources, as in Fig. 4, except that the terminations are arbitrary. The complex power input to the multiport in the sinusoidal steady state will be $W = V^*I$, where V^* is the conjugate transpose of V. If you go through the details of substituting the normalized variables for the actual ones, you will find that the expression for power is invariant to normalization. Thus

$$W = V_n^* I_n = (a^* + b^*)(a - b)$$
$$= (a^*a - b^*b) + (b^*a - a^*b). \tag{53}$$

Here (42) was used to replace the normalized voltage and current vectors by the scattering variables. The last term in parentheses on the far right is the difference of two conjugate quantities, since

$$(a*b) = (b*a)* = \overline{(b*a)}.$$

The last step here follows because a vector(inner) product is a scalar and the transpose of a scalar is itself. But the difference of two conjugates is imaginary. Hence the real power $-P = \text{Re } W-$ will be

$$P = a*a - b*b = a*a - a*S*Sa$$
$$= a*(U - S*S)a. \tag{54}$$

This was obtained by substituting **Sa** for **b**. This equation should be compared with (19) for the one-port case.

The properties of the scattering matrix for different classes of networks can be established from (54). First observe that the right side is a quadratic form. For convenience, define

$$Q = U - S*S, \tag{55}$$

so

$$P = a*Qa. \tag{56}$$

Let us take the conjugate transpose of **Q**; thus

$$Q* = (U - S*S)* = U - S*S = Q. \tag{57}$$

Now, a matrix that is equal to its own conjugate transpose is said to be *Hermitian*. Thus **Q** is a Hermitian matrix. Its elements are related by $q_{ij} = \overline{q}_{ji}$, which requires the diagonal elements to be real. This we have established without any conditions on the network type.

6.4.1   Properties for Passive Multiports

We are usually interested, though, in particular classes of networks: active and (lossless or lossy) passive, reciprocal and nonreciprocal. There is not much of a specific nature that can be said about active networks. Hence we shall concentrate mainly on passive networks, which may be reciprocal or nonreciprocal. We shall also focus on the lossless subclass of passive networks, which also may be reciprocal or nonreciprocal.

First, for passive networks in general, the real power delivered to the multiport from sinusoidal sources at the ports must never be negative. Hence

$$U - S^*S \text{ is positive semidefinite.} \tag{58}$$

This is the fundamental limitation on the scattering matrix of a passive multiport. It should be compared with (23) for the one-port case.

A necessary and sufficient condition for a matrix to be positive semidefinite is that its principal cofactors be not less than zero. The diagonal elements of Q are among the principal cofactors and hence must be non-negative. In terms of the elements of S, this means

$$q_{jj} = 1 - \sum_i \bar{S}_{ij} S_{ij} = 1 - \sum_i |S_{ij}|^2 \geqslant 0. \tag{59}$$

Each term in the summation is positive. The expression tells us that a sum of positive terms cannot exceed unity. This requires, *a fortiori*, that each term not exceed unity, or

$$|S_{ij}(j\omega)| \leqslant 1. \tag{60}$$

This is a fundamental limitation imposed on the scattering parameters as a consequence of passivity. It tells us that *for a passive network, the magnitude of a reflection coefficient cannot exceed unity, nor can the magnitude of a transmission coefficient.*

Next, consider a (passive) lossless multiport, whether reciprocal or nonreciprocal. In this case no power is dissipated within the multiport. Hence, the real-power input to all ports shown in (56) must be identically zero for any possible vector a. This is possible only if the matrix of the quadratic form vanishes; that is,

$$Q = U - S^*S = 0$$

or

$$S^*S = U = SS^*. \tag{61}$$

By definition of the inverse, we see that $S^{-1} = S^*$. A matrix whose inverse equals its conjugate transpose is called a *unitary matrix*. Thus *the scattering matrix of a lossless (passive) multiport is unitary.*

The unitary property imposes some constraints on the elements of the scattering matrix that can be established by expanding the products in (61). The result will be

$$|S_{1j}|^2 + |S_{2j}|^2 + |S_{3j}|^2 + \ldots + |S_{nj}|^2 = 1$$

$$\bar{S}_{1j}S_{1k} + \bar{S}_{2j}S_{2k} + \ldots + \bar{S}_{nj}S_{nk} = 0,$$

which can be written concisely as

$$\sum_{i=1}^{n} \overline{S}_{ij} S_{ik} = \delta_{jk}. \tag{62a}$$

and

$$|S_{j1}|^2 + |S_{j2}|^2 + |S_{j3}|^2 + \ldots + |S_{jn}|^2 = 1$$
$$S_{j1}\overline{S}_{k1} + S_{j2}\overline{S}_{k2} + \ldots + S_{jn}\overline{S}_{kn} = 0,$$

from which

$$\sum_{i=1}^{n} S_{ji} \overline{S}_{ki} = \delta_{jk}. \tag{62b}$$

This expression does for the rows of **S** what (62a) does for the columns.

6.4.2 Properties for Passive, Lossless Two-Port Networks

The immediately preceding equations give expression to properties of the scattering parameters of multiports. We shall examine these in detail for a two-port network, specifically limited to (*passive*) *lossless networks, both reciprocal and nonreciprocal.*

First, with $n = 2$, set $j = k = 1$ in (62a); then $j = k = 2$ in (62b). The results will be

$$|S_{11}|^2 + |S_{21}|^2 = 1, \tag{63a}$$

$$|S_{21}|^2 + |S_{22}|^2 = 1. \tag{63b}$$

Subtracting one from the other gives

$$|S_{11}(j\omega)|^2 = |S_{22}(j\omega)|^2. \tag{64}$$

Thus, *for a lossless two-port, whether reciprocal or nonreciprocal, the magnitudes of the reflection coefficients at the two ports are equal.*

This result can be extended to complex frequencies by analytic continuation. Using the symbol ϱ for reflection coefficient, the result can be written as follows:

$$\varrho_1(s)\varrho_1(-s) = \varrho_2(s)\varrho_2(-s). \tag{65}$$

In terms of poles and zeros, we conclude the following: The poles and zeros of $\varrho_1(s)\varrho_1(-s)$ and $\varrho_2(s)\varrho_2(-s)$ are identical, and they occur with quadrantal symmetry. In making the assignment of poles and zeros to $\varrho_1(s)$ from those of $\varrho_1(s)\varrho_1(-s)$, the only consideration is stability. No poles of $\varrho_1(s)$ can lie in the right half-plane. Hence the left half-plane poles of $\varrho_1(s)\varrho_1(-s)$ must be poles of $\varrho_1(s)$. As for the zeros, no limitation is imposed by stability; zeros of $\varrho_1(s)\varrho_1(-s)$ can be assigned to $\varrho_1(s)$ from either the left or the right half-plane, subject of course to the limitation that these zeros, plus their images in the $j\omega$-axis, must account for all the zeros of $\varrho_1(s)\varrho_1(-s)$. Similar statements can be made about the poles and zeros of $\varrho_2(s)$.

Let us return again to (62a) and this time set $j = k = 2$. The result will be

$$|S_{12}|^2 + |S_{22}|^2 = 1. \tag{66}$$

When this is compared with (63b), we see that

$$|S_{12}(j\omega)|^2 = |S_{21}(j\omega)|^2; \tag{67}$$

that is, the magnitude of the forward-transmission coefficient equals that of the reverse-transmission coefficient. This is not surprising for reciprocal networks, since then $S_{12}(s) = S_{21}(s)$, but it is true for non-reciprocal networks also. In fact, even more detailed relationships can be found by setting $j = 2$, $k = 1$ in (62a). The result will be

$$S_{11}(j\omega) = -\frac{S_{21}(j\omega)}{\overline{S}_{12}(j\omega)}\overline{S}_{22}(j\omega) \tag{68a}$$

or

$$\varrho_1(s) = -\frac{S_{21}(s)}{S_{12}(-s)}\varrho_2(-s). \tag{68b}$$

This applies to both reciprocal and nonreciprocal lossless two-ports. For the reciprocal case $S_{12} = S_{21}$; hence the ratio of $S_{21}(s)$ to $S_{12}(-s)$ will then be an all-pass function. Since $\varrho_1(s)$ can have no poles in the right half-plane, the zeros of this all-pass function must cancel the right-half-plane poles of $\varrho_2(-s)$.

6.4.3 First Application—Filtering or Equalizing

A number of different applications can be handled by the configuration shown in Fig. 11(a). A lossless coupling network $\mathcal{N}$ is to be designed for insertion between a source with a real internal impedance and a real load. The network may be required to perform the function of filtering or equalizing; that is, shaping the frequency response in a prescribed way.

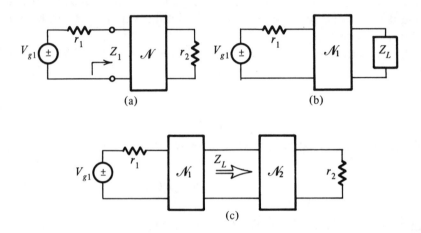

(a) (b)

(c)

Fig. 11 Filter, equalizer, or matching network

Alternatively, the load may be an impedance Z_L as shown in Fig. 11(b), and the coupling network is to be designed to provide a match to the resistive source over a band of frequencies. This case can be related to the former one by using Darlington's realization theorem. (See Chapter 12.) That is to say, Z_L can be realized as a lossless two-port $\mathcal{N}_2$ terminated in a resistance r_2, as shown in Fig. 11(c). The cascade combination of $\mathcal{N}_1$ and $\mathcal{N}_2$ plays the role of the lossless network $\mathcal{N}$ in Fig. 11(a).

Let us concentrate on the filter or equalizer problem. What is specified is the transducer power gain as a function of frequency. We shall label this function $G(\omega^2)$. According to (48), $G(\omega^2)$ is simply the magnitude square of $S_{21}(j\omega)$. But $|S_{21}(j\omega)|^2$ is related to the magnitude of the input reflection coefficient by (63a). If this expression is analytically continued, it can be written as

$$\varrho_1(s)\varrho_1(-s) = 1 - S_{21}(s)S_{21}(-s) = 1 - G(-s^2), \qquad (69)$$

where we have again replaced S_{11} by ϱ_1. If $G(\omega^2)$ is specified, the right-hand side is a known even function. It is now only necessary to assign the poles and zeros of the right side appropriately to $\varrho_1(s)$.

Furthermore, the reflection coefficient ϱ_1 and the impedance Z_1 looking into the input terminals of $\mathcal{N}$ with the output terminated in r_2 are related by (46), which can be solved for Z_1 as follows:

$$\frac{Z_1(s)}{r_1} = \frac{1 + \varrho_1(s)}{1 - \varrho_1(s)}. \tag{70}$$

Hence, once $\varrho_1(s)$ has been determined from (69), the input impedance Z_1 becomes known as a function of s. The task is then reduced to an application of Darlington's realization theorem; namely, realizing $Z_1(s)$ as a lossless two-port terminated in a resistance.

To illustrate this discussion let the transducer power gain be given as

$$G(\omega^2) = \frac{1}{1 + \omega^6}.$$

This is a third-order Butterworth filter function. The continuation is obtained through replacing ω^2 by $-s^2$. When this is inserted into (69), the result is

$$\varrho_1(s)\varrho_1(-s) = 1 - \frac{1}{1 - s^6} = \frac{-s^6}{1 - s^6} = \frac{-s^6}{(1 + s)(1 + s + s^2)(1 - s)(1 - s + s^2)}.$$

In the last step the denominator has been factored, placing in evidence the left and right half-plane poles. The left half-plane poles must belong to $\varrho_1(s)$, as opposed to $\varrho_1(-s)$. In the example the zeros also are uniquely assignable: three zeros at the origin to $\varrho_1(s)$ and three to $\varrho_1(s)$. The only ambiguity arises in the appropriate sign. There is no *a priori* reason why $\varrho_1(s)$ must have a positive sign. The conclusion is that $\varrho_1(s)$ must be the following:

$$\varrho_1(s) = \frac{\pm s^3}{(s + 1)(s^2 + s + 1)}.$$

When this is inserted into (70), the impedance is found to satisfy

$$\frac{Z_1(s)}{r_1} = \frac{2s^3 + 2s^2 + 2s + 1}{2s^2 + 2s + 1} \quad \text{or} \quad \frac{2s^2 + 2s + 1}{2s^3 + 2s^2 + 2s + 1},$$

depending on the sign chosen for $\varrho_1(s)$. But these are inverse impedances, and their realizations will be duals. In the present case one realization is rather simply obtained by expanding in a continued fraction. Thus, using the first function, we obtain

$$\frac{Z_1(s)}{r_1} = s + \cfrac{1}{2s + \cfrac{1}{s+1}}.$$

The networks realizing this function and its dual are shown in Figs. 12(a) and 12(b), respectively. These are the normalized realizations. Recall that the normalized impedance matrix Z_n is obtained by premultiplying and postmultiplying Z by $r^{-1/2}$. To undo this normalization, Z_n must be written down and then be premultiplied and postmultiplied by $r^{1/2}$. Suppose $r_1 = r_2 = r$; then the denormalized network (with the actual source and load resistances) corresponding to the normalized network in Fig. 12(a), is as shown in Fig. 12(c).

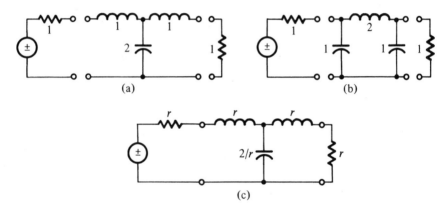

Fig. 12   Illustrative example

6.4.4   Second Application—Limitations Introduced by Parasitic Capacitance

The general matching problem, illustrated in Fig. 11(b) and (c), takes on some additional significance for the special case shown in Fig. 13(a), where the load impedance is the parallel combination of a capacitor and a resistor. This configuration is identical with that of a network working between two resistive terminations R_1 and R_2, but constrained by a parasitic shunt capacitance across the output terminals, which can be treated as part of the two-port, as suggested in Fig. 13(b). This is similar

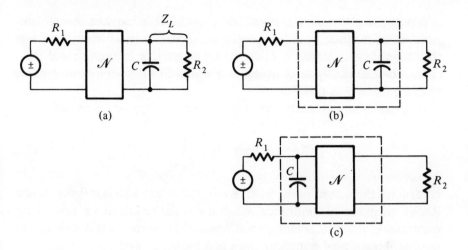

Fig. 13   Two-port constrained by parasitic capacitance

to the situation illustrated in Fig. 13(c), where a parasitic shunt capacitance occurs across the input port.

We shall here derive an integral constraint on the reflection coefficient due to the parasitic capacitance and use it to find a limitation on the transducer power gain.

The two situations in Fig. 13(b) and (c) are similar and can be treated simultaneously by considering Fig. 14, where R is either R_1 or R_2. In the first case, $R = R_1$, Z is the impedance Z_1 looking into the left-hand port of the dashed two-port in Fig. 13(c), with R_2 as the load; ϱ is the corresponding reflection coefficient ϱ_1. For $R = R_2$, Z is the impedance Z_2 looking into the right-hand port of the dashed two-port in Fig. 13(b), with the other port terminated in R_1; ϱ is the corresponding reflection coefficient ϱ_2. In either case,

$$\varrho = \frac{Z - R}{Z + R}.$$

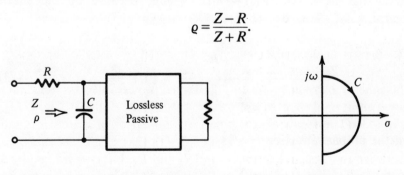

Fig. 14   Shunt capacitance constraint   **Fig. 15   Complex plane contour**

Ideally, under matched conditions, $\varrho = 0$. This requires $Z = R$ independent of frequency, at least over the frequency band of interest. But this cannot be achieved exactly; it might only be approximated. If ϱ cannot be identically zero, at least we would like to make its magnitude as close to zero as possible.

It is customary to define another quantity related to ϱ as follows:

$$\text{return loss} = \ln\frac{1}{|\varrho(j\omega)|}. \tag{71}$$

Under matched conditions, when $\varrho = 0$, the return loss is infinite; under totally mismatched conditions, when $\varrho = 1$, the return loss is zero. Thus maximizing the return loss over a band of frequencies is a measure of the optimization of matching over this band.

An integral constraint on the return loss can be obtained by taking the contour integral of $\ln(1/\varrho)$ around the contour consisting of the $j\omega$-axis and an infinite semicircle to the right, as shown in Fig. 15. To apply Cauchy's theorem from complex variables theory, the integrand must be regular in the right half-plane. However, although ϱ is regular in the right half-plane, $1/\varrho$ need not be. Hence we first multiply $1/\varrho$ by an all-pass function A, as follows:

$$\frac{1}{\varrho(s)}A(s) = \frac{Z(s)+R}{Z(s)-R} \times \frac{(s-s_1)(s-s_2)\dots(s-s_n)}{(s+s_1)(s+s_2)\dots(s+s_n)}, \tag{72}$$

where each s_k is a pole of $1/\varrho$ in the right half-plane. The resulting function is regular in the right half-plane, and the contour integration can be carried out. There will be contributions to the total contour integral from the $j\omega$-axis and from the infinite semicircle. To evaluate the latter, observe that as $s \to \infty$, $Z(s) \to 1/s\hat{C}$, where, because of the shunt capacitor, $\hat{C} \geqslant C$. Hence

$$\frac{Z(s)+R}{Z(s)-R} \xrightarrow{s\to\infty} \frac{\dfrac{1}{s\hat{C}}+R}{\dfrac{1}{s\hat{C}}-R} \xrightarrow{s\to\infty} -\left(1+\frac{2}{R\hat{C}s}\right). \tag{73}$$

Also, the all-pass function

$$A(s) = \frac{s^n - s^{n-1}\sum s_k + \dots}{s^n + s^{n-1}\sum s_k + \dots} \xrightarrow{s\to\infty} 1 - \frac{2\sum s_k}{s}. \tag{74}$$

As a consequence

$$\frac{1}{\varrho(s)}A(s) \xrightarrow{s \to \infty} -\left[1+\frac{2}{s}\left(\frac{1}{R\hat{C}}-\sum s_k\right)\right]. \tag{75}$$

The negative sign before the right-hand side suggests that we take the logarithm of $-A/\varrho$ instead of $+A/\varrho$. Thus, since $\ln(1+x) \to x$ for $|x| \ll 1$,

$$\int_c \ln\left(-\frac{A(s)}{\varrho(s)}\right)ds \to \int_c \frac{2}{s}\left(\frac{1}{R\hat{C}}-\sum s_k\right)ds = -j2\pi\left(\frac{1}{R\hat{C}}-\sum s_k\right), \tag{76}$$

where c is the infinite semicircular part of the contour and $\int_c ds/s = -j\pi$.

Along the $j\omega$-axis

$$\int_{-\infty}^{\infty} \ln\left(-\frac{A(j\omega)}{\varrho(j\omega)}\right)jd\omega = \int_{-\infty}^{\infty} \ln\left|\frac{1}{\varrho(j\omega)}\right|jd\omega + \int_{-\infty}^{\infty} j\arg\left(-\frac{A(j\omega)}{\varrho(j\omega)}\right)jd\omega$$

$$= j2\int_0^{\infty} \ln\frac{1}{|\varrho(j\omega)|}d\omega. \tag{77}$$

The first step follows from the fact that the magnitude of an all-pass function is unity on the $j\omega$-axis, so $\ln|A(j\omega)/\varrho(j\omega)| = \ln|1/\varrho(j\omega)|$. The last step follows because $\ln|1/\varrho(j\omega)|$ is an even function of ω, whereas the angle is an odd function.

From Cauchy's theorem, the sum of the integrals on the left sides of the last two equations equals zero. Hence

$$\int_0^{\infty} \ln\frac{1}{|\varrho(j\omega)|}d\omega = \pi\left(\frac{1}{R\hat{C}}-\sum s_k\right). \tag{78}$$

Recall that s_k is a pole of $1/\varrho$ in the right half-plane, so that its real part is positive. The sum of all such poles will, therefore, be real and positive. If $1/\varrho$ has no poles in the right half-plane, this sum will vanish. The final result will therefore be

$$\int_0^{\infty} \ln\frac{1}{|\varrho(j\omega)|}d\omega \leqslant \frac{\pi}{R\hat{C}} \leqslant \frac{\pi}{RC}. \tag{79}$$

This is a fundamental limitation on the return loss (or the reflection coefficient) when a two-port matching network is constrained by a shunt capacitor across one port.

This constraint places a limitation on the achievable transducer power gain also. To illustrate this, suppose the band of interest is the low-frequency region $0 \leqslant \omega \leqslant \omega_c$, which is the passband, the remainder of the frequency range being the stopband. There will be contributions to the integral in (78) from both bands. The most favorable conditions will occur when $1/\varrho$ has no poles in the right half-plane and the magnitude of ϱ is very small, ideally constant — say of value $|\varrho_0|$ — in the passband. Then

$$\int_0^\infty \ln\frac{1}{|\varrho(j\omega)|}d\omega = \int_0^{\omega_c} \ln\frac{1}{|\varrho_0|}d\omega + \int_{\omega_c}^\infty \ln\frac{1}{|\varrho(j\omega)|}d\omega$$

$$= \omega_c\ln\frac{1}{|\varrho_0|} + \int_{\omega_c}^\infty \ln\frac{1}{|\varrho(j\omega)|}d\omega = \frac{\pi}{R\hat{C}} \tag{80}$$

Outside the passband, there should be a total mismatch and $|\varrho|$ should ideally equal 1. A more practical view is: Although its value will be less than 1, it should be close to 1. Hence, $\ln(1/|\varrho|)$ will be a small positive number, rather than the ideal zero. Therefore the integral from ω_c to ∞ will be positive, and, consequently, (80) yields

$$\ln\frac{1}{|\varrho_0|} \leqslant \frac{\pi}{\omega_c R\hat{C}} \leqslant \frac{\pi}{\omega_c RC} \quad \text{or} \quad \frac{1}{|\varrho_0|} \leqslant e^{\pi/\omega_c RC} \quad \text{or} \quad |\varrho_0| \geqslant e^{-\pi/\omega_c RC}. \tag{81}$$

When this expression is combined with (63b), it is found that the magnitude squared of S_{21} must satisfy

$$|S_{21}(j\omega)|^2 \leqslant 1 - e^{-2\pi/\omega_c RC} \tag{82}$$

in the passband. This puts an upper limit on the achievable transducer power gain, $|S_{21}(j\omega)|^2$, over a wide passband, which might be unacceptable even if we assume a constant value is achievable over that passband. For a fixed shunt capacitance, the wider the frequency band of interest, the more stringent will this limitation become. Note that the immediately preceding result is valid for Fig. 13(c); it also applies to Fig. 13(b) by invoking (64) and (67).

In the application illustrated in Fig. 13(a), the load on the two-port $\mathcal{N}$ is not real. The procedure carried out took the load capacitor and lumped it with the two-port, thus leaving real terminations. Such a procedure permits normalization with real normalizing numbers. The question arises: Can't we use *complex* normalizing numbers so that matching to complex terminating impedances can be achieved? Furthermore, how about normalization to a *function of s* as opposed to a complex *number*? The answer is that both of these procedures are possible and they permit handling a wider range of applications. However, because of limitations of space, they will not be treated in this text.

CHAPTER 7
Frequency- and Time-Domain Representations of Network Functions

It is our purpose in this chapter to discuss ways in which network functions are represented and to begin the study of properties of network functions as analytic functions of a complex variable. We shall here concentrate largely on those properties that apply generally to network functions, without regard to their specific nature as driving-point or transfer functions. We shall also study the relationships that exist between parts of a network function — real and imaginary parts, magnitude and angle — and observe how the function is represented by any one of its component parts. We shall conclude with a brief discussion of the relationship of a network function to the evaluation of a network response.

7.1 POLES AND ZEROS

Recall that a network function is defined as the ratio of the Laplace transform of a response to that of an excitation when the network is initially relaxed. Let us begin by observing a few elementary properties of network functions that should have become clear by now, even though some of them may not have been stated explicitly.

We are dealing with lumped, linear, time-invariant networks. The network function of such a network is a *rational function*, the ratio of two polynomials. Let us confirm this by examining the state equations for a non-degenerate network. Thus, from Chapter 4,

$$\frac{d}{dt}\mathbf{x} = \mathbf{A}\mathbf{x} + \sum_{i=0}^{\sigma} \mathbf{B}_i \mathbf{u}^{(i)} \tag{1a}$$

$$\mathbf{w} = \mathbf{C}\mathbf{x} + \sum_{i=0}^{\sigma-1} \mathbf{D}_i \mathbf{u}^{(i)} \tag{1b}$$

where **x**, **u** and **w** are the state, excitation, and output vectors, respectively.

Assuming the network is initially relaxed, let us take the Laplace transforms of these equations, solve the first one for $X(s)$, and substitute that expression for $X(s)$ into the second. The result will be*

$$X(s) = (sU - A)^{-1} \sum_{i=0}^{\sigma} B_i s^i U(s) \tag{2a}$$

$$W(s) = \{C(sU - A)^{-1} \sum_{i=0}^{\sigma} B_i s^i + \sum_{i=0}^{\sigma-1} D_i s^i\} U(s) \tag{2b}$$

The quantity in braces is the transfer matrix $H(s)$, each of whose elements is a network function. Thus,

$$H(s) = C(sU - A)^{-1} \sum_{i=0}^{\sigma} B_i s^i + \sum_{i=0}^{\sigma-1} D_i s^i. \tag{3}$$

Consider the first term of (3), in particular, $(sU - A)^{-1}$. We know that

$$(sU - A)^{-1} = \frac{\text{adj}\{sU - A\}}{\det\{sU - A\}}. \tag{4}$$

Now the elements of adj$\{sU - A\}$ are simply cofactors of $sU - A$ and hence are polynomials. This fact is not modified when adj $(sU - A)$ is premultiplied by **C** and postmultiplied by $\Sigma_{i=0}^{\sigma} B_i s^i$. Hence the first term is a matrix whose elements are polynomials divided by $\det\{sU - A\}$ — a polynomial in s. We have thus verified that the elements of the first term of (3) are rational functions of s. Since the elements of the second term, $\Sigma_{i=0}^{\sigma-1} D_i s^i$, are polynomials in s, the elements of the transfer matrix $H(s)$ — the sum of these two terms — are rational functions in s.

---

* Note that $u^{(i)}(0)$, $i = 0, \ldots, \sigma - 1$, does not appear in (2b) even though the derivatives of **u** appear in (1). This is dictated by the requirement that the network be initially relaxed. The reason is: Algebraic constraints on the dynamic component variables — inductor currents and capacitor voltages — may be found during Step 7 of the State Equation Algorithm; these constraints may require some (possibly linear combination of) elements of the $u^{(i)}(0)$ to be zero so as to meet the condition that the network be initially relaxed; so, we set all these elements of the $u^{(i)}(0)$ to zero. As it is only these elements of $u^{(i)}(0)$ — possibly as linear combinations — that can actually affect the response $W(s)$, we set the remaining elements of the $u^{(i)}(0)$ to zero for the convenience of not having the $u^{(i)}(0)$ appear even formally in the expression for $W(s)$. For example, if there is a loop having one independent voltage source and, otherwise, capacitors, then setting initial capacitor voltages to zero requires that the initial voltage source value also be zero. If this were the only such constraint, the output would be unaffected by any other initial source value; therefore, they could be set to zero for convenience.

Let $F(s)$ be the generic symbol for a network function. Since it is a rational function, it can be written as

$$F(s) = \frac{a_m s_m + a_{m-1} s^{m-1} + \ldots + a_1 s + a_0}{b_n s^n + b_{n-1} s^{n-1} + \ldots + b_1 s + b_0} \tag{5a}$$

or

$$F(s) = K\frac{(s-s_{z1})(s-s_{z2})\ldots(s-s_{zm})}{(s-s_{p1})(s-s_{p2})\ldots(s-s_{pn})}, \tag{5b}$$

where all the coefficients of s in (5a) are real because the elements of the matrices $\mathbf{A}$, $\mathbf{B}_i(i=1, \ldots, \sigma)$, $\mathbf{C}$, and $\mathbf{D}_i(i-1, \ldots, \sigma-1)$ are real. Now if s takes on only real values in (5a), then $F(s)$ will be real. A function of a complex variable that is real when the variable is real is called a *real function*. So network functions are real rational functions of s.

From this, the following *reflection property* immediately follows:

$$F(\bar{s}) = \bar{F}(s); \tag{6}$$

that is, a network function takes on conjugate values at conjugate points in the complex plane.

Now look at the second form in (5) in which the poles s_{pk} and the zeros s_{zk} are placed in evidence. Aside from a scale factor K, the network function is completely specified in terms of its poles and zeros, which determine its analytic properties. In fact, the poles and zeros provide a representation of a network function, as illustrated in Fig. 1. The zeros are shown by circles, and the poles, by crosses. We refer to such diagrams as *pole-zero patterns*, or *configurations*. Because of the reflection property (6), the poles and zeros of a network function are either real or occur in complex-conjugate pairs.

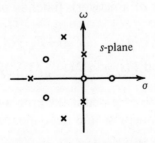

Fig. 1   Pole-zero pattern

Another simple property possessed by network functions follows from a consideration of stability. We know that the free response is governed by the poles of the network function. Since

$$\mathcal{L}^{-1}\left(\frac{a_{-k}}{(s-s_p)^k}\right) = \frac{a_{-k}t^{k-1}e^{s_p t}}{(k-1)!}, \tag{7}$$

we immediately conclude that the network function of a stable network cannot have any poles in the right half-plane, and any poles on the $j\omega$-axis must be simple. Otherwise, the free response would be unbounded and the network would be unstable.

This conclusion can be strengthened in the case of a driving-point function. Both driving-point impedance and admittance exhibit this property, and, since one is the reciprocal of the other, the driving-point functions can have neither poles nor zeros in the right half-plane. Furthermore, both poles and zeros on the $j\omega$-axis must be simple.

In the case of a transfer function, the reciprocal is not a network function. Hence we can say nothing about its zeros. They may lie anywhere in the complex plane, subject only to the reflection property.

7.2   EVEN AND ODD PARTS OF A NETWORK FUNCTION

Generally speaking, $F(s)$ will have both even and odd powers of s; it will be neither an even function nor an odd function of s. Hence we can write

$$F(s) = \text{Ev } F(s) + \text{Od } F(s), \tag{8}$$

where Ev $F(s)$ means "even part of $F(s)$," and Od $F(s)$ means "odd part of $F(s)$." Now an even function, say $g(s)$, is characterized by the property $g(-s) = g(s)$; and an odd function, say $h(s)$, by the property $h(-s) = -h(s)$. Using these properties together with (8), we can express the even and odd parts of a network function as follows:

$$\text{Ev } F(s) = \frac{1}{2}[F(s) + F(-s)], \tag{9a}$$

$$\text{Od } F(s) = \frac{1}{2}[F(s) - F(-s)]. \tag{9b}$$

Alternative forms can be obtained if the even and odd powers of s are grouped in both the numerator and denominator of $F(s)$. Thus, write

$$F(s) = \frac{m_1(s) + n_1(s)}{m_2(s) + n_2(s)}, \tag{10}$$

where $m_1(s)$ and $m_2(s)$ are even polynomials and $n_1(s)$ and $n_2(s)$ are odd polynomials. Then, using this in (9), we get

$$\text{Ev } F(s) = \frac{m_1(s)m_2(s) - n_1(s)n_2(s)}{m_2^2(s) - n_2^2(s)}, \tag{11a}$$

$$\text{Od } F(s) = \frac{n_1(s)m_2(s) - n_2(s)m_1(s)}{m_2^2(s) - n_2^2(s)}. \tag{11b}$$

Note that the denominator is the same for both the even and the odd part of $F(s)$, and it is an even polynomial. The numerator of Ev $F(s)$ is even, and that of Od $F(s)$ is odd, as they should be.

It is of interest to observe where the poles of both Ev $F(s)$ and Od $F(s)$ lie. From (9) it is clear that Ev $F(s)$ has poles where $F(s)$ has poles and also where $F(-s)$ has poles. But the poles of $F(-s)$ are the mirror images about the imaginary axis of the poles of $F(s)$. This can be illustrated by the following $F(s)$ and $F(-s)$:

$$F(s) = \frac{m_1(s) + n_1(s)}{(s+1)(s^2 + 2s + 2)},$$

$$F(-s) = \frac{m_1(s) - n_1(s)}{(-s+1)(s^2 + 2s + 2)}.$$

$F(s)$ has a negative real pole and a complex pair in the left half-plane. The poles of $F(-s)$ are the mirror images of these as shown in Fig. 2. Now Ev $F(s)$ has all the poles in Fig. 2, both those in the left half-plane (lhp) and those in the right half-plane (rhp).

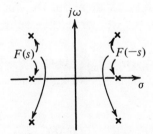

Fig. 2   Poles of Ev $F(s)$

The pole pattern in Fig. 2 possesses a certain symmetry. A pole configuration that has symmetry with respect to both the real and imaginary axes is said to have *quadrantal symmetry*. So we say that the poles of Ev $F(s)$ and Od $F(s)$ have quadrantal symmetry.

Now, $F(s)$ specifies a value of the function F for all complex values of s. Of all the values of s, of particular significence are those on the $j\omega$-axis. For $s = j\omega$, we are often interested in the behavior of one of the following quantities: real part, imaginary part, angle, and magnitude (or log magnitude). These are the quantities involved in the steady-state response to sinusoidal excitation. Any one of these quantities can be referred to as a *frequency response*. These components of a function are interrelated by

$$F(j\omega) = R(\omega) + jX(\omega) = |F(j\omega)|e^{j\phi(\omega)}, \tag{12}$$

where the meanings of the symbols are obvious.

Look at (9) under the assumption that $s = j\omega$; what becomes of the even and odd parts of $F(j\omega)$? Since $F(-j\omega) = F(\overline{j\omega}) = \overline{F}(j\omega)$ by (6), we see that

$$\text{Ev } F(j\omega) = \tfrac{1}{2}[F(j\omega) + \overline{F}(j\omega)] = \text{Re } F(j\omega) = R(\omega), \tag{13a}$$

$$\text{Od } F(j\omega) = \tfrac{1}{2}[F(j\omega) - \overline{F}(j\omega)] = j \text{ Im } F(j\omega) = jX(\omega). \tag{13b}$$

That is to say, the real part of a function on the $j\omega$-axis is its even part; the imaginary part on the $j\omega$-axis is its odd part divided by j. Another way of stating this is to say that the real part of $F(j\omega)$ is an even function of angular frequency ω, and the imaginary part is an odd function of ω.

7.3   MAGNITUDE AND ANGLE OF A NETWORK FUNCTION

Similar statements can be made about the magnitude and angle. Using the notation of (12), we can write the square of $F(j\omega)$ as follows:

$$F^2(j\omega) = F(j\omega)F(-j\omega)\frac{F(j\omega)}{F(-j\omega)} = |F(j\omega)|^2 e^{j2\phi(\omega)}$$

Hence,

$$|F(j\omega)|^2 = F(j\omega)F(-j\omega), \tag{14a}$$

$$\phi(\omega) = \frac{1}{2j}\ln\frac{F(j\omega)}{F(-j\omega)}. \tag{14b}$$

Upon replacing ω by $-\omega$, it is seen that the *magnitude-squared function* is an even rational function of ω. Observe also that $|F(j\omega)|^2$ is the value of the even rational function $G(s) = F(s)F(-s)$ on the $j\omega$-axis. It is of interest to note that both the poles and zeros of $G(s)$ occur in quadrantal symmetry, a fact that is true of any even rational function.

For the angle—also known as the phase—we get

$$\phi(-\omega) = \frac{1}{2j}\ln\frac{F(-j\omega)}{F(j\omega)} = -\frac{1}{2j}\ln\frac{F(j\omega)}{F(-j\omega)} = -\phi(\omega). \qquad (15)$$

Hence, we are tempted to say that the angle is an odd function of ω. However, the angle is a multivalued function. Only by remaining on the appropriate Riemann surface can that claim about the *angle* (or *phase*) *function* be made.

A transfer function will be called *ideal* if it is of the form $F(s) = e^{-s\tau}$. For $s = j\omega$, the magnitude identically equals 1, and the angle is proportional to ω. If a network having this transfer function is excited by a signal $u(t)$, the response of the network, in view of the shifting theorem of Laplace transform theory, will be $w(t) = u(t - \tau)$. The response signal is the same as the excitation except that it is delayed in time by an amount τ, called the *time delay*. Since $\phi(\omega) = -\omega\tau$ for the ideal function, the time delay is the negative derivative of the angle function.

On the basis of the preceding, a function called the delay is defined for an arbitrary transfer function as the negative derivative of the phase function. Thus,

$$\tau(\omega) = -\frac{d}{d\omega}\phi(\omega) \qquad (16)$$

is the *delay function*. In contrast with the angle function, the delay is a rational function and even.

As an illustration of this fact, consider the transfer function

$$F(s) = \frac{s+1}{s+2}.$$

Corresponding to this function,

$$\phi(\omega) = \frac{1}{2j}\ln\frac{(1+j\omega)(2-j\omega)}{(1-j\omega)(2+j\omega)} = \frac{1}{2j}\ln\ e^{j2(\tan^{-1}\omega - \tan^{-1}\omega/2)}$$

Then, the delay function is

$$\tau(\omega) = -\frac{d\phi}{d\omega} = -\frac{d}{d\omega}\left(\tan^{-1}\omega - \tan^{-1}\frac{\omega}{2}\right)$$

$$= -\frac{1}{1-\omega^2} + \frac{2}{1-(\omega/2)^2} = \frac{1 - \frac{7}{4}\omega^2}{(1 - \frac{1}{4}\omega^2)(1 - \omega^2)}$$

This is seen to be an even function.

7.4 MINIMUM-PHASE FUNCTIONS

As we observed earlier in this chapter, the zeros of transfer functions can occur in any part of the complex plane. However, those functions that have no zeros in the right half-plane have certain distinct properties. We say that a transfer function that has no zeros in the right half-plane is *minimum phase*. Conversely, any transfer function that has zeros (even one zero) in the right half-plane is labeled *non-minimum-phase*.

In order to determine the effect of right half-plane zeros on the magnitude and angle of a transfer function, consider Fig. 3(a). This shows a pair of conjugate zeros in the left half-plane and the right half-plane image of this pair. Let $P_r(s)$ and $P_l(s)$ be quadratic polynomials that have the right half-plane pair of factors and the left half-plane factors, respectively; that is,

$$P_r(s) = (s - s_0)(s - \bar{s}_0), \qquad (17a)$$

$$P_l(s) = (s + s_0)(s + \bar{s}_0). \qquad (17b)$$

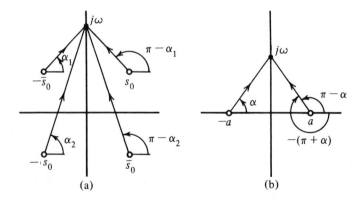

(a)   (b)

Fig. 3   Complex and real zeros in quadrantal symmetry

It is clear that $P_r(s) = P_l(-s)$. The geometrical construction in the figure indicates that the magnitudes of $P_r(s)$ and $P_l(s)$ are the same when $s = j\omega$. As for the angles, we find

$$\arg P_r(j\omega) = \pi - \alpha_1 + [(\pi - \alpha_2) - 2\pi] = -(\alpha_1 + \alpha_2), \qquad (18a)$$

$$\arg P_l(j\omega) = \alpha_1 + \alpha_2 = -\arg P_r(j\omega). \qquad (18b)$$

Note that in order for the angle of P_r to be zero at $\omega = 0$—as it must be if the angle is to be an odd function—we had to write the angle of $(s - \bar{s}_0)$ as $-(\pi + \alpha_2)$, rather than $\pi - \alpha_2$. The difference of 2π corresponds to specifying the angle on one Riemann surface rather than on another. The main reason for the desire that the angle be odd is that it simplifies the statement of many theorems that we shall present later in the chapter.

It is clear from Fig. 3 that $\alpha_1 + \alpha_2$, the angle contributed by the left half-plane zeros, is positive for all positive ω. It runs from 0 at $\omega = 0$ to π at infinity. This is illustrated in Fig. 4. It follows, then, that the angle of a pair of conjugate right half-plane zeros is always negative for positive values of ω, running from 0 at $\omega = 0$ to $-\pi$ at infinity.

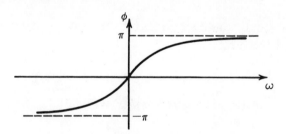

Fig. 4   Angle of a pair of complex left half-plane zeros

Let us now consider the situation in Fig. 3(b), which shows a real zero on the negative real axis and its right half-plane image. Again, the magnitudes of the two factors $(j\omega + a)$ and $(j\omega - a)$ are equal. The angle of the left half-plane factor $(j\omega + a)$ is α for a positive ω. (It will be $-\alpha$ for negative ω.) We shall choose the angle of the right half-plane factor $(j\omega - a)$ to be $-(\pi + \alpha)$ for positive ω and $\pi - \alpha$ for negative ω in order to make the angle function odd. Sketches of these angles are shown in Fig. 5. Note that there is a discontinuity of 2π in the second figure that is introduced simply by our desire to make the angle an odd function. This discontinuity corresponds to jumping from one Riemann surface to another.

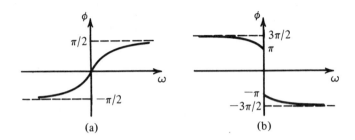

Fig. 5 **Examples of angle functions:** (a) arg $(j\omega + a)$;
(b) arg $(j\omega - a)$

Now, if we have two real right half-plane zeros, we can define the angles in such a way that this discontinuity is eliminated. The situation becomes similar to the case of a pair of conjugate right half-plane zeros. Thus, a jump in phase occurs at the origin only when a transfer function has an odd number of right half-plane zeros.

7.4.1 All-Pass and Minimum-Phase Functions

With this discussion as background, let us now consider the following two transfer functions:

$$F_1(s) = (s - s_0)(s - \bar{s}_0)F(s) = P_t(-s)F(s), \tag{19a}$$

$$F_2(s) = (s + s_0)(s + \bar{s}_0)F(s) = P_t(s)F(s), \tag{19b}$$

where s_0 and its conjugate lie in the right half-plane. These two functions are identical except that $F_1(s)$ has a pair of right half-plane zeros, whereas in $F_2(s)$ these are replaced by their left half-plane images. (The common function $F(s)$ may have additional right half-plane factors.) Suppose we multiply numerator and denominator of $F_1(s)$ by the left half-plane factors $(s + s_0)(s + \bar{s}_0) = P_t(s)$. The result will be

$$F_1(s) = \frac{P_t(s)}{P_t(s)}P_t(-s)F(s) = F_2(s)\frac{P_t(-s)}{P_t(s)} = F_2(s)F_0(s), \tag{20}$$

where

$$F_0(s) = \frac{P_t(-s)}{P_t(s)} = \frac{(s - s_0)(s - \bar{s}_0)}{(s + s_0)(s + \bar{s}_0)}. \tag{21}$$

Let us define an *all-pass function* as a transfer function all of whose zeros are in the right half-plane and whose poles are the left half-plane images of its zeros. It is clear, therefore, that an all-pass function has unit magnitude for all values of $s = j\omega$. (This is the reason for its name.) A consideration of the last equation now shows that $F_0(s)$ is an all-pass function. It is a second-order all-pass function, the order referring the the number of poles. From (18), the angle of $F_0(j\omega)$ is found to be

$$\arg F_0(j\omega) = \arg P_t(-j\omega) - \arg P_t(j\omega) = -2(\alpha_1 + \alpha_2). \quad (22)$$

From this we conclude that the angle of an all-pass function is negative for all positive frequencies.

Using this equation and (20), we can now write

$$\arg F_1(j\omega) = \arg F_2(j\omega) + \arg F_0(j\omega) < \arg F_2(j\omega) \ (\omega > 0). \quad (23)$$

This result tells us that, at all positive frequencies the angle of a function having right half-plane zeros is less than that of the function obtained when a pair of these zeros is replaced by its left half-plane image.

This procedure of expressing a transfer function as the product of two others may be repeated. At each step a pair of complex zeros or a real zero from the right half-plane is replaced by the left half-plane images. A sequence of functions, of which F_1 and F_2 are the first two, will be obtained. Each member of the sequence will have fewer right half-plane zeros than the preceding one. The last member in this sequence will have no right half-plane zeros. Let us label it $F_m(s)$. By definition, $F_m(s)$ is a minimum-phase function (as the subscript is meant to imply). Using (23), and similar results for the other functions, we can write

$$\arg F_1(j\omega) < \arg F_2(j\omega) < \ldots < F_m(j\omega) \ (\omega > 0). \quad (24)$$

Each of the functions in this sequence will have the same j-axis magnitude, but the angles get progressively larger. Paradoxically, the minimum-phase function will have the largest angle of all (algebraically, but not necessarily in magnitude). The reason for this apparent inconsistency is the following. We have defined a transfer function as the ratio of an output transform to an input transform. When the minimum-phase concept was first introduced by Bode, he defined a transfer function in an inverse manner. With such a definition the inequalities in (24) would be reversed, and the minimum-phase function would have the smallest angle algebraically.

At each step in the above procedure a second-order or first-order all-pass function is obtained. The product of any number of all-pass functions is again an all-pass function. It follows that *any non-minimum-phase transfer function can be written as the product of a minimum-phase function and an all-pass function*; that is,

$$F(s) = F_m(s)F_a(s), \tag{25}$$

where F_m is a minimum phase and F_a an all-pass function.

7.4.2 Net Change in Angle

We can establish one other result from a consideration of the variation of the angle of an all-pass function as ω increases from zero to infinity. Equation 22, together with Fig. 3(a), shows that the change in angle, defined as the angle at $\omega = +\infty$ minus the angle at $\omega = 0$, for a second-order all-pass function is -2π. Similarly, for a first-order all-pass function, we can show that this change is $-\pi$, not counting the discontinuity at $\omega = 0$. If n is even, there will be no discontinuity; however, if n is odd, there will be a discontinuity of $-\pi$, and the total change in angle will become $-n\pi - \pi$. Thus,

$$\Delta\phi = -n\pi \quad (n \text{ even})$$
$$= -(n+1)\pi \quad (n \text{ odd}). \tag{26}$$

Consider now a non-minimum-phase function that has n zeros in the right half-plane. This can be expressed as the product of a minimum-phase function and an nth-order all-pass function. The net change in angle of the non-minimum-phase function as ω varies from zero to plus infinity will be the net change in angle of the corresponding minimum-phase function, plus the net change in angle of the all-pass function. Since this latter is a negative quantity, it follows that a non-minimum-phase function has a smaller net change in angle (again, only algebraically), as ω varies from zero to infinity, than the corresponding minimum-phase function, the difference being $n\pi$ or $(n+1)\pi$, where n is the number of right half-plane zeros.

It is also of interest to determine what the net change in the angle of a minimum-phase function will be as ω varies from zero to plus infinity. The angle contributed by each zero to this net change is $\pi/2$, whereas that contributed by each pole is $-\pi/2$. Hence the net change in angle will be $\pi/2$ times the number of finite zeros minus the number of finite poles. Thus, *if a transfer function is regular at s = ∞, the minimum-phase function will have a smaller* $|\Delta\phi|$ *than the corresponding non-minimum-phase function*, since both angles are nonpositive.

7.4.3 Hurwitz Polynomials

Let us now consider another aspect of minimum-phase and non-minimum-phase functions; namely, some relationships between the coefficients of a polynomial and the locations of its zeros. Polynomials with no zeros in the open right half-plane are called *Hurwitz polynomials*. If, in addition, there are no zeros on the $j\omega$-axis, the polynomial is called *strictly Hurwitz*, for emphasis. Thus the numerator polynomial of a minimum phase function is Hurwitz.

Now a necessary condition for a polynomial to be Hurwitz is that all its coefficients have the same sign; however, that is not a sufficient condition. (You can easily make up a counterexample to demonstrate this.) That is to say, some polynomials with zeros in the right half-plane can have all positive (or all negative) coefficients. However, if a polynomial has coefficients of only one sign, there will be a limitation on the permissible locations of its zeros. The limitation is given by the following theorem:

THEOREM 2. *If a real polynomial P(s) of degree n has coefficients of only one sign, it will have no zeros in the open s-plane sector given by* $|\arg s| < \pi/n$.

The excluded region is shown in Fig. 6.* In the limiting case, if the only nonzero coefficients of a polynomial are the first and last, that is, if $P(s) = a_n s^n + a_0$, then there will be a zero on the boundary; that is, with $|\arg s| = \pi/n$.

Note that the converse of the theorem is not generally true; that is, if the zeros of a polynomial are excluded from the sector $|\arg s| < \pi/n$, the coefficients need not all have the same sign. Thus the polynomials

$$P_1(s) = s^3 + 0.2s^2 + 0.2s + 1,$$

$$P_2(s) = s^3 + s^2 - 0.44s + 1.8,$$

$$P_3(s) = s^3 - 0.3s^2 + 0.6s + 0.5$$

---

* For a proof using the principle of the argument see Norman Balabanian, *Network Synthesis*, Prentice-Hall, Englewood Cliffs, N.J., 1958.

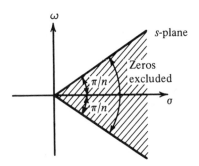

**Fig. 6   Forbidden region for zeros of a polynomial
with coefficients of one sign**

all have a real negative zero and the same right half-plane factor
$s^2 - 0.8s + 1$ whose zeros do not lie in the sector $|\arg s| < \pi/3$; yet two of
the polynomials have coefficients with different signs.

7.5   DETERMINING A NETWORK FUNCTION FROM ITS MAGNITUDE

The preceding sections have been largely concerned with giving
characterizations of and determining the properties of a network function. Given a rational function, it is possible to determine, among other
things, its real and imaginary parts, and its magnitude and angle. We
shall now consider the inverse operation, that of reconstructing a network function when only its magnitude or angle is known. The corresponding reconstruction task starting with its real part or imaginary
part is left for you to do as a project. (See Proj. 4.)

We start first with a consideration of the magnitude-squared function. (This is simpler to talk about than the magnitude function.)
Necessary conditions for a rational function $G(j\omega)$ to be the magnitude
squared of a network function on the $j\omega$-axis are quite simple: $G(j\omega)$
must be an even function of ω and, for a passive network, the degree of
the numerator must not exceed that of the denominator by more than 2.
(This is because the network function of a passive network cannot have
more than a simple pole at infinity.) In addition, any finite poles of $G(s)$
on the $j\omega$-axis must be double, since the poles of a (stable) network
function itself on the $j\omega$-axis must be simple. A similar statement
applies to $j\omega$-axis zeros in the case of a driving-point function.

Given such a $G(j\omega)$, we replace $j\omega$ by s; then all that is left is to identify the poles and zeros of the network function $F(s)$ from those of $G(s)$.
The poles and zeros of $G(s)$ occur with quadrantal symmetry. Since $F(s)$
must be regular in the right half-plane, we see, by looking at (15), that

all the left half-plane poles of $G(s)$ must be assigned to the network function $F(s)$. [The right half-plane poles of $G(s)$ will be mirror images of these and will automatically become poles of $F(-s)$.] Any poles of $G(s)$ on the $j\omega$-axis will be double and will be assigned as simple poles to $F(s)$. As for the zeros, the answer is not as clear-cut. There is generally no limitation on the locations of zeros of a network function, unless it is a driving-point function in which case the zeros must lie in the closed left half-plane, being simple on the $j\omega$-axis. For transfer functions, we need not assign to $F(s)$ all the left half-plane zeros of $G(s)$. Thus the zeros of $F(s)$ are not uniquely determined from a given $G(s)$, unless the transfer function is specified to be minimum-phase. In this case the zeros of $F(s)$, as well as the poles, must lie in the closed left half-plane.

7.5.1   Examples: Filter Functions

Let us now consider some examples that illustrate this procedure and are of practical interest. The requirement on most common electrical filters is for a transfer function whose $j\omega$-axis magnitude is ideally constant over a given frequency interval—referred to as the *pass band*—and ideally zero over the rest of the $j\omega$-axis—referred to as the *stop band*. It is not possible for the $j\omega$-axis magnitude of a rational function to behave in this manner. (Why?) However, it is possible to find transfer functions whose $j\omega$-axis magnitudes approximate the desired magnitude in some fashion or other.

Consider the ideal low-pass filter function shown in Fig. 7(a). Two possible ways of approximating this ideal function are shown in parts (b) and (c) of the figure. The first of these is called a *maximally flat*, or *Butterworth*, *approximation*, whereas the second one is called an *equal-ripple*, or *Chebyshev*, *approximation*. The Butterworth approximation is monotonic in both the pass and the stop band, the maximum error occurring near the edge of the band. On the other hand, the Chebyshev

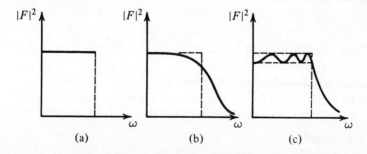

(a)   (b)   (c)

Fig. 7   Low-pass filter: (a) ideal; (b) Butterworth; (c) Chebyshev

approximation is oscillatory in the pass band, the peaks of the ripples being equal. In this way the error is distributed more uniformly over the pass band.

Aside from a scale factor, analytical forms of these functions, for a normalized bandwidth of unity, are given by

$$|F(j\omega)|^2 = \frac{1}{1 + \omega^{2n}} \text{ (maximally flat)} \tag{27}$$

and

$$|F(j\omega)|^2 = \frac{1}{1 + \delta^2 T_n^2(\omega)} \text{ (equal ripple)}, \tag{28}$$

where δ is a small number that controls the ripple amplitude and $T_n(\omega)$ is a Chebyshev polynomial* defined by

$$T_n(s/j) = \cosh(n \cosh^{-1} s/j), \tag{29}$$

which reduces, on substituting $s = j\omega$, to

$$T_n(\omega) = \cos(n \cos^{-1} \omega) \text{ for } |\omega| \leqslant 1. \tag{30}$$

Our problem now is to find the transfer function $F(s)$ when its $j\omega$-axis squared magnitude is known. Note: Maximally flat filters can have finite zeros; only those maximally-flat filters having no finite zeros are called Butterworth filters.

7.5.2 Maximally Flat Response

Let us first consider the Butterworth response. According to the preceding discussion, we first replace ω^2 by $-s^2$ in (27). The result is

$$G(s) = F(s)F(-s) = \frac{1}{1 + (-1)^n s^{2n}}. \tag{31}$$

---

* The use of the letter T for the Chebyshev polynomial is a legacy of the past. Some of Chebyshev's work was first published in French, leading to the use of the French alliteration "Tschebyscheff," or its variation "Tchebycheff." This spelling of the name has now been discarded in the American literature.

This function has no finite zeros, so we need only factor the denominator. In the present case this is a relatively simple task. The zeros of the denominator are found by writing

$$s^{2n} = e^{j(2k-1+n)\pi} \tag{32}$$

which is simply

$$s^{2n} = -(-1)^n.$$

Taking the $2n$th root in (32), we find the poles of $G(s)$ to be

$$s_k = e^{j(2k-1+n)\pi/2n}, \quad k = 1, 2, \ldots, 2n. \tag{33}$$

Thus, there are $2n$ poles, each of which has unit magnitude. The poles are uniformly distributed on the unit circle, as shown in Fig. 8 for the case $n = 4$. Notice that the imaginary parts of the poles lie in the pass band — in the range $\omega < 1$.

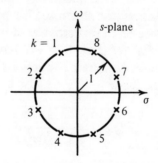

Fig. 8   Butterworth pole distribution for $n = 4$

To form $F(s)$ we simply take the n left half-plane poles of $G(s)$. These are the ones given by values of k from 1 to n. For $n = 4$ these will be

$$s_1 = e^{j(5\pi/8)}, \qquad\qquad s_3 = e^{j(9\pi/8)},$$

$$s_2 = e^{j(7\pi/8)}, \qquad\qquad s_4 = e^{j(11\pi/8)}.$$

Finally, for the case $n = 4$,

$$F(s) = \frac{1}{(s-s_1)(s-s_2)(s-s_3)(s-s_4)}$$

$$= \frac{1}{1 + 2.613s + 3.414s^2 + 2.613s^3 + s^4} \tag{34}$$

The coefficients of the Butterworth polynomials up to order 10 and the factors of these polynomials are given in Tables 1 and 2, respectively, for reference purposes.

The designation "maximally flat" is a result of the following consideration. Suppose a Taylor series of the function in (27) is written (by long division, say) for the region $\omega < 1$. The error between the desired magnitude function in this range, namely 1, and the series will be

$$1 - |F(j\omega)|^2 = \omega^{2n} - \omega^{4n} + \dots \tag{35}$$

In view of the relationship of the coefficients in a Taylor series to derivatives of a function and since the Taylor series for the error starts with the ω^{2n} power, this means the first $n-1$ derivaties with respect to ω^2 are 0 at $\omega = 0$. Hence the name maximally flat.

The Butterworth function just illustrated is a particularly simple maximally flat function, since all of its zeros are at infinity. It is possible to introduce a maximally flat function that will have some finite zeros. A glance back at the magnitude-squared functions in (27) and (28) shows that they are both of the form

$$|F(j\omega)|^2 = \frac{1}{1 + f(\omega^2)}. \tag{36}$$

where $f(\omega^2)$ is an even function of ω; the argument is expressed as ω^2 to accent this fact. In the case of the Butterworth function, $f(\omega^2)$ is simply a power of ω^2. (In the equal-ripple case, it is a not-so-trivial polynomial of ω^2.)

Now suppose that $f(\omega^2)$ is the rational function

$$f(\omega^2) = \frac{\omega^{2n}}{P(\omega^2)}, \tag{37}$$

where

$$P(\omega^2) = 1 + a_2\omega^2 + a_4\omega^4 + \dots + a_{2k}\omega^{2k}$$

Table 1 Coefficients of Butterworth Polynomials: $b_0 + b_1 s + \ldots + b_n s^n$

Order n	b_1	b_2	b_3	b_4	b_5	b_6	b_7	b_8	b_9
2	1.4142	2.0000							
3	2.0000	3.4142	2.6131						
4	2.6131	5.2361	5.2361	3.2361					
5	3.2361	7.4641	9.1416	7.4641	3.8637				
6	3.8637	10.0978	14.5920	14.5920	10.0978	4.4940			
7	4.4940	13.1371	21.8462	25.6884	21.8462	13.1371	5.1258		
8	5.1528	16.5817	31.1634	41.9864	41.9864	31.1634	16.5817	5.7588	
9	5.7588	20.4317	42.8021	64.8824	74.2334	64.8824	42.8021	20.4317	6.3925

Note: b_0 and b_n are always unity.

Table 2 Factors of Butterworth Polynomials

Order n	Factors
1	$s + 1$
2	$s^2 + 1.4142s + 1$
3	$(s + 1)(s^2 + s + 1)$
4	$(s^2 + 0.7654s + 1)(s^2 + 1.8478s + 1)$
5	$(s + 1)(s^2 + 0.6180s + 1)(s^2 + 1.6180s + 1)$
6	$(s^2 + 0.5176s + 1)(s^2 + 1.4142s + 1)(s^2 + 1.9319s + 1)$
7	$(s + 1)(s^2 + 0.4450s + 1)(s^2 + 1.2470s + 1)(s^2 + 1.8019s + 1)$
8	$(s^2 + 0.3002s + 1)(s^2 + 1.1111s + 1)(s^2 + 1.1663s + 1)(s^2 + 1.9616s + 1)$
9	$(s + 1)(s^2 + 0.3473s + 1)(s^2 + s + 1)(s^2 + 1.5321s + 1)(s^2 + 1.8794s + 1)$
10	$(s^2 + 0.3129s + 1)(s^2 + 0.9080s + 1)(s^2 + 1.4142s + 1)(s^2 + 1.7820s + 1)(s^2 + 1.9754s + 1)$

is a polynomial whose order, $2k$ in ω, is less than $2n$. Then $|F(j\omega)|^2$ and the difference between the desired function in the pass band, namely 1, and this function will be, respectively,

$$|F(j\omega)|^2 = \frac{P(\omega^2)}{P(\omega^2) + \omega^{2n}}, \qquad (38)$$

and

$$1 - |F(j\omega)|^2 = \frac{\omega^{2n}}{P(\omega^2) + \omega^{2n}} = \omega^{2n}[1 - a_2\omega^2 + (a_4 + a_2^2)\omega^4 - \ldots]. \qquad (39)$$

In the last step a power series was obtained by long division. Again the series starts with the term ω^{2n}, and so the first $n-1$ derivatives of the error with respect to ω^2 are 0 at $\omega = 0$. The magnitude-square function in (38) is, therefore, also maximally flat. In contrast with the Butterworth function, it does have some finite zeros.

As an illustration consider the following magnitude-squared function:

$$|F(j\omega)|^2 = \frac{1.838 - 1.346\omega^2 + 0.246\omega^4}{1.838 - 1.346\omega^2 + 0.246\omega^4 + \omega^8} = \frac{(1.355 - 0.496\omega^2)^2}{(1.355 - 0.496\omega^2)^2 + \omega^8}.$$

Note that corresponding coefficients of numerator and denominator are equal up to the highest power of the numerator, as required by (38). Setting $\omega^2 = -s^2$ leads to

$$F(s)F(-s) = \frac{(1.355 + 0.496s^2)^2}{(1.355 + 0.496s^2)^2 + s^8)}$$

$$= \frac{(1.355 + 0.496s^2)}{(s^2 + 1.9s + 1)(s^2 + 1.05s + 1.355)}$$

$$\times \frac{(1.355 + 0.496s^2)}{(s^2 - 1.9s + 1)(s^2 - 1.05s + 1.355)}$$

or

$$F(s) = \frac{0.496(s^2 + 2.73)}{(s^2 + 1.9s + 1)(s^2 + 1.05s + 1.355)}.$$

Note that the imaginary axis double zeros of $F(s)F(-s)$ are assigned equally to $F(s)$ and to $F(-s)$. The locations of the poles and zeros of

$F(s)$ are shown in Fig. 9 and are compared with the poles of the fourth-order Butterworth function, indicated by the large dots.

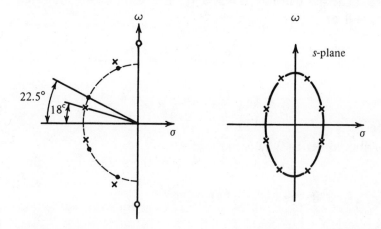

Fig. 9 Pole locations for example (Dots correspond to poles of Butterworth response.)

Fig. 10 Chebyshev pole distribution for $n = 4$

7.5.3 Chebyshev Response

Next let us consider the Chebyshev response in (28). The first step is to replace $j\omega$ by s. We then set the denominator equal to zero in order to locate the poles. The result using (29) is

$$T_n\left(\frac{s}{j}\right) = \cosh\left(n \cosh^{-1}\frac{s}{j}\right) = \frac{\pm j}{\delta}. \qquad (40)$$

In order to solve this equation let us define a new variable $w = x + jy$ and write

$$s = j \cosh w = j \cosh(x + jy). \qquad (41)$$

Consequently,

$$T_n\left(\frac{s}{j}\right) = \cosh nw = \cosh n(x + jy) = \frac{\pm j}{\delta}. \qquad (42)$$

If we now expand $\cosh nw$ in the last equation and equate real parts and imaginary parts on both sides of the equation, we will find the values of

x and y that satisfy the equation. When these values are substituted into (41) we find the corresponding values of s. These are the pole locations. If we designate them by $s_k = \sigma_k + j\omega_k$, the result of the indicated operations will be

$$\sigma_k = \sinh\left(\frac{1}{n}\sinh^{-1}\frac{1}{\delta}\right)\sin\frac{2k-1}{n}\frac{\pi}{2}, \tag{43a}$$

$$\omega_k = \cosh\left(\frac{1}{n}\sinh^{-1}\frac{1}{\delta}\right)\cos\frac{2k-1}{n}\frac{\pi}{2}. \tag{43b}$$

You should verify these equations.

In order to get some interpretation for these seemingly monstrous expressions, divide each of them by the hyperbolic function, square both sides, and add; the result will be

$$\frac{\sigma_k^2}{\sinh^2\left(\dfrac{1}{n}\sinh^{-1}\dfrac{1}{\delta}\right)} + \frac{\omega_k^2}{\cosh^2\left(\dfrac{1}{n}\sinh^{-1}\dfrac{1}{\delta}\right)} = 1. \tag{44}$$

This is the equation of an ellipse in the s-plane. The major axis of the ellipse will lie along the $j\omega$-axis, since the hyperbolic cosine of a real variable is always greater than the hyperbolic sine. The pole locations for $n = 4$ are shown in Fig. 10.

Finally, the left half-plane poles of $G(s)$ are allotted to $F(s)$, and the task is again complete.

For a typical case, if the permissible ripple is given as $\delta = 0.1$ and the order is $n = 4$, the pole locations are found from (43), from which we get the transfer function

$$\begin{aligned}
F(s) &= \frac{1}{(s^2 + 0.644s + 1.534)(s^2 + 1.519s + 0.823)}\\[2mm]
&= \frac{1}{s^4 + 2.16s^3 + 3.31s^2 + 2.86s + 1.26}.
\end{aligned}$$

7.6 INTEGRAL RELATIONSHIPS BETWEEN REAL AND IMAGINARY PARTS

In the preceding section, algebraic procedures were described or alluded to for determining a network function as a rational function of s, given one of the components of the function as a rational function, where by "a component of a function" we mean one of the quantities: magnitude, angle (actually, the associated tangent function), real part, or imaginary part. One drawback of these procedures is that the given component must already be in a realizable rational form. If, say, the magnitude is specified graphically or even analytically but not as a rational function, it is necessary first to find a realizable rational approximation to the given function before proceeding to find the network function and, from that, any of the other components.

Network functions are analytic functions of a complex variable, and hence their real and imaginary parts are related by the Cauchy-Riemann equations. For $s = \sigma + j\omega$ and with $F(s)$ written as $R(\sigma,\omega) + jX(\sigma,\omega)$, these equations are:

$$\frac{\partial R}{\partial \sigma} = \frac{\partial X}{\partial \omega} \tag{45a}$$

$$\frac{\partial X}{\partial \sigma} = -\frac{\partial R}{\partial \omega} \tag{45b}$$

Clearly, these equations are implicit relationships and do not provide explicit formulas for computing one component from the other. In this section we shall present a number of relationships between the parts of a network function. These are well known in mathematics as *Hilbert transforms*. However, since they were first used in network theory by Bode, we shall refer to them as the *Bode formulas*. One immediate advantage of these relationships is that the specified component of a function can be given merely as a graph; beyond this, the Bode formulas have many useful implications and applications, some of which we shall discuss.

Since we are dealing with analytic functions of a complex variable, one point of departure for relating components of a function could be Cauchy's integral formula, which states that

$$F(s) = \frac{1}{2\omega j} \oint_C \frac{F(z)}{z-s} dz. \tag{46}$$

In this expression C is a closed contour within and on which $F(s)$ is regular; z represents points on the contour, whereas s is any point inside. If we were to let the contour be a circle and express both z and s in polar coordinates, we could express the real and imaginary parts of $F(s)$ in terms of either its real part or its imaginary part on the circle. Then, by means of a transformation, the circle would be mapped into the imaginary axis. The expressions, relating the real and imaginary parts that would ensue are referred to as Hilbert transforms.

An alternative approach, which we shall adopt, is to start with Cauchy's integral theorem. This theorem states that the contour integral of a function around a path within and on which the function is regular will vanish. In order to apply this theorem, it is necessary to know (1) the integration contour and (2) the function to be integrated. In the present problem the contour of integration should include the $j\omega$-axis, since we want the final result to involve the $j\omega$-axis real and imaginary parts of a network function. Consequently, since the functions we are dealing with are regular in the entire right half-plane, the contour of integration we shall choose will consist of the $j\omega$-axis and an infinite semicircular arc in the right half-plane. By Cauchy's theorem, the complete contour integral will be zero. Hence it remains only to calculate the contributions from each part of the contour.

Let $F(s)$ be a network function of either the driving-point or the transfer type; in the usual way write

$$F(j\omega) = R(\omega) + jX(\omega), \tag{47a}$$

or

$$\ln F(j\omega) = \alpha(\omega) + j\phi(\omega), \tag{47b}$$

where $\alpha(\omega) = \ln|F(j\omega)|$ is the (logarithmic) gain function and $\phi(\omega)$ is the angle function. If $F(s)$ is a driving-point function, it will have neither zeros nor poles in the right half-plane. Hence $\ln F(s)$ will be regular there. If $F(s)$ is a transfer function, then $\ln F(s)$ will be regular in the right half-plane only if $F(s)$ is a minimum-phase function. Hence the results we develop will apply both to $F(s)$ and to $\ln F(s)$ so long as $F(s)$ is a minimum-phase function.

Let us now consider possible poles of $F(s)$ on the finite $j\omega$-axis. We know that any such poles must be simple. In carrying out the contour integration such poles must be bypassed by a small indentation to the right. The contribution of this indentation to the total integral is $2\pi j$ times half the residue of the integrand at the pole. Our objective is to obtain expressions relating the real part of a network function to the imaginary part, so that when one of these is given, the other can be calculated. Thus we are not likely at the outset to know the residues at the $j\omega$-axis poles. Hence we shall assume that $F(s)$ has no poles on the $j\omega$-axis, including the points zero and infinity. So, $F(s)$ is assumed regular at zero and infinity.

If $F(s)$ has a pole on the $j\omega$-axis, then $\ln F(s)$ will have a logarithmic singularity there. If the integrand in question involves $\ln F(s)$, we shall again indent the contour about this singularity. But because the singularity is logarithmic, this indentation will contribute nothing to the contour integral. Hence, if the integrand we choose involves $\ln F(s)$, we can permit $F(s)$ to have simple poles on the $j\omega$-axis. In the following discussion we shall always take the function in the integrand to be $F(s)$. However, identical results apply if we replace $F(s)$ by $\ln F(s)$. In the formulas $R(\omega)$ can be replaced by $\alpha(\omega)$, and $X(\omega)$ by $\phi(\omega)$.

Let us now consider integrating a network function $F(s)$, which is regular on the extended $j\omega$-axis, around the contour shown in Fig. 11(a), which consists of the entire $j\omega$-axis and an infinite semicircular arc to the right. By Cauchy's theorem, the integral of $F(s)$ will be zero. Our procedure will be to evaluate the contributions of those parts of the contour that we can evaluate and then to express the remaining parts in terms of these. With these ideas, it is obvious that we shall not be able to obtain the type of relationship we are looking for with $F(s)$ alone as the integrand. No particular point on the $j\omega$-axis is singled out and attention directed thereto.

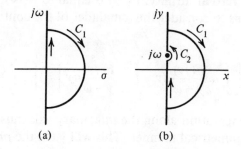

Fig. 11   Path of integration

Suppose we divide $F(s)$ by $s - j\omega_0$ before integrating, where ω_0 is any value of ω. This will put a pole of the integrand on the $j\omega$-axis. In order to apply Cauchy's theorem, we shall have to bypass this pole with a small semicircular arc C_2, as shown in Fig. 11(b). The contour now includes the arc C_2. Thus, the contribution on arc C_2 will have to be evaluated. This will focus attention on the value of $F(s)$ at $s = j\omega_0$. Note that the result of the integration will not be a function of s, which is only a dummy variable of integration, but of ω_0, which is an arbitrary point on the $j\omega$-axis. It will be convenient to use a different symbol for the dummy variable; let us use $z = x + jy$. Then the point $j\omega_0$ can be relabeled $j\omega$.

If $F(s)$ is a network function that is regular in the closed right half-plane, application of Cauchy's theorem leads to the following result:

$$\oint_C \frac{F(z)}{z-j\omega}dz=0, \tag{48}$$

where the closed contour is the one shown in Fig. 11(b).

The complete contour consists of three parts; the large semicircle C_1, the small semicircular indentation C_2 about the point $z=j\omega$, and the imaginary axis. The contribution from the small indentation to the overall integral is $2\pi j$ times half the residue of the integrand at $z=j\omega$; this residue is simply $F(j\omega)$. To compute the contribution on the infinite semicircle, let us initially assume a finite radius, with $z=R_0 e^{j\theta}$. Then

$$\int_{C_1} \frac{F(s)}{z-j\omega}dz = \int_{C_1} \frac{F(R_0 e^{j\theta})}{R_0 e^{j\theta}-j\omega}jR_0 e^{j\theta}d\theta \xrightarrow{R_0-\infty} jF(\infty)\int_{\pi/2}^{-\pi/2} d\theta$$
$$= -j\pi F(\infty), \tag{49}$$

where $F(\infty)$ is the value of $F(s)$ at $s=\infty$. Thus, as R_0 approaches infinity, the integral on C_1 approaches $-j\pi F(\infty)$. Since the imaginary part of $F(s)$ must be zero at infinity, $F(\infty)$ is equal to $R(\infty)$.

Now it remains to consider the remainder of the contour. This can be written

$$\lim_{\substack{R_0-\infty \\ r-0}} \left[\int_{-R_0}^{\omega-r} \frac{F(jy)}{y-\omega}dy + \int_{\omega+r}^{R_0} \frac{F(jy)}{y-\omega}dy \right] = \int_{-\infty}^{\infty} \frac{F(jy)}{y-\omega}dy \tag{50}$$

Note that the integration along the imaginary axis must avoid the pole at $z=j\omega$ in a symmetrical manner. This will yield the *principal value* of the integral on the right. In all the subsequent integrals we must keep this point in mind. Now collecting all these results and substituting into (48) we can write

$$\int_{-\infty}^{\infty} \frac{F(jy)}{y-\omega}dy = j\pi[F(\infty)-F(j\omega)]. \tag{51}$$

If we next write $F(j\omega)$ and $F(jy)$ in terms of their real and imaginary parts, and equate reals and imaginaries on both sides of the equation, we get, finally,

$$R(\omega) = R(\infty) - \frac{1}{\pi}\int_{-\infty}^{\infty} \frac{X(y)}{y-\omega}dy, \tag{52a}$$

$$X(\omega) = \frac{1}{\pi}\int_{-\infty}^{\infty} \frac{R(y)}{y-\omega}dy. \tag{52b}$$

We are leaving the algebraic details of these steps for you to work out.

The message carried by these two expressions is very important. The second one states that when a function is specified to be the real part of a network function over all frequencies, the imaginary part of the function is completely determined at all frequencies, assuming the network function has no poles on the $j\omega$-axis. Similarly, if the imaginary part is specified over all frequencies, the real part is completely determined at all frequencies to within an additive constant.

Remember that the same results apply if $F(s)$ is replaced by its logarithm. However, now we must also require that $F(s)$ be minimum-phase if it represents a transfer function. On the other hand, we can relax the requirement of regularity of $F(s)$ on the $j\omega$-axis. A simple pole of $F(s)$ on the $j\omega$-axis becomes a logarithmic singularity of $\ln F(s)$, and such a singularity will contribute nothing to the integral, as mentioned earlier. Thus, for minimum-phase transfer functions, (52) with R and X replaced by α and ϕ, relate the gain and phase functions over all frequencies.

Let us now obtain alternative forms for the two basic expressions in (52) that will throw additional light on the relationships and will bring out points that are not at once apparent from these expressions. Remember that the real and imaginary parts are even and odd functions of frequency, respectively. Let us use this fact and write (52b) as follows:

$$X(\omega) = \frac{1}{\pi}\int_{-\infty}^{0} \frac{R(y)}{y-\omega}dy + \frac{1}{\pi}\int_{0}^{\infty}\frac{R(y)}{y-\pi}dy. \tag{53}$$

In the first of these integrals, replace y by $-y$ and change the limits accordingly. The result is

$$\int_{-\infty}^{0}\frac{R(y)}{y-\omega}dy = \int_{\infty}^{0}\frac{R(-y)}{-(y+\omega)}(-dy) = -\int_{0}^{\infty}\frac{R(y)}{y+\omega}dy. \tag{54}$$

The last step follows from the fact that $R(y) = R(-y)$. Substituting this into (53), we get

$$X(\omega) = \frac{1}{\pi}\int_{0}^{\infty}R(y)\left(\frac{1}{y-\omega} - \frac{1}{y+\omega}\right)dy = \frac{2\omega}{\pi}\int_{0}^{\infty}\frac{R(y)}{y^2-\omega^2}dy. \tag{55}$$

In a completely similar way, starting with (52a) we get

$$R(\omega) = R(\infty) - \frac{2}{\pi}\int_{0}^{\infty}\frac{yX(y)}{y^2-\omega^2}dy. \tag{56}$$

In the last two expressions it still appears that the integrand goes to infinity on the path of integration at the point $y = \omega$. This is really illusory, since we must understand the integral as the principal value. Even this illusory difficulty can be removed if we note by direct integration that

$$\int_0^\infty \frac{dy}{y^2 - \omega^2} = 0, \tag{57}$$

again using the principal value of the integral. Hence we can subtract $R(\omega)/(y^2 - \omega^2)$ from the integrand in (55) and $\omega X(\omega)/(y^2 - \omega^2)$ from the integrand in (56) without changing the values of these integrals. The results of these steps will be

$$R(\omega) = R(\infty) = \frac{2}{\pi} \int_0^\infty \frac{yX(y) - \omega X(\omega)}{y^2 - \omega^2} dy, \tag{58a}$$

$$X(\omega) = \frac{2\omega}{\pi} \int_0^\infty \frac{R(y) - R(\omega)}{y^2 - \omega^2} dy. \tag{58b}$$

A very important feature of the results that we have established is the fact that it is not necessary to have the real part (or the imaginary part) as a realizable rational function. Corresponding to any given real part, whether in analytical or in graphical form, an imaginary part can be computed from the integral. As a matter of fact, the expressions are quite useful when a desired real part is specified in a vague sort of way and it is desired to obtain the approximate behavior of the imaginary part.

For example, suppose it is desired to know the approximate behavior of the angle function inside the passband of a low-pass filter. In this discussion we shall interpret R and X to represent the gain α and the angle ϕ, respectively. In the passband the gain is approximately zero up to some frequency ω_0. Hence in (58b) the lower limit becomes ω_0. Furthermore, the point ω, which lies in the passband, is less than ω_0; thus in the integrand we can neglect ω compared with y, since y varies from ω_0 to infinity. Thus an approximate value is given by

$$\phi(\omega) \approx \frac{2\omega}{\pi} \int_{\omega_0}^\infty \frac{\alpha(y)}{y^2} dy. \tag{59}$$

Now let us make the change of variable $y = 1/p$; then $dy/y^2 = -dp$. After appropriately modifying the limits of integration as well, this equation becomes

$$\phi(\omega) \approx \frac{2\omega}{\pi} \int_0^{1/\omega_0} \alpha\left(\frac{1}{p}\right) dp. \tag{60}$$

Note that the integral in (59) or (60) is not a function of ω and that, for a given vlaue of the band edge ω_0, it will be simply a constant. Thus the angle will be approximately a linear function of ω within the passband.* Of course, the approximation will get progressively worse as we approach the band edge, since then ω can no longer be neglected in comparison to y in the integrand of (58).

7.6.1 Phase Area and Attentuation-Integral Theorems

The two pairs of expressions obtained so far in (52) and (58) relate the imaginary part at any frequency to the real part at all frequencies; or the real part at any frequency to the imaginary part at all frequencies. We should be able to find limiting forms for these expressions when the frequency approaches zero or infinity.

First consider (58a) when ω approaches zero. This leads immediately to the result

$$\int_0^\infty \frac{X(y)}{y} dy = \frac{\pi}{2}[R(\infty) - R(0)]. \tag{61}$$

This expression is referred to as the *reactance-integral theorem*. It states that the integral of the imaginary part over all frequencies, weighted by the reciprocal of frequency, is proportional to the difference of the real part at the two extreme frequencies. It is also called the *phase-area theorem*, since the result remains valid when $F(s)$ is replaced by its logarithm, R by α and X by ϕ.

A more convenient expression is obtained if a change to logarithmic frequency is made. Define

$$u = \ln\frac{y}{\omega}, \quad \text{or} \quad \frac{y}{\omega} = e^u, \tag{62}$$

where ω is some arbitrary reference frequency. Then dy/y becomes du, and (61) can be written as follows:

---

* Such a linear phase characteristic corresponds to a constant time delay in the transmission of sinusoidal functions over this range of frequencies. Therefore for signals that have essentially only this frequency range we get distortionless transmission. For this reason a linear phase characteristic is desirable.

$$\int_{-\infty}^{\infty} X(y)du = \frac{\pi}{2}[R(\infty) - R(0)].$$ (63)

Note the change in the lower limit, since $u = -\infty$ when $y = 0$. The argument of $X(y)$ has been retained as y for simplicity, although the integrand should more accurately be written as $X(\omega e^u)$. Alternatively, a new function $\hat{X}(u) = X(\omega e^u)$ could be defined. However, this introduces additional new notation to complicate matters. In subsequent equations we shall retain y as the argument of the integrands and write $X(y)$ or $R(y)$, as the case may be, with the understanding that we mean to convert to a function of u by the substitution $y = \omega e^u$ before performing any operations. Thus we see that *the area under the curve of the imaginary part, when plotted against logarithmic frequency, is proportional to the net change in the real part between zero and infinite frequency.*

Next let us multiply both sides of (58b) by ω and then take the limit as ω approaches infinity. Remember that the upper limit on the integral means that we integrate up to R_0 and then let R_0 approach infinity. Thus,

$$\lim_{\omega \to \infty} \omega X(\omega) = \frac{2}{\pi} \lim_{\omega \to \infty} \left[\lim_{R_0 \to \infty} \int_0^{R_0} \frac{R(y) - R(\omega)}{(y^2/\omega^2) - 1} dy \right].$$ (64)

There are two limiting operations involved on the right-hand side. If we interchange these two operations, the expression can be evaluated readily; but we must inquire whether this interchange is permissible. The answer is affirmative if the integral is uniformly convergent for all values of ω, which it is. Hence, interchanging the two operations and taking the limits leads to

$$\int_0^{\infty} [R(y) - R(\infty)]dy = -\frac{\pi}{2} \lim_{\omega \to \infty} \omega X(\omega).$$ (65)

The result expressed by this equation is referred to as the *resistance-integral theorem*. [It is also called the *attenuation-integral theorem*, since the result remains valid if $F(s)$ is replaced by its logarithm.] If the asymptotic behavior of the imaginary part of a network function is specified, then — no matter how the $j\omega$-axis real part behaves with frequency — the area under the curve of the real part, with the horizontal axis shifted upward by an amount $R(\infty)$, must remain constant. Looking at it from the opposite viewpoint, when the integral of the real part of a function over all frequencies is specified, then the infinite-frequency behavior of the imaginary part is fixed.

Consider the special case in which $F(s)$ has a simple zero at infinity; then $R(\infty) = F(\infty) = 0$. Furthermore,

$$\lim_{s \to \infty} sF(s) = - \lim_{\omega \to \infty} \omega X(\omega). \tag{66}$$

However, according to the initial-value theorem, the limit on the left-hand side is simply the initial value of the impulse response of the network, which is $f(t)$ — the inverse Laplace transform of $F(s)$ — evaluated at $t = 0$. In this case, when $F(s)$ has a simple zero at infinity, then (65) becomes

$$\int_0^\infty R(\omega)d\omega = \frac{\pi}{2} \lim_{s \to \infty} sF(s) = \frac{\pi}{2}f(0), \tag{67}$$

Note that the dummy variable has been changed to ω to suggest the physical meaning.

7.6.2   Limitations on Constrained Networks

What has just been developed can be used to determine some basic limitations on the behavior of networks, when allowance is made for certain inevitable parasitic effects. Consider the situation depicted in Fig. 12(a). The capacitance C accounts for parasitic effects that almost inevitably occur, such as junction capacitances in a transistor or just plain wiring capacitance. The presence of such a capacitance imposes some limitations that we shall now discuss.

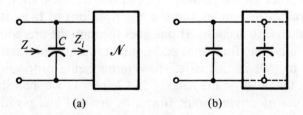

(a)   (b)

Fig. 12   Network constrained to have a shunt capacitance across its input terminals

Let $Z_i(s)$ be the impedance of the network $\mathcal{N}$ beyond the capacitance. The total impedance $Z(s)$ is given by

$$Z(s) = \frac{Z_i(s)}{CsZ_i(s) + 1} = \frac{1}{Cs + \frac{1}{Z_i(s)}}. \tag{68}$$

Whatever the behavior of $Z_i(s)$ may be at infinity, we observe that the total impedance $Z(s)$ will have a simple zero at infinity. We shall initially assume that the network $\mathcal{N}$ does not start with a shunt capacitor as in Fig. 12(b), meaning that $Z_i(s)$ has no zero at infinity. If it does, in fact, the result is an effective increase in the value of C.

With these stipulations, (66) is valid with $F(s) = Z(s)$. Inserting (68) into the right side of (66) and evaluating the limit yields

$$\lim_{s \to \infty} sZ(s) = \lim_{s \to \infty} \frac{sZ_i(s)}{CsZ_i(s) + 1} = \frac{1}{C}.$$

Finally, when this is inserted into (67), the result becomes

$$\int_0^\infty R(\omega)d\omega = \frac{\pi}{2C}. \tag{69}$$

We see that the shunt capacitance imposes an effective limit on the area under the curve of the real part. Although this resistance integral evolved as the limiting value of the general expression relating the real and imaginary parts of a network function, it appears to provide a figure of merit of some sort on network capability.

Since the resistance-integral theorem applies to functions having no poles on the $j\omega$-axis, (69) is valid for such a function. If a function does have such poles on the $j\omega$-axis, the contour of integration must be indented around these poles and the contributions of these indentations must be taken into account. If one goes through the preceding development carefully, one finds that additional terms are subtracted from the right side of (69) in this case, these terms being proportional to the residues at the poles on the $j\omega$-axis. In Chapter 11 we shall show that all such residues of driving-point functions are real and positive. Hence, when $Z(s)$ has poles on the $j\omega$-axis, the right side of (69) is reduced in value. For all cases, then, whether $Z(s)$ is regular on the $j\omega$-axis or not, the result can be written as follows:

$$\int_0^\infty R(\omega)d\omega \leqslant \frac{\pi}{2C}. \tag{70}$$

Further interpretaton of this important result can be obtained from a consideration of Fig. 13, where a two-port is terminated in a resistor R_L.

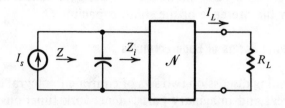

Fig. 13   Resistance-terminated two-port

Assuming sinusoidal excitation, a calculation of the real power delivered to the input terminals by the source and the power delivered by the network to the load will be

$$\text{power from source} = \tfrac{1}{2}|I_s(j\omega)|^2\text{Re } Z(j\omega), \tag{71a}$$

$$\text{power to load} = \tfrac{1}{2}|I_L(j\omega)|^2 R_L. \tag{71b}$$

Clearly, the load power cannot exceed the power from the source for a passive two-port. Hence, the second expression can be no greater than the first; so,

$$\left|\frac{I_L(j\omega)}{I_s(j\omega)}\right|^2 \leqslant \frac{1}{R_L}\text{Re } Z(j\omega). \tag{72}$$

The equality is valid when the two-port is lossless. Thus the squared magnitude of the current gain of a lossless two-port is proportional to the real part of the impedance at the input terminals of the two-port when the output is terminated in R_L. Thus, when (72) is inserted into (70) with $R(\omega)$ interpreted as Re $Z(j\omega)$, there results

$$\int_0^\infty \left|\frac{I_L(j\omega)}{I_s(j\omega)}\right|^2 d\omega \leqslant \frac{\pi}{2R_L C}. \tag{73}$$

Suppose the two-port in Fig. 13 is to be a filter with constant power gain over a given frequency band and zero outside this band. Then the integral in (73) will simply equal the constant-power gain times the bandwidth. In the more general case, even though the transfer function may not be an ideal-filter function, the area under the curve represented by this integral is dimensionally power gain times bandwidth. For this reason the integral in (73) is generally called the *gain-bandwidth integral*. Thus we find a basic limitation on the gain-bandwidth product introduced by the presence of the shunt capacitor C.

7.6.3   Alternative Forms of Bode Formulas

In the preceding discussion two sets of equivalent integral expressions relating the real and imaginary parts of network functions at all frequencies were found in (52) and (58). Still other forms are also possible, one of which is especially convenient for computation. This form is most relevant when $\ln F(s)$ is involved, rather than the network function itself. The expression utilizes the logarithmic frequency defined in (62).

Let us start with (58b) and perform some preliminary manipulations utilizing the logarithmic frequency variable. We shall also use α and ϕ instead of R and X. Thus,

$$
\begin{aligned}
\phi(\omega) &= \frac{2}{\pi} \int_0^\infty \frac{\alpha(y) - \alpha(\omega)}{\left(\dfrac{y}{\omega}\right) - \left(\dfrac{\omega}{y}\right)} \frac{dy}{y} \\[2mm]
&= \frac{2}{\pi} \int_{-\infty}^\infty \frac{\alpha(y) - \alpha(\omega)}{e^u - e^{-u}} du \\[2mm]
&= \frac{1}{\pi} \int_{-\infty}^\infty \frac{\alpha(y) - \alpha(\omega)}{\sinh u} du.
\end{aligned}
\tag{74}
$$

Note the change in the lower limit, since $u = -\infty$ when $y = 0$. The argument of $\alpha(y)$ has been retained as y, as discussed earlier.

As the next step, we integrate the last form by parts. Using the general formula

$$
\int a\, db = ab - \int b\, da
$$

with

$$
a = \alpha(y) - \alpha(\omega), \quad db = \frac{du}{\sinh u}
$$

$$
da = \frac{d\alpha(y)}{du} du, \quad b = -\ln \coth \frac{u}{2}.
$$

Hence (74) becomes

$$\phi(\omega) = -\frac{1}{\pi}\left\{[\alpha(y) - \alpha(\omega)]\ln\coth\frac{u}{2}\right\}\Bigg|_{-\infty}^{\infty}$$
$$+\frac{1}{\pi}\int_{-\infty}^{\infty}\frac{d\alpha(y)}{du}\ln\coth\frac{u}{2}du. \tag{75}$$

Note that coth $u/2$ is an odd function of u, being strictly positive when u is positive and strictly negative when u is negative. Hence its logarithm for negative u will be complex, the imaginary part being simply π. For negative u it can be written

$$\ln\coth\frac{u}{2} = \ln\coth\frac{|u|}{2} + j\pi, \quad u<0. \tag{76}$$

When $u = +\infty$, $\ln\coth u/2 = 0$; and when $u = -\infty$, $\ln\coth u/2 = j\pi$. Hence the integrated part of (75) becomes simply $j[\alpha(0) - \alpha(\omega)]$.

Now consider the remaining integral. If we use (76) for negative values of u, the result will be

$$\int_{-\infty}^{\infty}\frac{d\alpha(y)}{du}\ln\coth\frac{u}{2}du = \int_{-\infty}^{\infty}\frac{d\alpha(y)}{du}\ln\coth\frac{|u|}{2}du + j\pi\int_{-\infty}^{0}\frac{d\alpha(y)}{du}du$$
$$= \int_{-\infty}^{\infty}\frac{d\alpha(y)}{du}\ln\coth\frac{|u|}{2}du + j\pi\alpha(y)\Bigg|_{u=-\infty}^{u=0}$$

Finally, using all of these results in (75), we get

$$\phi(\omega) = \frac{1}{\pi}\int_{-\infty}^{\infty}\frac{d\alpha(y)}{du}\ln\coth\frac{|u|}{2}du. \tag{77}$$

This equation is quite easy to interpret even though it looks somewhat complicated. Note that the gain α is not an even function of the logarithmic frequency u, and so it is not possible to integrate over only half the range. The equation states that the angle at any frequency depends on the slope of the gain at all frequencies (when plotted against logarithmic frequency), the relative importance of different frequencies being determined by the weighting factor

$$\ln\coth\frac{|u|}{2} = \ln\left|\frac{y+\omega}{y-\omega}\right|. \tag{78}$$

This function is shown plotted in Fig. 14. It rises sharply in the vicinity of $u=0$ $(y=\omega)$, falling off to very small values on both sides of this point. This means that most of the contribution to the angle at a frequency ω comes from the slope of the gain in the immediate vicinity of ω.

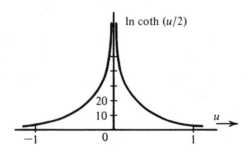

Fig. 14   Plot of weighting factor $\ln \coth \dfrac{|u|}{2} = \ln \left| \dfrac{y+\omega}{y-\omega} \right|$

Another useful form can be obtained by simply adding and subtracting the slope evaluated at $u=0$ $(y=\omega)$ under the integral in (77). We shall leave the details of this operation to you. The result will be

$$\phi(\omega) = \frac{\pi}{2} \frac{d\alpha(\omega)}{du} + \frac{1}{\pi} \int_{-\infty}^{\infty} \left[\frac{d\alpha(y)}{du} - \frac{d\alpha(\omega)}{du} \right] \ln \coth \frac{|u|}{2} du. \quad (79)$$

Note that by $d\alpha(\omega)/du$ we mean the slope of the gain as a function of u, evaluated when $u=0$ $(y=\omega)$. The slope $d\alpha(\omega)/du$ is measured in nepers per unit change of u. A unit change of u means a change in frequency by a factor e.

We see that the angle at any frequency is $\pi/2$ times the gain slope at the same frequency plus another term given by the integral. If the gain is a continuous function, then the difference in the integrand will be small in the vicinity of $y=\omega$, just where the weighting factor has large values. Hence, in this case, the contribution of the integral to the angle will always be relatively small. As a first approximation, then, we can say that the angle will have a value of $\pi/2$ radians whenever the gain slope is 1, a value of π radians whenever the gain slope is 2, etc.

Now suppose a gain function is given in graphical form. We can first approximate the curve by a series of straight-line segments having slopes of n, where n is an integer. An approximation to the (minimum-phase) angle function corresponding to the given gain function can now be quickly sketched according to the discussion of the last paragraph.

As an example of this procedure, suppose the gain plot* shown in Fig. 15 is given. The straight line approximation is superimposed. Now an approximate sketch of the angle, using only the approximate gain plot and completely neglecting the integral in (79), is the discontinuous function shown by the solid lines in the figure. The actual angle function might have the form shown by the smooth curve.

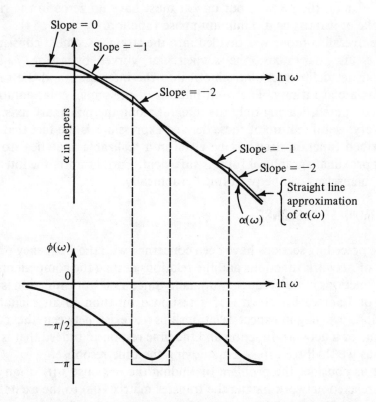

Fig. 15   Approximate angle corresponding to a given gain function

Let us now summarize the results of this section. The objective was to obtain relationships between the real and imaginary parts of a network function $F(s)$ (or between the gain and the phase), so that when one of these is prescribed the other can be calculated. The point of departure was Cauchy's integral theorem, the contour of integration consisting of the imaginary axis with an infinite semicircular arc joining the ends. An

---

* This is, with a scale change on both axes, the Bode diagram of $|F(j\omega)|$, which finds extensive use in control theory. The Bode diagram, which is just $20 \log |F(j\omega)|$ versus $\log \omega$, is discussed in most basic texts on control systems analysis.

292 Linear Network Theory

integrand was chosen involving $F(s)$ [or ln $F(s)$], multiplied by a weighting function. The contour was indented to bypass poles of the integrand introduced by this function.

If the integrand involves a network function $F(s)$, then the only restriction was that $F(s)$ be regular on the $j\omega$-axis, including the points at zero and infinity. If the integrand involves ln $F(s)$, then $F(s)$ need not be regular on the $j\omega$-axis, but now it must have no zeros in the right half-plane; it must be a minimum-phase function.

The overall contour was divided into the straight segment consisting of the imaginary axis, the semicircular curves bypassing $j\omega$-axis singularities deliberately introduced into the integrand, and the semi-circular arc at infinity. The contributions of the semicircular contours were computed, leaving only the integral along the imaginary axis.

A very useful feature of these derived expressions is the fact that the prescribed function need not be given in a realizable analytical form. An approximate graphical form is sufficient. Furthermore, the integrations themselves can be performed graphically.

7.7 IMPULSE RESPONSE

The preceding sections have been concerned with the frequency properties of network functions and the relations among the components of such functions in the frequency domain. Since a network function is the ratio of Laplace transforms of a response function to an excitation function, we might expect relationships to exist between the components of a network function and the time response. Indeed that is the case, as we shall see after first studying the time response.

Let us consider the problem of finding the response $\mathbf{w}(t)$ of an initally relaxed network having the transfer matrix $\mathbf{H}(s)$ to the excitation $\mathbf{u}(t)$. Now, $\mathbf{H}(s)$ must be the transform of a matrix of ordinary—not generalized—functions in order to apply the convolution theorem. This implies that $\mathbf{H}(s)$ tends to $\mathbf{0}$ as s tends to infinity within the sector of convergence for $\mathbf{H}(s)$. Let $W_\delta(t)$ denote the inverse transform of $\mathbf{H}(s)$; that is,

$$\mathcal{L}^{-1}\{\mathbf{H}(s)\} = \mathbf{W}_\delta(t). \tag{80}$$

The reason for this choice of notation will be clear shortly. Now we apply the convolution theorem to the frequency-domain expression

$$\mathbf{W}(s) = \mathbf{H}(s)\mathbf{U}(s). \tag{81}$$

The result is

$$\mathbf{w}(t) = \int_0^t \mathbf{W}_\delta(\tau)\mathbf{u}(t-\tau)d\tau = \int_0^t \mathbf{W}_\delta(t-\tau)\mathbf{u}(\tau)d\tau. \tag{82}$$

This is a very valuable result which permits expressing the time response of a network to an arbitrary excitation $\mathbf{u}(t)$ in terms of the inverse transforms of the transfer matrix of the network.

A further interpretation is possible if we are willing to admit the impulse function in our discussions.* Such an interpretation is not really needed, since (82) can stand on its own feet, so to speak. However, the interpretation may prove useful in some instances.

Now suppose that all excitations are zero except the jth one and that this one is an impulse. In this case the excitation vector, denoted by $\mathbf{u}_{\delta j}(t)$, has all elements equal to zero except the jth, this element being the impulse function $\delta(t)$. We may think of $\mathbf{u}_{\delta j}(t)$ as the jth column of the excitation matrix $\mathbf{U}_\delta(t)$. Thus, for example, $\mathbf{u}_{\delta 2}(t)$ is the second column vector of the excitation matrix $\mathbf{U}_\delta(t)$ shown below.

$$\mathbf{U}_\delta(t) = \begin{bmatrix} \delta(t) & 0 & 0 & \dots & 0 \\ 0 & \delta(t) & 0 & \dots & 0 \\ 0 & 0 & \delta(t) & \dots & 0 \\ \cdot & \cdot & \cdot & & \cdot \\ \cdot & \cdot & \cdot & & \cdot \\ \cdot & \cdot & \cdot & & \cdot \\ 0 & 0 & 0 & \dots & \delta(t) \end{bmatrix} = \delta(t)\mathbf{U}.$$

Similarly, let $\mathbf{w}_{\delta j}(t)$ be the response vector resulting from $\mathbf{u}_{\delta j}(t)$; that is, $\mathbf{w}_{\delta j}(t)$ is the collection of all the scalar responses when there is a single

---

* The impulse function $\delta(t)$ is not an ordinary function; rather, it is a generalized function. Symbolically, we may manipulate mathematical relations involving the impulse function and its derivatives as we would relations involving only ordinary functions. On the other hand, mathematical precision requires that we view each function as a generalized function, and each operation as defined on the space of generalized functions. Here it is enough to observe that the impulse function satisfies the following relations. With $a \leqslant \tau \leqslant b$,

$$\int_a^b \delta(t-\tau)d\tau = 1, \int_a^b f(\tau)\delta(t-\tau)d\tau = f(t), \text{ and}$$

$$\int_a^b \delta^{(i)}(t-\tau)f(\tau)d\tau = f^{(i)}(t).$$

For other values of τ, outside the range $[a, b]$, each of the above integrals yields zero.

excitation and this excitation is an impulse. Let these $\mathbf{w}_{\delta j}(t)$ vectors be arranged as the columns of a matrix designated $\mathbf{W}_\delta(t)$ and called the *impulse response* of the network. Note carefully that $\mathbf{W}_\delta(t)$ is a set of response vectors, one column for each column of $\mathbf{U}_\delta(t)$. It is thus not an observable response in the same sense that each of its columns is an observable response. On the other hand, the sum of elements in each row of $\mathbf{W}_\delta(t)$ is an observable (scalar) response — the response to the sum of all excitations, these excitations all being impulses.

Now consider the Laplace transforms. Since $\mathbf{U}_\delta(t) = \delta(t)\mathbf{U}$,

$$\mathcal{L}\{\mathbf{U}_\delta(t)\} = \mathcal{L}\{\delta(t)\mathbf{U}\} = \mathbf{U}. \tag{83}$$

Equation (81) relates corresponding columns of the transforms of $\mathbf{U}_\delta(t)$ and $\mathbf{W}_\delta(t)$. Hence, by using (83), we obtain

$$\mathcal{L}\{\mathbf{W}_\delta(t)\} = \mathbf{H}(s)\mathcal{L}\{\mathbf{U}_\delta(t)\} = \mathbf{H}(s) \quad \leftrightarrow \quad \mathbf{W}_\delta(t) = \mathcal{L}^{-1}\{\mathbf{H}(s)\}. \tag{84}$$

In words, the last equation states that the inverse transform of the network transfer function is equal to the impulse response of the network. We anticipated this result in using the notation in (80).

Let us return now to (82). We see that this equation expresses the fact that, once the impulse response of an initially relaxed network is known, the response to any other excitation $\mathbf{u}(t)$ is determined. What we must do is premultiply the excitation at each point τ by the impulse response — not at the same point, but at a point $(t - \tau)$ — and then integrate. Another viewpoint is that the input vector is weighted by the impulse response. This leads to the name of *weighting matrix* used by some authors for the impulse response.*

Let us elaborate on the concept of weighting with a simple example of a single-input, single-output network having the transfer function

$$F(s) = \frac{¾}{(s+1)^2},$$

which is the transfer function $V_2(s)/V_1(s)$ of the network of Fig. 16. Then the impulse response is given by

$$w_\delta(t) = ¾\, t e^{-t}$$

A plot of this function is given in Fig. 17.

---

* For the multi-input, multi-output networks discussed here this would be a generalization of the term *weighting function* for a single-input, single-output network used by such authors.

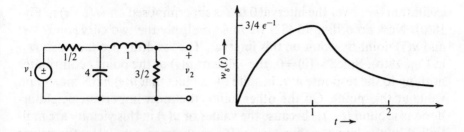

Fig. 16   Example for weighting function   Fig. 17   Impulse response of the
concept in convolution   network of Fig. 16

Suppose we wish to compute the response of this network to some driving function $u(t)$. For convenience of interpretation let us take the convolution of $w_\delta(t)$ and $u(t)$ in the second form given in (82). As τ is the integration variable, the excitation and impulse response must hereafter be viewed as functions of τ; thus, $u(\tau)$ and $w_\delta(\tau)$. To get the value of the response at any given time t, we first reverse the impulse response and translate it along the τ-axis so as to obtain $w_\delta(t-\tau)$ as a function of τ. Compare $w_\delta(t)$ versus t in Fig. 17 to $w_\delta(t-\tau)$ versus τ in Fig. 18(a). The

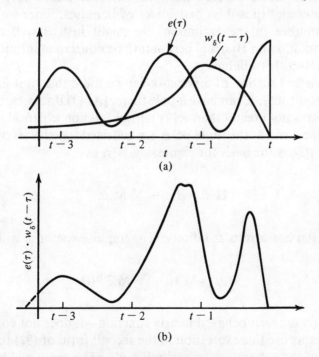

Fig. 18   Illustration of convolution

excitation $u(\tau)$ over the interval 0 to t is superimposed on $w_\delta(t - \tau)$ in Fig. 18(a). Now according to (82) we must multiply the two curves $w_\delta(t - \tau)$ and $u(\tau)$ point-by-point on this interval. The resulting product is shown in Fig. 18(b). Since $w_\delta(0) = 0$, the value of $u(\tau)$ at the point t contributes nothing to the response at t, in spite of the fact that $u(\tau)$ has a maximum value at this point. On the other hand, the most important neighborhood is around $(t - 1)$, because the values of $u(\tau)$ in this vicinity are multiplied by the largest values that $w_\delta(t - \tau)$ assumes. Similarly, the values of $u(\tau)$ for τ less than $(t - 2)$ do virtually nothing to the response at t. Thus $w_\delta(t - \tau)$ decides how much *weight* to attach to the values of $u(\tau)$ at various times. In this case the response [that by (82) is the integral of $w_\delta(t - \tau)u(\tau)$ from 0 to t] is decided almost entirely by the values of u for the previous two seconds, the most significant contribution coming from the values of u about one second prior to the time under consideration.

7.7.1 Transfer Function Nonzero at Infinity

The question now arises: What should we do if the network transfer function does not have a zero at infinity? In such a case $w_\delta(t)$ will contain impulses and (possibly) derivatives of impulses. Since we are permitting impulses in the excitation, we might just as well relax the original condition on $H(s)$ and permit it to be nonzero at infinity. Let us see what effect this will have.

The transfer function of a network can be more than just a nonzero constant at infinity, it can have a pole there. [As (3) discloses, the order of that pole is not greater than σ.] A partial fraction expansion of $H(s)$, in which the terms at the finite poles are collected together as the matrix function $\hat{H}(s)$, is the basis for expressing $H(s)$ as

$$H(s) = \hat{H}(s) + \sum_{i=0}^{\sigma} M_i s^i. \tag{85}$$

Clearly, $\hat{H}(s)$ has a zero at infinity. The impulse response will then be

$$W_\delta(t) = \hat{W}_\delta(t) + \sum_{i=0}^{\sigma} M_i \delta^{(i)}(t) \tag{86}$$

where $\hat{W}_\delta(t)$ is a well-behaved matrix function — it does not contain impulses. Let us use this expression in the second form of (82) to find the response of the network to an excitation $u(t)$. The result will be

$$w(t) = \int_0^t \hat{W}(t-\tau)u(\tau)d\tau + \int_0^t \left[\sum_{i=0}^{\sigma} M_i \delta^{(i)}(t-\tau) \right] u(\tau)d\tau$$

$$= \int_0^t \hat{W}_\delta(t-\tau)u(\tau)d\tau + \sum_{i=0}^{\sigma} M_i u^{(i)}(t). \tag{87}$$

The last step follows from the properties of impulse functions and their derivatives. This is the general form of the convolution integral for arbitrary networks.

7.7.2 Example

The application of the convolution integral in the solution of a problem is quite straightforward. It is necessary first to find the impulse response $W_\delta(t) = \mathcal{L}^{-1}\{H(s)\}$ and then to substitute this, together with the excitation, into the convolution integral. The excitation is to be expressed as some function — possibly different functions over different intervals of time. We shall illustrate this process in the following example.

In the initially relaxed network of Fig. 19, let the responses be v and i as shown. There is only a single source, having the voltage shown in the figure. Hence the excitation vector is order 1, and the response vector is order 2. The transfer-function matrix is

$$H(s) = \mathcal{L} \begin{bmatrix} v_\delta(t) \\ i_\delta(t) \end{bmatrix} = \begin{bmatrix} \dfrac{6}{(s+1)(s+6)} \\ \dfrac{6s(s+5)}{(s+1)(s+6)} \end{bmatrix} = \begin{bmatrix} \dfrac{6/5}{s+1} - \dfrac{6/5}{s+6} \\ 6 - \dfrac{24/5}{s+1} - \dfrac{26/5}{s+6} \end{bmatrix}.$$

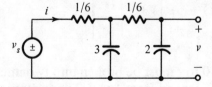
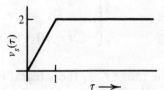

Fig. 19 Example

(You may go through the details of finding this, for example, by finding the state equations.) We see that the first element of $\mathbf{H}(s)$ has a zero at infinity, whereas the second one is nonzero at infinity. The impulse response, therefore, contains an impulse as seen in

$$\mathbf{W}_\delta(t) = \mathcal{L}^{-1}\{\mathbf{H}(s)\} = \frac{6}{5}\begin{bmatrix} e^{-t} - e^{-6t} \\ -4e^{-t} - 6e^{-6t} \end{bmatrix} + \begin{bmatrix} 0 \\ 6 \end{bmatrix}\delta(t).$$

Since the excitation has a different functional form for $0 \leqslant t \leqslant 1$ from the one it has for $t \geqslant 1$, the response for each of these ranges must be found separately. Thus,

$$v_s(t) = 2t \quad (0 \leqslant t \leqslant 1),$$
$$v_s(t) = 2 \quad (t \geqslant 1).$$

Hence, from (87), for $0 \leqslant t \leqslant 1$,

$$w(t) = \int_0^t \frac{6}{5}\begin{bmatrix} e^{-(t-\tau)} - e^{-6(t-\tau)} \\ -4e^{-(t-\tau)} - 6e^{-6(t-\tau)} \end{bmatrix} 2\tau\, d\tau + \begin{bmatrix} 0 \\ 6 \end{bmatrix} 2t$$

$$= \frac{12}{5}\begin{bmatrix} e^{-t}\int_0^t \tau e^\tau\, d\tau - e^{-6t}\int_0^t \tau e^{6\tau}\, d\tau \\ -4e^{-t}\int_0^t \tau e^\tau d\tau - 6e^{-6t}\int_0^t \tau e^{6\tau}\, d\tau \end{bmatrix} + \begin{bmatrix} 0 \\ 12t \end{bmatrix}$$

$$= \begin{bmatrix} 2t - \tfrac{7}{3} + \tfrac{12}{5}e^{-t} - \tfrac{1}{15}e^{-6t} \\ -12t + 10 - \tfrac{48}{5}e^{-t} - \tfrac{2}{5}e^{-6t} \end{bmatrix} + \begin{bmatrix} 0 \\ 12t \end{bmatrix}.$$

In the range $t \geqslant 1$, the integral from 0 to t must be broken into two integrals, the first going from 0 to 1, the second from 1 to t. The excitation in the first integral is $v_s(t) = 2t$, the same as in the calculation just completed. Hence in this next calculation it is enough to replace the limit t in the preceding integral by 1 and then to evaluate the second integral. Note that t is not replaced by 1 everywhere in the evaluated integral above, but only in the contribution coming from the upper limit. So, for $t \geqslant 1$,

$$w(t) = \frac{12}{5} \begin{bmatrix} e^{-t} \int_0^1 \tau e^\tau d\tau - e^{-6t} \int_0^1 \tau e^{6\tau} d\tau \\ -4e^{-t} \int_0^1 \tau e^\tau \, d\tau - 6e^{-6t} \int_0^1 \tau e^{6\tau} \, d\tau \end{bmatrix}$$

$$+ \frac{12}{5} \int_1^t \begin{bmatrix} e^{-(t-\tau)} - e^{-6(t-\tau)} \\ -4e^{-(t-\tau)} - 6e^{-6(t-\tau)} \end{bmatrix} d\tau + \begin{bmatrix} 0 \\ 6 \end{bmatrix} 2$$

$$= \begin{bmatrix} -{}^{12}\!/_{5} (1 - e^{-1})e^{-(t-1)} + {}^{1}\!/_{15} (1 - e^{-6})e^{-6(t-1)} + 2 \\ {}^{48}\!/_{5} (1 - e^{-1})e^{-(t-1)} + {}^{2}\!/_{5} (1 - e^{-6})e^{-6(t-1)} - 12 \end{bmatrix} + \begin{bmatrix} 0 \\ 12 \end{bmatrix}.$$

You should carry out the details of these calculations and verify that both expressions give the same value of $w(t)$ at $t = 1$.

7.8 STEP RESPONSE

In the last section we established that the response of an initially relaxed network to any arbitrary excitation can be found simply from a knowledge of the impulse response of the same network. In this section we shall show that the same conclusion applies as well to a knowledge of what is called the *step response* of the network.

Suppose that all excitations are zero except the jth one, which is a unit step. Denote by $\mathbf{u}_{uj}(t)$ an excitation vector with all its elements equal to zero except the jth, this one being a unit step $u(t)$. We can think of $\mathbf{u}_{uj}$ as the jth column of the matrix $\mathbf{U}_u(t) = u(t)\mathbf{U}$.

Similarly, let $\mathbf{w}_{uj}(t)$ denote the response vector resulting from $\mathbf{u}_{uj}(t)$; that is, $\mathbf{w}_{uj}(t)$ is the collection of all the scalar responses when there is a single excitation and this excitation is a unit step at the jth input. Suppose these $\mathbf{w}_{uj}$ vectors are arranged as the columns of a matrix designated $\mathbf{W}_u(t)$ and called the *step response* of the network.

Now consider the Laplace transforms. From (81) it follows that

$$\mathcal{L}\{\mathbf{W}_u(t)\} = \mathbf{H}(s)\{\mathbf{U}_u(t)\}. \tag{88}$$

However, since $\mathcal{L}\{U_u(t)\} = \mathcal{L}\{u(t)U\} = U/s$, it follows that

$$\mathcal{L}\{W_u(t)\} = \frac{1}{s}H(s). \tag{89}$$

This expression immediately tells us something about the relationship between the step response and the impulse response, since $H(s) = \mathcal{L}\{W_\delta(t)\}$. To determine the relationship between the time responses, we take the inverse transform of (89), either as it stands or after mutliplying through by s. The result will be

$$W_u(t) = \int_0^t W_\delta(\tau)d\tau, \tag{90}$$

Now substitute (86) in this expression to obtain

$$W_u(t) = \int_0^t W_\delta(\tau)d\tau + \sum_{i=0}^a M_i\delta^{(i-1)}(t), \tag{91}$$

where for $j > 0$ the function $\delta^{(-j)}(t) = t^{j-1}u(t)/(j-1)!$. [For example, $\delta^{(-1)}(t) = u(t)$ and $\delta^{(-2)} = tu(t)$.]

Note that if $W_\delta(t)$ contains a first-order impulse, $W_u(t)$ is not impulsive; if $W_\delta(t)$ contains the derivative of an impulse, $W_u(t)$ has an impulse but not the derivative of an impulse; etc. Hence $W_u(t)$ is always better behaved than $W_\delta(t)$.

Let us now return to our original task—evaluation of $W(t)$ using the step response $W_u(t)$. Assume at this time that $H(s)$ is regular at infinity. Then $M_0 = H(\infty)$ and $M_i = 0$ for $i > 0$. Equation (81) relates the transforms. This equation can be rewritten in one of several ways after multiplying numerator and denominator by s. Thus,

$$W(s) = s\left[\frac{H(s)}{s}U(s)\right] = s[\mathcal{L}\{W_u(t)\}U(s)], \tag{92a}$$

$$W(s) = \left[s\frac{H(s)}{s}\right]U(s) = [s\mathcal{L}\{W_u(t)\}]U(s), \tag{92b}$$

$$W(s) = \left[\frac{H(s)}{s}\right][sU(s)] = \mathcal{L}\{W_u(t)\}[sU(s)]. \tag{92c}$$

In each case we have used (89) to obtain the far-right side. To find $w(t)$ we shall now use the convolution theorem. Focus attention on (92a). This can be written as

$$\mathbf{W}(s) = s\mathbf{F}(s), \tag{93}$$

where

$$\mathbf{F}(s) = \mathcal{L}\{\mathbf{W}_u(t)\}\mathbf{U}(s). \tag{94}$$

By using the convolution theorem, we can write

$$\mathbf{f}(t) = \int_0^t \mathbf{W}_u(\tau)\mathbf{u}(t-\tau)d\tau = \int_0^t \mathbf{W}_u(t-\tau)\mathbf{u}(\tau)d\tau. \tag{95}$$

If we evaluate $\mathbf{f}(0)$, we find it must be zero, since $\mathbf{W}_u(t)$ is not impulsive because $\mathbf{H}(s)$ is regular at infinity. Then, by (93), $w(t)$ will be the derivative of $\mathbf{f}(t)$. Thus,

$$w(t) = \frac{d}{dt}\int_0^t \mathbf{W}_u(\tau)\mathbf{u}(t-\tau)d\tau \tag{96a}$$

$$= \frac{d}{dt}\int_0^t \mathbf{W}_u(t-\tau)\mathbf{u}(\tau)d\tau. \tag{96b}$$

We now have an expression for the response of an initially relaxed network to an excitation $\mathbf{u}(t)$ in terms of the step response. This result ranks in importance with (82). We can put the last equations in the following alternative forms by performing the differentiation; thus,

$$w(t) = \int_0^t \dot{\mathbf{W}}_u(t-\tau)\mathbf{u}(\tau)d\tau + \mathbf{W}_u(0)\mathbf{u}(t), \tag{97a}$$

$$w(t) = \int_0^t \mathbf{W}_u(\tau)\dot{\mathbf{u}}(t-\tau)d\tau + \mathbf{W}_u(t)\mathbf{u}(0). \tag{97b}$$

This will require that $\mathbf{u}(t)$ or $\mathbf{W}_u(t)$, as the case may be, be differentiable and that, correspondingly, $\mathbf{u}(0)$ or $\mathbf{W}_u(0)$ be finite.

These same expressions can be obtained in an alternative manner, starting from (92b) and (92c). To use (92b) let us first write

$$\mathcal{L}^{-1}\{s[\mathbf{W}_u(t)]\} = \mathcal{L}^{-1}\{s[\mathbf{W}_u(t)] - \mathbf{W}_u(0) + \mathbf{W}_u(0)\} \tag{98}$$

$$= \frac{d}{dt}\mathbf{W}_u(t) + \mathbf{W}_u(0)\delta(t).$$

We can now use the convolution theorem on (92b) with (98). The result will be

$$\mathbf{w}(t) = \int_0^t \left[\frac{d}{d\tau}\mathbf{W}_u(\tau) + \mathbf{W}_u(0)\delta(\tau) \right] \mathbf{u}(t-\tau)d\tau$$

$$= \int_0^t \dot{\mathbf{W}}_u(\tau)\mathbf{u}(t-\tau)d\tau + \mathbf{W}_u(0)\mathbf{u}(t) \qquad (99)$$

$$= \int_0^t \dot{\mathbf{W}}_u(t-\tau)\mathbf{u}(\tau)d\tau + \mathbf{W}_u(0)\mathbf{u}(t),$$

which is the same as (97a). In a similar manner, (97b) can be obtained starting from (92c). The details are left to you. (See Prob. 38.)

For future reference we shall collect all of the forms of these expressions that have been derived. They are as follows:

$$\mathbf{w}(t) = \mathbf{W}_u(t)\mathbf{u}(0) + \int_0^t \mathbf{W}_u(t-\tau)\dot{\mathbf{u}}(\tau)d\tau$$
$$= \mathbf{W}_u(t)\mathbf{u}(0) + \int_0^t \mathbf{W}_u(\tau)\dot{\mathbf{u}}(t-\tau)d\tau, \qquad (100)$$

$$\mathbf{w}(t) = \mathbf{W}_u(0)\mathbf{u}(t) + \int_0^t \dot{\mathbf{W}}_u(\tau)\mathbf{u}(t-\tau)d\tau$$
$$= \mathbf{W}_u(0)\mathbf{u}(t) + \int_0^t \dot{\mathbf{W}}_u(t-\tau)\mathbf{u}(\tau)d\tau, \qquad (101)$$

$$\mathbf{w}(t) = \frac{d}{dt}\int_0^t \mathbf{W}_u(\tau)\mathbf{u}(t-\tau)d\tau$$
$$= \frac{d}{dt}\int_0^t \mathbf{W}_u(t-\tau)\mathbf{u}(\tau)d\tau. \qquad (102)$$

These expressions, as scalar rather than vector equations, were originally used by DuHamel in 1833 in dynamics. They are variously known as the DuHamel integrals, Carson integrals, and superposition integrals. Carson himself called (102) *the fundamental formula of circuit theory*.

We leave to you the task of generalizing these results when the assumption that $\mathbf{H}(s)$ is regular at infinity is removed. (See Prob. 39.)

7.8.1 Example

In applying the superposition integrals to the evaluation of a network response, the first step is to find the response $\mathbf{W}_u(t)$. A decision is then required as to which term, $\mathbf{u}$ or $\mathbf{W}_u$, should be reversed and translated to the argument $(t-\tau)$. This choice is guided by the simplicity of the resulting integrals. Then a decision is needed as to which one, **u** or $\mathbf{W}_u$, should be differentiated. Sometimes there may be no choice, since one of them may not be differentiable.

To illustrate, consider again the example of Fig. 19 which was earlier evaluated by using the impulse response. Since we already have $\mathbf{W}_\delta(t)$, (90) can be used to find $\mathbf{W}_u(t)$. The result is

$$
\mathbf{W}_u(t) = \int_0^t \mathbf{W}_\delta(\tau)d\tau = \int_0^t \frac{6}{5}\begin{bmatrix} e^{-\tau} - e^{-6\tau} \\ -4e^{-\tau} - 6e^{-6\tau} \end{bmatrix} d\tau + \int_0^t \begin{bmatrix} 0 \\ 6 \end{bmatrix} \delta(\tau)d\tau
$$

$$
= \frac{1}{5}\, u(t) \begin{bmatrix} 5 - 6e^{-t} + e^{-6t} \\ 24e^{-t} + 6e^{-6t} \end{bmatrix}.
$$

Because of the functional form of the excitation, it is much simpler to differentiate $\mathbf{u}(\tau) = [v_s(\tau)]$ than $\mathbf{W}_u(t)$. The derivative is shown in Fig. 20; its analytical form is also given there.

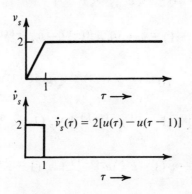

Fig. 20 Example

Let us use the second form of (90), which should be simpler than the first form, since $\dot{v}_s(t - \tau) = 2[u(t - \tau) - u(t - \tau - 1)]$, which is simply the square pulse in Fig. 20 reversed and shifted by t units. Since $\mathbf{u}(0) = [v_s(0)] = 0$, we get for $0 \leqslant t < 1$

$$w(t) = \int_0^t \frac{1}{5} \begin{bmatrix} 5 - 6e^{-\tau} + e^{-6\tau} \\ \\ 24e^{-\tau} + 6e^{-6\tau} \end{bmatrix} 2d\tau$$

$$= \begin{bmatrix} 2t - \frac{7}{3} + \frac{12}{5} e^{-t} - \frac{1}{15} e^{-6t} \\ \\ 10 - \frac{48}{5} e^{-t} - \frac{2}{5} e^{-6t} \end{bmatrix} .$$

This answer can be verified by comparing with the result previously found. Note that the integration was considerably simpler in this case.

This would be the response for all t if $\hat{v}_s$ would stay constant at 2; but it does not; it takes a negative step downward at $t = 1$. Hence, to find the response for $t \geqslant 1$, we simply replace t by $t - 1$ in the above expression — to get the response to a step at $t = 1$ — and subtract the result from the above expression. The result for $t \geqslant 1$ will be

$$w(t) = \begin{bmatrix} 2t - \frac{7}{3} + \frac{12}{5} e^{-t} - \frac{1}{15} e^{-6t} \\ \\ 10 - \frac{48}{5} e^{-t} - \frac{2}{5} e^{-6t} \end{bmatrix}$$

$$- \begin{bmatrix} 2(t-1) - \frac{7}{3} + \frac{12}{5} e^{-(t-1)} - \frac{1}{15} e^{-6(t-1)} \\ \\ 10 - \frac{48}{5} e^{-(t-1)} - \frac{2}{5} e^{-6(t-1)} \end{bmatrix}$$

$$= \begin{bmatrix} -\frac{12}{5} (1 - e^{-1})e^{-(t-1)} + \frac{1}{15} (1 - e^{-6})e^{-6(t-1)} + 2 \\ \\ \frac{48}{5} (1 - e^{-1})e^{-(t-1)} + \frac{2}{5} (1 - e^{-6})e^{-6(t-1)} \end{bmatrix}$$

This again agrees with the previously found result.

CHAPTER 8
Sensitivity Measures

In the preceding chapters we have developed mechanisms for (a) formulating equations for a given network; (b) symbolically solving these equations in the frequency-domain; (c) expressing these solutions in terms of appropriate network functions: driving point and transfer immittances, two-port parameters, scattering parameters, etc.; and (d) describing the network functions in terms of their magnitude and angle, their real and imaginary parts, and their poles and zeros. Generally speaking, any network function will depend on the values of the components of which the network is composed. As a component changes its value (due to temperature changes, aging, replacement, etc.), the network functions will also change. The change can be described as a change in the entire function itself, its magnitude, its angle, its pole locations, etc. It is of great importance to know how sensitive a network function is (as described by one of the measures above) to changes in one of the component parameter values. This is the subject of the present chapter.

8.1 VARIABILITY OF A NETWORK FUNCTION

We shall first be concerned with changes induced in the network function itself (as opposed to, say, its magnitude or its poles) when there is a change in parameter values. Let the component parameters (for example, resistance, capacitance, and gain) be designated p. A network function, say G, is a function of all the parameters. If the parameters are assumed to be varying, then the first order change in G due to changes in the individual parameters p_i can be written

$$\Delta G = \sum_i \frac{\partial G}{\partial p_i} \Delta p_i. \tag{1}$$

The *fractional change* in G is the change in G relative to its nominal value; thus,

$$\frac{\Delta G}{G} = \sum_i \frac{\partial G/\partial p_i}{G} \Delta p_i = \sum_i \left(\frac{p_i}{G} \frac{\partial G}{\partial p_i} \right) \frac{\Delta p_i}{p_i}. \tag{2}$$

This is called the *variability of G*. On the right side, both numerator and denominator were multiplied by p_i. The entire expression on the right is now in the form of a linear combination of fractional changes in the parameters of p_i; namely, the variabilities of p_i. Each coefficient of this linear combination is a measure of the contribution of the corresponding parameter change to the variability of G.

On the basis of the preceding discussion we define the *sensitivity of G to a parameter p* as

$$S_p^G \equiv \frac{\partial G/G}{\partial p/p} = \frac{\partial G}{\partial p} \frac{p}{G}. \tag{3}$$

Because the differential changes are normalized to their respective nominal values, this sensitivity is referred to as the *normalized sensitivity*. Sometimes it is convenient not to normalize one and/or the other (parameter and/or function); we will still refer to the corresponding expression as "the sensitivity" and will use the same symbol, S_p^G, but now the sensitivity will be unnormalized. The context will make evident what is meant.

There remains now the task of obtaining expressions for the sensitivity. For this purpose it would be useful to know what the functional dependence of G is on each of the network parameters. This can be readily established by a number of different approaches. One possibility is to review the formulations of the network equations in Chapter 4; for example, the tableau equations in (4-74b). The only submatrices in which the network parameters appear are $\hat{M}$ and $\hat{N}$. There are two cases to consider: (a) parameter p appears only once in $\hat{M}$ or $\hat{N}$, and (b) parameter p appears twice. The latter possibility occurs only in the case of the ideal transformer and the gyrator, where n or r appear in both of the component branch equations. For all other components, the parameter appears only once, in $\hat{M}$ or $\hat{N}$.

The process of solving for any variable in (4-74b) involves inverting the matrix on the left. The operations involved in inverting a matrix are multiplying entries together, then adding such products. In this process, if a parameter appears in only one entry of the matrix in (4-74b), it cannot be multiplied by itself and so will appear to the first power in the result of the matrix inversion. However, if a parameter appears in two entries of the matrix, it will appear to at most the second power in the result after inverting the matrix. Thus, if the network function is written as a rational function, namely as

$$G = \frac{N(p)}{D(p)}, \tag{4}$$

then, in the first case above, both N and D will be linear polynomials in p; in the second case they will be quadratics in p. For these two cases, G will have the following forms:

$$G(p) = \frac{N(p)}{D(p)} = \frac{N_0 + pN_1}{D_0 + pD_1}, \qquad \text{case (a),} \tag{5a}$$

and

$$G(p) = \frac{N(p)}{D(p)} = \frac{N_0 + pN_1 + p^2N_2}{D_0 + pD_1 + p^2D_2}, \qquad \text{case (b),} \tag{5b}$$

where N_i and D_i do not depend on p. Thus, the network function is *bilinear* in p in the first case and *biquadratic* in p in the second.*

As an illustration, consider the network in Fig. 1, assumed to be initially relaxed. Let the response function be V_4 so the network function is $G = V_4/V_g$. The network contains no ideal transformers or gyrators; hence, G should be bilinear in every parameter value. By any one of a number of methods, the expression for G can be found. If attention is to be focused on any one parameter, the expression for G can be rewritten to place it in the form of (5) with p representing that parameter. For example, with respect to the parameter α, the expression for G can be rewritten as

---

* These results can also be established by considering the expression for the appropriate graph gain of a signal-flow graph representing the network or the formula for the network function using topological methods. For these topics, see [48].

$$G(\alpha) = \frac{\{(1-\mu)G_3R_4\} + \alpha\{(\mu G_3 + Y_2)R_4\}}{\{(1+G_3R_4)(1+Z_1Y_2) + (1-\mu)Z_1G_3\} + \alpha\{-1\}}.$$

Similarly, with respect to the parameter G_3, we can rewrite the function G as

$$G(G_3) = \frac{\{\alpha Y_2R_4\} + G_3\{[1-\mu(1-\alpha)]R_4\}}{\{1+Z_1Y_2-\alpha\} + G_3\{(1+Z_1Y_2)R_4 + (1-\mu)Z_1\}}.$$

Illustrations of the biquadratic dependence of G on transformer turns ratio and gyration ratio are provided in the exercises. (See Exer. 51.)

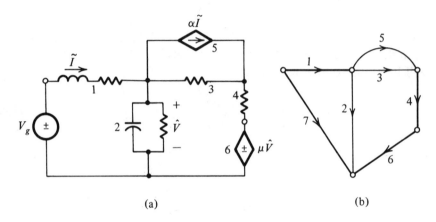

Fig. 1 Example

We are now ready to develop expressions for the sensitivity utilizing the bilinear and biquadratic forms in (5). For the bilinear function in (5a), differentiating G with respect to p and multiplying the result by p/G leads to

$$S_p^G = p\frac{N_1D - D_1N}{ND} = p\left(\frac{N_1}{N} - \frac{D_1}{D}\right), \text{ case (a).} \tag{6}$$

An alternate expression can be obtained by a simple manipulation of this one, utilizing the expressions for N and D from (5a); thus,

$$S_p^G = \frac{D_0}{D} - \frac{N_0}{N}, \text{ case (a).} \tag{7}$$

In a similar way, the following expressions for the sensitivity are obtained for the biquadratic case:

$$S_p^G = p \left(\frac{N_1}{N} - \frac{D_1}{D} \right) + 2p^2 \left(\frac{N_2}{N} - \frac{D_2}{D} \right), \text{ case (b)}, \qquad (8a)$$

or

$$S_p^G = 2 \left(\frac{D_0}{D} - \frac{N_0}{N} \right) + p \left(\frac{D_1}{D} - \frac{N_1}{N} \right), \text{ case (b)}, \qquad (8b)$$

or

$$S_p^G = \left(\frac{D_0}{D} - \frac{N_0}{N} \right) + p^2 \left(\frac{N_2}{N} - \frac{D_2}{D} \right), \text{ case (b)}. \qquad (8c)$$

You should verify that these expressions reduce to the corresponding ones in (6) and (7) in the event that $N_2 = 0$ and $D_2 = 0$.

It is clear from the preceding sensitivity expressions for both cases that the sensitivity has as poles all of the critical frequencies — zeros and poles — of the network function. It is thus, generally, a higher order function than the network function.

In specific cases, one or another expression for sensitivity may be simpler to use, as the following example will show. For the network of Fig. 2 the voltage gain function can be found to be

$$G(s) = \frac{V_o(s)}{V_i(s)} = \frac{\mu}{s^2 + (3 - \mu)s + 1} = \frac{\mu}{(s^2 + 3s + 1) + \mu(-s)}.$$

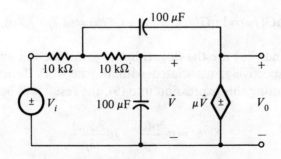

Fig. 2   Network of example

As expected, the gain is a bilinear function of the controlled source parameter μ. For the nominal value $\mu = 2$, this function is the low-pass, two-pole function

$$G(s) = \frac{2}{s^2 + s + 1}.$$

The sensitivity of the gain with respect to the parameter μ can be evaluated by either (6) or (7). The latter leads to an immediately simpler expression because $N_0 \equiv 0$. Thus, by (7),

$$S_\mu^{G(s)} = \frac{D_0(s)}{D(s)} = \frac{s^2 + 3s + 1}{s^2 + s + 1},$$

where μ in the denominator has been replaced by its nominal value $\mu = 2$.

8.2 GAIN AND PHASE SENSITIVITIES

Both a network function and its sensitivity with respect to a parameter are functions of the complex frequency variable s. Of particular interest are the frequencies $s = j\omega$, for which $G(j\omega)$ is a complex quantity. More detailed information about the variation of G can be obtained by examining the sensitivity of both the magnitude and angle of G, which we shall now do. Preparatory to this task, note that the definition of sensitivity in (3) can be written in an alternate form by using the identity $\partial \ln G / \partial G = 1/G$. Thus

$$S_p^G = p \frac{\partial \ln G}{\partial p}. \tag{9}$$

Now, for $s = j\omega$, we can write

$$\ln G(j\omega) = \ln |G(j\omega)| + j \arg G(j\omega) = \alpha(\omega) + j\beta(\omega), \tag{10}$$

where $\alpha(\omega)$ and $\beta(\omega)$ are the (logarithmic) gain function and the phase function, respectively, associated with the network function $G(j\omega)$. Upon substituting this expression into (9), the result will be

$$S_p^{G(j\omega)} = p \frac{\partial \alpha(\omega)}{\partial p} + jp \frac{\partial \beta(\omega)}{\partial p}. \tag{11}$$

Each term on the right is in the form of the right side of (3), except that the function is not normalized. (Each is, therefore, an unnormalized sensitivity.) Hence, (11) can be written as

$$S_p^{G(j\omega)} = S_p^{\alpha(\omega)} + jS_p^{\beta(\omega)}, \tag{12}$$

where

$$S_p^{\alpha(\omega)} = p\frac{\partial\alpha(\omega)}{\partial p} \tag{13a}$$

is the *gain sensitivity* and

$$S_p^{\beta(\omega)} = p\frac{\partial\beta(\omega)}{\partial p} \tag{13b}$$

is the *phase sensitivity*.

Observe that, when p is real, as is usually the case,

$$S_p^{\alpha(\omega)} = \text{Re}\{S_p^{G(j\omega)}\} = \text{Ev}\{S_p^{G(s)}\}|_{s=j\omega} \tag{14a}$$

and

$$S_p^{\beta(\omega)} = \text{Im}\{S_p^{G(j\omega)}\} = \frac{1}{j}\text{Od}\{S_p^{G(s)}\}|_{s=j\omega}. \tag{14b}$$

Thus, an expression for the sensitivity of G leads directly to expressions for the corresponding gain and phase sensitivities.

As an illustration, consider again the previous example for which we found the sensitivity

$$S_\mu^{G(s)} = \frac{s^2 + 3s + 1}{s^2 + s + 1}.$$

This can be written in terms of its even and odd parts as

$$S_\mu^{G(s)} = \frac{(s^4 - s^2 + 1)}{s^4 + s^2 + 1} + \frac{2s^3 + 2s}{s^4 + s^2 + 1}.$$

It follows that

$$S_\mu^{\alpha(\omega)} = \frac{\omega^4 + \omega^2 + 1}{\omega^4 - \omega^2 + 1} \quad \text{and} \quad S_\mu^{\beta(\omega)} = \frac{-2\omega^3 + 2\omega}{\omega^4 - \omega^2 + 1}$$

A sketch of each of these functions against ω will show how the gain and phase sensitivites vary with ω.

8.3 ZERO AND POLE SENSITIVITIES

The sensitivity defined in (3) is a measure of the variation of a function as a result of the variation of a parameter on which it depends. One way of describing the variation of the function was given in the preceding section; namely, in terms of the variations of the (logarithmic) gain function and the phase function. Another way of describing the variation of $G(s)$ will be discussed in this section.

As a network parameter varies, the locations of the poles and the zeros of a network function will generally shift. Some poles and zeros will move more than others will for the same fractional change of the parameter. A measure of these changes in pole and zero locations is the sensitivity of the poles and zeros, to be defined below.

Assume that all poles and zeros of a network function are simple. Then $G(s)$ can be expressed as

$$G(s) = G_0 \frac{\prod_{i=1}^{n_z}(s - z_i)}{\prod_{i=1}^{n_p}(s - p_i)}. \tag{15}$$

In order to use the alternate expression for sensitivity given in (9), we want the logarithm of this expression for $G(s)$; thus,

$$\ln G(s) = \ln G_0 + \sum_{i=1}^{n_z} \ln(s - z_i) - \sum_{i=1}^{n_p} \ln(s - p_i) \tag{16}$$

As p varies, the zeros z_i, the poles p_i, and the multiplying factor G_0 can all vary. Substituting (16) into (9) yields

$$S_p^G = p \frac{\partial \ln G}{\partial p} = \frac{p}{G_0} \frac{\partial G_0}{\partial p} - \sum_{i=1}^{n_z} \frac{p \partial z_i / \partial p}{s - z_i} + \sum_{i=1}^{n_p} \frac{p \partial p_i / \partial p}{s - p_i}. \tag{17}$$

The coefficients of the terms under the summation signs are in the form of unnormalized sensitivities. Let us define

$$S_p^{z_i} = p \frac{\partial z_i}{\partial p} \tag{18}$$

as the *zero sensitivites* of $G(s)$ and

$$S_p^{p_i} = p \frac{\partial p_i}{\partial p} \tag{19}$$

as the *pole sensitivites* of $G(s)$. Then, (17) can be rewritten as

$$S_p^G = S_p^{G_0} - \sum_{i=1}^{n_z} \frac{S_p^{z_i}}{s - z_i} + \sum_{i=1}^{n_p} \frac{S_p^{p_i}}{s - p_i}. \tag{20}$$

It has previously been demonstrated that the sensitivity function has as poles all the poles and zeros of the network function. The preceding expression confirms this; the right side is in the form of a partial fraction expansion. We see that the residues in the expansion are the (unnormalized) zero and pole sensitivities. To find the latter sensitivites, it is necessary only to expand S_p^G in partial fractions.

The preceding development is valid for simple poles and zeros. In the case of multiple poles or zeros, the sensitivity definitions in (18) and (19) are inappropriate.

As an illustration, return to the earlier example in which we found that the network function

$$G(s) = \frac{\mu}{(s^2 + 3s + 1) + \mu(-s)} \bigg|_{\mu=2}$$

had the sensitivity with respect to μ of

$$S_\mu^{G(s)} = \frac{s^2 + 3s + 1}{s^2 + s + 1}.$$

Now, $G(s)$ has no finite zeros and two simple poles:

$$p_1 = \frac{-1 + j\sqrt{3}}{2} \text{ and } p_2 = \frac{-1 - j\sqrt{3}}{2}.$$

The partial fraction expansion of the expression for the sensitivity is

$$S_\mu^{G(s)} = 1 + \frac{2 + j\sqrt{3}/3}{s - p_1} + \frac{2 - j\sqrt{3}/3}{s - p_2}.$$

It now follows from (20) that

$$S_\mu^{p_1} = 2 + j\sqrt{3}/3 \text{ and } S_\mu^{p_2} = 2 - j\sqrt{3}/3.$$

Observe, because $S_\mu^{G(s)}$ is a real rational function of s and $p_2 = \bar{p}_1$, that $S_\mu^{p_2}$ is the conjugate of $S_\mu^{p_1}$.

8.4 SENSITIVITY INVARIANTS

In the preceding discussion of sensitivity we considered only changes occurring in the values of individual components. But what happens if the values of all components of certain types are changed by the same multiplicative factor? Some quite useful results follow from a consideration of this question.

To begin, note that any network function G can be viewed as a function of the parameters of all the components constituting the network and hence can be written as $G(s; R_i, G_i, L_i, \Gamma_i, D_i, C_i, n_i, \mu_i, \alpha_i)$. The R_i and G_i include the parameters of gyrators, current-controlled voltage sources, and voltage-controlled current sources. Now suppose the following changes are made in the parameters: each R_i, L_i, and D_i is multiplied by a factor λ; each G_i, Γ_i, and C_i is multiplied by the factor $1/\lambda$; and the frequency variable is left unchanged. The resulting change in the network function depends on its type—impedance, admittance, or dimensionless gain. As a general proposition it can be said of the resulting function that

$$G(s; \lambda R_i, G_i/\lambda, \lambda L_i, \Gamma_i/\lambda, \lambda D_i, C_i/\lambda, n_i, \mu_i, \alpha_i)$$
$$= KG(s; R_i, G_i, L_i, \Gamma_i, D_i, C_i, n_i, \mu_i, \alpha_i), \tag{21}$$

where

$K = \lambda$, if $G(s)$ is an impedance function;

$\quad = 1$, if $G(s)$ is a voltage or current gain; and

$\quad = 1/\lambda$, if $G(s)$ is an admittance function.

In other words, under the specified changes, an impedance function becomes multiplied by λ and an admittance function by $1/\lambda$, but a voltage or current gain remains unchanged.

Now let us find the sensitivity of both sides of (21) with respect to λ evaluated at the nominal value of $\lambda = 1$. This implies differentiating (21) with respect to λ and dividing by G, with $\lambda = 1$. The right side is simple; λ appears only as a multiplier to the power of either 1, 0, or -1. The left side is more complicated. The final result of the proposed steps will be

$$\sum_i S_{R_i}^G - \sum_i S_{G_i}^G + \sum_i S_{L_i}^G - \sum_i S_{\Gamma_i}^G + \sum_i S_{D_i}^G - \sum_i S_{C_i}^G$$

$\quad = 1$, if G is an impedance,

$\quad = 0$, if G is a voltage or current gain, $\tag{22}$

$\quad = -1$, if G is an admittance.

In each instance the summation is over the number of parameters of the type indicated.

Observe that, no matter how the indicated parameters of a network vary, the algebraic sum of sensitivities on the left remains equal to the appropriate constant on the right. Thus, the network function might be highly sensitive to some particular parameters and less so to others. No matter; the algebraic sum of sensitivities indicated in this expression does not change. For this reason, the left side is called a *sensitivity invariant*.

In the preceding development, the frequency variable s was left unmodified. Suppose now that s is multiplied by $1/\lambda$; at the same time each L_i, Γ_i, D_i, and C_i is multiplied by λ so that each product $L_i s$, $\Gamma_i s$, $D_i s$, and $C_i s$ is unchanged. Since there has been no change in parameter impedances or admittances, we should expect no change in the network function. That is,

$$G(s/\lambda; R_i, G_i, \lambda L_i, \lambda \Gamma_i, \lambda D_i, \lambda C_i, n_i, \mu_i, \alpha_i)$$
$$= G(s; R_i, G_i, L_i, \Gamma_i, D_i, C_i, n_i, \mu_i, \alpha_i). \tag{23}$$

As before, we intend to calculate the sensitivity of both sides to λ; hence, we differentiate with respect to λ and divide by G, with $\lambda = 1$. Since λ does not appear on the right, the sensitivity of the right side will be zero. The final result is

$$\sum_i S_{L_i}^{G(s)} + \sum_i S_{\Gamma_i}^{G(s)} + \sum_i S_{D_i}^{G(s)} + \sum_i S_{C_i}^{G(s)} = S_s^{G(s)}. \tag{24}$$

Again, we see that no matter how the indicated parameters change, the sum of sensitivities on the left remains equal to the sensitivity of G with respect to s at the nominal parameter values. The expression on the left is, thus, another sensitivity invariant.

It is possible to derive a simple relationship between this sensitivity invariant and the gain and phase functions. First from (11), observe that

$$S_{j\omega}^{G(j\omega)} = \frac{\partial \alpha(\omega)}{\partial \omega / \omega} + j \frac{\partial \beta(\omega)}{\partial \omega / \omega} \tag{25a}$$

or, equivalently,

$$S_{j\omega}^{G(j\omega)} = \frac{\partial \alpha(\omega)}{\partial \ln \omega} + j \frac{\partial \beta(\omega)}{\partial \ln \omega}. \tag{25b}$$

Upon combining (25) and (24) with $s = j\omega$, we obtain

$$\text{Re}\left\{ \sum_i S_{L_i}^{G(j\omega)} + \sum_i S_{\Gamma_i}^{G(j\omega)} + \sum_i S_{D_i}^{G(j\omega)} + \sum_i S_{C_i}^{G(j\omega)} \right\}$$
$$= \omega \frac{\partial \alpha(\omega)}{\partial \omega} \tag{26a}$$
$$= \frac{\partial \alpha(\omega)}{\partial \ln \omega}$$

and

$$\text{Im}\left\{ \sum_i S_{L_i}^{G(j\omega)} + \sum_i S_{\Gamma_i}^{G(j\omega)} + \sum_i S_{D_i}^{G(j\omega)} + \sum_i S_{C_i}^{G(j\omega)} \right\}$$
$$= \omega \frac{\partial \beta(\omega)}{\partial \omega} \tag{26b}$$
$$= \frac{\partial \beta(\omega)}{\partial \ln \omega}$$

An interpretation for (26) is as follows: Suppose the gain function $\alpha(\omega)$ is plotted against ω on semi-log paper (or $|G(j\omega)|$ against ω on log-log paper). The slope of this curve at any frequency represents the real part of the sensitivity invariant at that frequency. Similarly, the slope of the curve of the phase function $\beta(\omega)$ plotted against ω on semi-log paper is the imaginary part of the sensitivity invariant at each frequency.

The two sensitivity invariants given in (22) and (24) involve the sensitivity of the network function G. It is possible to derive similar sensitivity invariants involving the pole or zero sensitivities. If $\hat{s}$ denotes an arbitrary critical frequency, zero or pole, then these invariants are

$$\sum_i S_{R_i}^{\hat{s}} - \sum_i S_{G_i}^{\hat{s}} + \sum_i S_{L_i}^{\hat{s}} - \sum_i S_{\Gamma_i}^{\hat{s}} + \sum_i S_{D_i}^{\hat{s}} - \sum_i S_{C_i}^{\hat{s}} = 0 \tag{27}$$

and

$$\sum_i S_{L_i}^{\hat{s}} - \sum_i S_{\Gamma_i}^{\hat{s}} - \sum_i S_{D_i}^{\hat{s}} + \sum_i S_{C_i}^{\hat{s}} = -\hat{s}. \tag{28}$$

You should supply the detailed development of these expressions. (See Prob. 40.) The last result is interesting. It states that, no matter how the indicated parameters change and even though a pole or zero may be more or less sensitive to changes in individual parameters, nevertheless, the sum of the sensitivities over all the indicated parameters remains equal to the original pole or zero location.

8.5 AN APPLICATION

Consider an active RC network realizing a voltage transfer function $G(s) = V_o(s)/V_i(s)$. Suppose the active components are voltage-controlled voltage sources − voltage amplifiers. Thus, $G(s) = G(s; R_i, C_i, \mu_i)$. Assuming that all capacitors are described by their capacitances (not their reciprocals) and all resistors by their resistances (not their reciprocals), the critical frequency invariants (27) and (28) become

$$\sum_i S^{\hat{s}}_{R_i} - \sum_i S^{\hat{s}}_{C_i} = 0$$

and

$$\sum_i S^{\hat{s}}_{C_i} = -\hat{s}.$$

Combining the two gives:

$$\sum_i S^{\hat{s}}_{R_i} = \sum_i S^{\hat{s}}_{C_i} = -\hat{s}. \tag{29}$$

Since the critical frequencies depend on the parameters R_i, C_i and μ_i, (1) with G replaced by $\hat{s}$ leads to

$$\Delta\hat{s} = \sum_i \frac{\partial\hat{s}}{\partial R_i}\Delta R_i + \sum_i \frac{\partial\hat{s}}{\partial C_i}\Delta C_i + \sum_i \frac{\partial\hat{s}}{\partial \mu_i}\Delta\mu_i.$$

If numerator and denominator of each term on the right is multiplied by the corresponding parameter − R_i, C_i, or μ_i − then this expression can be rewritten as

$$\Delta\hat{s} = \sum_i S^{\hat{s}}_{R_i}\frac{\Delta R_i}{R_i} + \sum_i S^{\hat{s}}_{C_i}\frac{\Delta C_i}{C_i} + \sum_i S^{\hat{s}}_{\mu_i}\frac{\Delta\mu_i}{\mu_i}. \tag{30}$$

Let us now assume that the relative resistance variations are equal − $\Delta R/R_i = \Delta R/R$ − and the relative capacitance variations are equal − $\Delta C_i/C_i = \Delta C/C$. (This is a reasonable assumption with hybrid integrated circuit fabrication of an active RC network.) The preceding expression will become

$$\Delta \hat{s} = \frac{\Delta R}{R} \sum_i S_{R_i}^{\hat{s}} + \frac{\Delta C}{C} \sum_i S_{C_i}^{\hat{s}} + \sum_i S_{\mu_i}^{\hat{s}} \frac{\Delta \mu_i}{\mu_i}. \tag{31}$$

By substitution of (29), this expression reduces to

$$\Delta \hat{s} = - \left(\frac{\Delta R}{R} + \frac{\Delta C}{C} \right) \hat{s} + \sum_i S_{\mu_i}^{\hat{s}} \frac{\Delta \mu_i}{\mu_i}. \tag{32}$$

A considerable simplification of this expression would be possible if it were possible to achieve

$$\frac{\Delta R}{R} = - \frac{\Delta C}{C}. \tag{33}$$

This is not unreasonable for hybrid integrated circuits. If the changes in R and C are due mainly to ambient temperature changes, then (33) translates to: The temperature coefficient of the resistors must be the negative of that of the capacitors. Such a match is well within reason for hybrid integrated circuits.

With (33) inserted into (32), the final result for the change in location of a critical frequency is

$$\Delta \hat{s} = \sum_i S_{\mu_i}^{\hat{s}} \frac{\Delta \mu_i}{\mu_i}. \tag{34}$$

Thus, if the variations of the R's and C's can be made to cancel each other out, the critical terms in an active RC network design are the voltage amplifier sensitivities $S_{\mu_i}^{\hat{s}}$—they should be made as low as possible to keep changes in pole and zero locations to small values, even with substantial variability in controlled-source gains.

Question Set: Part II

EXERCISES

1. In the network of Fig. E-1 solve for the voltage-gain function
   $V_2(s)/V_1(s)$. Do this by (a) using mixed-variable equations and (b)
   using node equations after expressing I_1 in terms of appropriate
   voltages.

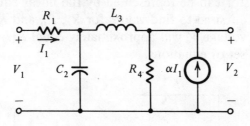

Fig. E-1

2. Figure E-2 shows an amplifier together with appropriate linear
   equivalents. It is desired to find the output impedance Z_o for both
   cases shown, when the output is taken from the collector and when
   it is taken from the emitter.
   (a) Do this by using node equations and an admittance representation for the controlled source.
   (b) Repeat (a) using loop equations. (How many are there?)
   (c) Repeat (a) using mixed-variable equations.

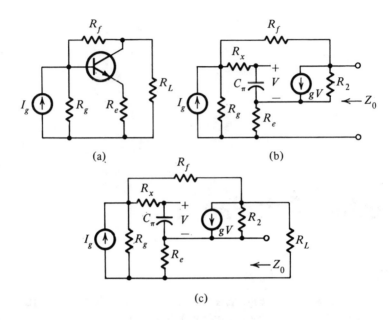

(a)   (b)

(c)

Fig. E-2

3. The diagram in Fig. E-3 shows a difference amplifier. Assume that
   each transistor can be represented by the linear equivalent circuit
   shown. It is desired to find values for R_L, R_f, and R_e in order that
   the output voltage V_o will approximately equal $K(I_2 - I_1)$. Use any
   convenient set of equations.

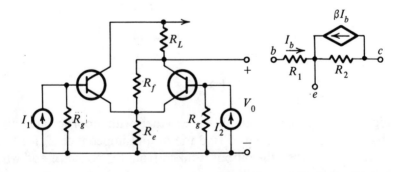

Fig. E-3

4. The diagram in Fig. E-4 is an approximate hybrid-π model of a
   transistor. Find the h-parameters.

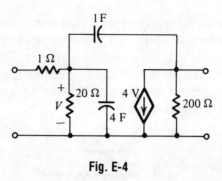

Fig. E-4

5. Find the hybrid h-matrix for each of the networks in Fig. E-5. (Replace each transistor by the simplest possible small-signal equivalent.)

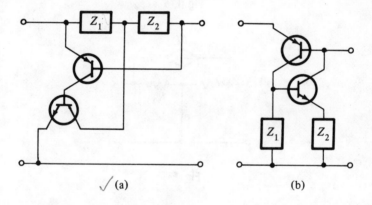

Fig. E-5

6. The two-port in Fig. E-6 is a simplified model of Fig. E-5(a); it is potentially a negative converter.
   (a) Find the hybrid h-parameters.
   (b) Specify the ratio R_2/R_1 in terms of β to make $h_{12}h_{21} = 1$.
   (c) Comment on the relative values of R_1 and R_2 for $\beta = 50$. ($\beta = 50$ is an easily realizable current gain.)
   (d) Is this a voltage or a current negative converter?

7. The two-port of Fig. E-7 is a simplified model of Fig. E-5(b); it is potentially a negative converter.
   (a) Find the hybrid h-parameters.
   (b) Find the ratio of R_2/R_1 in terms of β to make $h_{12}h_{21} = 1$.

(c) Draw an equivalent network based on the hybrid g-parameters for this two-port. Show all component values using the condition found in (b).

(d) Let $\beta = 50$. Design possible compensating networks to be placed in series or shunt at the ports in order to convert this two-port to an ideal negative converter.

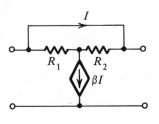

Fig. E-6

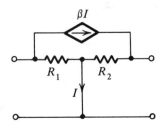

Fig. E-7

8. (a) Find the h-parameters of the two-port in Fig. E-8.

(b) Let $\beta_1 = 1$. Can you find values of β_2, R_2, and R_1 to make the two-port an ideal negative converter?

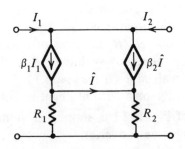

Fig. E-8

9. In Fig. E-9(a), a common-terminal gyrator has terminal 3 as the common terminal.
   (a) Determine the admittance matrix of the two-port obtained by making terminal 1 common instead.
   (b) Repeat (a) with terminal 2 made common.
   (c) The symbol for the gyrator is sometimes drawn as in Fig. E-9(b). Comment on the appropriateness of this symbol, in view of (a) and (b).

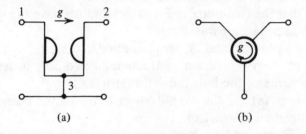

(a)   (b)

Fig. E-9

10. A certain nonreciprocal network can be represented by the network shown in Fig. E-10(a). It is desired to connect a resistor R_1 as shown in Fig. E-10(b) in order to stop reverse transmission (from right to left). Determine the required value of R_1.

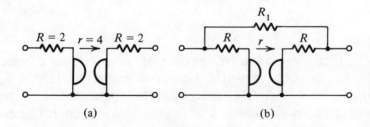

(a)   (b)

Fig. E-10

11. Fig. E-11 shows a two-port network terminated in an impedance Z_L. Show that

$$Z_{21}(s) = \frac{V_2(s)}{I_1(s)} = \frac{z_{21}Z_L}{z_{22} + Z_L}$$

$$Y_{21}(s) = \frac{I_2(s)}{V_1(s)} = \frac{y_{21}Y_L}{y_{22} + Y_L}.$$

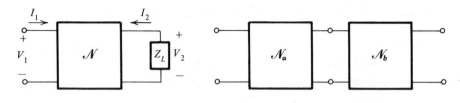

Fig. E-11   Fig. E-14

12. Verify that det $\mathbf{Y} = 1/\det \mathbf{Z}$ for a two-port.
13. Show that the two-ports in Fig. 15(c) and (d) have the same open-circuit impedance parameters.
14. Two two-ports $\mathcal{N}_a$ and $\mathcal{N}_b$ are connected in cascade, as in Fig. E-14.
    (a) Find the y_{21} function of the overall two-port in terms of the elements of the individual $\mathbf{Y}$ matrices.
    (b) Repeat (a) for the overall z_{21} in terms of the elements of the individual $\mathbf{Z}$ matrices.
15. Repeat Exercise 14 but with a voltage negative converter cascaded between $\mathcal{N}_a$ and $\mathcal{N}_b$, as in Fig. E-15.

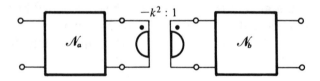

Fig. E-15

16. Fig. E-16 shows an interconnection of two-ports, one of which is a current negative converter. Obtain an expression for the voltage transfer ratio $V_2(s)/V_1(s)$ in terms of the y-parameters of $\mathcal{N}_a$ and $\mathcal{N}_b$ and the conversion ratio k of the negative converter. Compare, if the negative converter is not present.

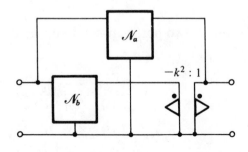

Fig. E-16

17. An ideal transformer is cascaded with a two-port, either on the input side or on the output side, as shown in Fig. E-17.
    (a) Find the overall **Z** matrix in terms of the turns ratio n and the **Z** matrix of $\mathcal{N}$.
    (b) Repeat (a) for the **Y** matrix.

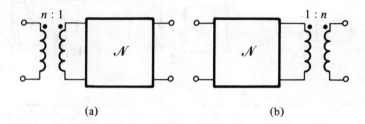

(a)   (b)

Fig. E-17

18. By direct application of the definitions, find the elements of the impedance, admittance, and hybrid matrices of the networks in Fig. E-18.

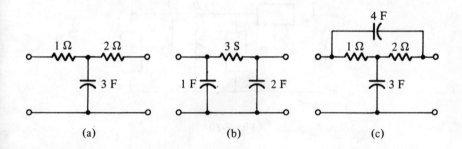

(a)   (b)   (c)

Fig. E-18

19. (a) Find h_{21} for the network in Fig. E-19(a), first with the switch in position A, then in position B. Use the Y matrix to describe network $\mathcal{N}$.
    (b) Repeat (a) for both positions of the switch if $\mathcal{N}$ has the structure of Fig. E-19(b).
20. Find the impedance Z in Fig. E-20, taking $f(s)$ to equal $Z_1(s)/Z_2(s)$.
21. Show that the voltage gain function for the network in Fig. E-21 is

$$\frac{V_2}{V_1} = \frac{-y_{21}}{y_{22} + G_1 - (g/G_3 - 1)Y},$$

where y_{21} and y_{22} refer to $\mathcal{N}$. (Note that the combination of G_1, G_2, and G_3 with the controlled source can represent a real amplifier for which the controlled source is the idealization.)

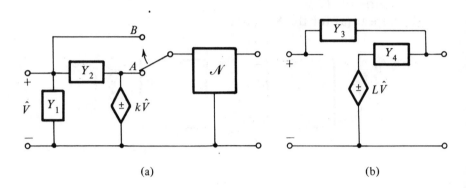

(a)   (b)

Fig. E-19

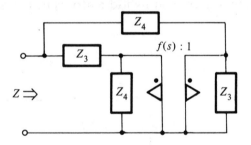

Fig. E-20

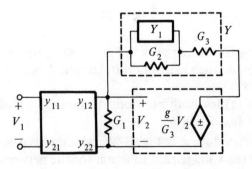

Fig. E-21

22. The hybrid matrix of the two-port $\mathcal{N}$ in Fig. E-22 is given as follows:

$$H = \begin{bmatrix} 5 & 3 \\ -3 & 4 \end{bmatrix}$$

From the basic definitions of h_{ij} find the **H** matrix of the overall two-port.

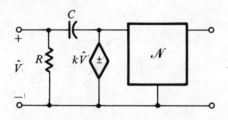

Fig. E-22

23. Find the transfer voltage ratio for the two networks in Fig. E-23 in terms of the amplifier gain μ and elements of the admittance matrices of the two-ports $\mathcal{N}_a$ and $\mathcal{N}_b$. Verify for Fig. E-23(b) that the limiting value as $\mu \to \infty$ is $V_2/V_1 = -y_{21b}/y_{21a}$.

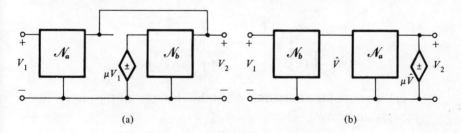

(a)   (b)

Fig. E-23

24. Find the chain matrix of the two-ports in Fig. E-24. The transformers are perfect.

25. Treat the bridged-tee network of Fig. E-25 first as the parallel connection of two two-ports and then as the series connection of two two-ports to find the overall y-parameters. (The answers should be the same.)

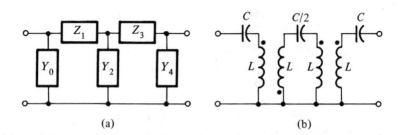

Fig. E-24

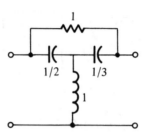

Fig. E-25

26. In Fig. E-26, $\mathcal{N}$ represents a linear, time-invariant two-port having the following hybrid equations:

$$\begin{bmatrix} V_a \\ I_2 \end{bmatrix} = \begin{bmatrix} 5 & 3 \\ -3 & 4 \end{bmatrix} \begin{bmatrix} I_a \\ V_2 \end{bmatrix}.$$

K is the gain of the amplifier. Find the elements of the matrix in the expression below.

$$\begin{bmatrix} V_1 \\ I_2 \end{bmatrix} = \begin{bmatrix} h_{11} & h_{12} \\ h_{21} & h_{22} \end{bmatrix} \begin{bmatrix} I_1 \\ V_2 \end{bmatrix}.$$

27. One of the sets of voltage-current relations of a linear, time-invariant, common-terminal two-port is as follows:

$$V_1 = z_{11}I_1 + z_{12}I_2$$

$$V_2 = z_{21}I_1 + z_{22}I_2$$

The networks shown in Fig. E-27 are realizations of these equations and so each is an "equivalent circuit" of a two-port. Notice that the equivalent circuit in Fig. E-27(b) has a single controlled source which vanishes when the two-port is reciprocal. Find other equivalent circuits of a two-port commencing with the two hybrid and the admittance representations.

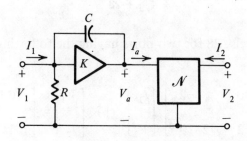

Fig. E-26

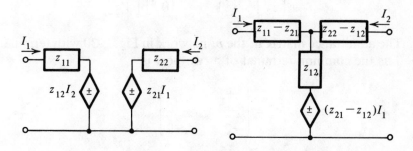

Fig. E-27

28. A two-port has the following hybrid V-I relationship:

$$\begin{bmatrix} V_1 \\ I_2 \end{bmatrix} = \begin{bmatrix} -75 & 1 \\ 1 & -10^3 \end{bmatrix} \begin{bmatrix} I_1 \\ V_2 \end{bmatrix}$$

Design compensating networks to be placed in series or shunt at the ports in Fig. E-28 in order to convert the resulting two-port to an ideal negative converter.

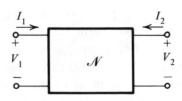

Fig. E-28

29. Repeat Exercise 28 for two-ports having the following V-I relationships:

(a) $$\begin{bmatrix} V_1 \\ I_2 \end{bmatrix} = \begin{bmatrix} 100 & -2 \\ -2 & 2\times10^{-3} \end{bmatrix} \begin{bmatrix} I_1 \\ V_2 \end{bmatrix}$$ (b) $$\begin{bmatrix} V_1 \\ I_2 \end{bmatrix} = \begin{bmatrix} -100 & 1 \\ 1 & 10^{-4} \end{bmatrix} \begin{bmatrix} I_1 \\ V_2 \end{bmatrix}$$

(c) $$\begin{bmatrix} V_1 \\ I_2 \end{bmatrix} = \begin{bmatrix} 100 & 1 \\ 1 & -10^{-4} \end{bmatrix} \begin{bmatrix} I_1 \\ V_2 \end{bmatrix}$$

30. The admittance matrix of the *pi*-network in Fig. E-30 with terminal 3 as the common terminal of a two-port is

$$\mathbf{Y}_3 = \begin{bmatrix} s+2 & -2 \\ -2 & 4s+2 \end{bmatrix} .$$

Find the admittance matrices when each of the other terminals is made the common terminal of a two-port.

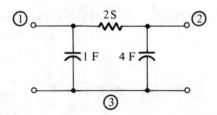

Fig. E-30

31. Let the hybrid **H** matrix for a transistor in the common-emitter connection be

$$H = \begin{bmatrix} h_{11} & h_{12} \\ h_{21} & h_{22} \end{bmatrix}$$

Find the **H** matrix of the transistor in the common-base and common-collector configurations through the agency of the indefinite admittance matrix.

32. The common-terminal two-port $\mathcal{N}$ shown in Fig. E-32(a) has the Y matrix given below. A new two-port is formed by reorienting $\mathcal{N}$ and adding components as shown in Fig. E-32(b). Find the admittance matrix of the new two-port.

$$Y = \begin{bmatrix} 2s+2 & -1 \\ -4 & 10 \end{bmatrix}$$

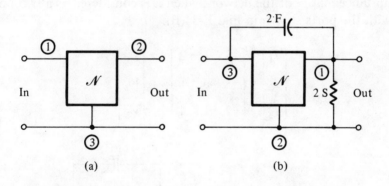

(a)   (b)

Fig. E-32

33. Fig. E-33(a) shows a common-terminal three-port with terminal 4 as the common terminal. The admittance matrix of this configuration is given below. (Take the elements of the matrix to be values of conductance.) It is desired to reconnect this network as a two-port, as shown in Fig. E-33(b), the input port being 3-2 and the output port being 1-2. Find the corresponding admittance matrix.

$$\begin{bmatrix} I_1 \\ I_2 \\ I_3 \end{bmatrix} = \begin{bmatrix} 1 & 2 & 3 \\ 6 & 5 & 4 \\ 7 & 8 & 9 \end{bmatrix} \begin{bmatrix} V_1 \\ V_2 \\ V_3 \end{bmatrix}$$

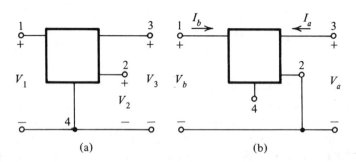

Fig. E-33

34. Fig. E-34(a) shows a four-terminal network connected as a common-terminal three-port. The admittance equations of this three-port are given below. It is desired to connect a unit capacitor between terminals 1 and 2, as shown in Fig. E-34(b). Find the admittance matrix of the network when it is considered as a two-port with the ports shown in Fig. E-34(B).

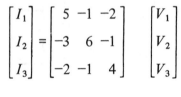

$$\begin{bmatrix} I_1 \\ I_2 \\ I_3 \end{bmatrix} = \begin{bmatrix} 5 & -1 & -2 \\ -3 & 6 & -1 \\ -2 & -1 & 4 \end{bmatrix} \begin{bmatrix} V_1 \\ V_2 \\ V_3 \end{bmatrix}$$

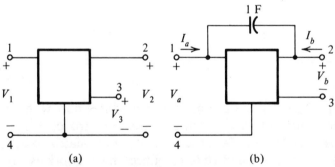

Fig. E-34

35. The sense of incident and reflected waves is related to what is taken to be the direction of power flow. Fig. E-35(a) shows a one-port with the usual references of voltage and current. The reflection coefficient for this one-port is ϱ_1. In Fig. E-35(b) the current in the one-port is reversed. The one-port is thus considered as supplying

power to the network to the left of the terminals. Find the new reflection coefficient ϱ_2 in terms of Z and ϱ_1.

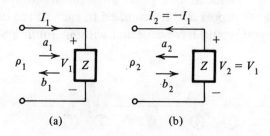

(a)   (b)

Fig. E-35

36. In Fig. E-36 are shown the two controlled sources that have no impedance or admittance representations. Find the scattering matrices for these two-ports.

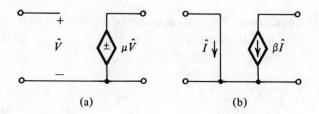

(a)   (b)

Fig. E-36

37. In Fig. E-37 are shown two controlled sources. One has no impedance representation; the other has no admittance representation. But they both have a scattering matrix. Find them.

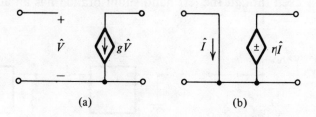

(a)   (b)

Fig. E-37

38. Each of the multiports in Fig. E-38 is an ideal junction consisting of direct connections between the ports. Find the scattering matrix of

each for 1Ω normalizing resistances at each port. In each case suppose that power is supplied by a voltage source in series with the terminating resistance at one port. Find the fraction of the power reflected at that port and transmitted to each of the other ports. Is this what you would have expected without finding **S**?

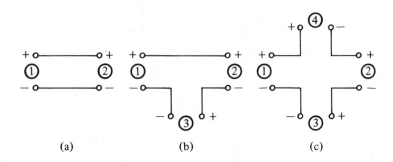

Fig. E-38

39. Find the even part, Ev $F(s)$, and the odd part, Od $F(s)$, of each of the following functions from the even and odd parts of the numerator and denominator:

(a) $F(s) = \dfrac{s^3 + 2s^2 + 3s + 4}{s^2 + 3s + 3}$
    (b) $F(s) = \dfrac{s^3 + s^2 + 2s + 2}{s^4 + 5s^3 + 6s^2 + 4s + 1}$

40. The polynomial $P_1(s) = s^2 - 6s + 12$ has a pair of zeros in the right half-plane. It is to be multiplied by another polynomial, $P_2(s)$, of degree n so that the resulting polynomial has no negative coefficients. What is the minimum value of n?

41. In Fig. E-41 find z_{21} and verify that there is no transmission zero at $s = -1$ even though the left hand shunt branch has an admittance pole at $s = -1$.

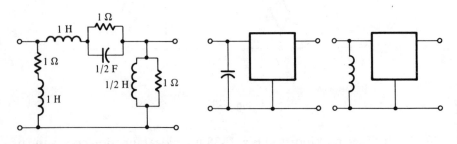

Fig. E-41   Fig. E-42

42. The shunt branch admittances in the diagrams in Fig. E-42 have a pole at infinity and zero, respectively. Show that the overall two-ports must have transmission zeros at these frequencies (unlike the case in the previous exercise), no matter what the rest of the network contains.

43. The following functions are specified as the real parts of impedance functions $Z(s)$. Find the functions $Z(s)$.

(a) $R(\omega) = \dfrac{16 - 8\omega^2 + \omega^4}{1 + \omega^8}$

(b) $R(\omega) = \dfrac{2 + 4\omega^2 + 3\omega^4 + \omega^6}{1 + \omega^8}$

(c) $R(\omega) = \dfrac{-\omega^2 + 2\omega^4 - \omega^8}{1 + \omega^8}$

(d) $R(\omega) = \dfrac{1 - 2\omega^2 + \omega^4}{1 - 2\omega^2 + \omega^4 + 4\omega^6}$

(e) $R(\omega) = \dfrac{(1 - \omega^2 + \omega^4)^2}{(\omega^4 - 4\omega^2 + 3)^2 + \omega^2(\omega^4 - 6\omega^2 + 8)^2}$

44. Suppose each function in Exercise 43 is the $j\omega$-axis magnitude squared of a network function. Find the function. If there is more than one possibility, find them all.

45. Each of the curves in Fig. E-45 is the magnitude $|F(j\omega)|$ of a transfer function for $\omega > 0$. Assuming the function is minimum-phase, find the corresponding angle function making appropriate approximations.

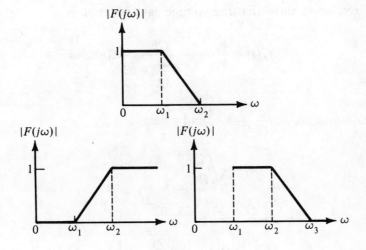

Fig. E-45

46. A real op-amp has an open loop gain which is frequency dependent, as follows:

$$A(s) = \frac{A_o \omega_a}{s + \omega_a} = \frac{\omega_t}{s + \omega_a},$$

where A_o is the dc gain (typically of the order of 10^5), ω_a is the low
frequency cut-off frequency (of the order of 10 to 100 rad/sec), and
$\omega_t = A_o \omega_a$ is the unity-gain frequency (of the order of 10^6 to 10^7
rad/sec). For the network in Fig. E-46 in which the op-amp has the
above open loop gain, find the input impedance and, from that,
draw an equivalent circuit at the input terminals.

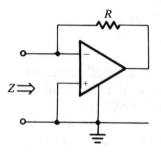

Fig. E-46

47. Either directly from the diagram in Fig. E-47 or from the result of
Exercise 46 show that the voltage gain function is

$$G(s) = \frac{V_2}{V_1} \approx \frac{G_o s}{s^2 + \frac{\omega_o}{Q} s + \omega_o^2} \quad \text{for } \omega \gg \omega_a$$

assuming $RC\omega_a \ll \frac{a+1}{a} \ll A_o$ and where

$$\omega_o = \sqrt{\frac{\omega_t}{RC}}$$

$$Q = \frac{a}{a+1} \sqrt{\omega_t RC}$$

$$G_o \equiv G(j\omega_o) = \frac{\omega_o Q}{a\omega_t} = \frac{1}{a+1}$$

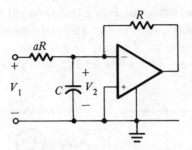

Fig. E-47

48. Suppose the op-amp used in the inverting and noninverting amplifiers in Fig. 1-13 has the frequency dependence given in Exercise 46.
Show that the transfer voltage ratio of each amplifier becomes

$$\frac{V_2}{V_1} = K \frac{\omega_t}{s + \omega_t/K_o}.$$

Determine the values of K_o and K in each case.

49. In Fig. E-49 the network of Fig. E-46 is shown connected across the
input terminals of a noninverting amplifier. Assume the op-amps
are identical and each has the gain given in Exercise 46.
(a) Determine the transfer voltage ratio V_2/V_1.
(b) Now suppose feedback is introduced by making the connection
shown by the dashed line. Show that the network will be a
linear oscillator — have a pole with zero real part — if

$$a \cong \frac{1-K}{1+K}$$

with a frequency ω_o approximated as $\omega_o^2 \cong a K \omega_t^2$.

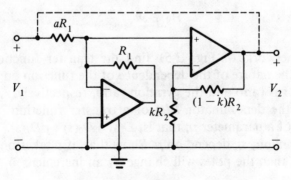

Fig. E-49

50. For each of the networks of Fig. E-50(a) to (d) with the transistor model of Fig. E-50(e), use (8-6) or (8-7) to determine the sensitivity of the transfer function V_o/V_i (a) to c, (b) to r, and (c) to g. The nominal values are $c = 100\mu F$, $r = 10^3\Omega$, and $g = 0.5S$.

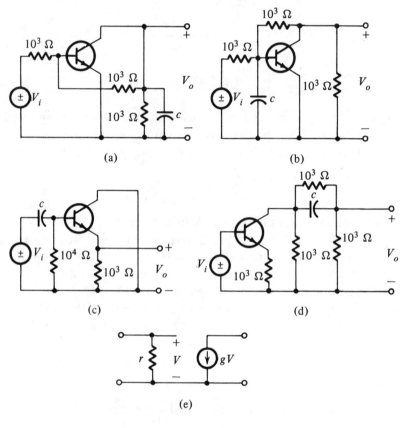

Fig. E-50

51. For the networks of Fig. E-51 find the transfer function V_2/V_1. Observe the nature of the dependence of the function on the transformer turns ratio and the gyration ratio, respectively.

52. Suppose the denominator $D(s)$ of a transfer function is a linear function of a parameter p; that is, $D(s) = D_0(s) + pD_1(s)$. The poles of the function, s_i, depend on p. Show that, if p takes on an increment Δp, then the poles will change by an increment

$$\Delta s_i = - \frac{D_1(s_i)}{dD/ds\big|_{s=s_i}} \Delta p.$$

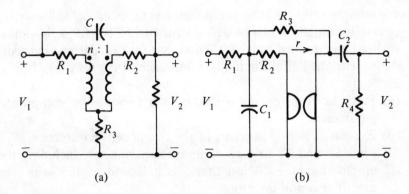

Fig. E-51

53. This exercise is intended to check the accuracy of Exercise 52. Let $D(s)$ be one of the following quadratic polynomials:

   (1) $D(s) = s^2 + (3 - K)s + 2$, $K_{nominal} = 1$

   (2) $D(s) = (K + 1)s^2 + s + 4$, $K_{nominal} = 0.5$

   The nominal value of the parameter K is specified for each. It is possible to find the location of the zeros of $D(s)$ both with the nominal value of the parameter and with a perturbed value.
   (a) Compare the answer so obtained with that derived using the result of Exercise 52 for $\Delta p = 20$ percent of p.
   (b) Repeat (a) for $\Delta p = 10$ percent of p.
   (c) Repeat (a) for $\Delta p = 5$ percent of p.
54. Let $f_1(x)$, $f_2(x)$, and $f(x)$ be functions of a parameter x. Demonstrate the following relations:

   (a) $S_{1/x}^{f(x)} = -S_x^{f(x)}$

   (b) $S_x^{1/f(x)} = -S_x^{f(x)}$

   (c) $S_x^{x^n} = n$

   (d) $S_{kx}^{f(kx)} = S_x^{f(x)}$

   (e) $S_x^{f_1(x)f_2(x)} = S_x^{f_1(x)} S_x^{f_2(x)}$

   (f) $S_{x_1+x_2}^{f} = S_{x_1}^{f} + S_{x_2}^{f}$

55. A biquadratic transfer function is often written as follows:

$$G(s) = \frac{N(s)}{s^2 + (\omega_o/Q)s + \omega_o^2},$$

where ω_o is the pole frequency (the magnitude of the poles) and Q is the quality factor. In a given network ω_o and Q are functions of the

component values. As the components vary, ω_o and Q will vary; so
sensitivity functions can be defined for each. That for ω_o is unnormalized and defined as in (8-13) and that for Q is defined in accordance with the definition in (8-3). For each of the networks in Fig.
E-55:

(a) Find the transfer voltage ratio as a function of component
    parameters.
(b) Express ω_o and Q in terms of the component parameters.
(c) Find S^{ω_o} and S^Q to each component parameter, including the
    amplifier gain $\pm K$. Note that ω_o is independent of K when the
    amplifier is non-inverting.

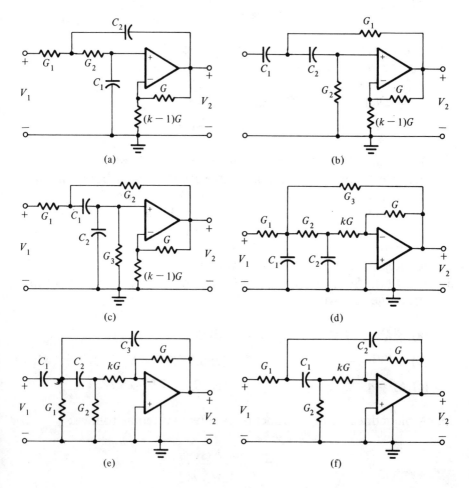

Fig. E-55

56. For the network shown in Fig. E-56:
    (a) Find the sensitivity of the transfer voltage ratio G to variations in each resistor for the given nominal values.
    (b) The total permissible change in G is to be 4 percent. Find the maximum tolerance for the resistors.

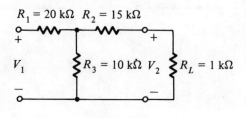

Fig. E-56

57. For the network in Fig. E-57, verify (8-27) and (8-28) by direct evaluation.

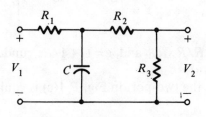

Fig. E-57

58. Fig. E-58 shows a number of RC networks.
    (a) Find the voltage gain function $G(s)$ for each network.
    (b) Verify (8-24) by direct evaluation; that is, verify that

$$\sum S_{C_i}^G = S_s^G.$$

    (c) Verify (8-27) and (8-28).

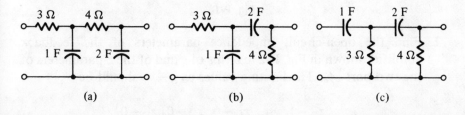

(a)   (b)   (c)

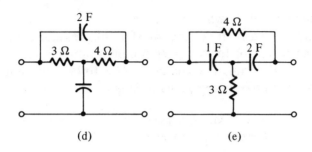

Fig. E-58

PROBLEMS

1. Assume that the model of each transistor in Fig. P-1(a) is a current-controlled current source, as shown in Fig. P-1(b).

   (a) Show that the Y matrix of the two-port is

   $$Y = \begin{bmatrix} g-G & -(g-G) \\ G & -G \end{bmatrix},$$

   where $G = R/R_{e1}R_{e2}$ and $g = G + 1/R_{e1}$ under the assumption that $R_{e2}/\beta_1 \ll R \ll \beta_2 R_{e2}$.

   (b) Verify that the two-port in Fig. P-1(c) is equivalent to this two-port.

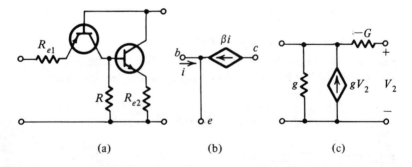

Fig. P-1

2. Find the open-circuit impedance parameters of the feedback amplifier shown in Fig. P-2 in terms of g and of the z-parameters of the two-port $\mathcal{N}_a$. The limiting values as $g \to \infty$ should be

$$z_{21} \to 1/y_{21a}, \quad z_{11} \to 0, \quad z_{22} \to 0, \quad z_{12} \to 0.$$

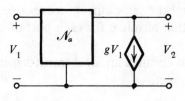

Fig. P-2

3. A two-port $\mathcal{N}_c$ with a resistance R across both its input and output ports is shown in Fig. P-3(a). The resulting two-port is denoted $\mathcal{N}_b$, and the z-parameters of $\mathcal{N}_b$ are z_{11b}, z_{12b}, z_{21b}, and z_{22b}. The network $\mathcal{N}_c$, after introducing either a series or shunt resistance R at its ports, is to be cascaded with the feedback amplifier of Problem 2. The two cascade configurations to be considered are shown in Fig. P-3(b) and (c). Show that the transfer impedance in both cascade cases is given by $z_{21} = z_{21b}/Ry_{21a}$ as $g \to \infty$. ($\mathcal{N}_f$ denotes the entire feedback structure of Fig. P-2.)

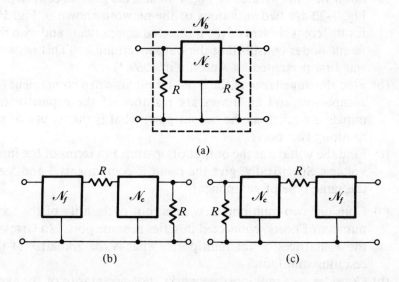

Fig. P-3

4. (a) For the series-parallel and parallel-series connections of two-ports in Fig. P-4, show that the h- and g-parameters of the component two-ports are added to give the overall h- and g-parameters, respectively.
   (b) State and prove conditions under which the series-parallel and parallel-series connections can be made without violating the

condition that the same current leaves one terminal of a port as enters the other terminal for each port of each component two-port.

(c) Show how to connect an ideal transformer so that these conditions can be met.

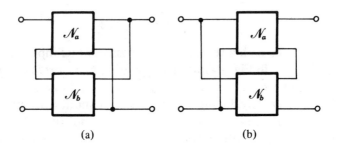

(a)   (b)

Fig. P-4

5. (a) Show that the gyrator of Fig. 1-18 and the general converter of Fig. 1-20 are two variations of the network shown in Fig. P-5 for different choices of the numbered components and with different nodes constituting the output terminals. (This network was first presented by Antoniu in 1969.*)

   (b) Find the impedance at the input terminals when component 4 is a capacitor and all others are resistors. If the capacitor terminals are taken as the output port, what is the nature of the resulting two-port?

   (c) Find the voltage at the output of op-amp 1 in terms of the input voltage. Specifically, give the result if components 3 and 5 are the same type of component.

6. (a) Consider two multiport networks, not necessarily of the same number of ports, connected in series at some ports. In terms of the $\mathbf{Z}$ matrices of the multiports, what is the $\mathbf{Z}$ matrix of the resulting multiport?

   (b) Consider two multiport networks, not necessarily of the same number of ports, connected in parallel at some ports. In terms of the $\mathbf{Y}$ matrices of the multiports, what is the $\mathbf{Y}$ matrix of the resulting multiport?

---

* A. Antoniu, "Realization of gyrators using operational amplifiers and their uses in *RC*-active network synthesis," *Proceedings of the IEE*, vol. 116, 1969, pp. 1838-1850.

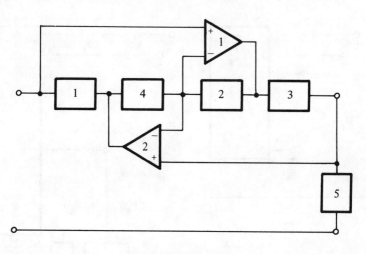

Fig. P-5

7. The n-terminal network shown in Fig. P-7(a) is linear, lumped, and time-invariant. It is represented by $\mathbf{I} = \mathbf{Y}_i \mathbf{V}$, where $\mathbf{Y}_i$ is the indefinite admittance matrix, and the currents and voltages are as defined on the diagram. It is proposed to retain the first k terminals as terminals and to connect the remaining ones to ground through impedances, as shown in Fig. P-7(b). Let $\mathbf{Z}$ be the diagonal matrix whose diagonal elements are the impedances Z_j. Find an expression relating the new terminal currents to the voltages in terms of $\mathbf{Z}$, $\mathbf{Y}_i$, and submatrices thereof.

8. (a) Prove that the impedance of an RLC network, without mutual inductance, will have a pole at $s = 0$ if and only if there is an all-capacitor cut-set that separates the two terminals.
    (b) Prove that the impedance will have a pole at infinity if and only if there is an all-inductor cut-set separating the terminals as in (a).

9. Prove that the admittance of an RLC network, without mutual inductance, will have a pole at $s = 0$ if and only if there is an all-inductor path between the terminals.
    (b) Prove that the admittance will have a pole at infinity if and only if there is an all-capacitor path between the terminals.

10. Use (6-42) in the text to find expressions for S_{11}, S_{12}, S_{21}, and S_{22} for a two-port in terms of the z-parameters.

11. It was shown in the text that $\mathbf{S} = \mathbf{U} - 2Y_{an}$ (see Equation 6-40), where $\mathbf{Y}_{an}$ is the $\mathbf{Y}$ matrix of the normalized augmented network, by

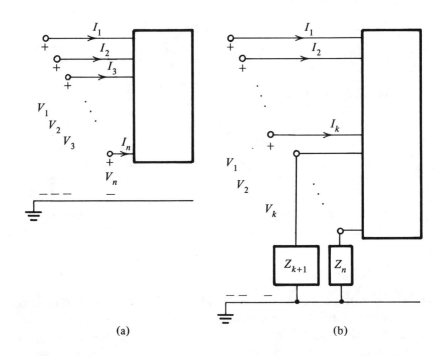

(a)   (b)

Fig. P-7

assuming that a multiport has an admittance matrix. Prove this result from the augmented network without making this assumption.

12. Show that $\mathbf{S} = 2(\mathbf{U} + \mathbf{Y}_n)^{-1} - \mathbf{U}$.

13. Consider a matched, nonreciprocal, lossless three-port. Starting with the general form of the scattering matrix, and using the appropriate properties of matched and lossless multiports, determine the elements of the scattering matrix. Can you identify the class of multiport from this scattering matrix?

14. (a) Write out a scattering matrix to represent a four-port circulator.

    (b) Take the transpose of this matrix and identify the kind of four-port it represents.

15. *Antimetrical* passive two-ports are defined as two-ports for which $z_{11} = y_{22}$, $z_{22} = y_{11}$, and $z_{12} = z_{21} = -y_{21} = -y_{12}$. Show that antimetrical two-ports are characterized by $S_{22} = -S_{11}$.

16. (a) Let the circulator of Fig. 6-10 be terminated in a resistance $-r$ at port 1 and r at port 3. Show that the relationship between the voltage and current at port 2 is that of a norator.

    (b) Interchange the terminations on the circulator and show that the relationship is that of a nullator.

See Problem 3 of Part I for the definitions of a norator and a nullator.

17. Show that

   (a) $(\mathbf{Z}_n + \mathbf{U})^{-1}(\mathbf{Z}_n - \mathbf{U}) = (\mathbf{Z}_n - \mathbf{U})(\mathbf{Z}_n + \mathbf{U})^{-1}$,

   (b) $\mathbf{r}^{-1}[\mathbf{Z}(s) - \mathbf{z}(-s)][\mathbf{Z}(s) + \mathbf{z}(s)]^{-1}\mathbf{r} = [\mathbf{Z}(s) + \mathbf{z}(s)]^{-1}[\mathbf{Z}(s) - \mathbf{z}(-s)]$,

   where $\mathbf{Z}_n$ is the impedance matrix of a multiport normalized to real numbers.

18. The structure in Fig. P-18 is a hybrid coil used in telephone systems. It consists of a three-winding ideal transformer from which a four-port is formed. The two transformer secondary windings have turns ratios of n_2 and n_3 relative to the primary. The equations characterizing the transformer are given in the figure. Assume each port is terminated in real normalizing resistances r_1, r_2, r_3, and r_4. The turns ratios and the normalizing resistances are chosen so that (a) when port 1 is excited (by a voltage source in series with its terminating resistance), there is to be no transmission to port 4, and vice versa; (b) when port 3 is excited, there is to be no transmission to port 4, and vice versa; and (c) all ports are matched—no reflections. Find the scattering matrix of this four-port in terms only of n_2 and n_3.

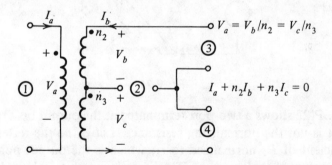

Fig. P-18

19. It is desired to investigate the possible existence of a lossless, reciprocal three-port that is match terminated with real impedances. Use the properties of the scattering matrix to determine the realizability of such a device. If realizable, find S_{12} and S_{13}.

20. Fig. P-20 shows a lossless, reciprocal three-port network that is assumed to be symmetrical. The three-port is not match terminated. When one of the ports is excited (by a voltage source in series with its termination), it is assumed that equal power is delivered to the other two ports. Find the maximum fraction of

available power that is delivered to each port under these conditions and find the fraction of power that is reflected.

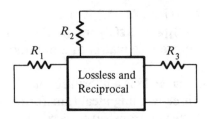

Fig. P-20

21. The network in Fig. P-21 is a lattice operating between two resistive terminations. Compute the transducer power gain. Determine conditions on the lattice elements that will make the gain identically unity, independent of frequency. Under these conditions find the reflection and transmission coefficients.

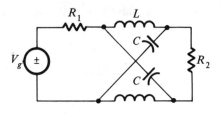

Fig. P-21

22. Fig. P-22 shows a two-port terminated at the output by a resistance that is not the normalizing resistance. Let ϱ_2 be the reflection coefficient of R_2 normalized to r_2, which is the output normalizing resistance of the two-port. The input is match-terminated; that is, r_1 is the normalizing resistance. Find the input reflection coefficient ϱ and the voltage gain V_{2n}/V_{gn} in terms of ϱ_2 and the scattering parameters of the two-port.

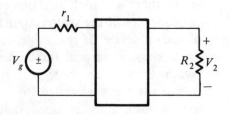

Fig. P-22

23. The four-port network in Fig. P-23 is a hybrid that is match terminated at two of the ports but not at the other two. Find the scattering matrix of the two-port within the dashed lines in terms of ϱ_3 and ϱ_4. Under what condition will the two-port have no reflections at either port?

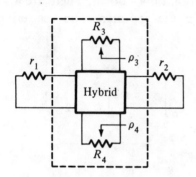

$$S = \frac{1}{\sqrt{2}} \begin{bmatrix} 0 & 0 & 1 & 1 \\ 0 & 0 & 1 & -1 \\ 1 & 1 & 0 & 0 \\ 1 & -1 & 0 & 0 \end{bmatrix}$$

(For the hybrid of Problem 18 with $n_2 = n_3$.)

Fig. P-23

24. In order to find the relationships among the port voltages and currents of a two-port that consists of the cascade connection of two sub-two-ports, it is convenient to express the port relationships of the sub-two-ports in terms of the chain matrix. It is desired to find a matrix T that can play a similar role for two cascaded two-ports; but this time the variables are scattering variables, rather than actual currents and voltages. For the network shown in Fig. P-24, let the desired overall relationship be written $x = Ty$.

(a) Determine the elements of the vectors x and y (from among the scattering variables) such that the overall T matrix equals $T_1 T_2$, where $x_1 = T_1 y_1$ and $x_2 = T_2 y_2$. Specify any condition on the normalizing resistances.

(b) Express the elements of the matrix T for a two-port in terms of the scattering parameters of that two-port.

(c) Determine a condition that the elements of T satisfy if the two-port is reciprocal.

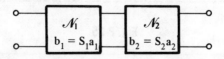

Fig. P-24

25. The four-port network within the dashed lines in Fig. P-25 represents a telephone repeater. The two-ports labeled L are low-pass filters, and those labeled H are high-pass filters. They are reciprocal and symmetric two-ports and hence are characterized by only two parameters each. The two-port labeled A is an amplifier that has transmission in one direction only — down. There are also two ideal three-port junctions in the repeater. The scattering matrices of each component are

$$S_L = \begin{bmatrix} \varrho_L & t_L \\ t_L & \varrho_L \end{bmatrix}, \quad S_H = \begin{bmatrix} \varrho_H & t_H \\ t_H & \varrho_H \end{bmatrix}, \quad S_A = \begin{bmatrix} \varrho_1 & 0 \\ t & \varrho_2 \end{bmatrix},$$

$$S_j = \frac{1}{3} \begin{bmatrix} 1 & 2 & 2 \\ 2 & 1 & -2 \\ 2 & -2 & 1 \end{bmatrix}$$

with all normalizing resistances being 1Ω. Find the scattering matrix of the four-port repeater. By examining the elements of this matrix, describe the reflection and transmission of low- and high-frequency signals at each of the ports.

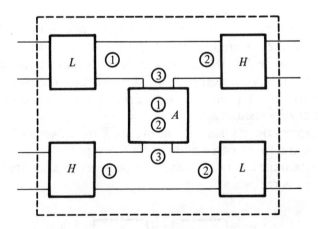

Fig. P-25

26. In Fig. P-26(a) a passive, lossless two-port is terminated in a -1Ω resistance. In Fig. P-26(b) the same two-port is terminated in a

$+1\Omega$ resistance. Show, by writing expressions for Z_1 and Z_2 in terms of the z- or y-parameters of the two-port, that $Z_2(s) = -Z_1(-s)$.

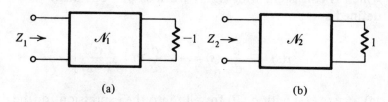

(a)   (b)

Fig. P-26

27. Let **S** be the scattering matrix of a passive, lossless three-port. From the unitary property of **S**, prove the following. [Where the argument of a parameter is not given, it is $j\omega$; thus, S_{12} means $S_{12}(j\omega)$.]

$$S_{11}(-j\omega) = S_{22}S_{33} - S_{23}S_{32} \qquad\qquad S_{21}(-j\omega) = S_{13}S_{32} - S_{12}S_{33}$$

$$S_{12}(-j\omega) = S_{23}S_{31} - S_{21}S_{33} \qquad\qquad S_{22}(-j\omega) = S_{11}S_{33} - S_{13}S_{31}$$

$$S_{13}(-j\omega) = S_{21}S_{32} - S_{22}S_{31} \qquad\qquad S_{23}(-j\omega) = S_{12}S_{31} - S_{11}S_{32}$$

$$S_{31}(-j\omega) = S_{12}S_{23} - S_{13}S_{22}$$

$$S_{32}(-j\omega) = S_{13}S_{21} - S_{11}S_{23}$$

$$S_{33}(-j\omega) = S_{11}S_{22} - S_{12}S_{21}$$

25. In a lossless, reciprocal three-port, suppose the $j\omega$-axis magnitude of one of the transmission coefficients is identically 1. Show from the unitary and symmetric properties of S that all the other scattering parameters must be identically zero.

29. Let the magnitude of a function be the maximally flat function in (7-27). Show that the angle is given by the following expression:

$$\phi(\omega) = -\frac{n}{\pi}\int_0^\infty \frac{1/y}{1+y^{-2n}}\ln\left|\frac{y+\omega}{y-\omega}\right|dy.$$

30. Let a transfer function be given by

$$F(s) = \frac{1 + a_1 s + a_2 s^2 + \ldots + a_n s^n}{1 + b_1 s + b_2 s^2 + \ldots + b_m s^m}$$

The *angle function* is defined as

$$\hat{\phi}(s) = \tfrac{1}{2} \ln \frac{F(s)}{F(-s)}$$

which is consistent with (7-14) when $s = j\omega$. The *delay function* is defined as

$$\tau(s) = -\frac{d}{ds}\hat{\phi}(s) = -\tfrac{1}{2}\frac{d}{ds} \ln \left[\frac{F(s)}{F(-s)} \right].$$

(a) Insert $F(s)$ with $a_i = 0$ for all i into the expression for the delay function. Find the values of the b_i coefficients if the delay is to be a maximally flat function for the cases $m = 3$, $m = 4$, and $m = 5$.

(b) Repeat (a) when $a_i \neq 0$ and with $n = m - 1$.

31. Prove that if all the coefficients of a real polynomial $P(s)$ of degree n have the same sign, then $P(s)$ will have no zeros in the sector $|\arg s| < \pi/n$.

32. Derive the resistance integral theorem in (7-65) by integrating the function $F(z) - R(\infty)$ around the basic contour consisting of the $j\omega$-axis and an infinite semicircle to the right.

33. Derive (7-55) by integrating the function $F(z)/(z^2 + \omega^2)$ around the basic contour with indentations at $z = \pm j\omega$.

34. Derive (7-56) by integrating the function $z[F(z) - R(\infty)]/(z^2 + \omega^2)$ around the basic contour with indentations at $z = \pm j\omega$.

35. By integrating the function $[F(z) - R(0)]/z(z^2 + \omega^2)$ around the basic contour with indentations at $z = 0$ and at $z = \pm j\omega$, derive the following relationship:

$$R(\omega) = R(0) - \frac{2\omega^2}{\pi} \int_0^\infty \frac{X(y)/y - X(\omega)/\omega}{y^2 - \omega^2} dy.$$

36. Give a derivation for (7-79), starting with (7-77).

37. Derive the reactance integral theorem (7-61) by integrating the function $F(z)/z$ around the basic contour with a small indentation around the origin.

38. Starting with (7-92c), derive (7-97b).

39. Generalize the results summarized in (7-100) through (7-102) to those wherein it is not necessary that $\mathbf{H}(s)$ be regular at infinity.

40. Let $\hat{s}$ represent a pole of a transfer function. Prove (8-27) and (8-28). Note that the sensitivities in those expressions are not normalized.

PROJECTS

1. Read Chapters 5, 6, and 8 (concentrating on section 7 of Chapter 8) of

S.-P. Chan, *Introductory Topological Analysis of Electrical Networks*, Holt, Rinehart, and Winston, New York, 1969.

or chapters 7 and 8 of

W. Mayeda, *Graph Theory*, Wiley-Interscience, New York, 1972.

and prepare a report, containing examples, of topological methods by which to determine driving-point and transfer functions of passive and active networks. One of the examples should include verification of (12-33). The report should also include a derivation of the *Fialkow-Gerst condition* for *RLC* two-port networks without mutual inductance. Specifically, if

$$z_{11}(s) = \frac{a_0 + a_1 s + \ldots + a_n s^n}{D(s)}$$

$$z_{22}(s) = \frac{b_0 + b_1 s + \ldots + b_m s^m}{D(s)}$$

$$z_{21}(s) = \frac{c_0 + c_1 s + \ldots + c_r s^r}{D(s)}$$

then: (a) For a noncommon terminal two-port, the c_k coefficients can be negative but are bounded by the corresponding b_k and a_k coefficients (which cannot be negative) as follows:

$$|c_k| \leqslant a_k, \ |c_k| \leqslant b_k.$$

(b) For a common terminal two-port, the bounds are the same except that c_k cannot be negative.

Comment also on the numerator coefficients of y_{11}, y_{22}, and $-y_{21}$. State the requirement on the denominators of the three functions in order for the Fialkow-Gerst condition to be valid. Use the following network to illustrate this requirement either for the z-parameters or the y-parameters.

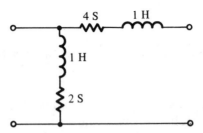

2. Read Chapter 8 (section 5) of

   N. Balabanian and T. A. Bickart, *Electrical Network Theory*, John Wiley & Sons, New York, 1969.

   and prepare a report, containing examples, on complex normaliization in scattering parameter methods.

3. Read Chapter 7 of

   S.-P. Chan, *Introductory Topological Analysis of Electrical Networks*, Holt, Rinehart, and Winston, New York, 1969.

   and prepare a report, containing examples, on signal-flow graph methods for the determination of network functions.

4. Read Chapter 6 (sections 5 and 6) of

   N. Balabanian and T. A. Bickart, *Electrical Network Theory*, John Wiley & Sons, New York, 1969.

   and read

   S. K. Mitra, "On the construction of a positive real impedance from a given even part," *Proceedings of the IEEE*, Vol. 51, 1963, p. 1267.

   and

   S. K. Mitra, "Construction of a network function from its given even (odd) part," *Proceedings of the IEEE*, vol. 52, 1964, pp. 197-198.

   Then, prepare a report, containing examples, on reconstructing network functions from their real and imaginary parts (alternatively, even and odd parts) and from their angle functions.

PART III
Computer-Aided Design

CHAPTER 9
Tellegen's Theorem and Adjoint Networks

The fundamental topological relationships on which network theory is based are the Kirchhoff current law and the Kirchhoff voltage law; these were considered at some length in Chapter 3. There exists an equally powerful relationship, first enunciated in 1948, called Tellegen's theorem. It deals with an equilibrium of power in a network, just as Kirchhoff's laws deal with an equilibrium of current and voltage. Since power is related to voltage and current, it should not be surprising that the two Kirchhoff laws and Tellegen's theorem are related to each other; any two of them imply the third, as we shall see. Of greater significance is the way in which Tellegen's theorem can be used to expand the concept of reciprocity of a single network to that of the interreciprocity of two different networks. This leads to the concept of adjoint networks which plays an important role in computer-aided network design.

9.1 TELLEGEN'S THEOREM

The concept of the conservation of energy has been with us for a long time. So when Tellegen published a paper in 1948 which seemed to confirm this fundamental law, not much of a stir was created. The more far-reaching implications of his basic result were not realized until much later. We shall first develop an elementary form of what is called Tellegen's Theorem (abbreviated TT).

Consider a network, $\mathcal{N}$, including sources. Assuming the voltage and current references are load references for all branches, including any sources, the total instantaneous power delivered to the collection of all components of $\mathcal{N}$ is

$$p = \sum_{\substack{\text{all} \\ \text{branches}}} v_k i_k = \mathbf{v'i}. \tag{1}$$

The second form expression of KCL, $\mathbf{i} = \mathbf{B'}i_c$ in Table 1, allows us to convert (1) to the following:

$$p = \mathbf{v'}(\mathbf{B'}i_c) = (\mathbf{Bv})'i_c. \tag{2}$$

The rightmost equality is a consequence of the identity $\mathbf{v'B'} = (\mathbf{Bv})'$. But $\mathbf{Bv} = \mathbf{0}$ by the first form expression of KVL in Table 1. Hence,

$$p = \mathbf{v'i} = 0. \tag{3}$$

This result, the elementary power form of TT, can be stated thus: *The power delivered to all components of a network at any instant of time is zero.*

This result does not seem to be profound. Because it is consistent with the conservation of energy principle, it should not be too surprising. However, its further generalization, which we shall now discuss, has some surprising elements.

Consider two topologically equivalent networks $\mathcal{N}$ and $\hat{\mathcal{N}}$. By that we mean the two networks are represented by the same graph but the components which make up the branches of the graph need not be the same. Or even if some of the corresponding components are the same, their parameter values may differ. The voltage and current variables of $\hat{\mathcal{N}}$ will carry the "^" symbol. Let us investigate the inner product of $\hat{\mathbf{v}}$ (voltage vector of network $\hat{\mathcal{N}}$) and $\mathbf{i}$ (current vector of $\mathcal{N}$); thus,

$$\hat{\mathbf{v}}'\mathbf{i} = \hat{\mathbf{v}}'(\mathbf{B'}i_c) = (\mathbf{B}\hat{\mathbf{v}})'i_c = (\hat{\mathbf{B}}\hat{\mathbf{v}})'i_c \tag{4}$$

or

$$\hat{\mathbf{v}}'\mathbf{i} = 0. \tag{5a}$$

All the steps but the last one on the right side of (4) are the same as the corresponding ones in (1) and (2). The equality $\mathbf{B} = \hat{\mathbf{B}}$ is a consequence of the topological equivalence of $\mathcal{N}$ and $\hat{\mathcal{N}}$. Although superficially (5a) looks just like (3), the meaning is different. The product $\hat{\mathbf{v}}'\mathbf{i}$ has nothing to do with the power delivered to a network, because the voltages are associated with one network and the currents with another. However, $\hat{\mathbf{v}}'\mathbf{i}$ is, dimensionally, power. Hence, it is often called the *quasi-power* associated with topologically equivalent networks. So (5a) can be stated thus: *The quasi-power associated with a pair of topologically equivalent networks is zero.*

The preceding result is a consequence of just the Kirchhoff laws and the topological equivalence of the two networks. It does not depend upon the components of the networks. Thus, $\mathcal{N}$ might be a nonlinear resistive network and $\hat{\mathcal{N}}$ might be a linear dynamic network. Furthermore, the result does not depend upon the domain of analysis. For example, $\mathcal{N}$ and $\hat{\mathcal{N}}$ might both be analyzed in the time-domain or both in the frequency-domain. or one might be analyzed in the time-domain and the other in the frequency-domain. (See Exer. 2.) To emphasize this, let us use capital letters to denote frequency-domain variables as customary, and rewrite the preceding general expression for Tellegen's theorem as follows:

$$\hat{\mathbf{V}}'\mathbf{I} = 0 \tag{5b}$$

$$\hat{\mathbf{V}}'\mathbf{i} = 0 \tag{5c}$$

$$\hat{\mathbf{v}}'\mathbf{I} = 0 \tag{5d}$$

Thus, for example from (5c), if the Laplace transform of the branch voltages in a linear network are multiplied by the corresponding branch currents, as functions of time, in another network which is nonlinear but which has the same topology as the first, the sum of the products will be zero.

It is trivial that $\mathcal{N}$ is topologically equivalent to itself. Therefore, if we take $\hat{\mathcal{N}}$ as $\mathcal{N}$, then (5a) yields (3) which is the condition on the power delivered to a network.

By Tellegen's theorem it is possible to establish that the complex power delivered to a network under sinusoidal steady state conditions is also, not surprisingly, zero. For this purpose, let V and I denote the vectors of branch voltage and branch current phasors associated with $\mathcal{N}$. Then, let $\hat{\mathcal{N}}$ be the same as $\mathcal{N}$ except for the sources; these are to have phasors which are the complex conjugates of those of $\mathcal{N}$. In this case we find that (5b) yields

$$\mathbf{V}^*\mathbf{I} = 0, \tag{6}$$

as expected.

The forms of Tellegen's theorem so far discussed are said to be *strong forms*. It is possible to derive alternate forms which are weaker, as follows. If the roles of $\mathscr{N}$ and $\hat{\mathscr{N}}$ are interchanged, the quasi-power can be written in the alternative form

$$\mathbf{v}\hat{\mathbf{i}} = 0. \tag{7}$$

Now, let us subtract (7) from (5a) to obtain

$$\hat{\mathbf{v}}'\mathbf{i} - \mathbf{v}'\hat{\mathbf{i}} = 0, \tag{8}$$

which is the quasi-power *difference form* of Tellegen's theorem. It is said to be a *weak form* because it is derivable from the previous (strong) form but the converse is not possible. (See Prob. 1 for another weak form.)

We have seen that, given the two Kirchhoff laws, Tellegen's theorem follows. But the relationship among these three things is even stronger, as expressed in this next theorem: *Any two* of KCL, KVL, *and* TT *imply the third*. In what follows, we will show only that KVL and TT imply KCL. The remaining case is left for you to verify. (See Prob. 2.)

We start with TT as expressed in (5a) and with KVL expressed as

$$\hat{\mathbf{v}} = \mathbf{Q}'\hat{\mathbf{v}}_c, \tag{9}$$

which derives from $\hat{\mathbf{v}} = \hat{\mathbf{Q}}'\hat{\mathbf{v}}_c$ since $\hat{\mathbf{Q}} = \mathbf{Q}$. Upon substituting (9) into (5a), we get, after a little manipulation

$$\hat{\mathbf{v}}'_c\mathbf{Qi} = 0. \tag{10}$$

Now, suppose KCL does not hold; that is, suppose $\mathbf{Qi} \neq 0$. In particular suppose the ith row of $\mathbf{Qi}$ is not zero. Since the preceding result is independent of the network components, let $\hat{\mathscr{N}}$ have only independent voltage sources as twigs and set $\hat{\mathbf{v}}_{ci} = 1$ and $\hat{\mathbf{v}}_{cj} = 0$ ($j \neq i$). Then, the product of $\hat{\mathbf{v}}_c$ with $\mathbf{Qi}$ cannot be zero. As this contradicts (10), the assumption that the ith row of $\mathbf{Qi}$ is nonzero cannot be true. Thus, all rows of $\mathbf{Qi}$ must be zero; hence, KCL must be true.

9.2 RECIPROCAL NETWORKS

In the preceding discussion, the nature of the components in the network was not at issue. Specifically, no distinction was made between independent sources and other components. However, the inputs and outputs of a network are of particular interest. For some purposes, therefore, we shall separate those branches which are inputs and outputs from those that are not.

9.2.1   Two-Ports

As a beginning, let $\mathcal{N}$ be a two-port* with the port conditions shown in Fig. 1(a). And let the topologically equivalent network $\hat{\mathcal{N}}$ be the same two-port with the reversed port conditions shown in Fig. 1(b). Observe that the references of all branches in these networks are to be load references, even the port branches. Thus, the port current references are opposite from the normal ones. This will introduce a change in sign in some expressions so care must be exercised.

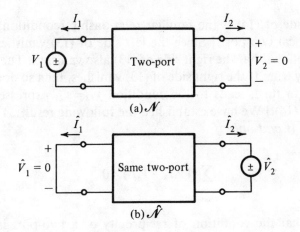

(a) $\mathcal{N}$

(b) $\hat{\mathcal{N}}$

Fig. 1   Networks $\mathcal{N}$ and $\hat{\mathcal{N}}$

Since we shall be dealing mainly with the frequency-domain, we shall henceforth use capital letters for the variables.

With the port branches shown explicitly, the quasi-power difference form of Tellegen's Theorem can be expressed as

$$0 = (\hat{V}_1 I_1 - V_1 \hat{I}_1) + (\hat{V}_2 I_2 - V_2 \hat{I}_2) + \sum_{k=3}^{b} (\hat{V}_k I_k - V_k \hat{I}_k). \qquad (12)$$

---

* Unless explicitly stated otherwise (see Prob. 13), any reference to a network as a multiport—in particular, a two-port—shall mean the multiport has no internal independent sources.

But, $V_2 = 0$ and $\hat{V}_1 = 0$; therefore, upon rearranging the port terms, this expression becomes

$$V_1 \hat{I}_1 - \hat{V}_2 I_2 = \sum_{k=3}^{b} (\hat{V}_k I_k - V_k \hat{I}_k). \tag{13}$$

The left side contains only port variables and the right side only nonport variables.

Now recall the condition, given in Chapter 1, for a two-port to be reciprocal: It is that, under the conditions of Fig. 1, if $\hat{V}_2 = V_1$, then $\hat{I}_1 = I_2$. Consequently, the left side of (13) vanishes; that is,

$$V_1 \hat{I}_1 - \hat{V}_2 I_2 = 0 \leftrightarrow \frac{\hat{I}_1}{\hat{V}_2} = \frac{I_2}{V_1} \tag{14}$$

[The right side of (14) is the familiar relationship (condition) $y_{12} = y_{21}$ for a reciprocal two-port.] Since the left side of (13) vanishes by reciprocity, it follows that the right side of (13) also vanishes. The converse is also clearly true: If the right side of (13) vanishes, then so does the left side. [This, in turn, leads to the condition $y_{12} = y_{21}$ expressed on the right side of (14).] We have established the following result: *A two-port is reciprocal if and only if*

$$\sum_{\substack{\text{nonport} \\ \text{branches}}} (\hat{V}_k I_k - V_k \hat{I}_l) = 0. \tag{15}$$

Observe that the condition of reciprocity of a two-port is initially defined in terms of relationships among the port voltage and current variables under specific excitations. What has been done above is to derive from these port-variable relationships another relationship among the variables *internal* to the two-port; namely (15).

Parenthetically, note that another approach might be to examine the contribution of specific types of components to the right side of (13). If this is done, it is found that the contributions of resistors, capacitors, inductors, and ideal transformers to the right side of (13) is zero. (See Prob. 3.) This establishes the following theorem: *A two-port containing just resistors, capacitors, inductors (possibly coupled), and ideal transformers is reciprocal.*

One final matter must be cleared up. Rather than the excitation being a voltage and the response being a current, as in Fig. 1, suppose the converse is true, as shown in Fig. 2. Then in (12) we would have $I_2 = 0$ and $\hat{I}_1 = 0$. Thus, (14) would be replaced by

$$-\hat{V}_1 I_1 + V_2 \hat{I}_2 = 0 \leftrightarrow \frac{V_2}{I_1} = \frac{\hat{V}_1}{\hat{I}_2}. \tag{17}$$

This is the relationship $z_{12} = z_{21}$ for reciprocal two-ports.

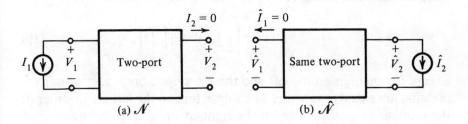

Fig. 2   Networks $\mathcal{N}$ and $\hat{\mathcal{N}}$ with current excitation

Finally, two other combinations of excitation-response (V-V and I-I) are possible. You should repeat the above procedures for these two cases and confirm that reciprocity implies $g_{12} = -g_{21}$ and $h_{12} = -h_{21}$, respectively.

9.2.2   N-Ports

Let us now extend the preceding discussion to n-ports. Let the ports of the network be numbered from 1 to n and the remaining branches $n+1$ to b. Some of the ports are to be excited by voltage sources and some by current sources. Let each port that is excited by a voltage source be labeled a *voltage port* and each one excited by a current source, a *current port*.

Suppose $\mathcal{N}$ refers to the network in which ports 1 to n_v are voltage ports and ports n_{v+1} to $n(= n_v + n_i)$ are current ports. And let $\hat{\mathcal{N}}$ refer to the same network with the same *types* of excitation (voltage or current) except that the values of the sources can be different. We say that $\mathcal{N}$ and $\hat{\mathcal{N}}$ are *consistently excited*. It should be noted that a short circuit can be viewed as a voltage source with zero voltage; and an open circuit can be viewed as a current source with zero current.

Now let us apply Tellegen's Theorem in the form of (8) to the two cases $\mathcal{N}$ and $\hat{\mathcal{N}}$ distinguished above. With the terms involving port variables transposed to one side, the result is

$$\sum_{\substack{\text{port}\\\text{branches}}} (-\hat{V}_k I_k + V_k \hat{I}_k) + \sum_{\substack{\text{nonport}\\\text{branches}}} (\hat{V}_k I_k - V_k \hat{I}_k). \tag{18}$$

It would be useful to write this expression in vector form. For this purpose, we will use subscript "p" for port variable and subscript "i" for nonport (internal) variables. Then (18) can be written as

$$-[-\hat{\mathbf{I}}_p'\ \hat{\mathbf{V}}_p']\begin{bmatrix} \mathbf{V}_p \\ \mathbf{I}_p \end{bmatrix} = [-\hat{\mathbf{I}}_i'\ \hat{\mathbf{V}}_i']\begin{bmatrix} \mathbf{V}_i \\ \mathbf{I}_i \end{bmatrix}. \tag{19}$$

Except for the sign on the left and the subscripts, both sides of this expression are exactly the same. The subvectors on the left are of order n, the number of ports; those on the right of order b-n, the number of non-port branches. In the sequel, we shall use the scalar form in (18) and the vector form in (19) interchangeably, as convenient.

Now let all current ports in $\mathcal{N}$ and $\hat{\mathcal{N}}$ be left open. In $\mathcal{N}$ let all voltage ports but one (say port j) be shorted, and in $\hat{\mathcal{N}}$ let all voltage ports but one (say port i) be shorted. The left side of (18) reduces to $-\hat{V}_i I_i + V_j \hat{I}_j$. Ports i and j in both $\mathcal{N}$ and $\hat{\mathcal{N}}$ are excited by voltage sources, one of which in each network happens to have the value zero.

Suppose that the two-port formed by ports i and j (with all other ports open or short) is reciprocal. In accordance with (14) this would mean

$$-\hat{V}_i I_i + V_j \hat{I}_j = 0 \leftrightarrow \frac{\hat{I}_j}{\hat{V}_i} = \frac{I_i}{V_j}. \tag{20}$$

This is the reciprocity condition $y_{ij} = y_{ji}$.

There are three other combinations of port excitations (or excitation-response combinations): (a) both j in $\mathcal{N}$ and i in $\hat{\mathcal{N}}$ are current-excited, (b) j in $\mathcal{N}$ is voltage-excited and i in $\hat{\mathcal{N}}$ current-excited, and (c) vice-versa; with all other ports being open or short. These would correspond to the conditions $z_{ij} = z_{ji}$, $g_{ij} = -g_{ji}$, and $h_{ij} = -h_{ji}$.

The condition in (20), together with the similar conditions mentioned in the preceding paragraph, are the conditions of reciprocity between two of the ports of the n-port. Suppose that the reciprocity condition is satisfied between each pair of ports (with $i \ne j$) of the n-port. Then we say that the n-port is reciprocal.

More fully, *an n-port is defined to be reciprocal if one of the reciprocity conditions is satisfied between each pair of ports, with all other ports being open or short.* Thus, a reciprocal n-port is defined as one for which the left side of (18) — or (19) in vector form — is zero. As a *consequence*, the right side will also be zero, or

$$\sum_{\substack{\text{nonport} \\ \text{branches}}} (\hat{V}_k I_k - V_k \hat{I}_k) = 0. \tag{22}$$

In vector form, this condition on the internal variables of a reciprocal multiport corresponds to setting the right side of (19) equal to zero; thus,

$$[-\hat{\mathbf{I}}'_i \ \hat{\mathbf{V}}'_i] \begin{bmatrix} \mathbf{V}_i \\ \mathbf{I}_i \end{bmatrix} = 0. \tag{23}$$

The preceding discussion of reciprocity might seem to be somewhat extended. However, we are preparing to introduce a new concept and this discussion of reciprocity will be helpful in clarifying it.

Preparatory to introducing this new concept, we shall place the general expression of Tellegen's Theorem in (18) in a modified form. Assume the voltage ports are excited by voltage sources V_{sk} (which may be zero, corresponding to a short circuit) and the current ports are excited by current sources I_{sk} (which may be zero, corresponding to an open circuit). *There are no independent sources internal to the multiport.*

The branch *V-I* equations in Chapter 3 are repeated here for convenience.

$$\mathbf{M}(\mathbf{V} - \mathbf{V}_s) + \mathbf{N}(\mathbf{I} - \mathbf{I}_s) = \mathbf{0} \tag{24a}$$

or

$$[\mathbf{M} \quad \mathbf{N}] \begin{bmatrix} \mathbf{V} - \mathbf{V}_s \\ \mathbf{I} - \mathbf{I}_s \end{bmatrix} = 0. \tag{24b}$$

Motivated by the form of these equations, we shall include source variables explicitly and consider a rewriting of Tellegen's theorem in (18) as follows:

$$\sum_{k=1}^{b} [(\hat{V}_k - \hat{V}_{sk})(I_k - I_{sk}) - (V_k - V_{sk})(\hat{I}_k - \hat{I}_{sk})] = 0 \tag{25}$$

In vector form, this can be written as

$$[-(\hat{\mathbf{I}}' - \hat{\mathbf{I}}'_s)\quad(\hat{\mathbf{V}}' - \hat{\mathbf{V}}'_s)]\begin{bmatrix}(\mathbf{V} - \mathbf{V}_s)\\ (\mathbf{I} - \mathbf{I}_s)\end{bmatrix} = 0. \qquad (26)$$

The summation extends over all branches, including the ports. For each voltage port, both $(V_k - V_{sk})$ and $(\hat{V}_k - \hat{V}_{sk})$ are zero; for each current port, both $(I_k - I_{sk})$ and $(\hat{I}_k - \hat{I}_{sk})$ are zero. Hence, each term in the summation in (25) that corresponds to a port is zero. That leaves the non-port branches; since these branches contain no independent sources, all the source terms for these branches vanish. Thus, (25) reduces to (22), the condition for n-port reciprocity. The conclusion is that *an n-port is reciprocal if and only if (25) — or the equivalent (26) — is satisfied.*

It should be observed that the form of (25) or (26) does not distinguish between port and non-port branches. Furthermore, the form of the component equations in (24) does not depend on whether the sources are viewed as separate components at the ports or constituents of general branches. It is possible, therefore, to conceive of a network as including its excitations, rather than as a multiport to which the excitations are external, without any influence on the forms of (24), (25) or (26). The concept of reciprocity can be extended to this more general setting. We say that *a network (as distinct from it as a multiport) is reciprocal if (25) — or its equivalent (26) — is satisfied.*

Though the *form* of (24) is not dependent on whether or not a source is accompanied, the *order* of the **M** and **N** matrices *will* be influenced by the choice made in treating sources. Note that when a source is accompanied, the quantities $(V_k - V_{sk})$ and $(I_k - I_{sk})$ in (25) are simply the voltage and current of the component accompanying the source.

These thoughts will be illustrated by an example. Consider the situation shown in Fig. 3. If the network is viewed as a two-port, with the

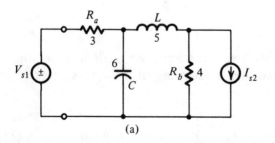

(a)

Branch equations

$V_1 - V_{s1} = 0$
$V_2 - I_{s2} = 0$
$V_3 - R_a I_3 = 0$
$V_4 - R_b I_4 = 0$
$V_5 - sLI_5 = 0$
$I_6 - sCV_6 = 0$

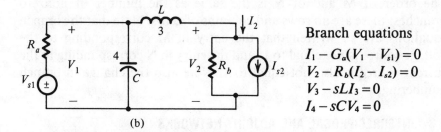

Branch equations

$$I_1 - G_a(V_1 - V_{s1}) = 0$$
$$V_2 - R_b(I_2 - I_{s2}) = 0$$
$$V_3 - sLI_3 = 0$$
$$I_4 - sCV_4 = 0$$

(b)

Fig. 3   Example

two sources constituting excitations at the ports, there will be a total of 6 branches. With the scalar branch equations as given in the figure, the branch equations as given in the form of (24) will be

$$
\begin{bmatrix}
1 & 0 & 0 & 0 & 0 & 0 \\
0 & 0 & 0 & 0 & 0 & 0 \\
0 & 0 & 1 & 0 & 0 & 0 \\
0 & 0 & 0 & 1 & 0 & 0 \\
0 & 0 & 0 & 0 & 1 & 0 \\
0 & 0 & 0 & 0 & 0 & -sC
\end{bmatrix}
\left\{
\begin{bmatrix} V_1 \\ V_2 \\ V_3 \\ V_4 \\ V_5 \\ V_6 \end{bmatrix}
-
\begin{bmatrix} V_{s1} \\ 0 \\ 0 \\ 0 \\ 0 \\ 0 \end{bmatrix}
\right\}
+
\begin{bmatrix}
0 & 0 & 0 & 0 & 0 & 0 \\
0 & 1 & 0 & 0 & 0 & 0 \\
0 & 0 & -R_a & 0 & 0 & 0 \\
0 & 0 & 0 & -R_b & 0 & 0 \\
0 & 0 & 0 & 0 & -sL & 0 \\
0 & 0 & 0 & 0 & 0 & 1
\end{bmatrix}
\left\{
\begin{bmatrix} I_1 \\ I_1 \\ I_3 \\ I_4 \\ I_5 \\ I_6 \end{bmatrix}
-
\begin{bmatrix} 0 \\ I_{s2} \\ 0 \\ 0 \\ 0 \\ 0 \end{bmatrix}
\right\}
= 0
$$

Note that in each of the vectors $\mathbf{V}_s$ and $\mathbf{I}_s$ there is only a single nonzero term. The matrices $\mathbf{M}$ and $\mathbf{N}$ are of order 6; each of these matrices has a row (and column) of zeros, each corresponding to one of the sources. The entry in $\mathbf{M}$ corresponding to the voltage source is 1; the entry in $\mathbf{N}$ corresponding to the current source is 1.

Now suppose the sources are combined with accompanying branches (the resistors, in this example) to form general branches. There are now only four branches. With the scalar branch equations as given in the figure, the branch equations in the form of (24) will be

$$
\begin{bmatrix}
-G_a & 0 & 0 & 0 \\
0 & 1 & 0 & 0 \\
0 & 0 & 1 & 0 \\
0 & 0 & 0 & -sC
\end{bmatrix}
\left\{
\begin{bmatrix} V_1 \\ V_2 \\ V_3 \\ V_4 \end{bmatrix}
-
\begin{bmatrix} V_{s1} \\ 0 \\ 0 \\ 0 \end{bmatrix}
\right\}
+
\begin{bmatrix}
1 & 0 & 0 & 0 \\
0 & -R_b & 0 & 0 \\
0 & 0 & -sL & 0 \\
0 & 0 & 0 & 1
\end{bmatrix}
\left\{
\begin{bmatrix} I_1 \\ I_2 \\ I_3 \\ I_4 \end{bmatrix}
-
\begin{bmatrix} 0 \\ I_{s2} \\ 0 \\ 0 \end{bmatrix}
\right\}
= 0.
$$

The order of **M** and of **N** is the same as the number of nonzero branches; there are no rows and columns of zeros. Note that the branch equations are so written that the entry in **M** corresponding to the voltage source *is not* equal to 1; and the entry in **N** corresponding to the current source is also not equal to 1. Note also the change in branch numbering.

9.3 INTERRECIPROCAL AND ADJOINT NETWORKS

Until now, $\mathcal{N}$ and $\hat{\mathcal{N}}$ were distinguished only by having different excitations; they were otherwise assumed to be the same interconnection of the same components. But the specific nature of the components was not invoked in deriving any of the preceding results (except for the parenthetical discussion of the reciprocity of networks containing R_s, L_s, C_s, and ideal transformers). That is, only topological considerations were used.

9.3.1 Interreciprocal Networks

Let us now suppose that $\mathcal{N}$ is a network and that $\hat{\mathcal{N}}$, though not necessarily the same, is a topologically equivalent network. The concept of reciprocity can be extended to this new situation.

Recall that reciprocity of a multiport, originally defined by relationships among port variables, was later equated to a condition on the nonport variables, namely (22) — equivalently (23). This led to condition (25) — equivalently (26) — which includes all variables; this, in turn, led to a generalization of reciprocity — that of a network as a whole, distinct from the network as a multiport. These latter conditions form the basis for an extension of the general concept of reciprocity.

We say that *the two topologically equivalent networks $\mathcal{N}$ and $\hat{\mathcal{N}}$ are interreciprocal if (25) — equivalently (26) — is valid*. Note: Interreciprocity of the networks as n-ports would be validated by (22) — equivalently (23). [When are (22) and (25) equivalent with respect to interreciprocity?]

The concept of interreciprocity extends considerably the types of components permitted in a network. Thus, a network containing a dependent source is not generally reciprocal although it may be for specific component values. (See Prob. 6.) On the other hand, interreciprocal networks may include controlled sources, gyrators, negative converters, etc., as we shall observe in greater detail below.

If two n-ports $\mathcal{N}$ and $\hat{\mathcal{N}}$ are interreciprocal, then (22) is satisfied. But from (18) it follows that

$$\sum_{k=1}^{n} (\hat{V}_k I_k - V_k \hat{I}_k) = 0 \tag{27}$$

is also true, where the variables here are the port source variables.

Let us take a port excitation approach similar to the procedure followed in the discussion of reciprocal n-ports. Specifically, let us focus attention on ports j and i. In $\mathcal{N}$, port j is excited by a voltage or a current source and the short circuit current or open circuit voltage at port i is measured, with all other ports either open or short. In $\hat{\mathcal{N}}$, the same two ports are consistently excited. For example, if port j in $\mathcal{N}$ was voltage excited and port i was shorted, then in $\hat{\mathcal{N}}$ port j is shorted and port i is excited by a voltage source. For this case (27) becomes

$$\hat{V}_i I_i - V_i \hat{I}_i = 0 \quad \leftrightarrow \quad \hat{y}_{ji} = y_{ij}. \tag{28}$$

There are a total of four possibilities, as summarized in Table 1. These lead to relationships between the transfer parameters of two interreciprocal multiports very much like those pertaining to reciprocal multiports.

Table 1

Excitations		Port-Variable Relations	Transfer Parameter Relations
Port j	Port i		
$\mathcal{N}$: voltage $\hat{\mathcal{N}}$: voltage($=0$)	voltage($=0$) voltage	$\hat{V}_i I_i - V_i \hat{I}_i = 0$	$\hat{y}_{ji} = y_{ij}$
$\mathcal{N}$: current $\hat{\mathcal{N}}$: current($=0$)	current($=0$) current	$\hat{V}_j I_j - V_i \hat{I}_i = 0$	$\hat{z}_{ji} = z_{ij}$
$\mathcal{N}$: current $\hat{\mathcal{N}}$: current($=0$)	voltage($=0$) voltage	$\hat{V}_j I_j + \hat{V}_i I_i = 0$	$\hat{h}_{ji} = -h_{ij}$
$\mathcal{N}$: voltage $\hat{\mathcal{N}}$: voltage($=0$)	current($=0$) current	$-V_j \hat{I}_j - V_i \hat{I}_i = 0$	$\hat{g}_{ji} = -g_{ij}$

Note that the derivation of the results in Table 1 starting in (27) does not guarantee the existence of specific transfer parameters. Thus, $\hat{y}_{ji} = y_{ij}$ requires voltage excitations (one being zero) at both ports of $\mathcal{N}$ and $\hat{\mathcal{N}}$. This might not be possible. For example, in a two-port consisting of an ideal transformer, it is not possible to excite one port with a nonzero voltage source while shorting the other port; so the short circuit parameters do not exist. The interpretation of Table 1 is that the interreciprocal multiport parameters are related as given there, assuming these parameters exist. You should verify that the entries in column two result from (27) for the specific excitation conditions of each row.

In addition to the transfer parameters it is possible to find relationships between the driving point parameters. In this case, only one port in each network is involved; the response is measured at the same port as the excitation. The result can be obtained from the second column of Table 1 in those rows (1 and 2) in which the excitations at both ports are the same, by setting $i = j$ (or $j = i$), yielding

$$\hat{y}_{jj} = y_{jj}$$
$$\hat{z}_{jj} = z_{jj}.$$

The conclusion from the preceding discussion is that, when they exist, the multiport admittance and impedance matrices of interreciprocal multiports are related by

$$\hat{\mathbf{Y}} = \mathbf{Y}' \tag{29a}$$
$$\hat{\mathbf{Z}} = \mathbf{Z}'. \tag{29b}$$

9.3.2 Adjoint Networks

When two networks are interreciprocal, we say that one is the *adjoint* of the other. In the preceding section we established relationships among the port parameters of interreciprocal multiports. What is of equal interest and importance is to examine the component relations of a network $\mathcal{N}$ and to determine what the corresponding component relations of the adjoint network $\hat{\mathcal{N}}$ must be and, from these, to determine the components in the adjoint network that correspond to specific components in $\mathcal{N}$.

Let us initiate the discussion by considering the component relations of network $\mathcal{N}$ in (24). Assuming that the network is not degenerate, matrix [**M N**] is of full rank (see Prob. 7) and thus, contains b linearly independent columns, some of them being columns of **M** and the rest columns of **N**. Suppose that the branches are so ordered as to group the linearly independent columns, leading to the following partitioned form:

$$[\mathbf{M} \ \mathbf{N}] = [[\mathbf{M}_a \ \mathbf{M}_b] \ [\mathbf{N}_a \ \mathbf{N}_b]], \tag{30}$$

where the columns of $\mathbf{M}_a$ and those of $\mathbf{N}_b$ are linearly independent, and so $[\mathbf{M}_a \; \mathbf{N}_b]$ is nonsingular. This partitioning is possible for all the basic components introduced in Chapter 1 except the ideal op-amp (and the ideal transistor introduced in the question set). The equations derived henceforth are valid for all networks except those containing ideal op-amps. (See Prob. 11 for a variation of the procedure for ideal op-amp networks.)

Upon similarly partitioning the voltages $\mathbf{V} - \mathbf{V}_s$ and the currents $\mathbf{I} - \mathbf{I}_s$, we can write (24a) as

$$[\mathbf{M}_a \quad \mathbf{M}_b] \begin{bmatrix} \mathbf{V}_a - \mathbf{V}_{sa} \\ \mathbf{V}_b - \mathbf{V}_{sb} \end{bmatrix} + [\mathbf{N}_a \quad \mathbf{N}_b] \begin{bmatrix} \mathbf{I}_a - \mathbf{I}_{sa} \\ \mathbf{I}_b - \mathbf{I}_{sb} \end{bmatrix} = 0. \tag{31}$$

Upon rearranging terms, this becomes

$$[\mathbf{M}_a \quad \mathbf{N}_b] \begin{bmatrix} \mathbf{V}_a - \mathbf{V}_{sa} \\ \mathbf{I}_b - \mathbf{I}_{sb} \end{bmatrix} + [\mathbf{N}_a \quad \mathbf{M}_b] \begin{bmatrix} \mathbf{I}_a - \mathbf{I}_{sa} \\ \mathbf{V}_b - \mathbf{V}_{sb} \end{bmatrix} = 0. \tag{32}$$

Since $[\mathbf{M}_a \; \mathbf{N}_b]$ is nonsingular, we obtain

$$\begin{bmatrix} \mathbf{V}_a - \mathbf{V}_{sa} \\ \mathbf{I}_b - \mathbf{I}_{sb} \end{bmatrix} = -[\mathbf{M}_a \quad \mathbf{N}_b]^{-1} [\mathbf{N}_a \quad \mathbf{M}_b] \begin{bmatrix} \mathbf{I}_a - \mathbf{I}_{sa} \\ \mathbf{V}_b - \mathbf{V}_{sb} \end{bmatrix} \tag{33}$$

For the networks under consideration, the branch relations can always be expressed such that $[\mathbf{M}_a \; \mathbf{N}_b] = \mathbf{U}$. We shall assume that this is the case. This means that $\mathbf{M}_a$ and $\mathbf{N}_b$ can be further partitioned as follows:

$$\mathbf{M}_a = \begin{bmatrix} \mathbf{U} \\ \mathbf{0} \end{bmatrix}, \qquad \mathbf{N}_b = \begin{bmatrix} \mathbf{0} \\ \mathbf{U} \end{bmatrix}. \tag{34}$$

If one also partitions $\mathbf{M}_b$ and $\mathbf{N}_a$ conformably, the overall $\mathbf{M}$ and $\mathbf{N}$ matrices can be written in partitioned form as

$$M = [M_a \quad M_b] = \begin{bmatrix} U & -H_{ab} \\ 0 & -Y_b \end{bmatrix} \tag{35a}$$

$$N = [N_a \quad N_b] = \begin{bmatrix} -Z_a & 0 \\ -H_{ba} & U \end{bmatrix}, \tag{35b}$$

where the partitions of M_b and N_a are easily identified. (The notation used for the submatrices will be clarified in a moment.)

When the partitioned forms of N_a and M_b are inserted into (33), the component relations finally become

$$\begin{bmatrix} V_a - V_{sa} \\ I_b - I_{sb} \end{bmatrix} = \begin{bmatrix} Z_a & H_{ab} \\ H_{ba} & Y_b \end{bmatrix} \begin{bmatrix} I_a - I_{sa} \\ V_b - V_{sb} \end{bmatrix}. \tag{36}$$

The matrix of these equations is a hybrid matrix, which explains the notation.

This expression gives the component relations of network $\mathcal{N}$, with all the sources counted as part of the network. If it were desired to consider the component relations of the nonsource components of the network, as a multiport without internal sources, they can be derived from (36).

Assume that no source is accompanied and recall that, in the original form of the component relations in (24), corresponding to an unaccompanied voltage source, there is a row and column of zeros in N, and corresponding to an unaccompanied current source, there is a row and column of zeros in M. Since the nonsingular submatrix $[M_a \ N_b]$ cannot have a row of zeros, it is necessary to put the columns corresponding to voltage sources in the "a" group and those corresponding to current sources in the "b" group. Hence, $I_{sa} = 0$ and $V_{sb} = 0$, so these vectors can be removed from the right side of (36), leading to

$$\begin{bmatrix} V_a - V_{sa} \\ I_b - I_{sb} \end{bmatrix} = \begin{bmatrix} Z_a & H_{ab} \\ H_{ba} & Y_b \end{bmatrix} \begin{bmatrix} I_a \\ V_b \end{bmatrix}. \tag{37}$$

On the left side of (36) the vector V_{sa} has nonzero elements only for those rows corresponding to voltage sources. The rows of the matrix on the right side of (37) corresponding to nonzero elements of V_{sa} must be zero because the entire component relation for an unaccompanied voltage source is $V - V_s = 0$. Similar comments apply to the rows corresponding to nonzero elements in $\mathbf{I}_{sb}$, which correspond to unaccompanied current sources. If we eliminate all these rows of zeros on the right (and the corresponding columns), as well as the corresponding elements of $(\mathbf{V}_a - \mathbf{V}_{sa})$, $(\mathbf{I}_b - \mathbf{I}_{sb})$, $\mathbf{I}_a$, and $\mathbf{V}_b$, then all source terms will be removed from (36) and the resulting component relations will apply only to the nonsource (internal) components. The result can be written as

$$
\begin{bmatrix} \mathbf{V}_{ia} \\ \mathbf{I}_{ib} \end{bmatrix} = \begin{bmatrix} \mathbf{Z}_a & \mathbf{H}_{ab} \\ \mathbf{H}_{ba} & \mathbf{Y}_b \end{bmatrix} \begin{bmatrix} \mathbf{I}_{ia} \\ \mathbf{V}_{ib} \end{bmatrix}, \tag{38}
$$

where the subscript i stands for internal. Strictly speaking, we should use different symbols for the submatrices in (38) because they are not the same as those in (36), having rows and columns corresponding to sources removed, and thus being generally of lower order. However, there is little likelihood of confusion in actual use.

Another way of treating the sources is to combine all of them with accompanying components to form general branches. When sources are treated in this way, the all hybrid matrix in (36) will be identical with that in (38) since there would have been no rows (and columns) of zeros to remove. (This statement assumes that the order of the branches is not changed and the nonsource branches are assigned to the same groups — "a" and "b.")

We will now illustrate these thoughts by again considering the network of Fig. 3 from two viewpoints: (a) no source accompanied [Fig. 3(a)], and (b) all sources accompanied [Fig. 3(b)]. In the first case, with branches 1 (the voltage source branch), 4, and 5 assigned to the "a" group, and consequently branches 2 (the current source branch), 3, and 6 in the "b" group, we obtain

$$
\begin{bmatrix} V_1 \\ V_4 \\ V_5 \\ \hline I_2 \\ I_3 \\ I_6 \end{bmatrix} - \begin{bmatrix} V_{s1} \\ 0 \\ 0 \\ \hline I_{s2} \\ 0 \\ 0 \end{bmatrix} = \begin{bmatrix} 0 & 0 & 0 & 0 & 0 & 0 \\ 0 & -R_b & 0 & 0 & 0 & 0 \\ 0 & 0 & -sL & 0 & 0 & 0 \\ \hline 0 & 0 & 0 & 0 & 0 & 0 \\ 0 & 0 & 0 & 0 & -G_a & 0 \\ 0 & 0 & 0 & 0 & 0 & -sC \end{bmatrix} \begin{bmatrix} I_1 \\ I_4 \\ I_5 \\ \hline V_2 \\ V_3 \\ V_6 \end{bmatrix} - \begin{bmatrix} 0 \\ 0 \\ 0 \\ \hline 0 \\ 0 \\ 0 \end{bmatrix}
$$

In the second case, with branches 2 and 3 placed in the "*a*" group and branches 1 and 4 put in the "*b*" group, we find

$$
\begin{bmatrix}
\begin{bmatrix} V_2 \\ V_3 \end{bmatrix} - \begin{bmatrix} 0 \\ 0 \end{bmatrix} \\
\begin{bmatrix} I_1 \\ I_4 \end{bmatrix} - \begin{bmatrix} 0 \\ 0 \end{bmatrix}
\end{bmatrix}
=
\begin{bmatrix}
-R_b & 0 & 0 & 0 \\
0 & -sL & 0 & 0 \\
0 & 0 & -G_a & 0 \\
0 & 0 & 0 & -sC
\end{bmatrix}
\begin{bmatrix}
\begin{bmatrix} I_2 \\ I_3 \end{bmatrix} - \begin{bmatrix} I_{s2} \\ 0 \end{bmatrix} \\
\begin{bmatrix} V_1 \\ V_4 \end{bmatrix} - \begin{bmatrix} V_{s2} \\ 0 \end{bmatrix}
\end{bmatrix} .
$$

When the component relations for the first case are modified by removing the rows and columns of zeros from the hybrid matrix, we obtain the hybrid matrix characterization of the internal branches of the network as a two-port which, as expected, is the same as the hybrid matrix for the second case. However, a difference is still evident in that, in the second case, source terms appear in the current and voltage vector; they do not appear in the first case.

To summarize, (36) is a general expression for the component relations, including sources (accompanied and/or unaccompanied), of a network. The disadvantage is that there are source vectors "attached" to the variable vectors, even though when no source is accompanied most of the elements of those source vectors on the left, and all of them on the right, will be zero, as shown in (37). On the other hand, (38) applies only to the nonsource components. We shall use both forms wherever appropriate.

The next task is to bring in the condition that one network is the adjoin of another. One possible expression, which includes the source terms, is given in (26). Another, for the network as a multiport without internal sources, is (23), which involves only the nonsource components. These two expressions can be rewritten as

$$
\begin{bmatrix} -\hat{\mathbf{I}} \\ \hat{\mathbf{V}} \end{bmatrix}' \begin{bmatrix} \mathbf{V} \\ \mathbf{I} \end{bmatrix} = 0
\tag{39a}
$$

$$
\begin{bmatrix} -(\hat{\mathbf{I}} - \hat{\mathbf{I}}_s) \\ (\hat{\mathbf{V}} - \hat{\mathbf{V}}_s) \end{bmatrix}' \begin{bmatrix} \mathbf{V} - \mathbf{V}_s \\ \mathbf{I} - \mathbf{I}_s \end{bmatrix} = 0
\tag{39b}
$$

(Remember that, unless all sources of the network are considered accompanied, the vectors in the first of these expressions are of lower order.)

For the following development we shall use (39b). The intention now is to use the component relations of $\mathcal{N}$ and somehow to get rid of the right hand vector in this expression, retaining only the "$\hat{\,}$" variables. To this end, let $\mathbf{W}$ be an arbitrary b-vector and premultiply the component relations of $\mathcal{N}$ in (30) by its transpose. Thus,

$$\mathbf{W}' \; [\mathbf{M} \quad \mathbf{N}] \begin{bmatrix} \mathbf{V} - \mathbf{V}_s \\ \mathbf{I} - \mathbf{I}_s \end{bmatrix} = 0$$

or, equivalently,

$$\left\{ \begin{bmatrix} \mathbf{M}' \\ \mathbf{N}' \end{bmatrix} \mathbf{W} \right\}' \begin{bmatrix} \mathbf{V} - \mathbf{V}_s \\ \mathbf{I} - \mathbf{I}_s \end{bmatrix} = 0. \tag{40}$$

Now compare this expression with (39b). Since $[\mathbf{M} \quad \mathbf{N}]$ is of full rank, it must be that

$$\begin{bmatrix} -(\hat{\mathbf{I}} - \hat{\mathbf{I}}_s) \\ \hat{\mathbf{V}} - \hat{\mathbf{V}}_s \end{bmatrix} = \begin{bmatrix} \mathbf{M}' \\ \mathbf{N}' \end{bmatrix} \mathbf{W} \tag{41}$$

for *some* $\mathbf{W}$. These are $2b$ independent branch relations in $3b$ variables for the adjoint network $\hat{\mathcal{N}}$.* The Kirchhoff laws provide the other b independent relations that are needed for a unique solution. If $\mathcal{N}$ is not degenerate, then these $3b$ equations have a unique solution for $\mathbf{W}$, $\hat{\mathbf{V}}$, and $\hat{\mathbf{I}}$, so $\hat{\mathcal{N}}$ is not degenerate. You should verify this fact.

To complete the development, we will insert in (41) the partitioned forms of M and N given in (35). The result will be

---

* The definition of adjoint networks as topologically equivalent networks satisfying (26) and the subsequent parametric formulation of the adjoint network equations (41) are due to C. A. Desoer as reported in "On the description of adjoint networks," *IEEE Transactions on Circuits and Systems*, vol. CAS-22, No. 7, 1975, pp. 585-587.

$$
\left[-\begin{bmatrix} \hat{I}_a - \hat{I}_{sa} \\ \hat{I}_b - \hat{I}_{sb} \end{bmatrix} \\ \begin{bmatrix} \hat{V}_a - \hat{V}_{sa} \\ \hat{V}_b - \hat{V}_{sb} \end{bmatrix} \right] = \left[\begin{bmatrix} U & 0 \\ -H'_{ab} & -Y'_b \end{bmatrix} \\ \begin{bmatrix} -Z'_a & -H'_{ba} \\ 0 & U \end{bmatrix} \right] W \quad . \tag{42}
$$

By regrouping the rows in this expression, it follows that

$$
\begin{bmatrix} -(\hat{I}_a - \hat{I}_{sa}) \\ \hat{V}_b - \hat{V}_{sb} \end{bmatrix} = \begin{bmatrix} U & 0 \\ 0 & U \end{bmatrix} W = W \tag{43}
$$

and

$$
\begin{bmatrix} \hat{V}_a - \hat{V}_{sa} \\ -(\hat{I}_b - \hat{I}_{sb}) \end{bmatrix} = \begin{bmatrix} -Z'_a & -H'_{ba} \\ -H'_{ab} & -Y'_b \end{bmatrix} W \quad . \tag{44}
$$

Finally, inserting W from the first of these expressions into the second one, we get

$$
\begin{bmatrix} \hat{V}_a - \hat{V}_{sa} \\ \hat{I}_b - \hat{I}_{sb} \end{bmatrix} = \begin{bmatrix} Z'_a & -H'_{ba} \\ -H'_{ab} & Y'_b \end{bmatrix} \begin{bmatrix} \hat{I}_a - \hat{I}_{sa} \\ \hat{V}_b - \hat{V}_{sb} \end{bmatrix} \quad . \tag{45}
$$

These are hybrid branch relations for the adjoint network in exactly the same form as for the original network $\mathcal{N}$, given in (36), counting sources as part of the network. If we use the "^" symbol to indicate the parameters of $\hat{\mathcal{N}}$, we find the following relationship between the hybrid parameters of $\hat{\mathcal{N}}$ and those of $\mathcal{N}$:

$$
\begin{aligned}
\hat{Z}_a &= Z'_a & \hat{H}_{ab} &= -H'_{ba} \\
\hat{Y}_b &= Y'_b & \hat{H}_{ba} &= -H'_{ab}
\end{aligned} \tag{46}
$$

Finally, the same observations about source terms can be made relative to (45) that were made relative to (36) and the hybrid branch equations of the nonsource components of the adjoint network, as a multi-port without internal sources, can be written as

$$
\begin{bmatrix} \hat{\mathbf{V}}_{ia} \\ \hat{\mathbf{I}}_{ib} \end{bmatrix} = \begin{bmatrix} \mathbf{Z}'_a & -\mathbf{H}'_{ba} \\ -\mathbf{H}'_{ab} & \mathbf{Y}'_b \end{bmatrix} \begin{bmatrix} \hat{\mathbf{I}}_{ia} \\ \hat{\mathbf{V}}_{ib} \end{bmatrix} \ , \tag{47}
$$

where the subscript i stands for internal. [Remember that the submatrices here are different from those in (45) by having the rows and columns of zeros in the latter corresponding to unaccompanied sources removed.]

Clearly the hybrid parameters of $\mathcal{N}$ determine those of $\hat{\mathcal{N}}$. Each component of $\mathcal{N}$ has an associated component in $\hat{\mathcal{N}}$, which is its *adjoint component*. For example, if branches k and l of $\mathcal{N}$ represent a current-controlled current source, then the contributions of these two branches to the hybrid matrix will be

$$
\begin{bmatrix} V_k \\ I_l \end{bmatrix} = \begin{bmatrix} 0 & 0 \\ \beta & 0 \end{bmatrix} \begin{bmatrix} I_k \\ V_l \end{bmatrix} \ .
$$

(Note that the positions of the elements of the matrix on the right, as they would appear in the overall hybrid matrix of the network of which this controlled source is a part, will be determined by the row and column indices k and l.) Now in accordance with (46), the contribution of the adjoint component to the adjoint network hybrid matrix will be

$$
\begin{bmatrix} \hat{V}_k \\ \hat{I}_l \end{bmatrix} = \begin{bmatrix} 0 & -\beta \\ 0 & 0 \end{bmatrix} \begin{bmatrix} \hat{I}_k \\ \hat{V}_l \end{bmatrix} \ .
$$

These are the equations of a voltage-controlled voltage source. The controlled and controlling branches have been interchanged and the gain has undergone a polarity reversal. This association of a *VCVS* with an *ICIS* is shown in Fig. 4. Similar analyses carried out for each of the basic components will determine the adjoint component of each. They

Table 2   Associated basic components of $\mathcal{N}$ and $\hat{\mathcal{N}}$

$\mathcal{N}$	$\hat{\mathcal{N}}$	$\mathcal{N}$	$\hat{\mathcal{N}}$
e v-source	$\hat{e}$	$f(s):1$ Voltage General Converter	$f(s):1$
j i-source	$\hat{j}$	VCVS	VCVS
R Resistor	R	VCIS	VCIS
C Capacitor	C	ICVS	ICVS
L Inductor	L	ICIS	ICIS
r Gyrator	r		
$n:1$ Ideal transformer	$n:1$		
$f(s):1$ Current General Converter	$f(s):1$		

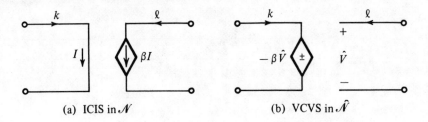

(a) ICIS in $\mathcal{N}$ (b) VCVS in $\hat{\mathcal{N}}$

Fig. 4   Component and its adjoint component

are given in Table 2. You should verify the remaining entries in this table.

Thus, given a network $\mathcal{N}$ with specified branches, the adjoint network $\hat{\mathcal{N}}$ can be immediately constructed by reference to Table 2.

CHAPTER 10
Computer-Aided Network Design

Network design is a process which starts from the specification of a desired performance measure. The measure for a filter might be band width for the pass-band and attenuation in the stop-band, or permissible deviation from linear phase, or overshoot in the step-response. The design consists of the creation of a prototype network — selection of the network structure and specification of the types of components — and the determination of the component values, such that the desired performance is achieved subject to any specified constraints.

The availability of a computer to aid in the design gives a wider scope to the design process. Starting with an initial design — configuration and component values — a computer-aided network design (CAND) process follows an iterative procedure to yield an improved design, one that meets the performance measure more closely.

In this chapter, we will start the study of CAND by developing relationships between incremental variations of network parameters and changes induced in response variables, by invoking Tellegen's Theorem. We will then devise algorithms, in which these relationships play an essential role, to optimize — minimize or maximize — specified network performance measures.

10.1 INCREMENTED NETWORKS

Let $\mathcal{N}$ be a nondegenerate network and $\hat{\mathcal{N}}$ be its adjoint. With port and internal (nonsource) branches taken separately, the difference form of Tellegen's theorem is

$$-\hat{\mathbf{V}}'_p \mathbf{I}_p + \hat{\mathbf{I}}'_p \mathbf{V}_p = \hat{\mathbf{V}}'_i \mathbf{I}_i - \hat{\mathbf{I}}'_i \mathbf{V}_i \ . \tag{1}$$

Assume that the component values in $\mathscr{N}$ are varying and let $\mathscr{N}_\Delta$ refer to $\mathscr{N}$ with its element values changed. The voltages and currents of $\mathscr{N}_\Delta$ can be expressed as variations on those of $\mathscr{N}$. Since $\mathscr{N}$ and $\mathscr{N}_\Delta$ are topologically equivalent, so are $\mathscr{N}_\Delta$ and $\hat{\mathscr{N}}$. So, again by Tellegen's theorem,

$$-\hat{\mathbf{V}}_p'(\mathbf{I}_p + \Delta\mathbf{I}_p) + \hat{\mathbf{I}}_p'(\mathbf{V}_p + \Delta\mathbf{V}_p) = \hat{\mathbf{V}}_i'(\mathbf{I}_i + \Delta\mathbf{I}_i) - \hat{\mathbf{I}}_i'(\mathbf{V}_i - \Delta\mathbf{V}_i) \qquad (2)$$

Subtracting (2) from (1) yields

$$-\hat{\mathbf{V}}_p'\Delta\mathbf{I}_p + \hat{\mathbf{I}}_p'\Delta\mathbf{V}_p = \hat{\mathbf{V}}_i'\Delta\mathbf{I}_i - \hat{\mathbf{I}}_i'\Delta\mathbf{V}_i \qquad (3)$$

Now let us partition the voltage and current vectors into the "a" and "b" groups as defined in Chapter 9. Then (3) becomes

$$-[\hat{\mathbf{V}}_{pa}' \quad \hat{\mathbf{V}}_{pb}']\begin{bmatrix}\Delta\mathbf{I}_{pa}\\ \Delta\mathbf{I}_{pb}\end{bmatrix} + [\hat{\mathbf{I}}_{pa}' \quad \hat{\mathbf{I}}_{pb}']\begin{bmatrix}\Delta\mathbf{V}_{pa}\\ \Delta\mathbf{V}_{pb}\end{bmatrix}$$

$$\qquad (4)$$

$$= [\hat{\mathbf{V}}_{ia}' \quad \hat{\mathbf{V}}_{ib}']\begin{bmatrix}\Delta\mathbf{I}_{ia}\\ \Delta\mathbf{I}_{ib}\end{bmatrix} - [\hat{\mathbf{I}}_{ia}' \quad \hat{\mathbf{I}}_{ib}']\begin{bmatrix}\Delta\mathbf{V}_{ia}\\ \Delta\mathbf{V}_{ib}\end{bmatrix}.$$

A simplifiction is possible on the left side. Note that in both $\mathscr{N}$ and $\hat{\mathscr{N}}$, voltage sources must be in the "a" group and current sources in the "b" group. Furthermore, there is no variation in the value of a voltage source or a current source. Hence, the left side of (4) reduces to

$$[-\hat{\mathbf{V}}_{pa}' \quad \hat{\mathbf{I}}_{pb}']\begin{bmatrix}\Delta\mathbf{I}_{pa}\\ \Delta\mathbf{V}_{pb}\end{bmatrix}. \qquad (5)$$

As for the right side of (4), it can be simplified by using the component relations in (9-38). From those relations

$$\Delta\mathbf{V}_{ia} = \Delta\mathbf{Z}_a\mathbf{I}_{ia} + \Delta\mathbf{H}_{ab}\mathbf{V}_{ib} + \mathbf{Z}_a\Delta\mathbf{I}_{ia} + \mathbf{H}_{ab}\Delta\mathbf{V}_{ib} \qquad (6a)$$

$$\Delta\mathbf{I}_{ib} = \Delta\mathbf{H}_{ba}\mathbf{I}_{ia} + \Delta\mathbf{Y}_b\mathbf{V}_{ib} + \mathbf{H}_{ba}\Delta\mathbf{I}_{ia} + \mathbf{Y}_b\Delta\mathbf{V}_{ib}. \qquad (6b)$$

When (5) and (6) are substituted into (4), and the terms are appropriately grouped, the result becomes

$$
[-\hat{\mathbf{V}}_{pa}' \quad \hat{\mathbf{I}}_{pb}'] \begin{bmatrix} \Delta\mathbf{I}_{pa} \\ \Delta\mathbf{V}_{pb} \end{bmatrix} = [\hat{\mathbf{V}}_{ia}' \quad \hat{\mathbf{V}}_{ib}'] \left\{ \begin{bmatrix} 0 & 0 \\ \Delta\mathbf{H}_{ba} & \Delta\mathbf{Y}_b \end{bmatrix} \begin{bmatrix} \mathbf{I}_a \\ \mathbf{V}_{ib} \end{bmatrix} + \begin{bmatrix} \mathbf{U} & 0 \\ \mathbf{H}_{ba} & \mathbf{Y}_b \end{bmatrix} \begin{bmatrix} \Delta\mathbf{I}_{ia} \\ \Delta\mathbf{V}_{ia} \end{bmatrix} \right\}
$$

$$
- [\hat{\mathbf{I}}_{ia}' \quad \hat{\mathbf{I}}_{ib}'] \left\{ \begin{bmatrix} \Delta\mathbf{Z}_a & \Delta\mathbf{H}_{ab} \\ 0 & 0 \end{bmatrix} \begin{bmatrix} \mathbf{I}_{ia} \\ \mathbf{V}_{ib} \end{bmatrix} + \begin{bmatrix} \mathbf{Z}_a & \mathbf{H}_{ab} \\ 0 & \mathbf{U} \end{bmatrix} \begin{bmatrix} \Delta\mathbf{I}_{ia} \\ \Delta\mathbf{V}_{ib} \end{bmatrix} \right\}
$$

$$
= [-\hat{\mathbf{I}}_{ia}' \quad \hat{\mathbf{V}}_{ib}'] \begin{bmatrix} \Delta\mathbf{Z}_a & \Delta\mathbf{H}_{ab} \\ \Delta\mathbf{H}_{ba} & \Delta\mathbf{Y}_b \end{bmatrix} \begin{bmatrix} \mathbf{I}_{ia} \\ \mathbf{V}_{ib} \end{bmatrix} \tag{7}
$$

$$
+ \left\{ [\hat{\mathbf{V}}_{ia}' \quad \hat{\mathbf{V}}_{ib}'] \begin{bmatrix} \mathbf{U} & 0 \\ \mathbf{H}_{ba} & \mathbf{Y}_b \end{bmatrix} - [\hat{\mathbf{I}}_{ia}' \quad \hat{\mathbf{I}}_{ib}'] \begin{bmatrix} \mathbf{Z}_a & \mathbf{H}_{ab} \\ 0 & \mathbf{U} \end{bmatrix} \right\} \begin{bmatrix} \Delta\mathbf{I}_{ia} \\ \Delta\mathbf{V}_{ib} \end{bmatrix}
$$

The last equality follows from the previous one with a simple rearrangement of terms. Upon substitution of the component relations of the adjoint network from (9-38), the last line of the last equality in the preceding equation vanishes. Hence, the final result becomes

$$
[-\hat{\mathbf{V}}_{pa}' \quad \hat{\mathbf{I}}_{pb}'] \begin{bmatrix} \Delta\mathbf{I}_{pa} \\ \Delta\mathbf{V}_{pb} \end{bmatrix} = [-\hat{\mathbf{I}}_{ia}' \quad \hat{\mathbf{V}}_{ib}'] \begin{bmatrix} \Delta\mathbf{Z}_a & \Delta\mathbf{H}_{ab} \\ \Delta\mathbf{H}_{ba} & \Delta\mathbf{Y}_b \end{bmatrix} \begin{bmatrix} \mathbf{I}_{ia} \\ \mathbf{V}_{ib} \end{bmatrix}. \tag{8}
$$

This expression relates changes in port voltages and currents, $\Delta\mathbf{V}_{pb}$ and $\Delta\mathbf{I}_{pa}$, which are presumably the responses, to changes in parameter values as expressed by changes in the submatrices of the hybrid matrix describing $\mathcal{N}$. It is a powerful tool for the calculation of the change in a response due to changes in one or more parameter values.

10.1.1 Example

As a simple illustration, consider the two-port in Fig. 1(a). Port 1 is excited with a voltage source and port 2 is left open. Thus, the possible responses are V_2 and I_1 or the transfer function V_2/V_1 and the input admittance $-I_1/V_1$. The gain A and conductance G_5 are the parameters that are assumed to be varying.

The first step in the process is to write the hybrid parameter equations in accordance with (9-38). To do this requires a partition of the branches into the "a" and "b" groups. Since branch 1 is a voltage source, it is in category "a." Similarly, since branch 2 is a current source

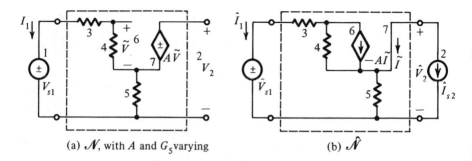

(a) $\mathcal{N}$, with A and G_5 varying   (b) $\hat{\mathcal{N}}$

Fig. 1   Network with varying parameters and its adjoint

(whose value happens to be zero), it is in category "b." The equations of the controlled source are

$$I_6 = 0 \quad \text{and} \quad V_7 = AV_6.$$

Hence, branch 6 should be in "b" and 7 in "a." Finally, since it is the *conductance* of branch 5 which is varying, the equation of this branch would be written $I_5 = G_5 V_5$, so branch 5 would be in "b." It is immaterial in which groups branches 3 and 4 are placed. Let us arbitrarily choose to put them in "a." The hybrid equations can now be written as

$$
\begin{bmatrix} V_3 \\ V_4 \\ V_7 \\ \hline I_5 \\ I_6 \end{bmatrix}
=
\begin{bmatrix}
R_3 & 0 & 0 & 0 & 0 \\
0 & R_4 & 0 & 0 & 0 \\
0 & 0 & 0 & 0 & A \\
\hline
0 & 0 & 0 & G_5 & 0 \\
0 & 0 & 0 & 0 & 0
\end{bmatrix}
\begin{bmatrix} I_3 \\ I_4 \\ I_7 \\ \hline V_5 \\ V_6 \end{bmatrix}
$$

There are variations only in (one element of) $\mathbf{H}_{ab}$ and (one element of) $\mathbf{Y}_b$, so the right side of (8) becomes

$$-\hat{\mathbf{I}}'_{ia}\Delta\mathbf{H}_{ab}\mathbf{V}_{ib} + \hat{\mathbf{V}}'_{ib}\Delta\mathbf{Y}_b\mathbf{V}_{ib}.$$

The next step is to construct the adjoint network $\hat{\mathcal{N}}$, remembering that it must be consistently excited; it is shown in Fig. 1(b). Under this constraint, the left side of (8) will become

$$-\hat{V}_{s1}\Delta I_1 + \hat{I}_{s2}\Delta V_2.$$

When the last two expressions are inserted into (8), with the varying entries in $\mathbf{H}_{ab}$ and $\mathbf{Y}_b$ explicitly shown, the result becomes

$$- \hat{V}_{s1}\Delta I_1 + \hat{I}_{s2}\Delta V_2 = (-\hat{I}_7 V_6)\Delta A + (\hat{V}_5 V_5)\Delta G_5$$

The numerical values of the sources in the adjoint network can be chosen for convenience and utility. For the two sets of values: $(\hat{V}_{s1} = 0, \hat{I}_{s2} = 1)$ and $(\hat{V}_{s1} = 1, \hat{I}_{s2} = 0)$ the following results are obtained.

$$\Delta V_2 = (-\hat{I}_7 V_6)\Delta A + (\hat{V}_5 V_5)\Delta G_5$$
$$\Delta I_1 = (-\hat{I}_7 V_6)\Delta A + (\hat{V}_5 V_5)\Delta G_5$$

The expressions on the right are identical, but this does not imply $\Delta V_2 = \Delta I_1$. True enough, the solutions for V_5 and V_6 in network $\mathcal{N}$ are the same for both cases but those for $\hat{V}_5$ and $\hat{I}_7$ in $\hat{\mathcal{N}}$ are not, because the adjoint sources are different in the two cases.

10.2   RESPONSE VARIATION VS. PARAMETER VARIATION

In the example just completed, notice the form of the right side in the last pair of expressions; the incremental change in a parameter value is multiplied by a factor which is a product of the corresponding voltage or current from both the original network $\mathcal{N}$ and the adjoint network $\hat{\mathcal{N}}$. This observation leads to the inquiry as to whether the right side of (8) can be written in this form generally. That is, instead of an expression in terms of changes in the submatrices of the hybrid matrix representing the component relations, it would be useful to have an expression directly involving the variations in the parameter values. To pursue this thought, we should examine each type of component and express the change in the appropriate hybrid submatrix in (8) in terms of the variation of that component's parameter value.

To illustrate, suppose branch j is a resistor expressed as a resistance. Then ΔR_j is the (j,j)th element — furthermore, the only nonzero element in row and column j — of the matrix in (8) and it is an element of ΔZ_a. Hence, the contribution of ΔR_j to the right side of (8) is

$$- \hat{I}_j I_j \Delta R_j. \tag{9}$$

Next suppose branches k and l are a current-controlled current source, with branch k controlling. Then $\Delta \beta_{lk}$ is the (l,k)th element —

furthermore, the only nonzero element in rows and columns k and $l-$ of the matrix in (8) and it is an element of $\Delta\mathbf{H}_{ba}$. Hence, the contribution of $\Delta\beta_{lk}$ is

$$\hat{V}_l I_k \Delta\beta_{lk}. \tag{10}$$

Both of the preceding expressions have the same form — the change in a network parameter multiplied by a coefficient. The coefficient is the product of one variable (current or voltage) from the adjoint network $\hat{n}$ and one variable from n. If we were to examine (8) in this manner with respect to each type of component, we would get similar terms, differing only in the factors comprising the coefficients. Collecting all such terms leads to the following expression:

$$[-\mathbf{V}_s' \quad \mathbf{I}_s'] \begin{bmatrix} \Delta\mathbf{I}_{V_s} \\ \Delta\mathbf{V}_{I_s} \end{bmatrix}$$

$$= \sum_{\text{Resistors}} (-\hat{I}_R I_R)\Delta R + \sum_{\text{Resistors}} \hat{V}_G V_G \Delta G$$

$$+ \sum_{\text{Gyrators}} (\hat{I}_i I_o - \hat{I}_o I_i)\Delta r + \sum_{\text{Gyrators}} (\hat{V}_i V_o - \hat{V}_o V_i)\Delta g$$

$$+ \sum_{\substack{\text{Ideal} \\ \text{Transformers}}} -(\hat{I}_i V_o + \hat{V}_o I_i)\Delta n \tag{11}$$

$$+ \sum_{\substack{\text{Current} \\ \text{Negative} \\ \text{Converters}}} \hat{V}_o I_i \Delta(k^2) + \sum_{\substack{\text{Voltage} \\ \text{Negative} \\ \text{Converters}}} \hat{I}_i V_o \Delta(k^2)$$

$$+ \sum_{\substack{\text{Dependent} \\ \text{Sources}}} (-\hat{I}_o I_i \Delta r - \hat{I}_o V_i \Delta\mu + \hat{V}_o I_i \Delta\beta + \hat{V}_o V_i \Delta g)$$

$$+ \sum_{\text{Capacitors}} j\omega \hat{V}_C V_C \Delta C + \sum_{\text{Capacitors}} -\frac{1}{j\omega}\hat{I}_C I_C \Delta D$$

$$+ \sum_{\text{Inductors}} -j\omega\hat{I}_L I_L \Delta L + \sum_{\text{Inductors}} \frac{1}{j\omega}\hat{V}_L V_L \Delta\Gamma.$$

A number of observations should be made about this expression. On the left side, the port variables — $\hat{V}_{pa}$ and $\hat{I}_{pb}$ in (8) — are simply the voltage and current sources in the adjoint network, so the notation has been modified appropriately. Similarly, $\mathbf{I}_{pa}$ and $\mathbf{V}_{pb}$ in (8) are the currents through the voltage sources and the voltages across the current sources in the original network. These are the responses. Even though no source may be shown in the given network at the position where a response is specified, it is assumed an appropriate source of zero value is present. Thus, in Fig. 1(a), the response V_2 across the open circuit is assumed to be across a current source of zero value. The modified notation on the left side of (11) reflects these ideas.

On the right side, each summation extends over all components in n of the type designated. For the two-branch components, subscript i designates input and o, output. When a component has both an impedance and an admittance representation, the change could be designated as a change in the parameter itself or in its reciprocal, but obviously not both.

Finally, a word is in order about the last two terms in (11), involving the dynamic components L and C. From the form of these terms it is clear that the variables have been taken as phasors and the analysis is in the frequency-domain. In the absence of L and C, the analysis can still be in the frequency-domain; but since all variables will be in-phase, a time-domain analysis would lead to exactly the same results except that the variables would be functions of time, possibly constant functions of time.

Some notational simplification can be introduced in (11) by noting that this expression gives the change in a function as a linear combination of changes in the parameters on which this function depends. Thus, suppose a function F depends on a set of parameters p_i. Then the first order change in F can be written as

$$\Delta F = \sum_i \frac{\partial F}{\partial p_i} \Delta p_i = \sum_i S_{p_i}^F \Delta p_i. \tag{12}$$

The partial derivatives in the first equality in this expression are the unnormalized sensitivities of F with respect to p_i; this leads to the second equality.

But the right side of (11) has exactly the same form as the right side of (12), namely, a linear combination of parameter variations. Thus, the coefficients of the parameter variations in (11) play the role of (have the significance of) sensitivities. Without indicating what they are the sensitivity of, (11) can therefore be written as

$$[-\hat{\mathbf{V}}_s' \quad \hat{\mathbf{I}}_s'] \begin{bmatrix} \Delta \mathbf{I}_{V_s} \\ \Delta \mathbf{V}_{I_s} \end{bmatrix} = \sum S_{p_i} \Delta p_i \tag{13}$$

$$= \mathbf{S}' \, \Delta \mathbf{p}$$

In the last line, the summation has been written in vector form. The elements of the *sensitivity vector* **S** are the (scalar) sensitivites S_{p_i}; the elements of the parameter vector **p** are the individual parameters of the network.

10.3 APPLICATIONS OF ADJOINT NETWORKS

The major application of the preceding development is to computer-aided network design. However, before embarking on that extensive subject, we shall develop some other applications in this section. (Proj. 6 also involves other applications of Tellegen's theorem and adjoint networks.)

10.3.1 Vratsanos' Theorem

Consider the current-excited one-port $\mathcal{N}$ depicted, with its adjoint one-port $\hat{\mathcal{N}}$, in Fig. 2. The combination of (8), (11), and (13) can be written as follows:

$$[-\hat{\mathbf{V}}_s' \quad \hat{\mathbf{I}}_s'] \begin{bmatrix} \Delta \mathbf{I}_{V_s} \\ \Delta \mathbf{V}_{I_s} \end{bmatrix} = [-\hat{\mathbf{I}}_{ia}' \quad \hat{\mathbf{V}}_{ib}'] \begin{bmatrix} \Delta \mathbf{Z}_a & \Delta \mathbf{H}_{ab} \\ \Delta \mathbf{H}_{ba} & \Delta \mathbf{Y}_b \end{bmatrix} \begin{bmatrix} \mathbf{I}_{ia} \\ \mathbf{V}_{ib} \end{bmatrix} = \mathbf{S}' \Delta \mathbf{p} \tag{14}$$

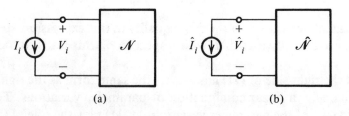

(a)   (b)

Fig. 2 One-port and its adjoint one-port

where the elements of **S** are the coefficients of the parameter changes in (11). Since there are no voltage sources and only one current source, this expression reduces to

$$\hat{I}_i \Delta V_i = \mathbf{S}' \Delta \mathbf{p}. \tag{15}$$

But, because the source value is fixed, $V_i = -Z_{in}I_i$ implies $\Delta V_i = -(\Delta Z_{in})I_i$. Hence, (5) yields

$$\Delta Z_{in} = -\frac{1}{I_i \hat{I}_i} \mathbf{S}' \Delta p. \tag{16a}$$

As a second possibility, suppose $\mathcal{N}$ in Fig. 2 is voltage excited. If we repeat the procedure just carried out, we get

$$\Delta Y_{in} = \frac{1}{V_i \hat{V}_i} \mathbf{S}' \Delta p. \tag{16b}$$

Let us suppose that the parameter of just one two-terminal component is varying. Then, if it is the admittance of branch k or the impedance of branch l, we get, from (16),

$$\frac{\Delta Z_{in}}{\Delta Y_k} = \frac{V_k \hat{V}_k}{I_i \hat{I}_i} \quad \text{and} \quad \frac{\Delta Y_{in}}{\Delta Y_k} = \frac{V_k \hat{V}_k}{V_i \hat{V}_i} \tag{17a}$$

$$\frac{\Delta Z_{in}}{\Delta Z_l} = \frac{I_l \hat{I}_l}{I_i \hat{I}_i} \quad \text{and} \quad \frac{\Delta Y_{in}}{\Delta Z_l} = -\frac{I_l \hat{I}_l}{V_i \hat{V}_i}. \tag{17b}$$

These expressions are referred to as *Vratsanos' Theorem*. They are the unnormalized sensitivities of the input impedance and of the input admittance of a one-port with respect to a parameter of the network realizing the one-port.

The four expressions of (17) are particularly simple. To find the change in the input impedance or admittance to a change in the parameter of one two-terminal component, we need find only two branch voltages or currents, one in the original one-port $\mathcal{N}$ and one in its adjoint $\hat{\mathcal{N}}$. Alternatively, we can view this as requiring the calculation of two network functions, one in each one-port. For example, the voltage gains V_k/V_i and $\hat{V}_k/\hat{V}_i$ in the second case of (17a).

10.3.2 Thévenin's and Norton's Theorems

In the usual determination of the Thévenin equivalent of a network, at a pair of terminals, two separate calculations are required; one to find the open-circuit voltage at the terminals with all the internal sources in place and another to find the impedance at the terminals with all the internal (independent) sources deactivated. The concepts of interreciprocity and adjoint networks permits a greatly simplified procedure.

Consider a three-port network $\mathcal{N}$ with no internal independent sources and its adjoint $\hat{\mathcal{N}}$, excited as depicted in Fig. 3. Then, by (9-27) — the port condition for interreciprocity of multiports — we have

$$(\hat{V}_1 I_1 - V_1 \hat{I}_1) + (\hat{V}_2 I_2 - V_2 \hat{I}_2) + (\hat{V}_3 I_3 - V_3 \hat{I}_3) = 0. \qquad (18)$$

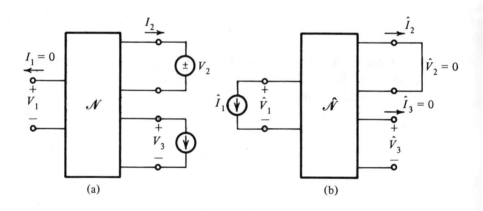

Fig. 3   Three-port and adjoint three-port

As $I_1 = \hat{V}_2 = \hat{I}_3 = 0$, it follows that the open-circuit voltage at port 1 of $\mathcal{N}$, which is V_1 and alternatively denoted V_{oc}, can be expressed as

$$V_{oc} = -\frac{\hat{I}_2}{\hat{I}_1} V_k + \frac{\hat{V}_3}{\hat{I}_1} I_3. \qquad (19)$$

If the network had contained other independent sources, each could have been considered to be connected to another port. Additional terms like those within the parentheses would have been included in (18), one for each source. Then (19) would be replaced by

$$V_{oc} = - \sum_{\substack{\text{voltage} \\ \text{sources}}} \frac{\hat{I}_k}{\hat{I}_1} V_k + \sum_{\substack{\text{current} \\ \text{sources}}} \frac{\hat{V}_k}{\hat{I}_1} I_k. \tag{20}$$

You can easily convince yourself of this fact. Let the input impedance of $\mathcal{N}$ be denoted by Z_t. From the discussion immediately following Table 9-1 this impedance is the same as the input impedance of the adjoint, $\hat{\mathcal{N}}$, at the corresponding port. Hence,

$$Z_t = - \frac{\hat{V}_1}{\hat{I}_1}. \tag{21}$$

These two quantities $- V_{oc}$ and $Z_t -$ are precisely those appearing in the Thévenin equivalent network at port 1 of $\mathcal{N}$, as depicted in Fig. 4(a).

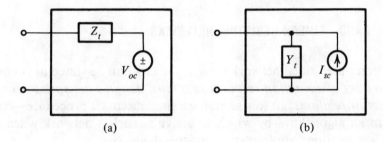

Fig. 4 Thévenin (a) and Norton (b) equivalent networks

In summary, then, given a network $\mathcal{N}$ containing independent sources, suppose it is desired to find the Thévenin equivalent at a pair of terminals, labeled port 1. Create the adjoint network $\hat{\mathcal{N}}$, with each independent source assigned the value zero. Apply an arbitrary excitation of value $\hat{I}_1$ — the simplest possibility is $\hat{I}_1 = 1$ — at port 1 of the adjoint. Analyze $\hat{\mathcal{N}}$, in the process determining $\hat{V}_1$, and the currents through the short-circuits and the voltages across the open-circuits standing in place of the independent sources. Then, simple algebra yields V_{oc} and Z_t according to (20) and (21).

The most important fact to be noted from this summary is: Only one analysis — that of $\hat{\mathcal{N}}$ — is needed to secure the Thévenin equivalent of $\mathcal{N}$ at the identified port 1.

By a development dual to that above (you should supply the details) the short-circuit current I_{sc} and input admittance $Y_t (= 1/Z_t)$ at port 1 of

$\mathcal{N}$ — the two quantities appearing in the Norton equivalent network at port 1 — are found to be

$$I_{sc} = \underbrace{\sum \frac{\hat{I}_k}{\hat{V}_1} V_k}_{\substack{\text{voltage} \\ \text{sources}}} - \underbrace{\sum \frac{\hat{V}_k}{\hat{V}_1} I_k}_{\substack{\text{current} \\ \text{sources}}} \tag{22}$$

and

$$Y_t = -\frac{\hat{I}_1}{\hat{V}_1}, \tag{23}$$

where $\hat{V}_1$ is the voltage excitation at port 1 of $\mathcal{N}$. The Norton equivalent is shown in Fig. 4(b). Its determination too requires but one analysis of the adjoint network.

10.4 CAND—LINEAR RESISTIVE NETWORKS

In computer-aided network design, the task can be stated as follows: *Given a set of excitation-response relations, design a network to exhibit this set of relations.* In this section we shall discuss a procedure — codified in an algorithm — by which to arrive at such a network when the specified relations are frequency independent.

The first step is to select the topology and component types of a candidate network which intuition or experience leads you to believe is potentially capable of meeting the requirements, provided the components have appropriate values. Obviously, this step requires a certain degree of experience in network analysis and design. Since the specified relations are independent of frequency, only nondynamic components will be involved here.

At the outset a performance function must be specified. In a great many applications, what is required is for one or more response voltages or currents to deviate as little as possible — absolutely — from some specified values. For dynamic networks one must add: over a specified time interval or a specified frequency interval. A number of different performance functions are possible. But whatever peformance function is chosen, it should be a nonnegative function which vanishes when each response variable is identical to its specified desired value. (See Problems 17 and 18.)

In order to accommodate any number of response variables, and to emphasize or deemphasize some of them relative to others, we shall take the following weighted quadratic sum to be our performance function.

$$\mathcal{E} = \frac{1}{2}[(\mathbf{I}_{pa} - \mathbf{I}_{pad})' \quad (\mathbf{V}_{pb} - \mathbf{V}_{pbd})'] \quad \mathbf{W} \begin{bmatrix} (\mathbf{I}_{pa} - \mathbf{I}_{pad}) \\ (\mathbf{V}_{pb} - \mathbf{V}_{pbd}) \end{bmatrix}$$

$$(24)$$

$$= \frac{1}{2} \sum_k |I_{pak} - I_{padk}|^2 w_{kk} + \frac{1}{2} \sum_k |V_{pbk} - V_{pbdk}|^2 w_{kk}$$

The vectors $\mathbf{I}_{pad}$ and $\mathbf{V}_{pbd}$ have as elements the *desired* response values, dictated by the desired excitation/response relations and some selected set of excitation values. The latter can be selected arbitrarily since the relations are treated as linear. The deviations from the desired values (or the errors) are $(\mathbf{I}_{pa} - \mathbf{I}_{pad})$ and $(\mathbf{V}_{pb} - \mathbf{V}_{pbd})$. The *weight matrix* $\mathbf{W}$ in (24) is diagonal and its diagonal elements have values in the interval $[0,1]$; that is,

$$\mathbf{W} = diag \{\ldots, w_{kk}, \ldots\} \text{ with } 0 \leqslant w_{kk} \leqslant 1. \quad (25)$$

The performance function chosen in (24) can be assigned the dimension of power, although this is not necessary for it to serve as a valid mathematical performance function. In this case, the diagonal elements of W are either resistance or conductance, as appropriate. Thus, those in the first summation in the second line of (24) are dimensionally resistance, those in the second summation, conductance.

Not all currents in the voltage sources or voltages across current sources will, in general, be chosen as output variables and have their desired values specified. To take care of such a case, the weighting parameter w_{kk} corresponding to each of these unspecified variables will be set equal to zero. For the variables specified as outputs, we shall require that $0 < w_{kk} \leqslant 1$. The relative values of w_{kk} indicate the degree of importance assigned to the various designated responses.

The first candidate network initially selected is not likely to be the best design, yielding output variables exactly equal to the desired values. The performance function (or error), therefore, will have a nonzero value. What is needed is a systematic method for varying the parameter values so that the performance function is reduced. If the smallest value of $\mathcal{E}$ is zero and we are able to reach that value by proper selection of the component values, the corresponding network realizes the desired excitation/response relations. An even more valuable circumstance would be if the systematic procedure would also show how to change the structure of the candidate network, as well as its component values.

The value of $\mathscr{E}$ varies when the response currents and voltages vary as a consequence of variations of the network parameters. The first order change in $\mathscr{E}$ is found to be

$$\Delta\mathscr{E} = [(\mathbf{I}_{pa} - \mathbf{I}_{pad})' \quad (\mathbf{V}_{pb} - \mathbf{V}_{pbd})'] \ \mathbf{W} \begin{bmatrix} \Delta\mathbf{I}_{pa} \\ \Delta\mathbf{V}_{pb} \end{bmatrix} \qquad (26)$$

Recall that (8) related variations in response variables to variations in parameter values. We see that the right side of (26) and the left side of (8) have the same form. In fact, the two can be made identical by an appropriate choice of the source values in the adjoint network; thus,

$$[\hat{\mathbf{V}}'_{pa} \ - \hat{\mathbf{I}}'_{pb}] = - [(\mathbf{I}_{pa} \ - \mathbf{I}_{pad})' \quad (\mathbf{V}_{pb} \ - \mathbf{V}_{pbd})']\mathbf{W}. \qquad (27)$$

Partitioning $\mathbf{W}$ as

$$\mathbf{W} = \begin{bmatrix} \mathbf{W}_a & 0 \\ 0 & \mathbf{W}_b \end{bmatrix}, \qquad (28)$$

permits the separation of (27) into

$$\hat{\mathbf{V}}_{pa} = - \mathbf{W}_a(\mathbf{I}_{pa} \ - \mathbf{I}_{pad}), \qquad (29a)$$

$$\hat{\mathbf{I}}_{pb} = \mathbf{W}_b(\mathbf{V}_{pb} \ - \mathbf{V}_{pbd}), \qquad (29b)$$

where we used $\mathbf{W}'_a = \mathbf{W}_a$ and $\mathbf{W}'_b = \mathbf{W}_b$, since $\mathbf{W}$ is symmetric.

What this means is that, at the voltage ports where no current response is to be measured in $\mathscr{N}$ (so that the corresponding diagonal element in $\mathbf{W}_a$ is zero), the value of the port voltage in $\hat{\mathscr{N}}$ is set equal to zero. Similarly, at the current ports where no voltage response is specified in $\mathscr{N}$, the value of port current in $\hat{\mathscr{N}}$ is set equal to zero. With the selection of adjoint network sources in accordance with (27), the right side of (26) is identical with the left side of (8); hence, $\Delta\mathscr{E}$ must equal the right side of (8). Thus,

$$\Delta\mathscr{E} = [-\hat{\mathbf{I}}'_{ia} \quad \hat{\mathbf{V}}'_{ib}] \begin{bmatrix} \Delta\mathbf{Z}_a & \Delta\mathbf{H}_{ab} \\ \Delta\mathbf{H}_{ba} & \Delta\mathbf{Y}_b \end{bmatrix} \begin{bmatrix} \mathbf{I}_{ia} \\ \mathbf{V}_{ib} \end{bmatrix} \qquad (30)$$

But the right side of (8) had previously been rewritten in (11) in terms of the actual parameter changes and this expression had been given, in simplified form in (13), in terms of the sensitivity and parameter change vectors. Using these results, (30) becomes

$$\Delta\mathcal{E} = \sum_k S^{\mathcal{E}}_{p_k}\Delta p_k = (\mathbf{S}^{\mathcal{E}})'\Delta\mathbf{p} \tag{31}$$

Since we are dealing with nondynamic networks, the last two summations on the right side of (11) are not included in (31). We see now that the coefficients of the parameter changes in (11) are *the sensitivites of the performance measure with respect to variations in the parameter values*; this has been indicated by the notation $S^{\mathcal{E}}_{p_k}$.

The preceding expression is very valuable. From the theory of n-dimensional vector spaces, we note that the change in a scalar function is the inner product of the gradient of that function with the change in the vector of coordinates on which the function depends. In this case $\Delta\mathbf{p}$ plays the role of the vector change in coordinates and $\mathcal{E}$ is the scalar function; hence, the sensitivity vector is the gradient of $\mathcal{E}$ with respect to these coordinates. Thus,

$$\mathbf{S}^{\mathcal{E}} = \mathbf{grad}\ \mathcal{E} \tag{32}$$

Using this expression, (31) becomes

$$\Delta\mathcal{E} = (\mathbf{grad}\ \mathcal{E})'\Delta\mathbf{p} \tag{33}$$

This is a more useful expression than (31) because it has a counterpart for dynamic networks. Hence, this is the expression we shall use in what follows.

It is known from vector theory that, as the parameter space coordinates change, $\mathcal{E}$ will decrease most rapidly in the direction of its negative gradient. This gives a clue as to the numerical procedure to follow in the course of a design. Let us designate with a superscript k the present value of a parameter or a variable. The next value after an iteration will be denoted by the superscript $(k+1)$. Hence, as we perturb the parameters, it is intuitively reasonable that we vary the vector $\mathbf{p}$ in the direction of the negative gradient of $\mathcal{E}$. So, our choice for the next value of $\mathbf{p}$ would be

$$\mathbf{p}^{(k+1)} = \mathbf{p}^{(k)} - \Delta\mathbf{p}^{(k)} \tag{34a}$$

$$\text{with } \Delta\mathbf{p}^{(k)} = \gamma^{(k)}(\mathbf{grad}\ \mathcal{E})^{(k)} \tag{34b}$$

where $\gamma^{(k)}$ is a positive constant whose value remains to be chosen.

Using this value of $\Delta p^{(k)}$ in (33), $\Delta\mathscr{E}^{(k)}$ becomes

$$\Delta\mathscr{E}^{(k)} = -\gamma^{(k)}[(\text{grad }\mathscr{E})^{(k)}]'[(\text{grad }\mathscr{E})^{(k)}] = -\gamma^{(k)}|S^\ell|^2 \qquad (35)$$

If this change in $\mathscr{E}$ is set equal to the negative of the present value of $\mathscr{E}$, then the next value of $\mathscr{E}$ should be zero — the minimum value of $\mathscr{E}$. The value of $\gamma^{(k)}$ for which $\Delta\mathscr{E}^{(k)} = -\mathscr{E}^{(k)}$ is

$$\gamma^{(k)} = \frac{\mathscr{E}^{(k)}}{[(\text{grad }\mathscr{E})^{(k)}]'[(\text{grad }\mathscr{E})^{(k)}]} = \frac{\mathscr{E}^{(k)}}{|S^\ell|^2} \qquad (36)$$

This desired result, $\mathscr{E}^{(k+1)} = 0$, will actually occur if $\mathscr{E}$ is a linear function of the paramter space coordinates; this, unfortunately, cannot reasonably be expected. Thus for finite changes in the parameters, although generally $\mathscr{E}$ will not be reduced to zero in one step, the preceding choice of $\gamma^{(k)}$ will most likely lead to a reduced value of $\mathscr{E}$; that is, $\mathscr{E}^{(k+1)} < \mathscr{E}^{(k)}$. The procedure should then be repeated until $\mathscr{E}$ becomes essentially equal to zero.

This method of bringing $\mathscr{E}$ to its minimum is a *gradient method* and, because we are using the Euclidean (vector) norm in the parameter space, it is also a *steepest descent method*. The step length selection procedure — selection of $\gamma^{(k)}$ — is due to Cauchy. There are other minimization methods (of these and other types) and there are other step size selection procedures. We will introduce some of them in the problems and projects.

The ingredients for the design procedure are now all at hand. At the outset, the desired responses $\mathbf{I}_{pad}$ and $\mathbf{V}_{pbd}$, if not known, are evaluated for some specified excitations from desired excitation-response relations, and the weighting matrices $\mathbf{W}_a$ and $\mathbf{W}_b$ are chosen. Then we select the initial network $\mathscr{N}$, including its parameter values, and solve for the appropriate currents and voltages. Using this network, together with expression (29) for the adjoint sources, we determine the adjoint network $\hat{\mathscr{N}}$ and solve for its currents and voltages. From these established current and voltage values, we evaluate $\mathscr{E}$, as in (24), and grad $\mathscr{E} = \mathbf{S}^\ell$, whose elements are the coefficients of the Δp in (11). The constant γ is then calculated, as in (36), and used to determine the next set of parameter values for the network according to (34). Now, the process is repeated until such time as $\mathscr{E}$ is effectively zero — less than some preselected small positive value.

This procedure is codified in Algorithm 1 in Table 1. The value of $\mathscr{E}_{fuzz}$ to be used in step 6 is set by the user and reflects a choice of that positive value below which $\mathscr{E}^{(k)}$ is viewed as being effectively zero. The value of k_{lim} used in step 7 is also set by the user and reflects a choice of that positive integer beyond which the number of stages k is viewed as excessive — convergence is too slow.

Table 1   Algorithm 1: CAND Algorithm for Linear Resistive Networks

STEP 1: Set $k = 1$ and select the initial network $\mathscr{N}^{(1)}$.

STEP 2: Solve for $\mathbf{I}_{ia}$ and $\mathbf{V}_{ib}$ of $\mathscr{N}^{(k)}$

STEP 3: Evalute $\mathscr{E}^{(k)}$ as in (24).

STEP 4: If $k = 1$, then go to step 6.

STEP 5: If $\mathscr{E}^{(k)} > \mathscr{E}^{(k-1)}$, then stop — $\mathscr{E}$ is diverging.

STEP 6: If $\mathscr{E}^{(k)} < \mathscr{E}_{fuzz}$, then stop — $\mathscr{E}$ has converged to a sufficiently small, effectively zero, value.

STEP 7: If $k > k_{lim}$, then stop — $\mathscr{E}$ is not converging fast enough.

STEP 8: Evaluate $\hat{\mathbf{V}}_{pa}$ and $\hat{\mathbf{I}}_{pb}$ of $\hat{\mathscr{N}}^{(k)}$ as in (29).

STEP 9: Solve for $\hat{\mathbf{I}}_{ia}$ and $\hat{\mathbf{V}}_{ib}$ of $\hat{\mathscr{N}}^{(k)}$.

STEP 10: Evaluate:
    (a) **grad** $\mathscr{E}^{(k)}$, the sensitivity vector;
    (b) $\gamma^{(k)}$, say as in (36); and
    (c) $\mathbf{p}^{(k+1)}$ as in (34).

STEP 11: Increment k by 1 and go to step 2.

10.4.1 Example

As an illustration of this algorithm we shall examine a very simple design problem. The specific task is: Design a voltage attenuator to have a 3Ω input resistance and an attenuation of $\frac{2}{3}$. As depicted in Fig. 5, for an input voltage of 1 volt the input current should be $\frac{1}{3}$ ampere and the output voltage should be $\frac{2}{3}$ volt.

We shall suppose the desired network has the structure depicted in Fig. 6(a). The current through the voltage source must be an element of $\mathbf{I}_a$ and the voltage across the current source must be an element of $\mathbf{V}_b$, since they are the desired response variables. Upon labeling the port branches up from 1 we arrive at the labels shown on the network graph in Fig. 6(b). Branches 3 and 4 may be in either group a or group b.

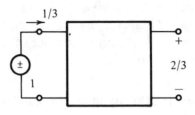

Fig. 5   Attenuator

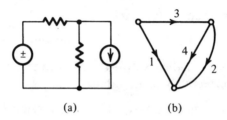

(a)   (b)

Fig. 6   Attenuator: structure and graph

Thus, either of the following two hybrid sets of branch relations for the internal branches may be used:

$$\begin{bmatrix} V_3 \\ \hline I_4 \end{bmatrix} = \begin{bmatrix} R_3 & 0 \\ \hline 0 & G_4 \end{bmatrix} \begin{bmatrix} I_3 \\ \hline V_4 \end{bmatrix} \quad \text{or} \quad \begin{bmatrix} I_3 \\ \hline I_4 \end{bmatrix} = \begin{bmatrix} G_3 & 0 \\ \hline 0 & G_4 \end{bmatrix} \begin{bmatrix} V_3 \\ \hline V_4 \end{bmatrix}$$

We have quite arbitrarily decided to use the former set.

Having labeled the branches we can now list the desired variables and their values, as previously noted and as displayed in Fig. 5; thus,

$$I_{d1} = -\tfrac{1}{3} \text{ and } V_{d2} = \tfrac{2}{3}.$$

Next, the diagonal weighting matrix $\mathbf{W} = \text{diag}\{\mathbf{W}_a, \mathbf{W}_b\} = \text{diag}\{w_{11}, w_{22}\}$ can be specified. We shall view the input resistance and the attenuation as being of equal importance. Thus we choose the diagonal elements of $\mathbf{W}$ as follows.

$$w_{11} = 1 \text{ and } w_{22} = 1.$$

To accomplish step 1 of the algorithm we must set $k = 1$ and define $\mathcal{N}^{(1)}$. This we do by picking parameter values for the components in the attenuator of Fig. 6(a). Past experience can be a guide in selecting those values; for this illustration, we have chosen the values shown in Fig. 7. Note: The value of the voltage source V_{s1} was previously set to 1 volt. (See Fig. 5.)

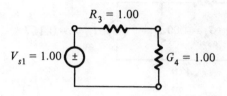

$R_3 = 1.00$

$V_{s1} = 1.00$ $\pm$

$G_4 = 1.00$

Fig. 7 Attenuator network $\mathcal{N}^{(1)}$

The results, together with some intermediate calculations, for steps 2 and 3 are presented in Fig. 8. Since $k = 1$ at step 4 during this first stage of the algorithm, a jump to step 6 takes place. And, since the computed value 2.78×10^{-2} of $\mathscr{E}^{(1)}$ is not less than 1.00×10^{-8}, the value we have chosen for $\mathscr{E}_{fuzz}$, we continue on to step 7. Since the value of k does not exceed 25, the value we have chosen for k_{lim}, we proceed to step 8. The results, with some calculations, for steps 8, 9, and 10 are also given in Fig. 8. The resulting attenuator network $\mathcal{N}^{(2)}$ is found at the top of Fig. 9. Stage 1 of the algorithm is completed by step 11 by incrementing k from 1 to 2, and jumping back to step 2 to start the next stage.

STAGE 1

STEP 2

$R_3 = 1.00$

$V_{s1} = 1.00$ $\pm$

$G_4 = 1.00$

$\mathcal{N}^{(1)}$

$I_1 = -0.500$

$V_2 = 0.500$

STEP 3

$$\mathscr{E}^{(1)} = \tfrac{1}{2}[1 \times (-0.500 + 0.333)^2 + 1 \times (0.500 - 0.667)^2] = 0.0278$$

STEP 8

$$\hat{V}_{s1} = -1 \times (-0.500 + 0.333) = 0.167$$

$$\hat{I}_{s2} = 1 \times (0.500 - 0.667) = -0.167$$

STEP 9

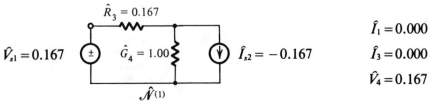

$\hat{R}_3 = 0.167$

$\hat{V}_{s1} = 0.167$ $\hat{G}_4 = 1.00$ $\hat{I}_{s2} = -0.167$

$\hat{\mathcal{N}}^{(1)}$

$\hat{I}_1 = 0.000$

$\hat{I}_3 = 0.000$

$\hat{V}_4 = 0.167$

STEP 10

$$(\text{grad}\,\mathcal{E})^{(1)} = \begin{bmatrix} -\hat{I}_3\,I_3 \\ \\ \hat{V}_4\,V_4 \end{bmatrix} = \begin{bmatrix} -0.000 \times 0.500 \\ \\ 0.167 \times 0.500 \end{bmatrix} = \begin{bmatrix} 0.000 \\ \\ 0.0833 \end{bmatrix}$$

$$\gamma^{(1)} = \frac{0.0278}{(0.000)^2 + (0.0833)^2} = 4.000$$

$$\begin{bmatrix} R_3 \\ \\ G_4 \end{bmatrix}^{(2)} = \begin{bmatrix} 1.00 \\ \\ 1.00 \end{bmatrix} - 4.000 \begin{bmatrix} 0.000 \\ \\ 0.0833 \end{bmatrix} = \begin{bmatrix} 1.00 \\ \\ 0.667 \end{bmatrix}$$

Fig. 8   Algorithm 1: stage 1, steps 2, 3, 8, 9, and 10

STAGE 2

STEP 2

$R_3 = 1.00$

$V_{s1} = 1.00$ $G_4 = 0.667$

$\mathcal{N}^{(2)}$

$I_1 = -0.400$

$V_2 = 0.600$

STEP 3

$$\mathscr{E}^{(2)} = \tfrac{1}{2}[1 \times (-0.400 + 0.333)^2 + 1 \times (0.600 - 0.667)^2] = 0.00444$$

STEP 8

$$\hat{V}_{s1} = -1 \times (-0.400 + 0.333) = 0.0667$$
$$\hat{I}_{s2} = 1 \times (0.600 - 0.667) = -0.0667$$

STEP 9

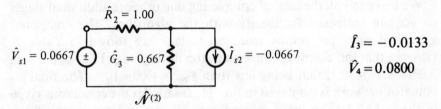

$\hat{I}_3 = -0.0133$

$\hat{V}_4 = 0.0800$

STEP 10

$$(\text{grad}\,\mathscr{E})^{(2)} = \begin{bmatrix} 0.0133 \times 0.400 \\ 0.0800 \times 0.600 \end{bmatrix} = \begin{bmatrix} 0.00533 \\ 0.0480 \end{bmatrix}$$

$$\gamma^{(2)} = \frac{0.00444}{(0.00533)^2 + (0.0480)^2} = 1.91$$

$$\begin{bmatrix} R_3 \\ G_4 \end{bmatrix}^{(3)} = \begin{bmatrix} 1.00 \\ 0.667 \end{bmatrix} - 1.91 \begin{bmatrix} 0.00533 \\ 0.0480 \end{bmatrix} = \begin{bmatrix} 0.990 \\ 0.575 \end{bmatrix}$$

Fig. 9   Algorithm 1: stage 2, steps 2, 3, 8, 9, and 10

The second stage of the algorithm proceeds very much as the first. Relevant results, and some calculations are presented in Fig. 9. The one difference is that step 5 is not skipped. However, as $\mathscr{E}^{(2)} = 4.44 \times 10^{-3}$ is less than $\mathscr{E}^{(1)} = 2.78 \times 10^{-2}$, a stop does not occur at step 5. The resulting attenuator network $\mathcal{N}^{(3)}$ is shown in Fig. 10.

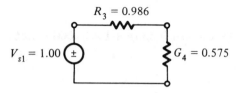

$R_3 = 0.986$

$V_{s1} = 1.00$ $\pm$ $G_4 = 0.575$

Fig. 10   Attenuator network. $\mathcal{N}^{(3)}$

We leave to you the task of completing one or more additional stages to acquire increased familiarity with the algorithm. The computer-generated principal results from each stage are shown in Table 2. Observe that the algorithm came to a stop during stage 17 at step 6 with $\mathcal{E}^{(17)} = 6.77 \times 10^{-9}$, that being less than $\mathcal{E}_{fuzz} = 1.00 = 10^{-8}$. The final attenuator network is displayed in Fig. 11. It satisfies the conditions given in the task; it has an input resistance of 3Ω and an attenuation of $\frac{2}{3}$.

Table 2   Algorithm 1: Stage-by-Stage Results

STAGE	R_3	G_4	$\mathcal{E}$
1	1.00	1.00	2.78×10^{-2}
2	1.00	0.667	4.44×10^{-3}
3	0.990	0.575	9.85×10^{-4}
4	0.986	0.537	2.36×10^{-4}
5	0.985	0.518	5.95×10^{-5}
6	0.985	0.509	1.64×10^{-5}
7	0.986	0.503	5.93×10^{-6}
8	0.991	0.499	3.25×10^{-6}
9	0.993	0.502	1.65×10^{-6}
10	0.995	0.500	8.56×10^{-7}
11	0.996	0.501	4.29×10^{-7}
12	0.998	0.500	2.15×10^{-7}
13	0.998	0.500	1.08×10^{-7}
14	0.999	0.500	5.41×10^{-8}
15	0.999	0.500	2.71×10^{-8}
16	0.999	0.500	1.35×10^{-8}
17	1.00	0.500	6.77×10^{-9}

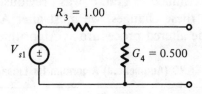

Fig. 11 Attenuator

10.4.2 More than One Set of Excitations

Equation (24) embodies an assumption of which, in all likelihood, you were unaware and which we did not discuss at the time. Reread the sentence following (24): "...and *some* selected set of excitation values." It may be that the desired excitation-response relations cannot be characterized by the set of responses to *one* selected set of excitations. For example, such would be the case if the desired relations had been both driving point resistances and both transfer resistances of a two-port. As you know from Chapter 5, it takes two linearly independent sets of excitations (and two responses for each set of excitations) to determine the four two-port parameters.

Thus, in the design of networks we must anticipate the need to use several linearly independent sets of excitations to probe a network under design. Corresponding to each we would have an expression of the form (24) which we would want to minimize. We can minimize each by minimizing their sum. We will next set up the procedure for doing so.

Index the several linearly independent sets of excitations by a subscript j with $j = 1, \ldots, n$. Corresponding to each j we have an $\mathcal{E}_j$ computed as in (24). Set

$$\mathcal{E} = \sum_{j=1}^{n} \mathcal{E}_j. \tag{37}$$

We can still use the gradient method (34), possibly with (36), to evaluate a next **p**; however, we must evaluate the gradient of $\mathcal{E}$ as

$$\mathbf{grad}\ \mathcal{E} = \sum_{j=1}^{n} (\mathbf{grad}\ \mathcal{E}_j), \tag{38}$$

where **grad** $\mathcal{E}_j$ is determined as **grad** $\mathcal{E}$ was previously.

To accommodate these changes, we must alter Algorithm 1 somewhat. We present the altered procedure as Algorithm 2 in Table 3.

Table 3   Algorithm 2: CAND (Augmented) Algorithm for Linear Resistive Networks

---

STEP 1:   Set $k=1$ and select the initial network $\mathcal{N}_j^{(1)}$.

STEP 2:   Set $j=1$.

STEP 3:   Solve for $\mathbf{I}_{ia}$ and $\mathbf{V}_{ib}$ of $\mathcal{N}_j^{(k)}$

STEP 4:   Evalute $\mathcal{E}_j^{(k)}$ as in (24).

STEP 5:   If $j=\mathcal{N}$, then go to step 7.

STEP 6:   Increment j by 1 and go to step 3.

STEP 7:   Evaluate $\mathcal{E}^{(k)}$ as in (37).

STEP 8:   If $k=1$, then go to step 10.

STEP 9:   If $\mathcal{E}^{(k)}>\mathcal{E}^{(k-1)}$, then stop$-\mathcal{E}$ is diverging.

STEP 10:   If $\mathcal{E}^{(k)}<\mathcal{E}_{fuzz}$, then stop$-\mathcal{E}$ has converged to a sufficiently small, effectively zero, value.

STEP 11:   If $k>k_{lim}$, then stop$-\mathcal{E}$ is not converging fast enough.

STEP 12:   Set $j=1$.

STEP 13:   Evaluate $\hat{\mathbf{V}}_{pa}$ and $\hat{\mathbf{I}}_{pb}$ of $\hat{\mathcal{N}}_j^{(k)}$ as in (29).

STEP 14:   Solve for $\hat{\mathbf{I}}_{ia}$ and $\hat{\mathbf{V}}_{ib}$ of $\hat{\mathcal{N}}_j^{(k)}$.

STEP 15:   Evaluate $(\mathbf{grad}\ \mathcal{E}_j)^{(k)}$.

STEP 16:   If $j=n$, then go to step 18.

STEP 17:   Increment j by 1 and go to step 12.

STEP 18:   Evaluate:
        (a) **grad** $\mathcal{E}^{(k)}$ as in (38);
        (b) $\gamma^{(k)}$, say as in (36); and
        (c) $\mathbf{p}^{(k+1)}$ as in (34).

STEP 19:   Increment k by 1 and go to step 2.

10.4.3   Example

As an illustration of Algorithm 2, consider the following problem: Design a two-port to have the following admittance matrix:

$$Y = \begin{bmatrix} 2 & 0 \\ -2 & 2 \end{bmatrix}$$

The two-port parameters—driving point and transfer conductances—can be characterized by the responses to two linearly independent sets of excitations, such as depicted in Fig. 12.

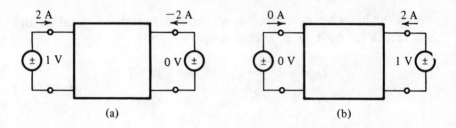

Fig. 12   **Two-port with excitations**

Since **Y** is not symmetric, the network will not be reciprocal. To obtain a non-reciprocal network, we will include a gyrator in our postulated network structure, shown in Fig. 13(a). Both source currents must be elements of I_a as they are desired response variables. There are no other constraints on element assignments to groups a and b. The

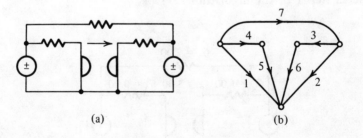

Fig. 13   **Initial design: structure and graph**

labels on the branches of the network graph show the mandated group a branches, the two (voltage) sources, numbered up from 1. We have chosen, quite arbitrarily, to assign all internal branches to group b. The corresponding set of branch relations is

$$
\begin{bmatrix} I_3 \\ I_4 \\ I_5 \\ I_6 \\ I_7 \end{bmatrix} = \begin{bmatrix} G_3 & 0 & 0 & 0 & 0 \\ 0 & G_4 & 0 & 0 & 0 \\ 0 & 0 & 0 & g & 0 \\ 0 & 0 & -g & 0 & 0 \\ 0 & 0 & 0 & 0 & G_7 \end{bmatrix} \begin{bmatrix} V_3 \\ V_4 \\ V_5 \\ V_6 \\ V_7 \end{bmatrix} .
$$

With the branches now labeled, we can list the desired variables and their values for each set of excitations; thus,

$$
\begin{aligned}
I_{d1} &= -2 & V_{s1} &= 1 \\
I_{d2} &= 2 & V_{s2} &= 0
\end{aligned}
\qquad \text{for } (j=1)
$$

and

$$
\begin{aligned}
I_{d1} &= 0 & V_{s1} &= 0 \\
I_{d2} &= -2 & V_{s2} &= 1
\end{aligned}
\qquad \text{for } (j=2).
$$

Note: We also indicated the value of j assigned to each set of excitations. The currents in branches 1 and 2 are the only desired response variables; for these, we have chosen equal weights of 1 for w_{11} and w_{22}.

The values initially assigned to the parameters to create $\mathcal{N}_j^{(1)}$ are shown in Fig. 14. Together with the previously given source values, this completes step 1 of the algorithm.

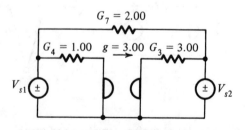

Fig. 14   Two-port network. $\mathcal{N}_j^{(1)}$

The results of the remaining steps, exclusive of step 7 through 11, are shown in Fig. 15, together with some calculations. With $\mathscr{E}_{fuzz} = 10^{-7}$ and $k_{lim} = 29$, no stop occurs during steps 7 through 10. The resulting two-port $\mathscr{N}_j^{(2)}$ is found at the top of Fig. 16. The incrementing of k by 1 and the return to step 2 completes stage 1. In Fig. 16 are also displayed the data pertinent to stage 2. The two-port $\mathscr{N}_j^{(3)}$, which derives from the end result of stage 2, is shown in Fig. 17. Stage 2 is then completed by incrementing k to 3 and returning to step 2. The principal results from stages 1 through 5 and every fifth stage thereafter through 30 are presented in Table 4. Observe that the algorithm came to a stop during

STAGE 1

STEPS 2-6

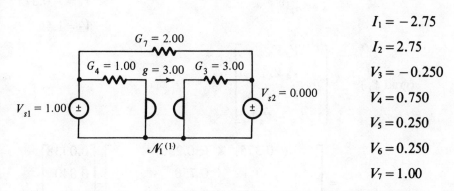

$$I_1 = -2.75$$
$$I_2 = 2.75$$
$$V_3 = -0.250$$
$$V_4 = 0.750$$
$$V_5 = 0.250$$
$$V_6 = 0.250$$
$$V_7 = 1.00$$

$$\mathscr{E}_1^{(1)} = \tfrac{1}{2}[1 \times (-2.75 + 2.00)^2 + 1 \times (2.75 - 2.00)^2 = 0.563$$

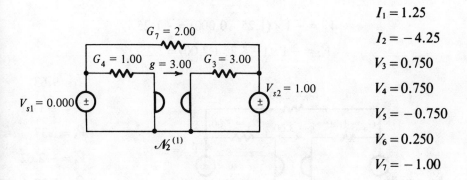

$$I_1 = 1.25$$
$$I_2 = -4.25$$
$$V_3 = 0.750$$
$$V_4 = 0.750$$
$$V_5 = -0.750$$
$$V_6 = 0.250$$
$$V_7 = -1.00$$

$$\mathscr{E}_2^{(1)} = \tfrac{1}{2}[1 \times (1.25 - 0.000)^2 + 1 \times (-4.25 + 2.00)^2] = 3.31$$

STEP 7
$$\mathscr{E}^{(1)} = 0.563 + 3.31 = 3.87$$

STEPS 12-17
$$\hat{V}_{s1} = -1 \times (-2.75 + 2.00) = 0.750$$
$$\hat{V}_{s2} = -1 \times (2.75 - 2.00) = -0.750$$

$\hat{I}_1 = -4.12$

$\hat{I}_2 = 4.12$

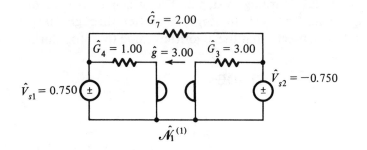

$\hat{V}_3 = -0.375$

$\hat{V}_4 = 1.12$

$\hat{V}_5 = -0.375$

$\hat{V}_6 = -0.375$

$\hat{V}_7 = 1.50$

$$(\textbf{grad } \mathscr{E}_1)^{(1)} = \begin{bmatrix} \hat{V}_3 V_3 \\ \hat{V}_4 V_4 \\ \hat{V}_7 V_7 \\ \hat{V}_5 V_6 - \hat{V}_6 V_5 \end{bmatrix}$$

$$= \begin{bmatrix} (-0.375) \times (-0.250) \\ 1.12 \times 0.750 \\ 1.50 \times 1.00 \\ (-0.375) \times 0.250 + 0.375 \times 0.250 \end{bmatrix} = \begin{bmatrix} 0.0938 \\ 0.840 \\ 1.50 \\ 0.000 \end{bmatrix}$$

$$\hat{V}_{s1} = -1 \times (1.25 - 0.000) = -1.25$$
$$\hat{V}_{s2} = -1 \times (-4.25 + 2.00) = 2.25$$

$\hat{I}_1 = 9.63$

$\hat{I}_2 = -11.1$

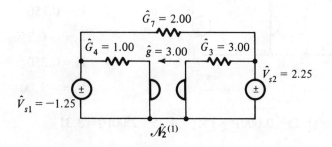

$\hat{V}_3 = 1.37$

$\hat{V}_4 = -2.62$

$\hat{V}_5 = 1.37$

$\hat{V}_6 = 0.875$

$\hat{V}_7 = -3.50$

$$(\text{grad}\,\mathscr{E}_2)^{(1)} = \begin{bmatrix} 1.37 \times 0.750 \\ (-2.62) \times 0.750 \\ (-3.50) \times (-1.00) \\ 1.37 \times 0.250 - 0.875 \times (-0.750) \end{bmatrix} = \begin{bmatrix} 1.03 \\ -1.97 \\ 3.50 \\ 0.999 \end{bmatrix}$$

STEP 18

$$(\text{grad}\,\mathscr{E})^{(1)} = \begin{bmatrix} 0.0938 \\ 0.840 \\ 1.50 \\ 0.000 \end{bmatrix} + \begin{bmatrix} 1.03 \\ -1.97 \\ 3.50 \\ 0.999 \end{bmatrix} = \begin{bmatrix} 1.12 \\ -1.12 \\ 5.00 \\ 1.00 \end{bmatrix}$$

$$\gamma^{(1)} = \frac{3.87}{(1.12)^2 + (-1.12)^2 + (5.00)^2 + (1.00)^2} = 0.136$$

$$\begin{bmatrix} G_3 \\ G_4 \\ G_7 \\ g \end{bmatrix}^{(1)} = \begin{bmatrix} 3.00 \\ 1.00 \\ 2.00 \\ 3.00 \end{bmatrix} - 0.136 \begin{bmatrix} 1.12 \\ -1.12 \\ 5.00 \\ 1.00 \end{bmatrix} = \begin{bmatrix} 2.85 \\ 1.15 \\ 1.32 \\ 2.86 \end{bmatrix}$$

Fig. 15 Algorithm 2: stage 1, steps 2, ..., 6, 12, ..., 18

STAGE 2

STEPS 2-6

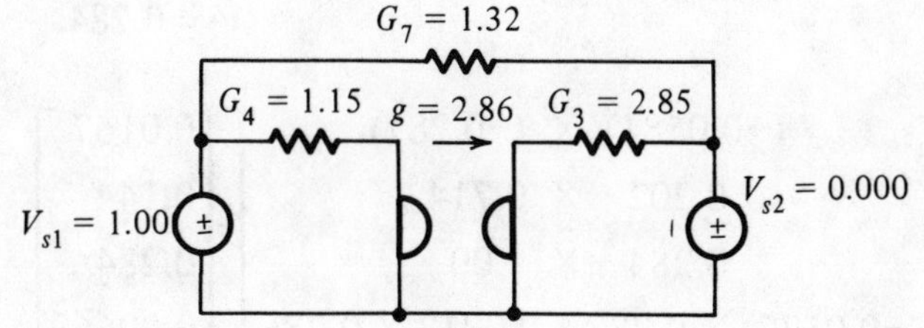

$$I_1 = -2.14$$
$$I_2 = 2.14$$
$$V_3 = -0.287$$
$$V_4 = 0.714$$
$$V_5 = 0.286$$
$$V_6 = 0.287$$
$$V_7 = 1.00$$

$$\mathscr{E}_1^{(2)} = \tfrac{1}{2}[1 \times (-2.14 + 2.00)^2 + 1 \times (2.14 - 2.00)^2 = 0.0196$$

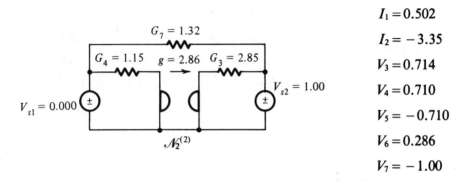

$$I_1 = 0.502$$
$$I_2 = -3.35$$
$$V_3 = 0.714$$
$$V_4 = 0.710$$
$$V_5 = -0.710$$
$$V_6 = 0.286$$
$$V_7 = -1.00$$

$$\mathscr{E}_2^{(2)} = \frac{1}{2}[1 \times (0.502 - 0.000)^2 + 1 \times (-3.35 + 2.00)^2] = 1.04$$

STEP 7

$$\mathscr{E}^{(2)} = 0.0196 + 1.04 = 1.06$$

STEPS 12-17

$$\hat{V}_{s1} = -1 \times (-2.14 + 2.00) = 0.144$$
$$\hat{V}_{s2} = -1 \times (2.14 - 2.00) = -0.139$$

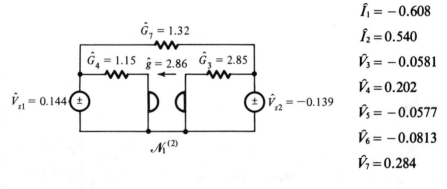

$$\hat{I}_1 = -0.608$$
$$\hat{I}_2 = 0.540$$
$$\hat{V}_3 = -0.0581$$
$$\hat{V}_4 = 0.202$$
$$\hat{V}_5 = -0.0577$$
$$\hat{V}_6 = -0.0813$$
$$\hat{V}_7 = 0.284$$

$$(\text{grad }\mathscr{E}_1)^{(2)} = \begin{bmatrix} (-0.0581) \times (-0.287) \\ 0.202 \times 0.714 \\ 0.284 \times 1.00 \\ (-0.0577) \times 0.287 + 0.0813 \times 0.286 \end{bmatrix} = \begin{bmatrix} 0.0167 \\ 0.144 \\ 0.284 \\ 0.00669 \end{bmatrix}$$

$$\hat{V}_{s1} = -1 \times (0.502 - 0.000) = -0.502$$
$$\hat{V}_{s2} = -1 \times (-3.35 + 2.00) = 1.35$$

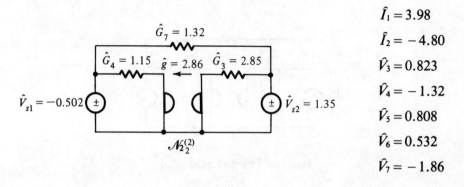

$$\hat{I}_1 = 3.98$$
$$\hat{I}_2 = -4.80$$
$$\hat{V}_3 = 0.823$$
$$\hat{V}_4 = -1.32$$
$$\hat{V}_5 = 0.808$$
$$\hat{V}_6 = 0.532$$
$$\hat{V}_7 = -1.86$$

$$(\text{grad } \mathcal{E}_2)^{(2)} = \begin{bmatrix} 0.823 \times 0.714 \\ (-1.32) \times 0.710 \\ (-1.86) \times (-1.00) \\ 0.818 \times 0.286 - 0.532 \times (-0.710) \end{bmatrix} = \begin{bmatrix} 0.588 \\ -0.937 \\ 1.86 \\ 0.612 \end{bmatrix}$$

STEP 18

$$(\text{grad } \mathcal{E})^{(2)} = \begin{bmatrix} 0.0167 \\ 0.144 \\ 0.284 \\ 0.00669 \end{bmatrix} + \begin{bmatrix} 0.588 \\ -0.937 \\ 1.86 \\ 0.612 \end{bmatrix} = \begin{bmatrix} 0.605 \\ -0.793 \\ 2.14 \\ 0.618 \end{bmatrix}$$

$$\gamma^{(2)} = \frac{1.06}{(0.605)^2 + (-0.793)^2 + (2.14)^2 + (0.618)^2} = 0.179$$

$$\begin{bmatrix} G_3 \\ G_4 \\ G_7 \\ g \end{bmatrix}^{(2)} = \begin{bmatrix} 2.85 \\ 1.15 \\ 1.32 \\ 2.86 \end{bmatrix} - 0.179 \begin{bmatrix} 0.605 \\ -0.793 \\ 2.14 \\ 0.618 \end{bmatrix} = \begin{bmatrix} 2.74 \\ 1.29 \\ 0.939 \\ 2.75 \end{bmatrix}$$

Fig. 16   Algorithm 2: stage 2, steps 2, ..., 6, 12, ..., 17, and 18

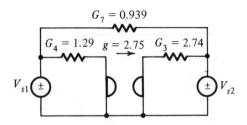

Fig. 17   Two-port network $\mathcal{N}_j^{(3)}$

Table 4   Algorithm 2: Results at various stages

STAGE	G_3	G_4	G_7	g	$\mathcal{E}$
1	3.00	1.00	2.00	3.00	$3.87 = 10^0$
2	2.85	1.15	1.32	2.86	$1.06 = 10^0$
3	2.74	1.29	0.939	2.75	$3.59 = 10^{-1}$
4	2.59	1.55	0.714	2.60	$1.90 = 10^{-1}$
5	2.51	1.68	0.967	2.57	1.26×10^{-1}
10	2.25	1.90	0.892	2.31	2.37×10^{-2}
15	2.06	1.99	1.01	2.13	$5.19 = 10^{-3}$
20	2.03	2.00	0.985	2.06	5.14×10^{-4}
25	2.01	2.00	1.00	2.02	$6.63 = 10^{-5}$
30	2.00	2.00	1.00	2.00	$3.84 = 10^{-6}$

stage 30 at step 11 because $k = 30$ exceeded $k_{lim} = 29$. This stop occurred because convergence to zero $- \mathcal{E} < \mathcal{E}_{fuzz} = 10^{-7}$ — was too slow, as indicated by the value of k_{lim} set before invoking the algorithm. However, an examination of the data discloses that $\mathcal{E}^{(30)} = 3.84 \times 10^{-6}$ is not very much greater than $\mathcal{E}_{fuzz}$ and that $\mathcal{N}^{(30)}$ with parameter values as indicated in Table 4 possesses the desired short circuit admittance matrix. The two-port we have just designed is shown in Fig. 18.

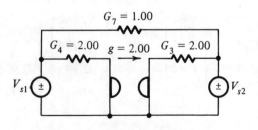

Fig. 18   Two-port

10.5 CAND—LINEAR DYNAMIC NETWORKS

We shall now turn our attention to computer-aided dynamic network design. Such networks are characterized by ordinary differential equations of a real variable in the time-domain or algebraic equations of a complex variable in the frequency-domain. Thus, a new dimension—time variable or frequency variable—has been added to those we must consider. Carrying out a design which provides good performance at a single instant of time or at a single frequency would not be adequate. What is needed is to optimize a performance function over some set of values of the variable, usually by minimizing an integral of a performance function. Such a performance measure is known as a *performance functional*. In the treatment of dynamic network design that follows, we will limit ourselves to the frequency domain, the complex frequency variable assuming values only on the imaginary axis. That is, the voltage and current variables will be treated as phasors. Time-domain design has been suggested as a project.

The beginning point is a performance functional. As for resistive networks, we would seek an expression for the gradient of that functional. Then, we would need a way of determining the change in parameters required from their present value in order to move toward a reduction of the performance functional. The details differ but little from those for the resistive network case, so we will rapidly outline the procedure.

Let us begin with the following performance functional.

$$\mathscr{E} = \int_\Omega d\omega \left\{ \frac{1}{2}[(\mathbf{I}_{pa} - \mathbf{I}_{pad})^* \quad (\mathbf{V}_{pb} - \mathbf{V}_{pbd})^*] \, \mathbf{W} \begin{bmatrix} \mathbf{I}_{pa} - \mathbf{I}_{pad} \\ \mathbf{V}_{pb} - \mathbf{V}_{pbd} \end{bmatrix} \right\} \tag{39}$$

Although the variables are complex, this expression is a real function of frequency. The diagonal elements of the weighting matrix $\mathbf{W}$ can here be functions of ω. The set of frequencies Ω over which the integral is taken can be in a single interval or can belong to a union of intervals. For example, in the design of a low-pass filter of bandwidth ω_0 we might have $\Omega = [\omega_0/10, 10\omega_0]$—one interval.

The adjoint network sources will be chosen as follows,

$$\hat{\mathbf{V}}_{pa} = -\mathbf{W}_a(\mathbf{I}_{pa} - \mathbf{I}_{pad})^* \tag{40a}$$

$$\hat{\mathbf{I}}_{pb} = \mathbf{W}_{pb}(\mathbf{V}_{pb} - \mathbf{V}_{pbd})^*. \tag{40b}$$

For resistive networks, the expression for the change in $\mathcal{E}$ was given in (31).In the present case,this same expression is valid only at a single frequency. The appropriate quantity would be its integral; thus,

$$\Delta\mathcal{E} = \int_\Omega d\omega \, \text{Re}\{(S^\iota)'\Delta\mathbf{p}\} \tag{41}$$

where S^ι is obtained from the right side of (11) with the provision that the variables are phasors.

Observe that the integration with respect to frequency and the real part operation in (41) can be interchanged. Thus,

$$\Delta\mathcal{E} = \left[\text{Re} \int_\Omega d\omega(S^\iota)' \right]\Delta\mathbf{p}. \tag{42}$$

But, repeating (33),

$$\Delta\mathcal{E} = (\text{grad } \mathcal{E})'\Delta\mathbf{p}. \tag{43}$$

Hence,

$$\text{grad } \mathcal{E} = \text{Re} \int_\Omega d\omega S^\iota. \tag{44}$$

This expression for **grad** $\mathcal{E}$, with S^ι determined from (11), is the relation we sought.

An interesting fact is that, for other performance functionals, **grad** $\mathcal{E}$ and S^ι are still evaluated by (44) and (11). Only the expressions defining the adjoint network sources must be changed in such cases. As a specific case, suppose it is the magnitude (or its square) of the desired excitation/response relations which is given, as is common in the case of frequency-domain design. Then, the performance functional in (39) is not appropriate. Rather than this, suppose we take the following as our performance functional:

$$\mathcal{E}= \int_\Omega d\omega \left\{ \tfrac{1}{4} \left[\sum_{j=1}^{n_a} w_{jj}(\bar{I}_j I_j - \bar{I}_{dj} I_{dj})^2 + \sum_{j=n_a+1}^{n_a+n_b} w_{jj}(\bar{V}_j V_j - \bar{V}_{dj} V_{dj})^2 \right] \right\}, \tag{45}$$

Note: The sources are assumed to be numbered up from 1, first those in the a group and then those in the b group; the number of sources in the a and b groups are denoted by n_a and n_b, respectively. The integrand of this performance functional is a weighted sum of the square of the difference of the magnitude squared of each response value and the magnitude squared of the corresponding desired response value. Now, it can be shown (see Prob. 19) that (44) and (11) remain valid if the elements of the adjoint network source variables $\hat{\mathbf{V}}_{pa}$ and $\hat{\mathbf{I}}_{pb}$ are assigned values as follows:

$$\hat{V}_{paj} = -w_{jj}(\bar{I}_j I_j - \bar{I}_{dj} I_{dj})\bar{I}_j \ _{for} \ j = 1, \ \ldots, \ n_a \qquad (46a)$$

$$\hat{I}_{pbj} = w_{jj}(\bar{V}_j V_j - \bar{V}_{dj} V_{dj})\bar{V}_j \ _{for} \ j = n_a + 1, \ \ldots, \ n_a + n_b, \qquad (46b)$$

instead of the values in (40). An examination of (45) shows that $\mathscr{E}$ in this case is a quartic in the current and voltage phasor variables; hence, it will not equal power, dimensionally, unless the diagonal elements are given appropriate, but artificial dimensions.

10.5.1   Approximate Integration Methods

We must now consider some approximate methods by which to evaluate the integrals of (39) or (45) and of (44). We will do so by considering the general integration problem: Evaluate

$$\int_{\Omega} \mathbf{f}(\omega)d\omega. \qquad (47)$$

Suppose Ω is a union of disjoint intervals; that is, $\Omega = \cup_{i=1}^{m}[\omega_{il}, \ \omega_{ih}]$. Then, since

$$\int_{\Omega} \mathbf{f}(\omega)d\omega = \sum_{i=1}^{m} \int_{\omega_{il}}^{\omega_{ih}} \mathbf{f}(\omega)d\omega, \qquad (48)$$

it is sufficient to consider just the simpler problem of evaluating the integral over a single frequency interval. Thus,

$$\int_{\omega_{il}}^{\omega_{ih}} \mathbf{f}(\omega)d\omega. \qquad (49)$$

Now, divide the interval into n_j contiguous subintervals Δ_{ik} and let

$$\omega_{i0} = \omega_{il} \qquad (50a)$$

and

$$\omega_{ij} = \omega_{ij-1} + \Delta_{ij} \text{ for } j = 1, \ldots, n_i. \qquad (50b)$$

Note: $\omega_{ih} = \omega_{in_i}$. The integral (49) can be approximated by either of the first order Euler formulas

$$\int_{\omega_{il}}^{\omega_{ih}} \mathbf{f}(\omega)d\omega \approx \sum_{j=1}^{n_i} \mathbf{f}(\omega_{ij-1})\Delta_{ij} \qquad (51)$$

or

$$\int_{\omega_{il}}^{\omega_{ih}} \mathbf{f}(\omega)d\omega \approx \sum_{j=1}^{n_i} \mathbf{f}(\omega_{ij})\Delta_{ij}. \qquad (52)$$

Or it can be approximated by their average, the second order trapezoidal formula:

$$\int_{\omega_{il}}^{\omega_{ih}} \mathbf{f}(\omega)d\omega \approx \sum_{j=1}^{n_i} \tfrac{1}{2}[\mathbf{f}(\omega_{ij-1}) + f(\omega_{ij})]\Delta_{ij}$$

$$= \mathbf{f}(\omega_{i0})\frac{\Delta_{i1}}{2} + \sum_{j=1}^{n_i-1} \mathbf{f}(\omega_{0j})\frac{\Delta_{ij} + \Delta_{ij+1}}{2}$$

$$+ \mathbf{f}(\omega_{in_i})\frac{\Delta_{in_i}}{2}. \qquad (53)$$

Observe, by virtue of the definition of a Riemann integral, that the two sides of (51) — and of (52) — would be equal were we to take the limit of the right side as $\max_{1 \leqslant j \leqslant n_i} \Delta_{ij}$ went to zero. We will consider higher order approximations to the integral (49) in Projects.

It is common practice on a small interval to make all the subintervals Δ_{ij} equal; that is,

$$\Delta_{ij} = \Delta_i = \frac{\omega_{ih} - \omega_{il}}{n_i} \text{ for } j = 1, \ldots, n_i. \qquad (54)$$

However, in network design it is often true that the desired excitation-response relations are specified on an interval for which ω_{ih} is orders of magnitude greater than ω_{il}. In that case it is usually preferable to use subintervals which form a geometric progression. For example, suppose we set $\Delta_{il} = \Delta_i$ and $\Delta_{ij} = 2\Delta_{ij-1}$ for $j = 2, \ldots, n_i$ or, equivalently,

$$\Delta_{ij} = 2^{j-1}\Delta_i \text{ for } j = 1, \ldots, n_i. \qquad (55)$$

Then, since

$$\omega_{ih} = \omega_{il} + \sum_{j=1}^{n_i} \Delta_{ij} = \omega_{il} + \Delta_i \sum_{j=1}^{n_i} 2^{j-1} = \omega_{il} + \Delta_i \frac{2^{n_i} - 1}{2 - 1} \quad (56)$$

in a succession of easy-to-verify equalities, we find that Δ_i should be selected as follows:

$$\Delta_i = \frac{\omega_{ih} - \omega_{il}}{2^{n_i} - 1}. \quad (57)$$

10.5.2 Step-Length Selection Procedure

Unlike resistive network design problems, dynamic network design problems are often stated as approximation problems. For example, in some problems the task is to design a network with certain attributes having responses which most nearly approximate the desired responses, which are often ideal and physically unrealizable. The approximation is made in the sense of minimizing $\mathscr{E}$. Thus, it must be anticipated that the least attainable value of $\mathscr{E}$ might not be zero. It would be inappropriate in this instance to select $\gamma^{(k)}$ as in (36); rather, (36) should be replaced by

$$\gamma^{(k)} = \frac{\mathscr{E}^{(k)} - \mathscr{E}_{min}}{[(\mathbf{grad}\,\mathscr{E})^{(k)}]'[(\mathbf{grad}\,\mathscr{E})^{(k)}]}. \quad (58)$$

Unfortunately, $\mathscr{E}_{min}$ is not likely to be known. Thus, we must develop an alternate step-length selection procedure.

Suppose

$$\|[\mathbf{grad}\,\mathscr{E}(\mathbf{p}_1)] - [\mathbf{grad}\,\mathscr{E}(\mathbf{p}_2)]\| \leqslant \mu \|\mathbf{p}_1 - \mathbf{p}_2\| \quad (59)$$

in some domain D of the parameter space within which $\mathscr{E}$ attains its least value. Suppose also that $\mathbf{p}^{(k)}$ is contained in D. Then, it can be shown (see Prob. 20) that for $\gamma^{(k)}$ sufficiently small,

$$\mathscr{E}^{(k+1)} \leqslant \mathscr{E}^{(k)} - \gamma^{(k)}(1 - \tfrac{1}{2}\mu\gamma^{(k)})[(\mathbf{grad}\,\mathscr{E})^{(k)}]'[(\mathbf{grad}\,\mathscr{E})^{(k)}]. \quad (60)$$

The right hand side, which is a bound on $\mathscr{E}^{(k+1)}$, is minimized by setting

$$\gamma^{(k)} = 1/\mu. \quad (61)$$

In this case we know that

$$\mathcal{E}^{(k+1)} \leqslant \mathcal{E}^{(k)} - \tfrac{1}{2}\gamma^{(k)}[(\text{grad } \mathcal{E})^{(k)}]'[(\text{grad } \mathcal{E})^{(k)}] \qquad (62)$$

or, equivalently, that $\mathcal{E}^{(k)}$ is a non-increasing sequence. Whether $\gamma^{(k)}$ is sufficiently small is determined by whether $\mathbf{p}^{(k+1)} = \mathbf{p}^{(k)} - \gamma^{(k)}(\text{grad } \mathcal{E})^{(k)}$ is contained in D. In any algorithm invoking this procedure for evaluating $\gamma^{(k)}$ we would assume $\mathbf{p}^{(k+1)}$ was in D provided $\mathcal{E}^{(k+1)} \leqslant \mathcal{E}^{(k)}$.

The task now befalling us is that of estimating μ. We observe that at each step a lower bound on μ can be determined from (59) as

$$\mu \geqslant \frac{\|(\text{grad } \mathcal{E})^{(k)} - (\text{grad } \mathcal{E})^{(k-1)}\|}{\|\mathbf{p}^{(k)} - \mathbf{p}^{(k-1)}\|} = \frac{\|(\text{grad } \mathcal{E})^{(k)} - (\text{grad } \mathcal{E})^{(k-1)}\|}{\gamma^{(k-1)}\|(\text{grad } \mathcal{E})^{(k-1)}\|}. \qquad (63)$$

Then, step-after-step we can refine the lower bound on μ as

$$\mu \geqslant \max_{2 \leqslant j \leqslant k} \frac{\|(\text{grad } \mathcal{E})^{(j)} - (\text{grad } \mathcal{E})^{(j-1)}\|}{\gamma^{(j-1)}\|(\text{grad } \mathcal{E})^{(j-1)}\|}. \qquad (64)$$

As an estimate of μ at step k we will use this lower bound increased by a multiplicative factor $\nu^{(k)} \geqslant 1$. It then follows by (61) for $\gamma^{(k)}$ that

$$\gamma^{(k)} = \frac{1}{\nu^{(k)} \times \max_{2 \leqslant j \leqslant k} \dfrac{\|(\text{grad } \mathcal{E})^{(j)} - (\text{grad } \mathcal{E})^{(j-1)}\|}{\gamma^{(j-1)}\|(\text{grad } \mathcal{E})^{(j-1)}\|}}, \quad k = 2, 3, \ldots . \qquad (65)$$

Let us observe that as k increases, the lower bound on μ given in (64) becomes more refined and rather likely provides an increasingly true estimate of μ itself. Thus, we can anticipate that, whereas ν_k might have to be moderately large for small k, it could reasonably be allowed to assume a decreasing (to not less than unity) value for increasing k. For example, we might use

$$\nu_k = \alpha + \beta \delta^k \qquad (66)$$

with $\alpha \geqslant 1$, $\beta \geqslant 0$, and $0 \leqslant \delta < 1$. We now have a procedure by which to select $\gamma^{(k)}$ for all but $k = 1$. We will use $\gamma^{(1)}$ of (36) diminished by the multiplicative factor x, $0 < x < 1$; that is, we will set

$$\gamma^{(1)} = x \frac{\mathcal{E}^{(1)}}{[(\text{grad } \mathcal{E})^{(1)}]'[(\text{grad } \mathcal{E})^{(1)}]}. \qquad (67)$$

10.5.3 Algorithm

We have now completed the preparations for Algorithm 3 (see Table 5), an algorithm for CAND of linear dynamic networks. This algorithm is the dynamic networks counterpart of Algorithm 1. That is, it applies only to those cases for which one set of excitations is sufficient to probe the network. Furthermore, the algorithm is limited to the case wherein Ω is just one interval — m of (48) is unity. For this reason the subscript i,

Table 5 Algorithm 3: CAND for Linear Dynamic Networks

STEP 1: Set $k = 1$, create the lists of frequencies $\{\omega_0, \ldots, \omega_n\}$ as in (50) with frequency intervals $\{\Delta_1, \ldots, \Delta_n\}$ as in (54) [alternatively, (55) with (57)], and select the initial network $\mathcal{N}^{(1)}$.

STEP 2: Set $j = 0$.

STEP 3: Solve for $\mathbf{I}_{ia}$ and $\mathbf{V}_{ib}$ of $\mathcal{N}^{(k)}$ at ω_j.

STEP 4: Evaluate the integral for $\mathscr{E}^{(k)}$ as in (39) [alternatively, (46)] by (49) through the term in ω_j.

STEP 5: Evaluate $\hat{\mathbf{V}}_{pa}$ and $\hat{\mathbf{I}}_{pb}$ of $\hat{\mathcal{N}}^{(k)}$ as in (40) [alternatively, (47)].

STEP 6: Solve for $\hat{\mathbf{I}}_{ia}$ and $\hat{\mathbf{V}}_{ib}$ of $\hat{\mathcal{N}}^{(k)}$ at ω_j.

STEP 7: Evaluate the integral for $\Delta\mathscr{E}^{(k)}$ as in (44) by (53) through the term in ω_j.

STEP 8: If $j = n$, then go to step 10.

STEP 9: Increment j by 1 and go to step 3.

STEP 10: Evaluate
(a) $\gamma^{(k)}$ as in (67) for $k = 1$ and as in (65) for $k = 2, 3, \ldots$ and
(b) $\mathbf{p}^{(k)}$ as in (34).

STEP 11: If $k = 1$, then go to step 13.

STEP 12: If $\mathscr{E}^{(k)} > \epsilon^{(k-1)}$, then stop — $\mathscr{E}$ is diverging.

STEP 13: Evaluate $\Delta\mathscr{E}^{(k)}$ as in (35).

STEP 14: If $|\Delta\mathscr{E}^{(k)}| < \varrho\epsilon^{(k)}$ then stop — $\mathscr{E}$ has converged to a value sufficiently close to $\mathscr{E}_{min}$.

STEP 15: If $k > k_{lim}$, then stop — $\mathscr{E}$ is not converging fast enough.

STEP 16: Increment k by 1 and go to step 2.

which was previously used to index the intervals in Ω, has been dropped in referring to frequencies and frequency intervals in the algorithm. We have chosen to invoke the trapezoidal formula in steps 4 and 7 simply because, for very little added computational effort, the order of accuracy is twice that for either Euler formula. [You are certainly free to use either Euler (or any other) formula instead.] We have presented this algorithm, which is somewhat restricted in its applicability, for ease of understanding. Once this algorithm is understood, the details of the more general case can be dealt with more easily. Problem 21 requires augmenting the algorithm so as to accommodate the case where Ω is the union of several intervals and where several linearly independent sets of excitations must be used to probe the network. Also note that we have chosen as our convergence test: Is $|\Delta\mathcal{E}|$ sufficiently small, less than a preselected fraction ϱ of $\mathcal{E}$. This means that the test for convergence cannot be made until after analysis of the adjoint network and determination of $(\mathbf{grad}\,\mathcal{E})^{(k)}$ and $\gamma^{(k)}$; thus, it appears near the end of the algorithm as step 14. In addition, the test for divergence is deferred until after analysis of the adjoint network; it appears as step 12. The reason is that if at each ω_j the adjoint network is analyzed immediately after analysis of the network itself, then the values of $\hat{\mathbf{I}}_{ia}$ and $\hat{\mathbf{V}}_{ib}$ for the several ω_j need not be stored for later use in evaluating the adjoint network source terms $\hat{\mathbf{V}}_{pa}$ and $\hat{\mathbf{I}}_{pb}$ at each ω_j. Note also that in some cases network equations for $\mathcal{N}$ — hence, also $\hat{\mathcal{N}}$ — can be expressed in terms of an admittance matrix — node or cut set equations — or of an impedance matrix — loop equations. In each such case the inverse of the matrix needed in the solution of the equations for $\hat{\mathcal{N}}$ can be derived from that needed for $\mathcal{N}$ by transposition. This is yet another reason why, at each frequency, the solution of the equations for $\hat{\mathcal{N}}$ would best take place following the solution of those for $\mathcal{N}$.

10.5.4 Example

The illustration of Algorithm 3 we have chosen has as its task: Design a three pole filter with a voltage transfer function magnitude which approximates that in Fig. 19.

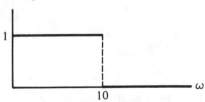

Fig. 19 Ideal voltage transfer function magnitude

For the initial design we chose the three pole, low-pass network structure shown in Fig. 20 together with its graph. The indicated branch labels correspond to the necessity of making the voltage source an "*a*" group branch and the (zero valued) current source—its voltage is a desired response—a "*b*" group branch. In fact, for unit (phasor) excitation, the desired response satisfies

$$\bar{V}_{d2}V_{d2} = 1, \quad 0 \leqslant \omega \leqslant 10$$
$$= 0, \quad 10 < \omega.$$

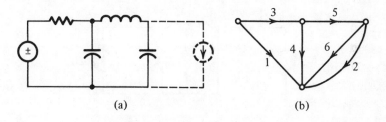

(a)   (b)

Fig. 20   Filter: structure and graph

Among the many acceptable component relations for this network, we chose

$$\begin{bmatrix} I_3 \\ I_4 \\ I_5 \\ I_6 \end{bmatrix} = \begin{bmatrix} G_3 & 0 & 0 & 0 \\ 0 & j\omega C_4 & 0 & 0 \\ 0 & 0 & \Gamma_5/j\omega & 0 \\ 0 & 0 & 0 & j\omega C_6 \end{bmatrix} \begin{bmatrix} V_3 \\ V_4 \\ V_5 \\ V_6 \end{bmatrix}$$

Given that the desired response is a magnitude—the phase is of no concern—we will use the performance functional of (46). Furthermore, we will let $\Omega = [2,20]$ and set

$$w_{11} = 0 \quad \text{and} \quad w_{22} = 1, \; 2 \leqslant \omega \leqslant 20.$$

As the last preparatory acts before invoking the algorithm, we will set

$$k_{lim} = 200,$$
$$\varkappa = 0.001,$$
$$\varrho = 0.001,$$

and

$$\nu^{(k)} = 1 + 2 \times 0.5^k.$$

At step 1 we will set

$$\omega_j = 2 + 2j, \; j = 0, \; \ldots, \; 9,$$

and, as a consequence,

$$\Delta_j = 2, \; j = 1, \; \ldots, \; 9.$$

Also at that step we must set the parameter values which define $\mathcal{N}^{(1)}$. This we will do such that $\mathcal{N}^{(1)}$ is as shown in Fig. 21.

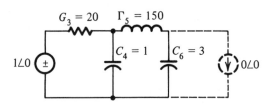

Fig. 21 Filter network $\mathcal{N}^{(1)}$

The results, with some calculations, for steps 3 through 7 during the first two phases ($j = 0, 1$) of the first stage ($k = 1$) are displayed in Fig. 22.

STAGE 1 PHASE 0

STEP 3

$I_1 = 7.84 \underline{/-113°}$

$V_3 = 0.392 \underline{/66.9°}$

$V_4 = 0.920 \underline{/-23.1°}$

$V_5 = 0.0800 \underline{/157°}$

$V_6 = 1.00 \underline{/-23.1°}$

STEP 4

$$\mathcal{E}_0^{(1)} = 0.000 + \tfrac{1}{4}\{1 \times [(1.00\underline{/23.1°})(1.00\underline{/-23.1°}) - 1.00]^2\}\frac{2.00}{2}$$

$$= 1.02 \times 10^{-9}$$

STEP 5

$$\hat{I}_{s2} = 1 \times [(1.00\underline{/23.1°})(1.00\underline{/-23.1°}) - 1.00](1.00\underline{/23.1°})$$

$$= 6.40 \times 10^{-5} \underline{/-157°}$$

STEP 6

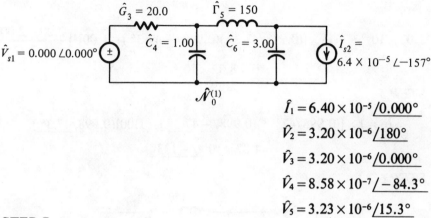

$$\hat{I}_1 = 6.40 \times 10^{-5} \underline{/0.000°}$$

$$\hat{V}_2 = 3.20 \times 10^{-6} \underline{/180°}$$

$$\hat{V}_3 = 3.20 \times 10^{-6} \underline{/0.000°}$$

$$\hat{V}_4 = 8.58 \times 10^{-7} \underline{/-84.3°}$$

$$\hat{V}_5 = 3.23 \times 10^{-6} \underline{/15.3°}$$

STEP 7

$$\mathbf{grad}\,\mathscr{E}_0^{(1)} = \begin{bmatrix} 0.000 \\ 0.000 \\ 0.000 \\ 0.000 \end{bmatrix}$$

$$+ \left\{ \mathrm{Re} \begin{bmatrix} (3.20 \times 10^{-6} \underline{/180°})(0.392 \underline{/66.9°}) \\ (2.00 \underline{/90.0°})(3.20 \times 10^{-6} \underline{/0.000°})(0.920 \underline{/-23.1°}) \\ (1/2.00 \underline{/90.0°})(8.58 \times 10^{-7} \underline{/-84.3°})(0.0800 \underline{/157°}) \\ (2.00 \underline{/90.0°})(3.23 \times 10^{-6} \underline{/15.3°})(1.00 \underline{/-23.1°}) \end{bmatrix} \right\} \frac{2.00}{2}$$

$$= \begin{bmatrix} -4.92 \times 10^{-7} \\ 2.31 \times 10^{-6} \\ 3.27 \times 10^{-8} \\ 8.72 \times 10^{-7} \end{bmatrix}$$

STAGE 1   PHASE 1

STEP 3

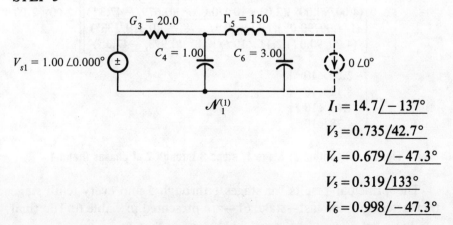

$$I_1 = 14.7 \underline{/-137°}$$

$$V_3 = 0.735 \underline{/42.7°}$$

$$V_4 = 0.679 \underline{/-47.3°}$$

$$V_5 = 0.319 \underline{/133°}$$

$$V_6 = 0.998 \underline{/-47.3°}$$

STEP 4

$$\mathscr{E}_1^{(1)} =$$

$$1.02 \times 10^{-9} + \tfrac{1}{4}\{1 \times [(0.998\underline{/47.3°})(0.998\underline{/-47.3°}) - 1.00]^2\}\frac{2.00 + 2.00}{2}$$

$$= 8.32 \times 10^{-6}$$

STEP 5

$$\hat{I}_{s2} = 1 \times [(0.998\underline{/47.3°})(0.998\underline{/-47.3°}) - 1.00](0.998\underline{/47.3°})$$

$$= 4.07 \times 10^{-3}\underline{/-133°}$$

STEP 6

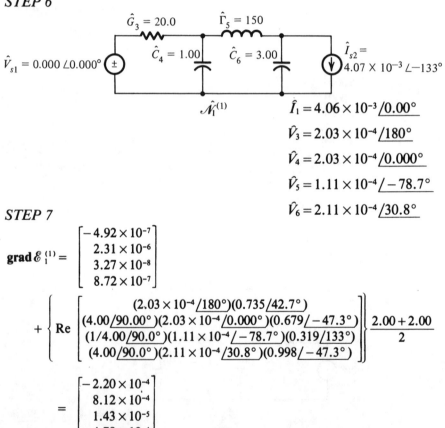

$$\hat{I}_1 = 4.06 \times 10^{-3}\underline{/0.00°}$$
$$\hat{V}_3 = 2.03 \times 10^{-4}\underline{/180°}$$
$$\hat{V}_4 = 2.03 \times 10^{-4}\underline{/0.000°}$$
$$\hat{V}_5 = 1.11 \times 10^{-4}\underline{/-78.7°}$$
$$\hat{V}_6 = 2.11 \times 10^{-4}\underline{/30.8°}$$

STEP 7

$$\mathbf{grad}\,\mathscr{E}_1^{(1)} = \begin{bmatrix} -4.92 \times 10^{-7} \\ 2.31 \times 10^{-6} \\ 3.27 \times 10^{-8} \\ 8.72 \times 10^{-7} \end{bmatrix}$$

$$+ \left\{ \mathrm{Re} \begin{bmatrix} (2.03 \times 10^{-4}\underline{/180°})(0.735\underline{/42.7°}) \\ (4.00\underline{/90.00°})(2.03 \times 10^{-4}\underline{/0.000°})(0.679\underline{/-47.3°}) \\ (1/4.00\underline{/90.0°})(1.11 \times 10^{-4}\underline{/-78.7°})(0.319\underline{/133°}) \\ (4.00\underline{/90.0°})(2.11 \times 10^{-4}\underline{/30.8°})(0.998\underline{/-47.3°}) \end{bmatrix} \right\}\frac{2.00 + 2.00}{2}$$

$$= \begin{bmatrix} -2.20 \times 10^{-4} \\ 8.12 \times 10^{-4} \\ 1.43 \times 10^{-5} \\ 4.78 \times 10^{-4} \end{bmatrix}$$

Fig. 22   Algorithm 3: Stage 1, steps 3 through 7 of phases 0 and 1

The principal results for stages 1 through 5 and every tenth stage thereafter until the last — stage 61 — are presented in Table 6. The final design for the network is as shown in Fig. 23. To give you a sense of the quality of the approximation to the ideal voltage transfer function magnitude of Fig. 19, we have displayed the realized function magnitude in Fig. 24.

Table 6   Algorithm 3: Results at various stages

STAGE	G_3	G_4	Γ_5	C_6	$\mathscr{E}$
1	20.0	1.00	150	3.00	1.88×10^{-1}
2	20.0	1.00	150	3.00	1.88×10^{-1}
3	20.1	1.19	150	2.63	1.22×10^{-1}
4	20.1	1.23	150	2.67	1.19×10^{-1}
5	20.1	1.29	150	2.69	1.16×10^{-1}
10	20.2	1.59	150	2.77	9.79×10^{-2}
20	20.4	2.01	150	2.90	7.89×10^{-2}
30	20.6	2.10	150	2.93	7.49×10^{-2}
40	20.8	2.12	150	2.94	7.28×10^{-2}
50	20.9	2.12	150	2.95	7.14×10^{-2}
60	21.0	2.12	150	2.96	7.05×10^{-2}
61	21.0	2.11	150	2.96	7.05×10^{-2}

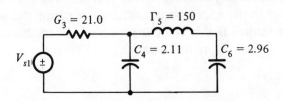

Fig. 23   Filter network

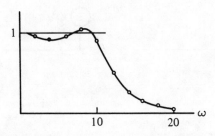

Fig. 24   Realized voltage transfer function magnitude

10.5.5 Design for a Variable Structure

In the procedure we have been discussing, the structure and component types of an initial design are chosen at the start. From then on, the
algorithm gives improved component values but does not improve the
structure. However, it is possible to formulate some small modifications which will permit "growing" additional components onto the initial structure.

To carry out the development, consider the network in Fig. 25(a),
which is the initial structure $\mathscr{N}$ for a design problem in which the specified function is V_2/V_1. In step 2 of Algorithm 1 (step 3 in Algorithms 2
and 3) the currents and voltages in $\mathscr{N}$ are calculated. Similarly, in step 9
of Algorithm 1 (steps 14 and 6 in Algorithms 2 and 3), the currents and
voltages of the adjoint network are calculated. From these, the gradient
is determined and the next value of the parameters found.

It is evident that, although no branch appears between nodes 1 and 2
in the initial structure, it is possible to imagine a branch there having
zero conductance, as shown in Fig. 25(b). (In the dynamic case the
branch could be taken as a capacitor with zero capacitance or an inductor with zero inverse inductance). The voltage across nodes 1 and 2,
both in the initial network and its adjoint, could be calculated. From
these, the corresponding element of the gradient could be calculated;
then, the change in the nonexistent conductance parameter and its next
value could be found. If this value is positive, a conductance could be
"grown" onto $\mathscr{N}$ between nodes 1 and 2.

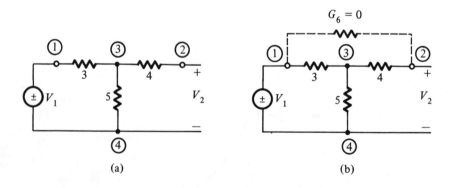

Fig. 25   "Growing" branches in an initial design

In a similar way, it is possible to grow branches in series with existing branches (or anywhere there is computable current). In the case of resistive networks, growing a resistor in series with another resistor is trivial. But in dynamic network design, the branch grown in series with another one might be of a different type. Again a branch having an appropriate parameter of zero value (resistance, inductance, or inverse capacitance) is assumed, and its current as well as the current in the adjoint calculated. These determine an element of the gradient, from which the next value of the parameter is found. If this value is positive, a new branch could be grown.

When a branch is grown in series in this way, not only is a new branch added to the network, but a new node is added. It is now possible to grow additional branches from this node to any other node in the network. Proceeding in this way, the initial design structure can be dramatically augmented. Clearly, cost becomes a factor in how far this branch growing procedure is pursued.

Question Set: Part III

EXERCISES

1. For each of the following networks in Fig. E-1, illustrate Tellegen's Theorem by validating (9-4) after solving for the branch voltages and currents. Assume all capacitor voltages are initially zero.

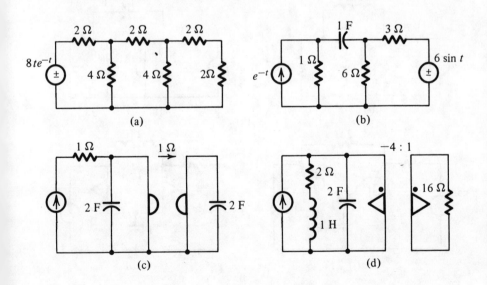

Fig. E-1

2. For each of the pairs of topologically equivalent networks in Fig. E-2 verify the quasi-power form of Tellegen's Theorem by validat-

ing (9-5) after solving for the branch currents of $\mathcal{N}$ and the branch voltages of $\hat{\mathcal{N}}$ according to the following schedule:

Case	Branch Currents of $\mathcal{N}$ in the	Branch Voltages of $\hat{\mathcal{N}}$ in the
a	time-domain	time-domain
b	time-domain	frequency-domain
c	frequency-domain	frequency-domain

Assume there is no initial stored energy.

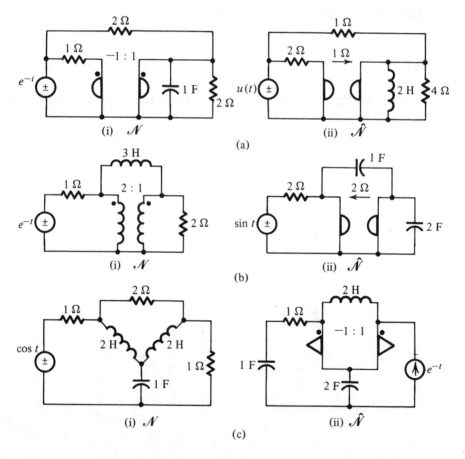

Fig. E-2

3. Show that the two-ports in Fig. E-3 are reciprocal by (a) showing that the left side of (9-19) is zero and (b) validating either (9-22) or (9-23).

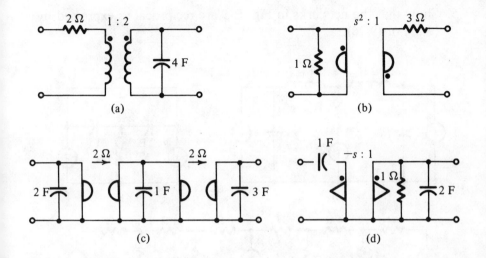

Fig. E-3

4. Show that the multiports in Fig. E-4 are reciprocal by (a) showing that the left side of (9-19) is zero and (b) validating either (9-22) or (9-23).

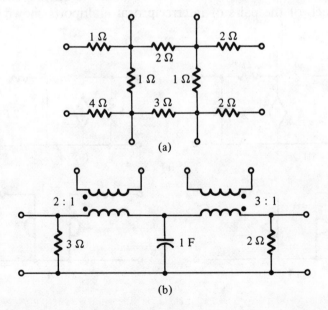

(a)

(b)

Fig. E-4

5. Show that the networks in Fig. E-5 are reciprocal as expressed by (9-25) or (9-26).

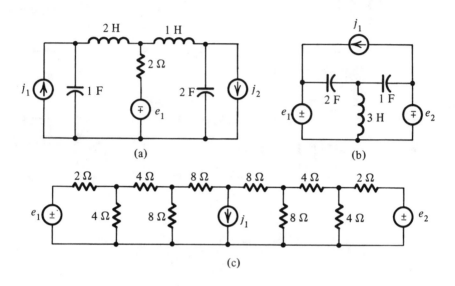

(a)   (b)

(c)

Fig. E-5

6. Verify that the transfer parameter relations of Table 9-1 are valid for each of the pairs of interreciprocal multiports shown in Fig. E-6.

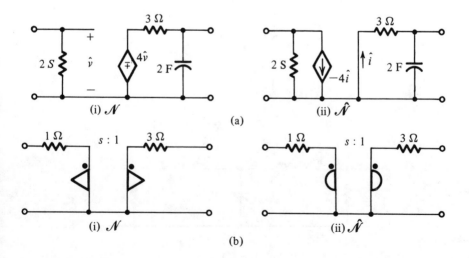

(i) $\mathcal{N}$ (ii) $\hat{\mathcal{N}}$

(a)

(i) $\mathcal{N}$ (ii) $\hat{\mathcal{N}}$

(b)

Fig. E-6

7. For each transistor model depicted in Fig. E-7, determine the adjoint transistor model.

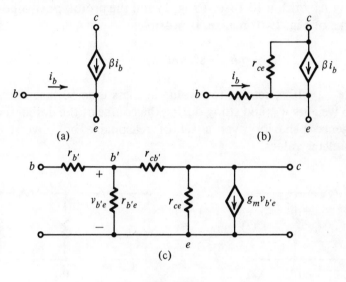

(a)

(b)

(c)

Fig. E-7

8. For each network in Fig. E-8, determine, using Table 9-2, the adjoint network.

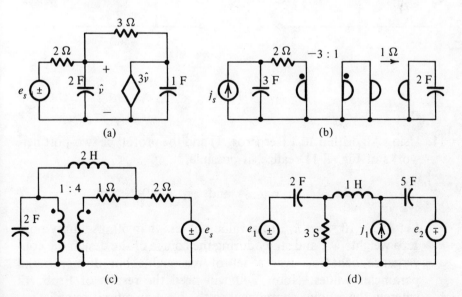

(a)

(b)

(c)

(d)

Fig. E-8

9. Continue the design of the attenuator in the illustration of Algorithm 10-1 through stage 5. (See pages 395 through 401.)

10. Using Algorithm 10-1 (see Prog. 1) and the prototype two-port networks of Fig. E-10 realize, if possible,

$$h_{11} = 8\Omega \text{ and } h_{21} = -\frac{1}{4}.$$

Let $\mathscr{E}_{fuzz} = 10^{-6}$, set k_{lim} to a value not less than 50, use unity nonzero weights w_{ii}, and study during the course of the design the convergence behavior over a set of reasonable but diverse initial parameter values.

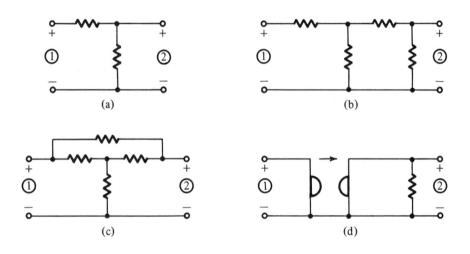

Fig. E-10

11. Using Algorithm 10-1 (see Prog. 1) and the prototype two-port networks of Fig. E-11 realize, if possible,

$$g_{11} = \frac{1}{100} \quad \text{and} \quad g_{21} = -9.$$

Let $\mathscr{E}_{fuzz} = 10^{-6}$, set k_{lim} to a value not less than 50, use unity nonzero weights w_{ii}, and study during the course of the design the convergence behavior over a set of reasonable but diverse initial parameter values. Note: You will need the results of Prob. 12 wherein the adjoint component to the ideal op-amp is established.

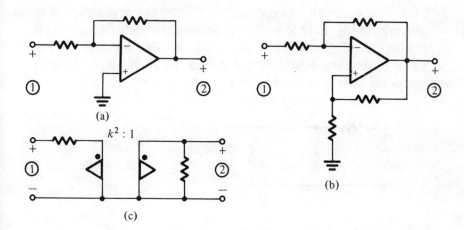

Fig. E-11

12. Repeat Exercise 11 for

$$g_{11} = 10 \quad \text{and} \quad g_{21} = 4$$

with respect to the networks of Fig. E-12.

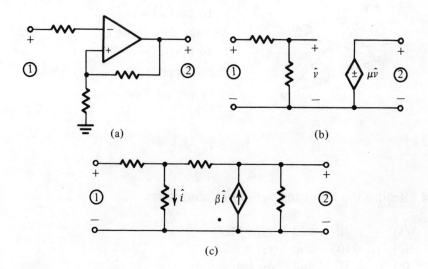

Fig. E-12

13. Using Algorithm 10-1 (see Prog. 1) optimize the parameters of the networks in Fig. E-13 to realize, if possible, the desired relations indicated. Let $\mathscr{E}_{fuzz} = 10^{-6}$ and set k_{lim} to a value not less than 50. Study during the course of the design the convergence behavior over a set of reasonable but diverse non-zero weights w_{ii}.

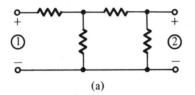

$z_{11} = 15\Omega$
$z_{21} = 10\Omega$

(a)

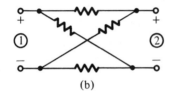

$g_{11} = \frac{1}{2}S$
$g_{21} = 3S$

(b)

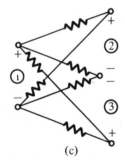

voltage gain (port 1 to port 2) = $\frac{1}{2}$

voltage gain (port 1 to port 3) = $\frac{1}{3}$

input impedance (port 1) = 5Ω

(c)

Fig. E-13

14. Realize the following two-port parameters:

(a) $z_{12} = 4\Omega$ and $z_{22} = 5\Omega$,
(b) $y_{11} = 10S$ and $y_{21} = -2S$,
(c) $h_{11} = 5\Omega$ and $h_{21} = 4$,
(d) $g_{12} = \frac{3}{5}$ and $g_{22} = 8\Omega$,
(e) $A = -2$ and $C = 20S$.

In each case, select a prototype network and then use Algorithm 10-1. (See Prog. 1.) Also determine the effect on the quality of the design achieved as $\mathscr{E}_{fuzz}$ is varied from 10^{-3} to 10^{-8} in decade steps. You should not change your selected initial parameter values as $\mathscr{E}_{fuzz}$ is varied. Select k_{lim} such that the algorithm terminates because convergence is achieved. Use unity non-zero weights w_{ii}.

15. Continue the design of the two-port in the illustration of Algorithm 10-2 through stage 5. (See pages 402 through 410.)

16. Using Algorithm 10-2 (see Prog. 2) and the prototype two-ports of Fig. E-16 realize, if possible,

$$G = \begin{bmatrix} 10 & 0 \\ -4 & 1 \end{bmatrix}$$

Let $\mathscr{E}_{fuzz} = 10^{-6}$, set k_{lim} to a value not less than 50, use unity non-zero weights w_{ii}, and study during the course of the design the convergence behavior over a set of reasonable but diverse initial parameter values. Note: You will need the results of Prob. 12 wherein the adjoint component to the ideal op-amp is established.

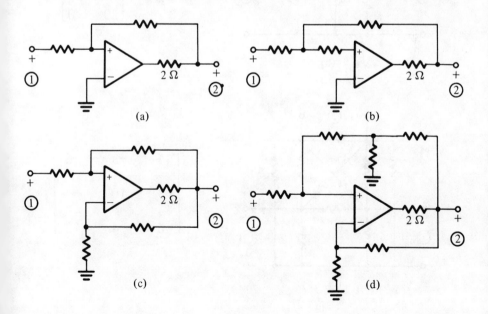

Fig. E-16

17. Using Algorithm 10-2 (see Prog. 2) and the prototype multiports of Fig. E-17 realize, if possible, the relations indicated. In each case, the selection of the initial parameter values, the values of the non-zero weights w_{ii}, the value of $\mathscr{E}_{fuzz}$, and the value of k_{lim} is left to you. Discuss the appropriateness of your choices in light of the network design achieved in each case.

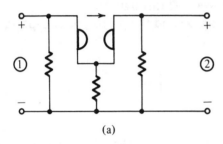

$$Y = \begin{bmatrix} 2 & -1 \\ 2 & 4 \end{bmatrix}$$

(a)

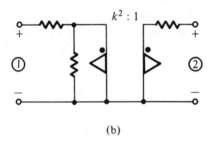

$$Z = \begin{bmatrix} 30 & -4 \\ 20 & 0 \end{bmatrix}$$

(b)

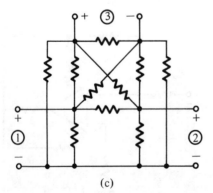

$$Y = \begin{bmatrix} 15 & -3 & -6 \\ -3 & 10 & -4 \\ -6 & -4 & 12 \end{bmatrix}$$

(c)

Fig. E-17

18. Realize the following two-port parameters:

(a) $Y = \begin{bmatrix} 5 & -2 \\ -3 & 6 \end{bmatrix}$ (b) $G = \begin{bmatrix} 4 & -1 \\ 2 & 1 \end{bmatrix}$

(c) $Z = \begin{bmatrix} 5 & -6 \\ -2 & 3 \end{bmatrix}$ (d) $H = \begin{bmatrix} 10 & 3 \\ 3 & 4 \end{bmatrix}$

In each case, select a prototype network and then use Algorithm 10-2 (see Prog. 2) after setting network initial parameter values, performance function weights w_{ii}, and algorithm control parameters $\mathcal{E}_{fuzz}$ and k_{lim}.

19. Continue the design of the (low-pass) filter in the illustration of Algorithm 10-3 through phase 5 of stage 1. (See pages 418 through 423).

20. Using Algorithm 10-3 (see Prog. 3) with the performance functional (10-45) and the trapezoidal integration method (10-53), realize a network approximating the ideal (low-pass) voltage transfer function of Fig. 10-19 and having the structure depicted in Fig. E-20. Set $\Omega = [2,20]$ and $k_{lim} = 200$.

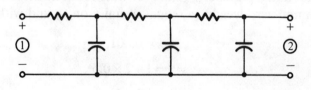

Fig. E-20

(a) With the non-zero weight w_{ii} equal to unity on Ω and with

$$\varrho = 0.001,$$
$$\varkappa = 0.001,$$
$$\nu^{(k)} = 1 + 2 \times 0.5^k,$$
$$\omega_j = 2 + j\Delta_j,$$
$$\Delta_j = 2.$$

Study during the course of the design the convergence behavior over a set of reasonable but diverse initial parameter values.

(b) With initial parameter values for which convergence occurs and with

$$\varrho = 0.001,$$

$$\varkappa = 0.001,$$

$$\nu^{(k)} = 1 + 2 \times 0.5^k,$$

$$\omega_j = 2 + j\Delta_j,$$

$$\Delta_j = 2.$$

Study during the course of the design the convergence behavior over the following set of weight functions.

Values of Non-zero w_{ii}	
$\omega \epsilon [2,10]$	$\omega \epsilon [10,20]$
1	1
1	½
1	¼
½	1
¼	1

(c) With initial parameter values for which convergence occurs, with the non-zero weight w_{ii} equal to unity on Ω, and with

$$\varkappa = 0.001,$$

$$\nu^{(k)} = 1 + 2 \times 0.5^k,$$

$$\omega_j = 2 + j\Delta_j,$$

$$\Delta_j = 2.$$

Study during the course of the design the convergence behavior over the set of convergence factors $\varrho = 0.05$, 0.02, 0.001, 0.0005, 0.0002, 0.0001.

(d) With initial parameter values for which convergence occurs, with the non-zero weight w_{ii} equal to unity on Ω, and with

$$\varrho = 0.001,$$

$$\nu^{(k)} = 1 + 2 \times 0.5^k,$$

$$\omega_j = 2 + j\Delta_j,$$

$$\Delta_j = 2.$$

Study during the course of the design the convergence behavior over the set of initial step control factors $\varkappa = 0.5$, 0.1, 0.05, 0.01, 0.005, 0.001, 0.0005.

(e) With initial parameter values for which convergence occurs, with the non-zero weight w_{ii} equal to unity on Ω, and with

$$\varrho = 0.001,$$

$$\varkappa = 0.001,$$

$$\nu^{(k)} = \alpha + \beta \times \delta^k,$$

$$\omega_j = 2 + j\Delta_j,$$

$$\Delta_j = 2.$$

Study during the course of the design the convergence behavior over the various combinations of $\alpha = 1$, 1.5, 2; $\beta = 1$, 2, 4; and $\delta = 0.25$, 0.5, 0.75

(f) With initial parameter values for which convergence occurs, with the non-zero weight w_{ii} equal to unity on Ω, and with

$$\varrho = 0.001,$$

$$\varkappa = 0.001,$$

$$\nu^{(k)} = 1 + 2 \times 0.5^k,$$

$$\omega_j = 2 + j\Delta_j.$$

Study during the course of the design the convergence behavior over the set of frequency intervals $\Delta_j = 2$, 1, 0.5, 0.25

(g) With initial parameter values for which convergence occurs, with the non-zero weight w_{ii} equal to unity on Ω, and with

$$\varrho = 0.001,$$

$$\varkappa = 0.001,$$

$$\nu^{(k)} = 1 + 2 \times 0.5^k,$$

$$\omega_j = 2 + (2^j - 1)\Delta,$$

$$\Delta_j = 2^{j-1}\Delta,$$

$$\Delta = 18/(2^n - 1).$$

Study during the course of the design the convergence behavior over the number of geometrically spaced frequency intervals $n = 10$, 20, 40, 80.

21. Repeat Exercise 20 for the ideal (band-pass) voltage transfer function of Fig. E-21(a) and network structure of Fig. E-21(b). In items (a) through (f) diminish Δ_j by an order of magnitude ($\times \frac{1}{10}$) and change the specifications for item (b) as follows:

Values of Non-zero w_{ii}		
$\omega\epsilon[2,10)$	$\omega\epsilon[10,12]$	$\omega\epsilon(12,20]$
1	1	1
$\frac{1}{2}$	1	$\frac{1}{2}$
$\frac{1}{4}$	1	$\frac{1}{4}$
1	$\frac{1}{2}$	1
1	$\frac{1}{4}$	1

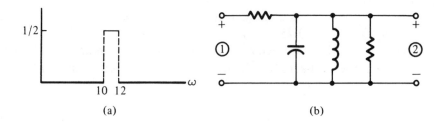

(a)   (b)

Fig. E-21

22. Repeat Exercise 20 with the performance functional (10-39) to realize the (low-pass) voltage transfer functions

(A) $\dfrac{120}{s^2 + 22s + 120}$

(B) $\dfrac{72}{s^2 + 12s + 72}$

(C) $\dfrac{960}{s^3 + 30s^2 + 148s + 960}$

(D) $\dfrac{720}{s^3 + 22s^2 + 192s + 720}$

(E) $\dfrac{13440}{s^4 + 44s^3 + 568s^2 + 3032s + 13440}$

(F) $\dfrac{9216}{s^4 + 28s^3 + 392s^2 + 2688s + 9216}$

using the structure (I) of Fig. 10-20(a) and (II) of Fig. E-20.

23. Determine the Thévenin equivalent network for each of the one-ports of Fig. E-23 by applying (10-20) and (10-21).

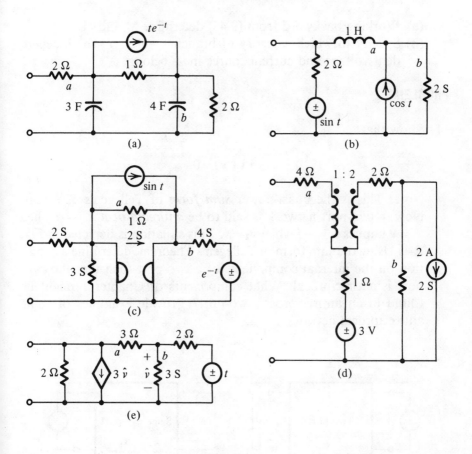

Fig. E-23

24. Determine the Norton equivalent network for each of the one-ports of Fig. E-23 by applying (10-22) and (10-23).

25. By application of Vratsano's Theorem, determine

$$\frac{\Delta Z_{in}}{\Delta Z_a}, \frac{\Delta Z_{in}}{\Delta Y_b}, \frac{\Delta Y_{in}}{\Delta Z_a}, \text{ and } \frac{\Delta Y_{in}}{\Delta Y_b}$$

for the branches labeled a and b in the networks of Fig. E-23.

26. Let $\hat{\mathscr{N}}$ be the adjoint of a network $\mathscr{N}$. The component relations of $\hat{\mathscr{N}}$ can be written

$$\hat{\mathbf{M}}(\hat{\mathbf{V}} - \hat{\mathbf{V}}_s) + \hat{\mathbf{N}}(\hat{\mathbf{I}} - \hat{\mathbf{I}}_s) = \mathbf{0}.$$

(a) Working backward from (9-45) determine $\hat{\mathbf{M}}$ and $\hat{\mathbf{N}}$.
(b) Specify to which category of branches—a or b—the independent voltage and current source in $\hat{\mathscr{N}}$ belong.

PROBLEMS

1. Show that

$$\hat{\mathbf{v}}'\mathbf{i} + \mathbf{v}'\hat{\mathbf{i}} = 0.$$

Note: This is the quasi-power *sum form* of Tellegen's Theorem. Now, a two-port network is said to be *antireciprocal* if $i_2 = i$ when $v_1 = v$ implies $i_1 = -i$ when $v_2 = v$. This situation is depicted in Fig. P-1. Using the sum form of Tellegen's Theorem, determine a condition on the internal components of a two-port such that the two-port is antireciprocal. What components of Chapter 1 might be found in an antireciprocal two-port? Provide examples of some antireciprocal networks.

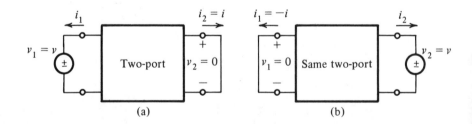

Fig. P-1

2. Prove that KCL and TT imply KVL.
3. Show when branch k in $\mathscr{N}$ and $\hat{\mathscr{N}}$ of Fig. 9-1 is (a) a capacitor or (b) an inductor that

$$\hat{v}_k i_k - v_k \hat{i}_k = 0.$$

Also show when branches k and l are coupled inductors that

$$(\hat{v}_k i_k - v_k \hat{i}_k) + (\hat{v}_l i_l - v_l \hat{i}_l) = 0.$$

4. Let $\mathcal{L}_v$ and $\mathcal{L}_i$ denote linear operators, such as scaling or differentiation. Show that

$$(\mathcal{L}_v \mathbf{v})'(\mathcal{L}_i \mathbf{i}) = 0.$$

This is referred to as the *generalized form* of Tellegen's Theorem. Determine the various alternative forms, such as the *generalized difference form*. Show that each of the forms by which Tellegen's Theorem was expressed in Chapter 9 is a special case of one of the generalized forms.

5. Verify, as stated following (9-20), that for a reciprocal multiport

   (a) $z_{ij} = z_{ji}$ $(j \neq i)$
   (b) $g_{ij} = -g_{ji}$ $(j \neq i)$
   (c) $h_{ij} = -h_{ji}$ $(j \neq i)$

This includes the two-port as a special case and so validates the relations stated following (9-17).

6. Show that the two-port depicted in Fig. P-6 is reciprocal even though it contains dependent sources.

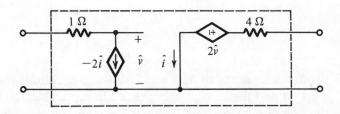

Fig. P-6

7. Suppose the network $\mathcal{N}$ is not degenerate. Show that $[\mathbf{M}\ \mathbf{N}]$, as found in (9-24), is of full rank. Hint: Since $\mathcal{N}$ is not degenerate the branch relations together with KVL and KCL must have a unique solution.

8. Verify the claim on pages 368-369 that for the basic components introduced in Chapter 1, exclusive of the ideal op-amp and the ideal transistor, the branch relations can always be expressed such that $[\mathbf{M}_a\ \mathbf{N}_b] = \mathbf{U}$.

9. Show that $\hat{\mathscr{N}}$, the adjoint network of $\mathscr{N}$, is not degenerate if $\mathscr{N}$ is not degenerate. Show also that (9-41), together with the Kirchhoff laws, must then exhibit a unique solution for $\hat{\mathbf{V}}$, $\hat{\mathbf{I}}$, and W.

10. With respect to interreprocity, when are (9-22) and (9-25) equivalent?

11. Show that, if a network is reciprocal, then it is *self-adjoint*.

12. In composing the branch relations (9-36) the branches of $\mathscr{N}$ were divided into two groups a and b. Correspondingly $\mathbf{V}$ and $\mathbf{I}$ were partitioned as

$$\mathbf{V} = \begin{bmatrix} \mathbf{V}_a \\ \mathbf{V}_b \end{bmatrix} \qquad \text{and} \qquad \mathbf{I} = \begin{bmatrix} \mathbf{I}_a \\ \mathbf{I}_b \end{bmatrix}.$$

In this way we could partition $\mathbf{M}$ and $\mathbf{N}$ such that $[\mathbf{M}_a\ \mathbf{N}_b] = \mathbf{U}$ when the network components were those of Chapter 1, exclusive of the ideal op-amp and the ideal transistor. We claim that this exclusion is not necessary if the two groups for the partition of $\mathbf{I}$ are allowed to be different from those for the partition of $\mathbf{V}$. Thus, let us write

$$\mathbf{V} = \begin{bmatrix} \mathbf{V}_{\bar{a}} \\ \mathbf{V}_{\bar{b}} \end{bmatrix} \qquad \text{and} \qquad \mathbf{I} = \begin{bmatrix} \mathbf{I}_{\hat{a}} \\ \mathbf{I}_{\hat{b}} \end{bmatrix}.$$

(a) From these partitions of $\mathbf{V}$ and $\mathbf{I}$, develop equations for the network $\mathscr{N}$ and the adjoint network $\hat{\mathscr{N}}$. In particular, (i) show that the component pairs of Table 9-2 remain correct and (ii) add the pairs corresponding to the ideal op-amp and the ideal transistor.

(b) Using the results of (a) develop the gradient equations for updating of the parameter vector of $\mathscr{N}$. Then, (i) show that the terms of (10-11) contributing to the gradient remain correct and (ii) add the terms corresponding to the ideal op-amp and the ideal transistor.

13. The concept of reciprocity (and interreciprocity) of a network is more general than the concept of reciprocity (and interreciprocity)

of a multiport. With respect to the concept of reciprocity, consider the network shown in Fig. P-13(a). Show that it is a reciprocal network in that (9-26) is satisfied. Though it is not necessary to do so, treat each independent source and its accompanying two-terminal nonsource component as a general component. Next, show that the network is reciprocal as a three-port [see Fig. P-13(b)] by showing that (9-23) — or (9-26) — is satisfied. Here treat each of the three independent sources — each corresponding to a port of the network — as distinct components. Lastly, consider the network as a two-port, as depicted in Fig. P-13(c). Show that the network as a two-port is not reciprocal in that (9-23) is not satisfied. The internal source can be treated as a distinct component or as a general component. Thus, a reciprocal network is not, in general, a reciprocal multiport. However, as Chapter 9 makes clear, it is reciprocal if every independent source is associated with a port.

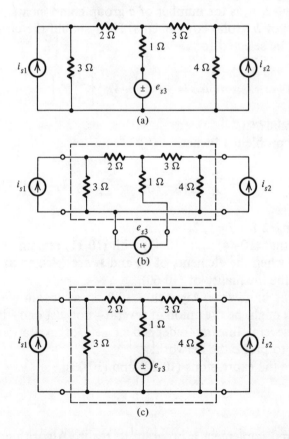

Fig. P-13

14. Illustrate the following statement: Interreciprocal networks are not, in general, interreciprocal multiports.

15. Consider a two-port component which has a (possibly singular) set of z-parameters. What are the z-parameters of the adjoint two-port? Repeat for the y-parameters, the g-parameters, the h-parameters, and the chain parameters. In the latter case you will find the results of Prob. 12 useful; they are actually necessary when the chain parameters are singular.

16. Starting with (9-39a) and (9-38), derive the component relations (9-47) of the adjoint network as a multiport without internal sources.

17. Let

$$\mathscr{E} = \frac{1}{p}\left[\sum_{j=1}^{n_a} w_{jj}|I_j - I_{dj}|^p + \sum_{j=n_a+1}^{n_a+n_b} w_{jj}|V_j - V_{dj}|^p \right],$$

where $p > 2$, n_a is the number of a group components, and n_b is the number of b group components. How should the elements of $\hat{\mathbf{V}}_{pa}$ and $\hat{\mathbf{I}}_{pb}$ be selected for

$$\Delta\mathscr{E} = -[\hat{\mathbf{V}}'_{pa} \quad -\hat{\mathbf{I}}'_{pb}]\begin{bmatrix} \Delta\mathbf{I}_{pa} \\ \Delta\mathbf{V}_{pb} \end{bmatrix}$$

to be valid?

18. Repeat problem 17 when

$$\mathscr{E} = \sum_{j=1}^{n_a} w_{jj}|I_j - I_{dj}|^{p_j} + \sum_{j=n_a+1}^{n_a+n_b} w_{jj}|V_j - V_{dj}|^{p_j},$$

where $p_j \geqslant 2$ for $j = 1, 2, \ldots, n_a + n_b$.

19. Verify that (10-44) and (10-41) with (10-11) remain valid for ϵ of (10-45) when the elements of $\hat{\mathbf{V}}_a$ and $\hat{\mathbf{I}}_b$ are selected as in (10-46).

20. Verify the inequality of (10-60).

21. Augment or rewrite Algorithm 10-3 so as to allow for the case where Ω might be the union of several — not just one — intervals and where several linearly independent sets of excitations might be needed to probe the network.

22. Validate the expressions (10-22) and (10-23).

PROGRAMS

1. Write and implement a program to realize Algorithm 10-1. Use a subroutine call for the analysis of the network — step 2 — and of its

adjoint—step 9. If unavailable, write this subroutine as well. Prepare a short report describing the input and output data structures and illustrating its use.

2. Repeat the task of program 1 for Algorithm 10-2.
3. Write and implement a program to realize Algorithm 10-3. Use a subroutine call for the analysis of the network—step 3—and of its adjoint—step 6. If unavailable, write the subroutine as well. Switch variables are to be included to allow the user to select the performance function of (10-39) or (10-45) and the integration method of (10-51) or (10-52) or (10-53). Prepare a short report describing the input and output data structures and illustrating its use.
4. Repeat the task of program 3 for the algorithm which is the result in solving problem 21.

PROJECTS

1. Read

   S. W. Director and R. A. Rohrer, "The generalized adjoint network and network sensitivities," *IEEE Transactions on Circuit Theory*, vol. CT-16, 1969, pp. 318-323.

   Using this paper as a guide develop the time-domain counterpart of the CAND procedure embodied in Algorithm 10-3. Prepare a short report which shows the development of all relevant equations, presents the resulting algorithm, and gives an illustrative application of the algorithm.

2. Read

   P. O. Scheibe and E. A. Huber, "The application of Carroll's optimization technique to network synthesis," *Proc. Third Annual Allerton Conf. on Systems and Circuits*, 1965, pp. 182-191.

   and any appropriate references cited in this paper so as to be able to prepare a report describing the synthesis procedure tendered by these authors. Include an algorithm which embodies the procedure.

3. Read

   R. Fletcher and M. J. D. Powell, "A rapidly convergent descent method for minimization," *Computer Jour.*, vol. 6, 1963, pp. 163-168.

This paper describes one of the most popular of the descent methods for minimization of a performance functional. Write a report describing the method. Include an algorithm, replacing Algorithm 10-1, embodying this method for minimization of the performance functional of (10-24). You may also find chapter 8 of the following supplemental reference of value:

> J. M. Ortega and W. C. Rheinboldt, *Iterative solution of nonlinear equations in several variables*, Academic Press, New York, 1970.

4. Read

> R. Fletcher and C. M. Reeves, "Function minimization by conjugate gradients," *Computer Jour.*, vol. 7, 1964, pp. 149-154

and

> W. Zangwill, "Minimizing a function without calculating derivatives," *Computer Jour.*, vol. 10, 1967, pp. 293-296.

These papers, the second refining the result of the first, describe a conjugate gradient method for minimization of a performance functional. Prepare a report describing this method. Discuss the use of this method in computer-aided network design. You may find the supplemental reference of Project 3 of value.

5. Read chapter 8, concentrating on section 3, of

> J. M. Ortega and W. C. Rheinboldt, *Iterative solution of nonlinear equations in several variables*, Academic Press, New York, 1970.

Then prepare a short report describing step-length selection procedures other than that due to Cauchy and presented in Chapter 10.

6. Read

> P. Penfield, Jr., R. Spence, and S. Duinker, *Tellegen's theorem and electrical networks*, M.I.T. Press, Cambridge, MA, 1970.

Then prepare notes (and transparencies) for a thirty minute talk which illustrates some of the many and diverse applications of Tellegen's Theorem.

PART IV
Network Synthesis

CHAPTER 11
Energy Functions and Positive Real Functions

Network synthesis is the process of designing and constructing a network to provide a prescribed response to a specified excitation. This is the converse of the analysis problem where a response is to be calculated when a prescribed excitation is applied to a given network. In contrast with the latter, the synthesis problem may not have a unique solution. In fact, it may not have any solution, since there may be no network that has the desired response to the given excitation. At the outset, then, one may be faced with the necessity of approximating the desired response with one that is obtainable.

Specification of the response and its approximation may be either in the time-domain or in the frequency-domain. In the frequency-domain the end result of the approximation process is the specification of one or more network functions that characterize the desired network. The realization is guided by the fact that there are various classes of networks. These classes can be characterized by the number of external terminals and ports (three-terminal two-port, four-terminal two-port, etc.), by the type of components (passive, reciprocal, etc.), by the structure (ladder, twin-tree, etc.), and so forth.

The first task in the realization process is to determine the properties of network functions that are appropriate for each class of network. These properties include permissible locations of poles and zeros, the signs of residues and real parts, and the relative sizes of coefficients. This is the task on which we shall concentrate in this chapter, with respect to the class of networks labeled passive. What we establish will greatly augment what was established in Chapter 5.

11.1 ENERGY FUNCTIONS

Let us now turn to the task of relating certain network functions to the energy stored and dissipated in a network. Then, from physical knowledge of the nature of this energy, we will draw some conclusions about the properties of network functions.

Consider a multiport excited by voltage sources at each port. Fig. 1 shows just a two-port, but the discussion will be carried out in terms of a general multiport. The multiport is assumed to be linear, time-invariant, and initially relaxed.

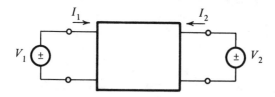

Fig. 1   Excited two-port

Now let us apply Tellegen's theorem to this network $\mathcal{N}$ and to its topological equivalent $\hat{\mathcal{N}}$, which is the same as $\mathcal{N}$ except possibly for the sources. We shall write the terms corresponding to the ports — subscript p — and to the internal branches — subscript i — separately. Since the port currents, oriented relative to the port voltage sources as shown, are the negative of the source currents using the orientation standard for Tellegen's theorem, (9-5b) becomes

$$\hat{\mathbf{I}}_p' \mathbf{V}_p = \hat{\mathbf{I}}_i' V_i, \tag{1}$$

with the roles of $\mathcal{N}$ and $\hat{\mathcal{N}}$ reversed. The vectors of the internal branch variables can be partitioned into the two categories a and b, such that the hybrid relations of (9-38) can be substituted;* the result becomes

---

* The validity of (9-38) required that the multiport be devoid of ideal op-amps; this limitation holds for the present development.

$$\hat{\mathbf{I}}_p' \, \mathbf{V}_p = [\hat{\mathbf{I}}_{ia} \quad \hat{\mathbf{I}}_{ib}] \begin{bmatrix} \mathbf{V}_{ia} \\ \mathbf{V}_{ib} \end{bmatrix}$$

$$\tag{2}$$

$$= [\hat{\mathbf{I}}_{ia}' \quad (\hat{\mathbf{H}}_{ba}\hat{\mathbf{I}}_{ia} + \hat{\mathbf{Y}}_b \hat{\mathbf{V}}_{ib})'] \begin{bmatrix} \mathbf{Z}_a\mathbf{I}_{ia} + \mathbf{H}_{ab}\mathbf{V}_{ib} \\ \mathbf{V}_{ib} \end{bmatrix}.$$

Suppose $\hat{\mathcal{N}}$ is the same as $\mathcal{N}$ and no special conditions are placed on the sources in $\hat{\mathcal{N}}$. Then (2) can be rewritten as

$$\hat{\mathbf{I}}_p'\mathbf{V}_p = \hat{\mathbf{I}}_a'\mathbf{Z}_a\mathbf{I}_a + \hat{\mathbf{V}}_b'\mathbf{Y}_b'\mathbf{V}_b + \hat{\mathbf{I}}_a'(\mathbf{H}_{ab} + \mathbf{H}_{ba}')\mathbf{V}_b. \tag{3}$$

(The subscripts i have been dropped for simplicity. In what follows any voltage and current not designated to be a port quantity is that of an internal, nonsource branch.)

Let us temporarily assume that all sources in $\mathcal{N}$ are sinusoidal at the same frequency and the variables in (3) pertaining to $\mathcal{N}$ are phasors (complex quantities) representing these sinusoids. Further, let the variables pertaining to $\hat{\mathcal{N}}$ be the complex conjugates of the corresponding variables in $\mathcal{N}$. We can rewrite (3) as

$$\mathbf{I}_p^*\mathbf{V}_p = \mathbf{I}_a^*\mathbf{Z}_a\mathbf{I}_a + \mathbf{V}_b^*\mathbf{Y}_b'\mathbf{V}_b + \mathbf{I}_a^*(\mathbf{H}_{ab} + \mathbf{H}_{ba}')\mathbf{V}_b. \tag{4}$$

(The notation $\mathbf{M}^*$ stands for the conjugate transpose of $\mathbf{M}$.) Each term on the right side is a bilinear form; the first two terms, in fact, are quadratic forms.

The left side of (4) is the complex power supplied to the network from the ports so its real part is the real (average) power supplied; its imaginary part is proportional to the net average energy stored in the network, the difference between the energy stored in the inductors and in the capacitors. Thus,

$$\text{Re} \, (\mathbf{I}_p^*\mathbf{V}_p) = P \tag{5a}$$

$$\text{Im} \, (\mathbf{I}_p^*\mathbf{V}_p) = \pm 2\omega(W_L - W_C). \tag{5b}$$

(The appropriate sign depends on the form of the expressions for W_L and W_C, as will become clear shortly.)

Nothing specific can be inferred from (4) for a general network containing arbitrary linear components; e.g., $\mathbf{Z}_a$ and $\mathbf{Y}_b$ are not necessarily symmetric or diagonal, and $\mathbf{H}_{ab}$ and $\mathbf{H}_{ba}$ are not necessarily zero. Nevertheless, the first quadratic form in (4) is a scalar representing the complex power into a network with branch impedance matrix $\mathbf{Z}_a$. Likewise for the second quadratic form in (4). More detailed interpretations will be given shortly.

Note that the value of a quadratic form is unchanged if the matrix of the form is replaced by its Hermitian part, which, because the matrices under consideration are real, is also its symmetric part. Hence, we shall hereafter remove the transpose symbol from $\mathbf{Y}_b'$ and, in general, assume that all matrices of quadratic forms have been replaced by their symmetric parts.

11.2 PASSIVE NETWORKS

Let us now restrict ourselves to passive networks: R, C, L, M and gyrator. For such networks the hybrid submatrices $\mathbf{H}_{ab}$ and $\mathbf{H}_{ba}$ will vanish. The real part of the complex power supplied to the network at its ports must be nonnegative, by the definition of passivity. Hence,

$$P = \mathrm{Re}\ \{\mathbf{I}_a^*\mathbf{Z}_a\mathbf{I}_a + \mathbf{V}_b^*\mathbf{Y}_b\mathbf{V}_b\} \geqslant 0$$

or

$$\mathbf{I}_a^*(\mathrm{Re}\ \mathbf{Z}_a)\mathbf{I}_a + \mathbf{V}_b^*(\mathrm{Re}\ \mathbf{Y}_b)\mathbf{V}_b \geqslant 0. \tag{6}$$

(The last expression follows because the complex nature of a quadratic form is not a result of the variables being complex but a result of the matrix being complex.) This expression imposes the condition that the *sum* of two specific quadratic forms cannot be negative; but what can be said about each one?

Let us assume that no compound branches have been formed in writing the branch relationships. Since each R, C, L (alone or coupled), and gyrator can be arbitrarily placed in either the a or the b category, it follows that *each* of the quadratic forms in (6) cannot be negative; each must be positive semi-definite. On one extreme, *all* the resistors (including gyrators) can be put in the a category; for this case let us designate $\mathrm{Re}\ (\mathbf{Z}_a)$ as $\mathbf{R}$, the *branch resistance matrix*. At the other extreme, all the resistors can be put in the b category; for this case let us designate Re ($\mathbf{Y}_b$) as $\mathbf{G}$, the *branch conductance matrix*. The conclusion from this discussion is that the *branch resistance and branch conductance matrices are positive semi-definite*. Note that since $\mathbf{Z}_a$ and $\mathbf{Y}_b$ are here the symmetric parts of an impedance matrix and an admittance matrix, respectively, any gyrator resistance or conductance will not appear. Hence, the names branch resistance matrix and branch conductance matrix are appropriate.

Now let us turn to the imaginary part of (4). Inductors and capacitors are the only things that contribute to the imaginary part of the right side. On one extreme, suppose all inductors (including coupled ones) and capacitors are put in the a category. At the other extreme suppose they are all put in the b category. In these two cases, we can write, respectively,

$$\text{Im}\ (\mathbf{Z}_a) = \omega \left(\mathbf{L} - \frac{1}{\omega^2}\mathbf{D} \right), \tag{7a}$$

$$\text{Im}\ (\mathbf{Y}_b) = \omega \left(\mathbf{C} - \frac{1}{\omega^2}\mathbf{\Gamma} \right), \tag{7b}$$

where $\mathbf{L}$ and $\mathbf{\Gamma}$ are the *branch inductance* and *reciprocal inductance matrices* and where $\mathbf{C}$ and $\mathbf{D}$ are the *branch capacitance* and *reciprocal capacitance matrices*, respectively. For the two cases considered, taking the imaginary part of (4) and substituting (5b) and (7), we can write

$$\omega \left(\mathbf{I}_a^* \mathbf{L} \mathbf{I}_a - \frac{1}{\omega^2}\mathbf{I}_a^* \mathbf{D} \mathbf{I}_a \right) = 2\omega(W_L - W_C) \tag{8a}$$

$$\omega \left(\mathbf{V}_b^* \mathbf{C} \mathbf{V}_b - \frac{1}{\omega^2}\mathbf{V}_b^* \mathbf{\Gamma} \mathbf{V}_b \right) = 2\omega(W_C - W_L). \tag{8b}$$

[Notice how it was necessary to choose the sign on the right of (5b).] The following interpretations of the various quadratic forms can immediately be made:

$$\frac{1}{2}\mathbf{I}_a^* \mathbf{L} \mathbf{I}_a \tag{9a}$$

$$\frac{1}{2\omega^2}\mathbf{V}_b^* \mathbf{\Gamma} \mathbf{V}_b \tag{9b}$$

$\left.\right\}$ average energy stored in inductors

$$\frac{1}{2}\mathbf{V}_b^* \mathbf{C} \mathbf{V}_b \tag{9c}$$

$$\frac{1}{2\omega^2}\mathbf{I}_a^* \mathbf{D} \mathbf{I}_a \tag{9d}$$

$\left.\right\}$ average energy stored in capacitors

Since the average energy stored in any capacitor or inductor can never be negative, we conclude that each of the quadratic forms in (9) is positive semi-definite.

Before going on, recall that, although no special notation was used, the variables in (4) and subsequent equations are (complex) phasors. Let us now return to (3); for the passive networks we are now considering, $\mathbf{H}_{ab}$ and $\mathbf{H}_{ba}$ are zero. Let us assume that the sources in $\hat{\mathcal{N}}$ are such that their Laplace transforms are the complex conjugates of the transforms of the corresponding sources in $\mathcal{N}$. The matrices $\mathbf{Z}_a$ and $\mathbf{Y}_b$ can be written in expanded form as

$$\mathbf{Z}_a = \mathbf{R} + s\mathbf{L} + \frac{\mathbf{D}}{s} \tag{10a}$$

$$\mathbf{Y}_b = \mathbf{G} + s\mathbf{C} + \frac{\mathbf{\Gamma}}{s}. \tag{10b}$$

With these changes, and assigning branches in the two possible extreme ways (all in a or all in b), (3) can be rewritten as

$$\mathbf{I}_b^* \mathbf{V}_p = \mathbf{I}_a^* \mathbf{R} \mathbf{I}_a + s\mathbf{I}_a^* \mathbf{L} \mathbf{I}_a + \frac{1}{s}\mathbf{I}_a^* \mathbf{D} \mathbf{I}_a \tag{11a}$$

$$= \mathbf{V}_b^* \mathbf{G} \mathbf{V}_b + s\mathbf{V}_b^* \mathbf{C} \mathbf{V}_b + \frac{1}{s}\mathbf{V}_b^* \mathbf{\Gamma} \mathbf{V}_b. \tag{11b}$$

Each of the quadratic forms on the right have been encountered before, in (6) and (9). Although the *variables* of the forms here are not the phasors encountered in (6) and (9), the *matrices* are exactly the same. Hence, the nature of the quadratic form (positive semi-definite) is retained.

Let us make the following definitions:

$$F_0(s) = \mathbf{I}_a^* \mathbf{R} \mathbf{I}_a = \sum_{k=1}^{b_R} R_k |I_k|^2 \tag{12a}$$

$$T_0(s) = \mathbf{I}_a^* \mathbf{L} \mathbf{I}_a = \sum_{k=1}^{b_L} \sum_{j=1}^{b_L} L_{jk} \bar{I}_j I_k \tag{12b}$$

$$V_0(s) = \mathbf{I}_a^* \mathbf{D} \mathbf{I}_a = \sum_{k=1}^{b_C} D_k |I_k|^2, \tag{12c}$$

where R_k and D_k are the kth diagonal elements of the diagonal matrices $\mathbf{R}$ and $\mathbf{D}$, respectively.

From our earlier physical interpretation, when the variables were phasors, the first of these is the real power dissipated in the network and cannot be negative; the second is twice the average energy stored in the inductors and the third is $2\omega^2$ times the average energy stored in the capacitors. Neither of these also can be negative. These functions are collectively called *energy functions*, notwithstanding the fact that one of them is not dimensionally energy even in the sinusoidal case, and none of them have the dimension of energy in the general case. The choice of symbols for these functions is an unfortunate one, since they can be confused with other quantities having similar symbols; but they have become quite standard in the literature, so we shall continue using them.

In terms of the energy functions, (11a) can be rewritten as

$$\mathbf{I}_p^* \mathbf{V}_p = F_0(s) + sT_0(s) + \frac{1}{s}V_0(s). \tag{13}$$

Recall that the currents appearing in the quadratic forms on the right are internal variables whereas the variables on the left side are port variables. But the port variables are related to each other through the multiport impedance matrix or admittance matrix, for example,

$$\mathbf{V}_p(s) = \mathbf{Z}(s)\mathbf{I}_p(s) \tag{14a}$$

or

$$\mathbf{I}_p(s) = \mathbf{Y}(s)\mathbf{V}_p(s). \tag{14b}$$

The first of these can be inserted directly into (3); the second can be inserted after taking the conjugate transpose of (13), which leads to

$$(\mathbf{I}_p^* \mathbf{V}_p)^* = \left(F_0 + sT_0 + \frac{1}{s}V_0 \right)$$

or

$$\mathbf{V}_p^* \mathbf{I}_p = F_0 + \overline{s}T_0 + \frac{1}{\overline{s}}V_0. \tag{15}$$

This last step follows because the quadratic forms are real scalars; hence, each is its own conjugate. The result of inserting (14a) into (13) and (14b) into (15) is

$$\mathbf{I}_p^* \mathbf{Z} \mathbf{I}_p = F_0 + sT_0 + \frac{1}{s}V_0 \tag{16a}$$

$$\mathbf{V}_p^* \mathbf{Y} \mathbf{V}_p = F_0 + \bar{s}T_0 + \frac{1}{\bar{s}}V_0. \tag{16b}$$

It is from these expressions that some of the most fundamental properties of network functions originate. We shall now embark on a study of these properties.

11.3 THE IMPEDANCE FUNCTION

Let us consider first the simplest multiport; namely, a one-port. In this case $\mathbf{Z}$ is the scalar $Z(s)$, the impedance of the one-port, and $\mathbf{I}_p$ reduces to the scalar input current. From (16a) the expression for $Z(s)$ becomes

$$Z(s) = \frac{1}{|I(s)|^2}\left\{ F_0(s) + sT_0(s) + \frac{1}{s}V_0(s) \right\}. \tag{17}$$

Note that the quadratic forms are functions of s only through the fact that the branch currents are functions of s and that the real, positive semidefinite nature of the quadratic forms does not depend on the current variables, but only on the branch-parameter matrices, which are constant matrices.

11.3.1 Real and Imaginary Parts Conditions

The preceding expression can be separated into real and imaginary parts after replacing s by $\sigma + j\omega$. Thus

$$\mathrm{Re}[Z(s)] = \frac{I}{|I(s)|^2}\left[F_0(s) + \sigma T_0(s) + \frac{\sigma}{\sigma^2 + \omega^2}V_0(s) \right] \tag{18a}$$

$$\mathrm{Im}\,[Z(s)] = \frac{\omega}{|I(s)|^2}\left[T_0(s) - \frac{V_0(s)}{\sigma^2 + \omega^2} \right]. \tag{18b}$$

Notice that these equations apply no matter what the value of s may be, except at zeros of $I(s)$. These two are extremely important equations, from which we can draw some interesting conclusions. For later reference let us state these results as a theorem.

Theorem 1. Let $Z(s)$ be the driving-point impedance of RLCM gyrator $-$ passive $-$ network $\mathcal{N}$. Then the following statements are true:

(a) *Whenever $\sigma \geqslant 0$, $\mathrm{Re}[Z(s)] \geqslant 0$.*

(b) *If $\mathcal{N}$ contains no resistances $[F_0(s) = 0]$, then*
   $\sigma > 0$ *implies* $\mathrm{Re}[Z(s)] > 0$,
   $\sigma = 0$ *implies* $\mathrm{Re}[Z(s)] = 0$,
   $\sigma < 0$ *implies* $\mathrm{Re}[Z(s)] < 0$.

(c) *If $\mathcal{N}$ contains no capacitances $[V_0(s) = 0]$, then*
   $\omega > 0$ *implies* $\mathrm{Im}[Z(s)] > 0$,
   $\omega = 0$ *implies* $\mathrm{Im}[Z(s)] = 0$,
   $\omega < 0$ *implies* $\mathrm{Im}[Z(s)] < 0$.

(d) *If $\mathcal{N}$ contains no inductances $[T_0(s) = 0]$, then*
   $\omega > 0$ *implies* $\mathrm{Im}[Z(s)] < 0$,
   $\omega = 0$ *implies* $\mathrm{Im}[Z(s)] = 0$,
   $\omega < 0$ *implies* $\mathrm{Im}[Z(s)] > 0$.

These results follow immediately from (18). Part (a) states that the value of $Z(s)$ corresponding to a value of s lying in the right half-plane must itself lie in the right half-plane. It leads to the discussion of positive real functions, which we shall take up in the next section. Part (b) leads to the historically important reactance theorem of Foster. Parts (c) and (d) lead to Cauer's results on RL and RC networks.

11.3.2 Angle Condition

Another property of the impedance function can be determined from (17). Note that $|I|^2$, F_0, T_0, and V_0 are all positive constants for any value of s. Hence $Z(s)$ can be written as

$$Z(s) = a_0 + a_1 s + \frac{a_2}{s}, \tag{19}$$

where each of the coefficients is positive. Let $s_0 = \sigma_0 + j\omega_0$ be a point in the right half-plane; that is, $\sigma_0 > 0$, as shown in Fig. 2(a). Each of the terms on the right of (19) can be represented by a directed line in the complex plane, as shown in Fig. 2(b) for the corresponding value of s. Whatever the lengths of these lines may be, the sum cannot lie outside the cross-hatched sector shown in Fig. 2(a). By observing from the diagram what happens for a number of possible angles of s, including 0 and $\pi/2$ radians, the following result is obtained:

$$|\arg Z(s)| \leqslant |\arg s| \quad \text{for } 0 \leqslant |\arg s| \leqslant \pi/2. \tag{20}$$

This seems to be a stronger condition on the impedance than the condition $\text{Re}[Z(s)] \geqslant 0$ for $\text{Re } s \geqslant 0$. Not only must $Z(s)$ be in the right half-plane when s is, but its location there is limited by a condition on its angle. It is not, however, a stronger condition, since it can be shown (see Prob. 1) that for any impedance expressible as in (17) it is true that $\text{Re } Z(s) \geqslant 0$ for $\text{Re } s \geqslant 0$ implies and is implied by $|\arg Z(s)| \leqslant |\arg s|$ for $\text{Re } s \geqslant 0$.

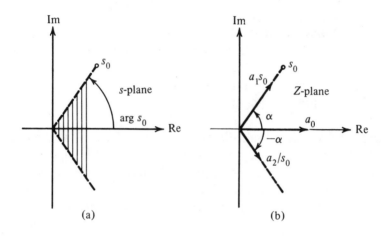

Fig. 2   Demonstration that $|\arg Z| \leqslant |\arg s|$ for $|\arg s| \leqslant \pi/2$

What has been done in this section was to start with a class of networks and to derive some properties that the driving-point impedance of such networks necessarily satisfies. This was done from considerations of energy in the frequency-domain. An alternative approach would have been to start from the definition of a passive network given in Chapter 1 and repeated here for a one-port:

$$\int_{-\infty}^{t} v(\tau)i(\tau)dr \geqslant 0. \tag{21}$$

Suppose the current and voltage at the terminals of a passive network are

$$i(t) = 2|I_0|e^{\sigma_0 t}\cos(\omega_0 t + \alpha) = I_0 e^{s_0 t} + \bar{I}_0 e^{\bar{s}_0 t}, \tag{22a}$$

$$v(t) = Z(s_0)I_0 e^{s_0 t} + Z(\bar{s}_0)\bar{I}_0 e^{\bar{s}_0 t}, \tag{22b}$$

where $s_0 = \sigma_0 + j\omega_0$ with $\sigma_0 > 0$ and $I_0 = |I_0|e^{j\alpha}$. Assume these signals were initiated at $t = -\infty$, at which time there was no initial energy stored in the network. Because $e^{\sigma_0 t} = 0$ for $t = -\infty$, both signals start from 0. There is, then, no question of a transient, and the given expressions for current and voltage represent the excitation and total response.

Inserting these expressions for v and i into (21) leads, after some manipulation, to

$$|I_0|^2 \frac{\text{Re}[Z(s_0)]}{\sigma_0} e^{2\sigma_0 t} + \text{Re}\left[\frac{Z(s_0)I_0^2}{s_0}e^{2s_0 t}\right] \geq 0. \tag{23}$$

Now express the multiplier of the exponential in the last brackets in terms of its magnitude and angle; thus,

$$\frac{Z(s_0)I_0^2}{s_0} = \frac{|Z(s_0)||I_0|^2}{|s_0|}e^{j\theta_0}. \tag{24}$$

When this is inserted into the preceding equation, the result will be:

$$|I_0|^2 e^{2\sigma_0 t}\left[\frac{\text{Re}[Z(s_0)]}{\sigma_0} + \frac{|Z(s_0)|}{|s_0|}\cos(2\omega_0 t + \theta_0)\right] \geq 0 \tag{25}$$

The worse case occurs when the cosine equals -1. For this case the condition reduces to:

$$\frac{\text{Re}[Z(s_0)]}{\sigma_0} - \frac{|Z(s_0)|}{|s_0|} \geq 0,$$

or

$$\frac{\text{Re}[Z(s_0)]}{|Z(s_0)|} \geq \frac{\sigma_0}{|s_0|}. \tag{26}$$

Each side of this expression is the real part divided by the magnitude of some complex quantity, so each side equals the cosine of the corresponding angle. Hence,

$$\cos[\arg Z(s_0)] \geq \cos[\arg s_0], \tag{27}$$

from which it follows that

$$|\arg Z(s_0)| \leq |\arg s_0|. \tag{28}$$

Since Re $s_0 = \sigma_0 > 0$, this is identical with (20).

This result established in the time-domain is extremely important because from it can be deduced the fact that the previous results established in the frequency-domain for *RLCM* gyrator networks, as expressed in Theorem 1, have wider validity — they are valid for passive networks in general.

This completes the development of the general necessary properties of impedance functions of passive networks. Completely similar properties could have been developed for the admittance function by starting from (16b) instead of (16a). Thus Theorem 1 and Equation (20) are true when $Z(s)$ is replaced by $Y(s)$.

We shall now define a class of mathematical functions having these same properties and shall investigate the detailed behavior of this class of functions.

11.4 POSITIVE REAL FUNCTIONS

A *positive real function* $F(s)$ is an analytic function of the complex variable $s = \sigma + j\omega$, which has the following properties:

1. $F(s)$ is regular for $\sigma > 0$.
2. $F(\sigma)$ is real.
3. $\sigma \geq 0$ implies $\operatorname{Re}[F(s)] \geq 0$.

This is a mathematical definition for a class of mathematical functions. Our motivation in making this definition is the fact that a passive network function of interest — namely, the driving-point impedance (or admittance) — possesses these properties. By making a mathematical study of this class of functions we can perhaps determine things about impedances that we could not establish from physical reasoning alone. The concept of a positive real function, as well as many of the properties of positive real functions that we shall consider, are due to Otto Brune.

We shall now show that, if a function is rational, as is the case for the lumped component networks considered in this book, and satisfies the last two of the above conditions, it will automatically be regular in the right half-plane and thus satisfy condition 1. We shall do this by first showing that a pole of order n of a real rational function is surrounded by $2n$ sectors in which the real part of the function is alternately positive and negative. Let s_0 be a pole of order n of the rational function $F(s)$. The case $n = 3$ is illustrated in Fig. 3. In the neighborhood of the pole of order n, the function has a Laurent expansion of the form:

$$F(s) = \frac{a_{-n}}{(s-s_0)^n} + \frac{a_{-n+1}}{(s-s_0)^{n-1}} + \ldots + \frac{a_{-1}}{s-s_0} + \sum_{j=0}^{\infty} a_j(s-s_0)^j. \quad (29)$$

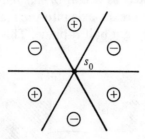

Fig. 3   Pole of order 3

If a sufficiently small neighborhood of s_0 is chosen, the first term of the Laurent expansion dominates the others and determines the nature of $F(s)$. We can show that the real part of this term, and hence that of $F(s)$ in this neighborhood will take on both positive and negative values. Write

$$a_{-n} = ke^{j\theta} \quad (30a)$$

$$(s-s_0) = \varrho e^{j\phi}, \quad (30b)$$

Then

$$\mathrm{Re}\left[\frac{a_{-n}}{(s-s_0)^n}\right] = \frac{k}{\varrho^n}\cos(\theta - n\phi). \quad (31)$$

Since θ is a fixed angle and ϕ can vary from 0 to 2π in this neighborhood, we see that the real part of this dominant term changes sign $2n$ times as ϕ varies from 0 to 2π. Therefore the real part of $F(s)$ also changes sign $2n$ times (although not necessarily at exactly the same values of ϕ, due to the other terms in the Laurent expansion).

Now suppose that the function $F(s)$ satisfies the last two conditions in the definition of a positive real function, but it has a pole in the interior of the right half-plane. According to what we have just proved, the real part of $F(s)$ will then take on both negative and positive values in the right half-plane, which contradicts condition 3.

We conclude that in the case of rational functions, whose only singular points are poles, condition 1 of the definition of a positive real function is a consequence of the other two conditions and hence is unnecessary.

As a further aid to understanding, the definition of a positive real function can be interpreted as a *conformal mapping*. A positive real function $F = F(s)$ maps the real s-axis into the real F-axis, and maps the right half s-plane into the right half F-plane. This is illustrated in Fig. 4.

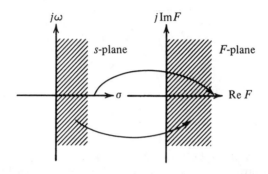

Fig. 4   Mapping by positive real functions

An immediate consequence of this interpretation is the fact that *a positive real function of a positive real function is itself positive real*; that is, if $F_1(s)$ and $F_2(s)$ are pr (this is used as an abbreviation for positive real), then

$$F(s) = F_2[F_1(s)] \qquad (32)$$

is also pr, because the right half s-plane goes into the right half F_1-plane, since $F_1(s)$ is positive real and because the right half F_1-plane goes into the right half F_2-plane, since F_2 is positive real. The composite mapping therefore maps the right half s-plane into the right half F-plane. The real axis is preserved throughout.

This is a useful result. We can use it to show immediately that, if $F(s)$ is pr, so are $1/F(s)$ and $F(1/s)$. To prove this result we merely observe that

$$\frac{1}{s} = \frac{\sigma}{\sigma^2 + \omega^2} - j\frac{\omega}{\sigma^2 + \omega^2} \qquad (33)$$

is a pr function. Now we use $1/s$ and $F(s)$ as $F_1(s)$ and $F_2(s)$ in (32), in both possible ways, and the results follow immediately.

From the fact that the reciprocal of a pr function is itself pr, it follows that a positive real function can have no zeros in the right half-plane; because if it did, then its reciprocal would have poles in the right half-plane, which is impossible. Since the impedance of a passive network is a pr function, its reciprocal — the admittance — is also a pr function.

From a conformal-mappping point of view, the points $F(s) = 0$ and ∞ — these are the zeros and poles of the functions — which are on the boundary of the right half F-plane, cannot be images of any interior points of the right half s-plane. They might, though, be images of boundary points of the right hand s-plane. Let us now inquire into the properties resulting when finite boundary points of the right half F-plane are in fact images of boundary points of the right half s-plane; that is, let a point on the $j\omega$-axis be mapped by a pr function $F(s)$ into a point on the imaginary axis of the F-plane. If $j\omega_0$ is the point in question, then:

$$F(j\omega_0) = jX_0, \tag{34}$$

where X_0 is real (positive, negative, or zero).

Consider a neighborhood of $j\omega_0$ in the s-plane and the corresponding neighborhood of jX_0 in the F-plane, as shown in Fig. 5. Let s_1 denote a point in the right half-plane in this neighborhood of $j\omega_0$. Let us now expand $F(s)$ in a Taylor series about $j\omega_0$ and evaluate it at $s = s_1$. The result is

$$F(s_1) - jX_0 = F^{(n)}(j\omega_0)(s_1 - j\omega_0)^n + F^{(n+1)}(j\omega_0)(s_1 - j\omega_0)^{n+1} + \ldots, \tag{35}$$

where $F^{(n)}(j\omega_0)$ is the first nonvanishing derivative of $F(s)$ at $j\omega_0$. (The real factors $1/n!$ of the Taylor coefficients are neglected.)

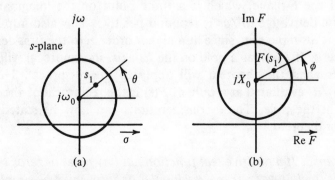

Fig. 5   Conformal mapping by positive real functions

As s_1 approaches $j\omega_0$, the dominant term on the right will be the first term. Let us define:

$$\phi = \arg[F(s_1) - jX_0], \tag{36}$$

$$\theta = \arg(s_1 - j\omega_0), \tag{37}$$

$$\beta = \arg[F^{(n)}(j\omega_0)], \tag{38}$$

Then, in the limit, we find from (35) that

$$\lim_{s_1 \to j\omega_0} \phi = \beta + n \lim_{s_1 \to j\omega_0} \theta. \tag{39}$$

But the positive real condition requires that $|\phi| \leqslant \pi/2$ as long as $|\theta| \leqslant \pi/2$. Therefore we conclude from (39) that

$$n = 1, \tag{40a}$$

$$\beta = 0. \tag{40b}$$

Thus the first nonvanishing derivative is the first one, and its angle is zero at $s = j\omega_0$. This is a very important result. For future reference we shall state it as a theorem:

Theorem 2. If any point on the $j\omega$-axis is mapped by a positive real function F into a finite point on the imaginary axis in the F-plane, then at this point the derivative dF/ds is real and positive.

That is, if $F(j\omega_0) = jX_0$, then $dF(s)/ds|_{s=j\omega_0} > 0$. A number of other results follow from this important theorem. Note that if $F(s)$ has a zero or a pole on the $j\omega$-axis, the conditions of the theorem are satisfied. In the case of a zero ($X_0 = 0$), a point on the $j\omega$-axis is mapped into the origin of the F-plane, which is a finite point on the imaginary axis. Hence the derivative dF/ds is real and positive. This also implies that the zero is a simple one, since at a higher order zero the first derivative will be zero. If $F(s)$ has a pole on the $j\omega$-axis, its reciprocal will have a zero there and the theorem will apply to the reciprocal. However, $d[1/F(s)]/ds$ evaluated at a pole of $F(s)$ is the reciprocal of the residue of $F(s)$ at the pole. These considerations can now be stated as the following theorem:

Theorem 3. If a positive real function has any poles or zeros on the $j\omega$-axis (including $s = 0, \infty$), such poles or zeros must be simple. At

*a simple zero on the jω-axis the derivative is real and positive. At a
simple pole on the jω-axis, the residue is real and positive.*

11.4.1 Necessary and Sufficient Conditions

We have up to this point collected quite a number of necessary conditions that a positive real function satisfies. What we would like to do is
to find a set from among these necessary conditions which proves to be
sufficient as well. The result is contained in the following theorem:

*Theorem 4. A rational function $F(s)$ with real coefficients is
positive real if and only if*
(a) *$F(s)$ is regular for $\sigma > 0$;*
(b) *Poles on the jω-axis (including $s = \infty$) are simple, with real
positive residues;*
(c) *$\mathrm{Re}[F(j\omega)] \geqslant 0$ for all ω, except at the poles.*

That these conditions are necessary is obvious from the definition of
a pr function and from Theorem 3. Therefore only the sufficiency needs
to be proved; that is, let us assume that a function $F(s)$ satisfies these
conditions and show that the function must be positive real. Let ω_1, ω_2,
..., ω_k be the poles on the jω-axis and let us examine the principal parts
at these poles. If there is a pole at the origin, the principal part is

$$F_0(s) = k_0/s,$$

where k_0 is real and positive. It is evident that $F_0(s)$ is itself pr and, in
addition, that

$$\mathrm{Re}[F(j\omega)] = 0.$$

Similarly, the principal part at a possible simple pole of $F(s)$ at infinity
is

$$F_\infty(s) = k_\infty s,$$

where k_∞ is real and positive, $F_\infty(s)$ is also pr and, in addition, its real
part on the jω-axis is zero; that is, $\mathrm{Re}[F_\infty(j\omega)] = 0$.

Any other poles on the jω-axis must occur in conjugate pairs and with
conjugate residues, since $F(s)$ is a real function. Since the residues are

real by hypothesis, the two residues are equal. Taking the principal parts at the conjugate poles $j\omega_i$ and $-j\omega_i$ together, we get

$$F_i(s) = \frac{k_i}{s - j\omega_i} + \frac{k_i}{s + j\omega_i} = \frac{2k_i s}{s^2 + \omega_i^2},$$

where k_i is real and positive. This function is also positive real and, in addition, has the property $\text{Re}[F_i(j\omega)] = 0$. (We may note that $F_0(s)$ is the impedance of a capacitor, $F_\infty(s)$ that of an inductor, and $F_i(s)$ that of a parallel connected capacitor and inductor.)

Thus we can subtract from the given function $F(s)$ the principal parts at all of its poles on the $j\omega$-axis. The remainder function $F_r(s)$ still has property (c) of the theorem; that is,

$$\text{Re}[F_r(j\omega)] = \text{Re}[F(j\omega)] \geqslant 0. \tag{41}$$

The remainder function $F_r(s)$ is a function that is regular in the right half-plane and on its entire boundary—the $j\omega$-axis, including the point at infinity. For such a function the minimum value of the real part throughout its region of regularity lies on the boundary. This can be proved by using the maximum-modulus theorem of complex function theory in the following way. Let $G(s) = e^{-F_r(s)}$. This function will have the same region of regularity as $F_r(s)$. Hence, according to the maximum-modulus theorem, the maximum magnitude of $G(s)$ for all $\sigma \geqslant 0$ lies on the $j\omega$-axis. Since

$$|G(s)| = e^{-\text{Re}[F_r(s)]} \tag{42}$$

the maximum magnitude of $G(s)$ will correspond to the smallest value of $\text{Re}[F_r(s)]$. This proves the desired result that the minimum value of $\text{Re}[F_r(s)]$ for all $\sigma \geqslant 0$ occurs on the $j\omega$-axis. Since according to (41) this value is nonnegative, the real part of $F_r(s)$ must be nonnegative everywhere in the right half-plane; that is,

$$\text{Re}[F_r(s)] \geqslant 0 \quad (\sigma \geqslant 0).$$

Since, in addition, $F_r(\sigma)$ is real, we conclude that $F_r(s)$ is a positive real function.

Now let us write

$$F(s) = F_r(s) + k_\infty s + \frac{k_0}{s} + \sum_i \frac{2k_i s}{s^2 + \omega_i^2}. \tag{43}$$

We have shown that each term on the right is pr. You can easily show that the sum of two (or more) pr functions is itself pr. Hence, $F(s)$ is positive real. This completes the proof of the sufficiency of the stated conditions.

Since the reciprocal of a pr function is also pr, we can restate these necessary and sufficient conditions in terms of the zeros of $F(s)$.

> *Theorem 5. A real rational function $F(s)$ is positive real if and only if:*
> (a) *$F(s)$ has no zeros in $\sigma > 0$.*
> (b) *Zeros on the $j\omega$-axis (including $s = \infty$) are simple, with real positive derivatives.*
> (c) *$\mathrm{Re}[F(j\omega)] > 0$ for all ω (except at poles).*

This theorem follows directly from the preceding one if we remember that the residue of a function at a simple pole is the reciprocal of the derivative of the reciprocal of the function.

11.4.2 Testing for Positive Realness

In testing a given function to determine positive realness, it may not always be necessary to use the necessary and sufficient conditions listed in the preceding two theorems. It may be possible to eliminate some functions from consideration by inspection because they violate certain simple necessary conditions. let us now discuss some of these conditions.

We have seen that a rational positive real function has neither zeros nor poles in the right half s-plane. We previously defined a *Hurwitz polynomial* as one that has no zeros in the right half s-plane. (This definition permits zeros on the $j\omega$-axis.) With this terminology, we see that a positive real function is the ratio of two Hurwitz polynomials.

The factors that constitute a Hurwitz polynomial must have one of the following two forms: $(s + a)$ for real zeros or $(s^2 + as + b)$ for a pair of complex zeros, with a being non-negative and b being positive. If any number of such factors are multiplied, the result must be a polynomial all of whose coefficients are non-negative. Furthermore, unless *all* the factors correspond to zeros on the $j\omega$-axis, *all* the coefficients of the polynomial will be strictly positive. If we introduce the added condition that zeros on the $j\omega$-axis be simple, then it is found that, when all the zeros are on the $j\omega$-axis, every other coefficient will be zero and the remaining coefficients will be strictly positive.

Even though this is a necessary condition for a Hurwitz polynomial, it is not sufficient, as the following counter-example readily demonstrates:

$$(s^2 - s + 4)(s + 2) = s^3 + s^2 + 2s + 8.$$

The polynomial on the right has no missing powers of s and all coefficients are positive, yet it has a pair of zeros in the right half-plane.

Hence, if a rational function is presented as a candidate for positive realness, this criterion can serve as a negative type of test. If the numerator or denominator polynomials have any negative coefficients or missing coefficients (other than all alternate coefficients as described above), the function can be discarded. On the other hand, if this test is passed, nothing definite can be said about the function.

Another simple test follows from the fact that a positive real function can have no more than a simple pole or a simple zero at zero or infinity (which are on the $j\omega$-axis). This requires that the highest powers of s in numerator and denominator not differ by more than unity; and similarly for the lowest powers.

To illustrate these thoughts we shall list some rational functions and see if they can be ruled out rapidly as not satisfying certain necessary conditions for positive real functions.

Function	Remarks
$F(s) = \dfrac{s^2 + 2s + 2}{s + 1}$	No more than simple pole at infinity; positive coefficients. Might be positive real.
$F(s) = \dfrac{s^4 + 3s^2 + 2s + 2}{s^3 + 4s^2 + s + 2}$	Coefficient of numerator cubic term missing. Not positive real.
$F(s) = \dfrac{s + 2}{s^3 + 5s^2 + 3s + 1}$	Double zero at infinity. Not positive real.
$F(s) = \dfrac{s^3 + 2s}{s^3 + 5s^2 + 2s + 5}$	Coefficients missing in numerator looks bad; but, all even powers missing. Might still be positive real. (In fact, it is.)
$F(s) = \dfrac{(s + 1)(s + 3)(s + 4)}{(s + 2)^3}$	No negative or missing coefficients, but triple pole at $s = -2$ might seem peculiar. Do not rule out. (In fact, it is positive real.)

11.4.3 The Angle Property of Positive Real Functions

An important property of the impedance of a passive network that was found earlier was the angle condition given in (20). This property can be proved mathematically, without recourse to energy considerations, simply from the definition of a positive real function. However, the proof is somewhat lengthy even though it is straightforward. It will therefore not be given but will be outlined in a problem. (See Prob. 1.) Furthermore, assuming the truth of (20) for a real function $F(s)$, it follows that $F(s)$ is positive real because

$$\text{Re}[F(s)] = |F(s)| \cos[\arg F(s)] \geqslant |F(s)| \cos[\arg s] \geqslant 0$$

$$\left(0 \leqslant |\arg s| \leqslant \frac{\pi}{2}\right).$$

Thus this angle property is not only necessary but sufficient as well. We shall therefore state it here as a theorem.

Theorem 6. A real rational function $F(s)$ is positive real if and only if

$$|\arg F(s)| \leqslant |\arg s| \quad \text{for} \quad 0 \leqslant |\arg s| \leqslant \frac{\pi}{2}. \tag{44}$$

11.4.4 Bounded Real Functions

It is possible to relate a function to a positive real function through a bilinear transformation. The function so obtained possesses some interesting properties. Consider the following bilinear transformation:

$$W(s) = \frac{1 - F(s)}{1 + F(s)} \quad \text{or} \quad F(s) = \frac{1 - W(s)}{1 + W(s)}. \tag{45}$$

The mapping between the F- and W-plane is shown in Fig. 6. The right half of the F-plane is mapped into (the interior of) the unit disk in the W-plane. The $j\omega$-axis becomes the boundary of the unit disk.

If $F(s)$ is a pr function, right half-plane values of s map into right half-plane values of F and so are mapped into the W-plane unit disk. When $s = j\omega$, $F(j\omega)$ takes on values in the right half-plane or on the Im

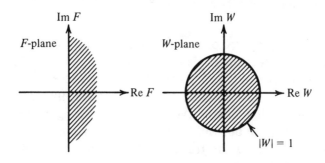

Fig. 6   Mapping of bilinear transformation

F-axis, and these fall inside or on the boundary of the W-plane unit disk. Hence, if $F(s)$ is pr and $W(s)$ is related to $F(s)$ through (45), then

$$|W(j\omega)| \leqslant 1. \qquad (46)$$

Now consider the poles of $W(s)$. From (45), these occur where $F(s) = -1$. Values of s for which this is true cannot lie in the closed right half-plane if $F(s)$ is pr, since that would require Re $F < 0$ for Re $s \geqslant 0$. Hence $W(s)$ must be regular both in the right half-plane and on the $j\omega$-axis.

A function $W(s)$ having these properties—namely $W(s)$ regular in the closed right half-plane and $|W(j\omega)| \leqslant 1$—is called *bounded real*. Thus *a bilinear transformation of a positive real function is bounded real*. The converse of this is also true; that is, *a bilinear transformation of a bounded real function is positive real*. Sketching the few steps in the proof is left to you.

This relationship of bounded real and positive real functions leads to an interesting conclusion. Suppose a pr function $F(s)$ is written as

$$F(s) = \frac{m_1(s) + n_1(s)}{m_2(s) + n_2(s)}, \qquad (47)$$

where m_1 and m_2 are even polynomials, and n_1 and n_2 are odd. Then the bilinear transformation (45) gives

$$W(s) = \frac{(m_2 - m_1) + (n_2 - n_1)}{(m_2 + m_1) + (n_2 + n_1)}. \qquad (48)$$

The magnitude squared function $|W(j\omega)|^2$ becomes

$$|W(j\omega)|^2 = \frac{(m_2 - m_1)^2 - (n_2 - n_1)^2}{(m_2 + m_1)^2 - (n_2 + n_1)^2}\bigg|_{s=j\omega} \leqslant 1. \tag{49}$$

Now suppose m_1 and m_2 are interchanged; clearly, the value of $|W(j\omega)|$ will not be affected, as observed from (49); neither will the poles of $W(s)$, as observed from (48), although the zeros of $W(s)$ will. Let the new W-function obtained by interchanging m_1 and m_2 be called $\hat{W}(s)$. It is clearly a bounded real function. From (48), $\hat{W}$ is found to be

$$\hat{W}(s) = \frac{(m_1 - m_2) + (n_2 - n_1)}{(m_1 + m_2) + (n_1 + n_2)}. \tag{50}$$

The corresponding pr function $\hat{F}(s)$ is found from the bilinear transformation (45) to be

$$\hat{F}(s) = \frac{m_2(s) + n_1(s)}{m_1(s) + n_2(s)}. \tag{51}$$

This is simply the original $F(s)$ with the even powers of the numerator and denominator interchanged. Since $F(s)$ is a bilinear transformation of a bounded real function, it is pr. The reciprocal of $\hat{F}$ is also pr. But the reciprocal of $\hat{F}$ is the same as the original $F(s)$, with $n_1(s)$ and $n_2(s)$ interchanged. The conclusion is given as the following theorem:

Theorem 7. If in a positive real function the even powers of the numerator and denominator, or the odd powers, are interchanged, the result is a positive real function.

11.4.5 Real Part Function

Since the real part of a pr function plays such a central role in its properties, we should examine the behavior of the real part of such a function on the $j\omega$-axis. Remember that the $j\omega$-axis real part of $F(s)$ is equal to the even part evaluated at $s = j\omega$; that is,

$$\begin{aligned} R(\omega) &= \text{Re}[F(j\omega)] = \text{Ev}\, F(s)|_{s=j\omega} \\ &= \tfrac{1}{2}[F(s) + F(-s)]|_{s=j\omega} \\ &= \tfrac{1}{2}[F(j\omega) + F(-j\omega)], \end{aligned} \tag{52}$$

so that statements made about the even part can easily be interpreted in terms of the real part on the $j\omega$-axis.

We already know that $R(\omega)$ is necessarily an even function of ω and non-negative for all ω. It is also easy to establish that the even part of $F(s)$ can have no poles on the $j\omega$-axis. Any poles of the even part would also have to be poles of $F(s)$; but on the $j\omega$-axis, these are simple. Now consider $F(s)$ given as a partial fraction expansion as in (43). The function $F(-s)$ will contain the same terms, but all those involving the poles on the $j\omega$-axis will have a negative sign. Hence, in forming the even part, $F(s) + F(-s)$, these will all cancel, leaving the function with no poles on the $j\omega$-axis. Interpreted in terms of the real part, this means that $R(\omega)$ *must be bounded for all* ω.

Now let us consider a possible zero of $R(\omega)$. Fig. 7 shows a sketch of $R(\omega)$ versus ω in the vincinity of a zero. Because of the positive real requirement, $R(\omega)$ must remain positive on both sides of the zero. It follows that a zero of $R(\omega)$ on the ω-axis cannot be of odd multiplicity; it must be of even multiplicity.

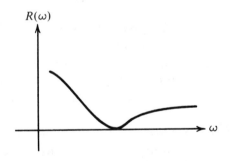

Fig. 7   Sketch of real part of positive real function

We have here determined certain necessary conditions for the $j\omega$-axis real part of a positive real function. Let us now list a set of necessary and sufficient conditions as a theorem.

Theorem 8. A real function $R(\omega)$ of a real variable ω is the real part of a rational positive real function $F(s)$ on the $j\omega$-axis if and only if
(a) *$R(\omega)$ is an even rational function with real coefficients,*
(b) *$R(\omega)$ is bounded for all ω, and*
(c) *$R(\omega) \geqslant 0$ for all ω.*

We have already seen that these conditions are necessary. It is a simple matter of actual construction to find a rational function from a given $R(\omega)$ satisfying the first two conditions. (See Question Set II, Ex. 43.) If condition (c) is also satisfied by $R(\omega)$, this is sufficient to make the rational function in question a positive real function.

11.5 TWO-PORT PARAMETERS

In the previous sections we studied some of the most important properties of driving-point functions of passive one-port networks. We shall now go on to a consideration of multiport networks; in particular, two-ports. The groundwork was laid in (16) for a consideration of the impedance and admittance matrices. The right-hand side of each of these equations is a positive real function. (The right-hand side of the second equation is the conjugate of that of the first.) The left-hand side of each equation is a quadratic form that is now seen to equal a positive real function. Just as we say that the matrix of a positive definite quadratic form is positive definite, so also we say that the matrix of a positive real quadratic form is positive real. The conclusion then is

Theorem 9. The impedance and admittance matrices of a passive, multiport network are positive real matrices.

The same result can be demonstrated in a different way. It will be illustrated for a two-port by the network shown in Fig. 8. The two pairs

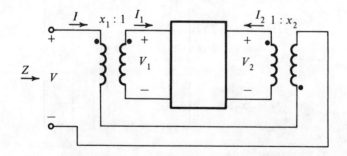

Fig. 8 Demonstration that the **Z** and **Y** matrices are positive real

of terminals of the two-port are connected in series through ideal transformers whose turns ratios are x_1:1 and x_2:1, respectively. The voltage and current at the input terminals will be

$$V = x_1 V_1 + x_2 V_2, \tag{53a}$$

$$I = \frac{I_1}{x_1} = \frac{I_2}{x_2}. \tag{53b}$$

If we now compute the driving-point impedance $Z(s) = V/I$ at the input terminals, we get

$$Z(s) = x_1^2 z_{11} + 2x_1 x_2 z_{21} + x_2^2 z_{22}$$

$$= [x_1 \quad x_2] \begin{bmatrix} z_{11} & z_{12} \\ z_{21} & z_{22} \end{bmatrix} \begin{bmatrix} x_1 \\ x_2 \end{bmatrix} \tag{54}$$

Since the impedance is positive real for all x_1 and x_2, this proves that the quadratic form on the right is also positive real. To prove the condition for the Y-matrix, the two pairs of terminals can be connected in parallel through ideal transformers and the overall input admittance calculated. This is left for you to do. (See Prob. 19.)

Let us now restrict ourselves to two-ports; the extension of the subsequent results to higher order multiports is simple and will become evident. The fact that Z and Y are positive real matrices has some interesting consequences. Let x_1 and x_2 be two arbitrary real numbers. Since the quadratic forms

$$Q_1 = [x_1 \quad x_2] \begin{bmatrix} z_{11} & z_{12} \\ z_{21} & z_{22} \end{bmatrix} \begin{bmatrix} x_1 \\ x_2 \end{bmatrix} \tag{55a}$$

$$Q_2 = [x_1 \quad x_2] \begin{bmatrix} y_{11} & y_{12} \\ y_{21} & y_{22} \end{bmatrix} \begin{bmatrix} x_1 \\ x_2 \end{bmatrix} \tag{55b}$$

are positive real functions, it follows by Theorem 4 that any pole of these functions on the $j\omega$-axis must be simple, and the residue at such a pole must be real and positive. Suppose, for instance, that the z-parameters have a pole at $s = j\omega_i$. Since this pole is a simple pole of the quadratic form, the residue of Q_1 is

$$\text{residue of } Q_1 = \lim_{s \to j\omega_i} (s - j\omega_i)[x_1 \quad x_2] \begin{bmatrix} z_{11} & z_{12} \\ z_{21} & z_{22} \end{bmatrix} \begin{bmatrix} x_1 \\ x_2 \end{bmatrix}$$

$$(56)$$

$$= \lim_{s \to j\omega_i} [x_1 \quad x_2] \begin{bmatrix} (s - j\omega_i)z_{11} & (s - j\omega_i)z_{12} \\ (s - j\omega_i)z_{21} & (s - j\omega_i)z_{22} \end{bmatrix} \begin{bmatrix} x_1 \\ x_2 \end{bmatrix}$$

If we give the residues of z_{11}, z_{12}, z_{21}, and z_{22} at the pole $s = j\omega_i$ the labels $k_{11}^{(i)}$, $k_{12}^{(i)}$, $k_{21}^{(i)}$, and $k_{22}^{(i)}$, respectively, then the residue of the quadratic form will become

$$\text{residue of } Q_1 = [x_1 \quad x_2] \begin{bmatrix} k_{11}^{(i)} & k_{12}^{(i)} \\ k_{21}^{(i)} & k_{22}^{(i)} \end{bmatrix} \begin{bmatrix} x_1 \\ x_2 \end{bmatrix} \quad (57)$$

Thus the residue of Q_1 itself is a quadratic form whose matrix is the matrix of residues of the z-parameters. However, this residue must be real and non-negative for all values of x_1 and x_2. Hence the symmetric part of the matrix of residues of the z-parameters at any poles on the $j\omega$-axis must be positive semidefinite. This requires that the determinant and all of the principal cofactors of the symmetric part of the matrix, which is

$$\begin{bmatrix} k_{11}^{(i)} & \frac{1}{2}(k_{12}^{(i)} + k_{21}^{(i)}) \\ \frac{1}{2}(k_{12}^{(i)} + k_{21}^{(i)}) & k_{22}^{(i)} \end{bmatrix}$$

be non-negative. Thus,

$$k_{11}^{(i)} \geqslant 0, \quad k_{22}^{(i)} \geqslant 0, \quad (58a)$$

$$k_{11}^{(i)} k_{22}^{(i)} - [\tfrac{1}{2}(k_{12}^{(i)} + k_{21}^{(i)})]^2 \geqslant 0. \quad (58b)$$

Observe that in the case of a reciprocal network this second condition can be simplified. For this case $z_{12} = z_{21}$, which implies that $k_{12}^{(i)} = k_{21}^{(i)}$. Thus, (58b) becomes

$$k_{11}^{(i)} k_{22}^{(i)} - (k_{21}^{(i)})^2 \geqslant 0 \quad \text{(reciprocal network)}. \quad (59)$$

The first line in (58) is already known, since z_{11} and z_{22} are driving-point functions and therefore positive real. The second line or its reciprocal network restriction in (59), however, is a new and important result. It is known as the *residue condition*.

What was done for the quadratic form Q_1 is also valid for Q_2. Thus the same conclusions follow for residues of **Y**. We shall state the result for reciprocal networks as a theorem.

*Theorem 10. At any $j\omega$-axis pole of **Z** or **Y** of a passive, reciprocal two-port network, the residues of the parameters satisfy the condition*

$$k_{11}k_{22} - k_{21}^2 \geq 0, \tag{60}$$

where k_{ij} is the residue of z_{ij} or y_{ij} at the $j\omega$-axis pole.

Let us now turn to another consequence of the positive real nature of **Z** and **Y**. By definition, positive realness is linked with the real part of a function. Hence we should expect to obtain some relationships among the real parts of the z- and y-parameters. Let us denote these real parts as r_{11}, r_{12}, r_{21}, and r_{22} for the z-parameters and as g_{11}, g_{12}, g_{21}, and g_{22} for the y-parameters. The real part of the quadratic forms Q_1 and Q_2 in (55) can then be written as follows:

$$\text{Re}(Q_1) = \begin{bmatrix} x_1 & x_2 \end{bmatrix} \begin{bmatrix} r_{11} & r_{12} \\ r_{21} & r_{22} \end{bmatrix} \begin{bmatrix} x_1 \\ x_2 \end{bmatrix} \tag{61a}$$

$$\text{Re}(Q_2) = \begin{bmatrix} x_1 & x_2 \end{bmatrix} \begin{bmatrix} g_{11} & g_{12} \\ g_{21} & g_{22} \end{bmatrix} \begin{bmatrix} x_1 \\ x_2 \end{bmatrix} \tag{61b}$$

Whenever s lies in the closed right half-plane, these quadratic forms must be positive semidefinite, since Q_1 and Q_2 are positive real functions. As in the case of the matrix of residues, it follows for Re $s \geq 0$ that

$$r_{11} \geq 0, \quad r_{22} \geq 0, \tag{62a}$$

and

$$r_{11}r_{22} - [\tfrac{1}{2}(r_{12} + r_{21})]^2 \geq 0 \tag{62b}$$

or

$$r_{11}r_{22} - r_{21}^2 \geqslant 0 \text{ (reciprocal network)} \tag{62c}$$

for the real parts of the z-parameters and that

$$g_{11} \geqslant 0, \ g_{22} \geqslant 0, \tag{63a}$$

and

$$g_{11}g_{22} - [\tfrac{1}{2}(g_{12} + g_{21})]^2 \geqslant 0 \tag{63b}$$

or

$$g_{11}g_{22} - g_{21}^2 \geqslant 0 \text{ (reciprocal network)} \tag{63c}$$

for the real parts of the y-parameters. Again the first lines in each set carry no surprises, since z_{11}, z_{22}, y_{11}, and y_{22} are driving-point functions and hence positive real. The second and third lines, however, express a new result, which is called the *real-part condition*. In fact, the real part condition alone is a sufficient condition that $\mathbf{Z}$ or $\mathbf{Y}$ be positive real matrices. (Verify this statement; see Prob. 22.)

CHAPTER 12
Passive (LC, RC, and RLC) Synthesis

We saw in the previous chapter that the driving-point function — impedance or admittance — of a passive (and lumped component) network is a positive real (and rational) function. We also established the more general result that the impedance and admittance matrices of a passive network are positive real matrices. It is quite reasonable now to ask: Are the converse implications true? We shall not attempt to develop an answer to this very general question to which others have devoted entire books. Rather, we shall establish a partial answer by devising synthesis procedures by which to realize a network exhibiting the positive real property under some added constraints. It is, of course, the existence of the synthesis procedure which affirms the reverse implication.

Let us therefore first turn our attention to one of several special types of positive real functions. These arise from a consideration of networks containing only two types of elements — LC, RC, and RL. Historically, such networks were studied before the more general ones, starting with the work done by Foster in 1924.

12.1 REACTANCE FUNCTIONS

We shall initially consider networks for which the energy function $F_0(s)$ is identically zero. Such networks are referred to as *lossless*, or *reactance*, or LC networks. The last name derives from the fact that networks with just inductors and capacitors — no resistors — are lossless, or reactive; that is, $F_0(s) \equiv 0$. In Theorem 11-1 we noted that the driving-point impedance of a lossless (necessarily passive) network is purely imaginary on the $j\omega$-axis; that is, $\text{Re}[Z(j\omega)] = 0$. Stated in terms of a transformation, the impedance of a lossless network maps the imaginary axis of the s-plane into the imaginary axis of the Z-plane. Having observed this property of the impedance of a network, we shall now revert to mathematics and make this property the basis of a definition. We shall make the following definition: *A reactance function is a positive real function that maps the imaginary axis into the imaginary axis*. In this terminology, the driving-point impedance of a lossless network is a reactance function.

12.1.1 Properties of Reactance Functions

We shall first show that the poles and zeros of a reactance function all lie on the $j\omega$-axis. Note that, just as a function that maps the real axis into the real axis has symmetry about the real axis [i.e., $F(\bar{s}) = \bar{F}(s)$], so also, a function that maps the imaginary axis into the imaginary axis has symmetry about the imaginary axis. To see this clearly let us rotate the two planes (the s-plane and the F-plane) clockwise by $\pi/2$ radians. We do this by defining

$$z = \frac{s}{j}, \tag{1a}$$

$$\psi(z) = \frac{1}{j}F(jz). \tag{1b}$$

These transformations are shown in Fig. 1. Note that the real s-axis becomes the imaginary z-axis, and vice versa. A similar case obtains for the other transformation. Now, when z is real, the argument of $F(jz)$ is

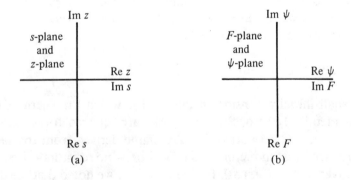

Fig. 1 **Transformation that rotates axes by $\pi/2$ radians**

imaginary, so by hypothesis $F(jz)$ will also be imaginary. Hence, $\psi(z)$ will be real when z is real. It then follows from the reflection property that

$$\psi(\bar{z}) = \bar{\psi}(z). \tag{2}$$

If we translate back through the transformations in (1) this reflection property implies

$$F(-\bar{s}) = -\bar{F}(s). \tag{3}$$

Note that the point $-\bar{s}$ is the image of the point s with respect to the imaginary axis. A similar case obtains for the points $-\bar{F}$ and F. Hence the result in (3) states that image points with respect to the imaginary axis in the s-plane go into image points with respect to the imgainary axis in the F-plane.

It follows that, if $F(s)$ has a pole or a zero in the left half-plane, then the image point in the right half-plane is also a pole or a zero, which is not possible for a pr function. Hence *the poles and zeros of a reactance function must all lie on the $j\omega$-axis.*

Let us turn back to Theorem 11-2 for a moment. There we saw that if a pr function maps a point on the $j\omega$-axis into a finite point on the imaginary axis, then the derivative of the function at that point is real and positive. But according to Theorem 11-1, a reactance function maps the entire $j\omega$-axis into the imaginary axis in the F-plane. Hence for such a function the derivative property will hold at all points except poles on the $j\omega$-axis. This is the basis of another very important property; namely, *the poles and zeros of a reactance function alternate on the $j\omega$-axis;* that is, between any two poles is a zero and between any two zeros is a pole.

As already noted, Theorem 11-2 applies at all points on the $j\omega$-axis except at poles. Hence the derivative dF/ds evaluated at $s=j\omega$ is real and positive. Let us compute the derivative of the function $F(s)$ along the $j\omega$-axis, which we are permitted to do since the derivative exists. The result will be

$$\left. \frac{dF}{ds} \right|_{s=j\omega} = \frac{dF(j\omega)}{d(j\omega)} = \frac{d[jX(\omega)]}{d(j\omega)} = \frac{jdX(\omega)}{jd\omega} = \frac{dX(\omega)}{d\omega} > 0. \tag{4}$$

We have used the usual notation $F(j\omega) = R(\omega) + jX(\omega)$, in which, since F is here a reactance function, $R(\omega)$ is zero. Notice that $X(\omega)$ is a real function of a real variable. Therefore, if there were no pole between two zeros of $X(\omega)$, the derivative would become negative somewhere in between, which, as we have just shown, is impossible. A similar conclusion applies to successive poles. Figure 2 illustrates the form that $X(\omega)$ would have for successive zeros or poles without intervening poles or zeros, respectively.

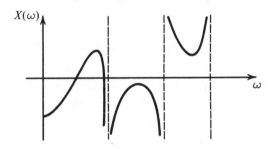

Fig. 2   Impossible behavior of a reactance function

The property that we have just established is referred to as the *alternation property* of the poles and zeros. From this property it is clear that the plot of $X(\omega)$ against ω must have the general shape shown in Fig. 3.

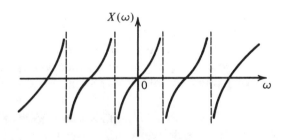

Fig. 3   Correct behavior of a reactance function

Since $X(\omega)$ is an odd function of ω and the alternation of poles and zeros must hold on the entire—positive and negative—imaginary axis, we conclude that the point $s=0$ is either a zero or a pole of a reactance function.

Note that, if $F(s)$ is a pr function mapping the imaginary axis into the imaginary axis, so is the function $F(1/s)$. With the transformation $s \to 1/s$, the point ∞ in the s-plane goes into the origin in the $1/s$-plane. Hence, by using the immediately preceding result, we find that the point $s = \infty$ is either a zero or a pole of a reactance function.

We have now discussed several properties of reactance functions. We should also remember that the properties of (general) pr functions apply in particular to reactance functions. Thus, since we have shown in Theorems 11-4 and 11-5 that poles and zeros of a pr function that lie on the $j\omega$-axis are simple and that residues at such poles are real and positive, we conclude that all poles and zeros of reactance functions are simple and that residues at all poles are real and positive.

We are now in a position to consolidate our results about reactance functions and to state necessary and sufficient conditions for a rational function of s to be a reactance function.

Theorem 1. A real rational function $\psi(s)$ is a reactance function if and only if
1. *All of its poles are simple and lie on the $j\omega$-axis;*
2. *The residues are all real and positive;*
3. *The function has either a pole or a zero at $s=0$ and at $s=\infty$; and*
4. *Re $\psi(j\omega)=0$ for some ω.*

Notice that this statement involves only the poles and the residues, not the zeros. We have already shown the preceding conditions to be necessary; it remains to prove that they are sufficient; that is, assuming a rational function to satisfy the stated conditions, we must show that the function is a reactance function. This is most easily done by considering the partial-fraction expansion of such a function. If we combine the two terms due to conjugate poles, the most general form of the partial-fraction expansion will be*

$$\psi(s) = \frac{k_0}{s} + k_\infty s + \sum_{i=1}^{n} \frac{2k_i s}{s^2 + \omega_i^2}, \tag{5}$$

---

* In the absence of condition 4 in Theorem 1, a constant term would be permitted in the expansion of (5). Condition 4 is required to eliminate this constant, which cannot be part of a reactance function.

where the summation runs over all the poles and all the k's are positive. Of course, the pole at the origin or at infinity, or both, may be absent. This expression is consistent with (11-43) with $F_r(s) = 0$, since in the present case there are no other poles except those on the $j\omega$-axis. The desired result follows immediately. Each term in this expansion is imaginary for imaginary values of s, so that $\psi(s)$ maps the imaginary axis into the imaginary axis, which makes $\psi(s)$ a reactance function by definition.

The alternation property of the poles and zeros forms the basis of an alternate set of necessary and sufficient conditions, stated as

Theorem 2. A real rational function of s is a reactance function if and only if all of its poles and zeros are simple, lie on the $j\omega$-axis, and alternate with each other.

Again, we have already proved that a reactance function necessarily satisfies these conditions. It remains to show that the conditions are sufficient. A real rational function that satisfies the given conditions must have the following form:

$$\psi(s) = K \frac{s(s^2 + \omega_1^2)(s^2 + \omega_3^2)\dots(s^2 + \omega_{2n-1}^2)}{(s^2 + \omega_0^2)(s^2 + \omega_2^2)\dots(s^2 + \omega_k^2)}, \tag{6}$$

where

$$0 \leqslant \omega_0 < \omega_1 < \omega_2 < \omega_3 < \dots < \omega_{2n-2} < \omega_{2n-1} < \omega_{2n} < \infty. \tag{7}$$

In (6) K is a positive constant, and $k = 2n - 2$ or $2n$ according as $\psi(s)$ has a pole or a zero at infinity. If $\psi(s)$ has a pole at $s = 0$, we take ω_0 to be zero. A factor s will then cancel. The desired result now follows immediately: Conditions 1, 3, and 4 of Theorem 1 are satisfied by inspection and condition 2 follows from an examination of the partial fraction expansion of (6); hence, by Theorem 1 the sufficiency of the conditions of Theorem 2 is established. [You should obtain the partial fraction expansion of (6) and indeed show that it is of the form of (5) with positive residues.]

12.2 REALIZATION OF REACTANCE FUNCTIONS

At the start of this discussion we showed that the driving-point impedance of a lossless network is necessarily a reactance function. Note that the driving-point admittance of a lossless network is also a reactance function; that is,

$$Y(s) = 1/Z(s) \tag{8}$$

is also imaginary for imaginary values of s if $Z(s)$ is.

The question now arises as to whether the converse of this condition is also true; that is, given a reactance function, is this the driving-point impedance (or admittance) of some lossless network? In order to answer this question in the affirmative, we shall have to construct a lossless network that has the given reactance function as its impedance or admittance. The question was answered in 1924 by Foster in his famous reactance theorem (although not in the form given here).

Theorem 3. A real rational function of s is a reactance function if and only if it is the driving-point impedance or admittance of a lossless network.

We have already estalished the sufficiency. It remains to show that, given a reactance function, it is necessarily the impedance or the admittance of a lossless network. To show this, turn back to the partial-fraction expansion of a reactance function given in (5). We recognize that each of the summands of the partial-fraction expansion is the impedance or admittance of a very simple reactance structure. These structures are shown in Table 1. Thus, if $\psi(s)$ [alternatively, $1/\psi(s)$] is to be an impedance, we can represent it as a series connection of the elementary one-port networks in column 2 of Table 1 or we can represent $1/\psi(s)$ [alternatively, $\psi(s)$] — an admittance — as a parallel connection of the elementary one-port networks in column 3. Clearly this statement remains true following an interchange of the words "impedance" and "admittance." The forms of the resulting networks are shown in Fig. 4. They are referred to as Foster's first and second forms.

We have now proved the theorem with a vengeance. We found that a given reactance function can be both the impedance and the admittance of some lossless network — not the same network, of course.

Let us illustrate this result with the following function. Let

$$Z(s) = \psi(s) = \frac{4(s^2+1)(s^2+9)}{s(s^2+4)} = 4s + \frac{9}{s} + \frac{15s}{s^2+4} \tag{9a}$$

or

$$Y(s) = \frac{1}{\psi(s)} = \frac{s(s^2+4)}{4(s^2+1)(s^2+9)} = \frac{(3/32)s}{s^2+1} + \frac{(5/32)}{s^2+9}. \tag{9b}$$

Table 1   Representation of Partial-Fraction Summands

Term	Network representation	
	Impedance	Admittance
$\dfrac{k_0}{s}$	 $C = 1/k_0$	 $L = 1/k_0$
$k_\infty s$	 $L = k_\infty$	 $C = k_\infty$
$\dfrac{2k_i s}{s^2 + \omega_i^2}$	$L = 2k_i/\omega_i^2$ $C = 1/2k_i$	$C = 2k_i/\omega_i^2$ $L = 1/2k_i$

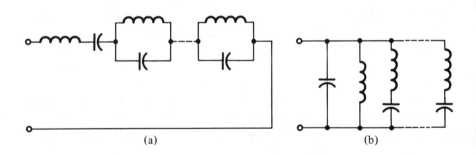

(a)   (b)

Fig. 4   Foster's forms of lossless one-ports

In the first of these, the term $4s$ is recognized as the impedance of a four-unit inductor. Similarly, $9/s$ is recognized as the impedance of a 1/9-unit capacitor. (The units are not henry or farad because this is presumably a normalized function.) The impedance of an inductor and capacitor in parallel is

$$Z = \frac{s/C}{s^2 + 1/LC}.$$

Hence, by direct comparison, the values of L and C are found to be $C = 1/15$, $L = 15/4$. (Confirm these values as those obtained by substitution in the expressions found in Table 1.) The network takes the form shown in Fig. 5(a).

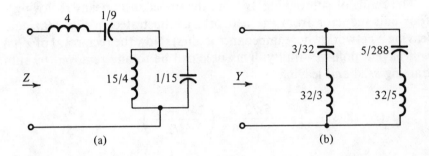

Fig. 5   Reactive network realizations

The admittance in (9b) is seen to consist of two terms, each of which can be realized by an inductor and a capacitor in a series. The admittance of such a series-tuned circuit is

$$Y = \frac{s/L}{s^2 + 1/LC}.$$

Hence the values of L and C for each of the two branches can be found by comparison of this expansion with each of the numerical terms in the given function. The result is shown in Fig. 5(b).

The two networks obtained are entirely equivalent at their terminals. No measurements made there could distinguish one from the other. You should complete this illustration by determining a series realization of $Z(s) = 1/\psi(s)$ and a parallel realization of $Y(s) = \psi(s)$.

The Foster forms are not the only possible network structures by which to realize a given function. (There are, in fact, an infinite number of alternative structures.) Before generalizing, let us illustrate this by finding a different structure realizing the impedance of the example already treated. The impedance in (9a) has a pole at infinity. If this entire pole is subtracted from $Z(s)$, the remaining function will no longer have a pole at infinity and so it must have a zero there. Thus

$$Z_1(s) = Z(s) - 4s = \frac{4(s^2+1)(s^2+9)}{s(s^2+4)} - 4s = \frac{24s^2+36}{s^3+4s}$$

$$= \left(\frac{s^3+4s}{24s^2+36}\right)^{-1} = \left(\frac{s}{24} + \frac{5s/2}{24s^2+36}\right)^{-1}.$$

The result of subtracting $4s$ from the impedance means removing a four-unit inductor from the network, as illustrated in Fig. 6(a), and leaving a network whose impedance is $Z_1(s)$. Now the reciprocal of $Z_1(s)$ will have a pole at infinity. This pole can be totally removed by subtracting $s/24$ and leaving

$$Y_2(s) = Y_1(s) - \frac{s}{24} = \frac{5s/2}{24s^2+36} = \left(\frac{24s^2+36}{5s/2}\right)^{-1} = \left(\frac{48s}{5} + \frac{72}{5s}\right)^{-1}.$$

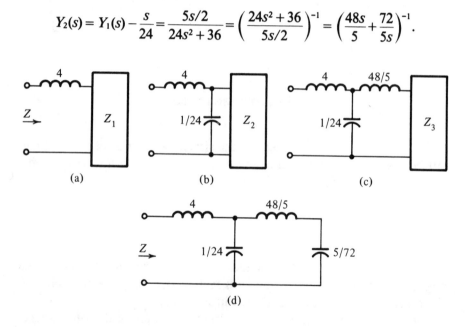

(a)   (b)   (c)

(d)

Fig. 6   Reactive (ladder) network realization

The network equivalent of subtracting $s/24$ from the admittance is to remove a 1/24-unit capacitor from across the input terminals of $Z_1(s)$, as shown in Fig. 6(b). The admittance $Y_2(s)$ remaining after this removal has no pole at infinity, but its reciprocal, $Z_2(s)$, does. This can be removed, leaving

$$Z_3(s) = Z_2(s) - \frac{48s}{5} = \frac{72}{5s}.$$

The network equivalent of subtracting an impedance of $48s/5$ is to remove a $48/5$-unit inductor, as shown in Fig. 6(c). The remaining impedance $Z_3(s)$ is simple enough to identify as a capacitor. The final network is shown in Fig. 6(d). It is in the form of a ladder network.

A ladder network having arbitrary branches is shown in Fig. 7. Its impedance can be written in the following *continued-fraction* form:

$$Z = Z_1 + \cfrac{1}{Y_2 + \cfrac{1}{Z_3 + \cfrac{1}{Y_4 + \cfrac{1}{Z_5 + \cfrac{1}{Y_6}}}}} \qquad (10)$$

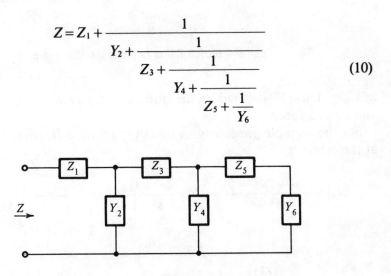

Fig. 7   Ladder network with arbitrary branch immittances

In the example just treated the process carried out step-by-step was actually a continued-fraction expansion, where each of the Z_i and Y_i functions in (10) is of the form ks, in which k is inductance or capacitance. The expansion deals exclusively with the pole at infinity, removing this pole alternately from an impedance and then the remaining admittance. The result of this process for an arbitrary reactance function will have the network structure shown in Fig. 8(a).

An alternate continued fraction expansion can be made by dealing with the pole at the origin, $s = 0$. The expansion is obtained by removing the pole at $s = 0$ alternately from an impedance and then the remaining admittance until the function is exhausted. In this case each of the Z_i and Y_i functions in (10) will be of the form k/s, where $1/k$ is capacitance or inductance. The resulting network structure is that shown in Fig. 8(b). You should bear in mind that, if $Z(s)$ does not have a pole at infinity in the first case or at the origin in the second case, then the first impedance Z_1 — an inductor or a capacitor, respectively — will be

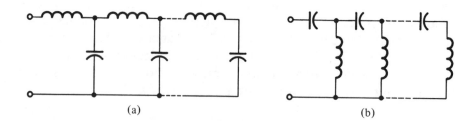

Fig. 8   First and second Cauer forms of lossless one-ports

missing. These lossless ladder structures are also known as Cauer's first and second forms.

For the example previously treated the continued fraction expansion at the origin is

$$Z(s) = \frac{4(s^2+1)(s^2+9)}{s(s^2+4)} = 9/s + \frac{4s^3+31s}{s^2+4} = 9/s + \cfrac{1}{4/31s + \cfrac{15s/31}{4s^2+31}}$$

$$= 9/s + \cfrac{1}{4/31s + \cfrac{1}{961/15s + \cfrac{1}{15/124s}}}$$

The resulting network is as in Fig. 8(b) with the first four elements being

$$C_1 = \frac{1}{9}, \; L_2 = \frac{31}{4}, \; C_3 = \frac{15}{961}, \text{ and } L_4 = \frac{124}{15}.$$

To summarize, we have shown that the impedance and admittance of a lossless, or LC, network are reactance functions; and conversely, given any reactance function, a number of networks can be found whose impedance or admittance is equal to the given reactance function.

12.3 HURWITZ POLYNOMIALS AND REACTANCE FUNCTIONS

We have found that a reactance function is an odd rational function, the ratio of an odd to an even polynomial, or vice versa, as observed in (6). If we denote even and odd polynomials by $m(s)$ and $n(s)$, respectively, then a reactance function $\psi(s)$ can be written as

$$\psi(s) = \frac{m(s)}{n(s)} \text{ or } \frac{n(s)}{m(s)}, \tag{11}$$

where m and n have no common factors.

Now consider the parallel connection of a lossless network and a one unit resistance. Taking $\psi(s)$ to be the admittance of the lossless network, the impedance of this combination will be

$$Z(s) = \frac{1}{1 + \psi(s)} = \frac{n(s)}{m(s) + n(s)} \text{ or } \frac{m(s)}{m(s) + n(s)}, \tag{12}$$

where (11) is used for $\psi(s)$. The impedance of this *RCL* network will be pr and regular on the $j\omega$-axis; hence its poles cannot lie in the closed right half-plane. The polynomial $m(s) + n(s)$ in (12) is therefore a strictly Hurwitz polynomial. This is a very useful result. We state a somewhat generalized version of this result, and its converse, as

Theorem 4. Let $m(s)$ and $n(s)$ be, respectively, the even and odd parts of the polynomial $P(s) = m(s) + n(s)$. Then, $P(s)$ is the product of a strictly Hurwitz polynomial and an even polynomial (which might just be the even polynomial of zero degree having the value 1) if and only if $m(s)/n(s)$ is a reactance function. *

This theorem provides us with a means for easily determining whether a given rational function is regular in the right half-plane, as positive realness requires. We take the ratio (or its reciprocal) of the even and odd parts of the denominator polynomial, then expand in a continued fraction or a partial fraction. To illustrate, let

$$P(s) = 2s^4 + 5s^3 + 6s^2 + 3s + 1.$$

Then

$$m(s) = 2s^4 + 6s^2 + 1,$$

$$n(s) = 5s^3 + 3s.$$

Now form the ratio m/n and expand in a continued fraction. The result will be

---

* A proof is outlined in Prob. 17 for you to work out. An alternate proof is given in Norman Balabanian, *Network Synthesis*, Prentice-Hall, Englewood Cliffs, N.J., 1958, pp. 77-81.

$$\frac{m(s)}{n(s)} = \frac{2s^4 + 6s^2 + 1}{5s^3 + 3s} = \frac{2s}{5} + \cfrac{1}{\cfrac{25s}{24} + \cfrac{1}{\cfrac{576s}{235} + \cfrac{1}{\cfrac{47s}{24}}}}.$$

The elements in a lossless network realization of this continued fraction will all be positive. Hence m/n is a reactance function and P is a strictly Hurwitz polynomial. In this example we assumed, without detailed investigation, the absence of a multiplicative even polynomial, other than the trivial one of value unity. A criterion for verifying this will evolve from the next example.

As another illustration consider

$$P(s) = s^5 + 2s^4 + 3s^3 + 6s^2 + 4s + 8,$$

$$m(s) = 2s^4 + 6s^2 + 8,$$

$$n(s) = s^5 + 3s^3 + 4s.$$

Then we form the ratio n/m and expand in a continued fraction.

$$\frac{n(s)}{m(s)} = \frac{s^5 + 3s^3 + 4s}{2s^4 + 6s^2 + 8} = \frac{s}{2} + 0.$$

Observe that $n/m = s/2$ is a reactance function; but the continued fraction expansion terminates prematurely because a non-trivial even polynomial

$$s^4 + 3s^2 + 4 = (s^2 - s + 2)(s^2 + s + 2)$$

is a factor of both the even and odd parts. (This is an even polynomial that has two zeros in the right half-plane and two in the left.) The original polynomial is

$$P(s) = (s + 2)(s^4 + 3s^2 + 4)$$

and is exactly a strictly Hurwitz polynomial times an even polynomial, in accordance with the theorem.

To conclude: Given a polynomial $P(s) = m(s) + n(s)$, in order to detect the presence of an even polynomial factor, we note that this must be a factor of both the even and odd parts. Hence, when the ratio is formed and a continued fraction expansion is carried out, a premature termination of the expansion signals the presence of such an even factor. The final divisor, just before the termination, is the even polynomial in question.

12.4 RC IMMITTANCE FUNCTIONS

Let us now turn to another type of two-element network, namely, RC networks. We could, if we wanted to, carry out a complete discussion of this case, without referring to the discussion of LC networks. However, this would be a waste of time, since it is possible to interrelate the driving-point functions of the two types of networks by means of suitable transformations. The procedure we shall follow was first used by Cauer in extending Foster's work to RC and RL networks.

Let $Z(s)$ be the driving-point impedance of an RC network $\mathcal{N}$. With the usual choice of loops, let the loop impedance matrix of $\mathcal{N}$ be

$$\mathbf{Z}_c(s) = [z_{cij}(s)], \tag{13}$$

where the elements of the matrix are

$$z_{cij}(s) = R_{ij} + \frac{1}{sC_{ij}}. \tag{14}$$

Let us replace each resistance in $\mathcal{N}$ by an inductance of equal value (R ohms becomes R henrys). Then the loop impedance matrix of the new network $\mathcal{N}'$ becomes

$$\zeta_c(s) = \left[sR_{ij} + \frac{1}{sC_{ij}} \right] = \left[s \left(R_{ij} + \frac{1}{s^2 C_{ij}} \right) \right] = s\mathbf{Z}_c(s^2). \tag{15}$$

The driving-point impedance of network $\mathcal{N}'$ is found from a solution of the corresponding loop equations; it will be given by the ratio of one of the first principal cofactors of ζ_c to $\det(\zeta_c)$. The impedance of network $\mathcal{N}$ will equal the ratio of the corresponding first principal cofactor of $\mathbf{Z}_c$ to $\det(\mathbf{Z}_c)$. But ζ_c and $\mathbf{Z}_c$ are related through (15). Hence, remembering the effect on the cofactors and the determinant of multiplication of a matrix by a scalar s, we find the driving-point impedance of the network $\mathcal{N}'$ to be

$$\psi(s) = sZ(s^2).$$

The network $\mathcal{N}'$ contains only capacitors and inductors, so that $\psi(s)$ in the last equation is a reactance function. Thus we have found that the impedance of an RC network can be transformed into a reactance function by replacing s by s^2 and then multiplying by s.

It would be of interest to see if the converse is also true; that is, given a reactance function $\psi(s)$, can we convert into the impedance of an RC network with the opposite transformation? To do this, consider the reactance function to be expanded in partial fractions, as shown in (5). Now divide the entire result by s and replace s by $\sqrt{s}$. (This is the opposite of the transformation just used.) The result will be

$$\frac{1}{\sqrt{s}}\psi(\sqrt{s}) = \frac{1}{\sqrt{s}}\left(\frac{k_0}{\sqrt{s}} + k_\infty\sqrt{s} + \sum_i \frac{2k_i\sqrt{s}}{s + \omega_i^2}\right)$$

$$= \frac{k_0}{s} + k_\infty + \sum \frac{2k_i}{s + \omega_i^2}.$$

Each term on the right is recognizable as the impedance of a simple RC structure. The term k_0/s is a capacitor, and k_∞ a resistor. Each of the other terms represents the impedance of a branch consisting of a resistor and a capacitor in parallel, given by $(1/C)/(s + 1/RC)$. The values of R and C are obtained by comparing the two expressions. As a matter of fact, the representations of column 2 in Table 1 apply, with inductances replaced by resistances. For convenient reference let us state this result as

Theorem 5. If $Z_{RC}(s)$ is the driving point impedance of an RC network, then

$$\psi(s) = sZ_{RC}(s^2) \tag{16}$$

is a reactance function. Conversely, if $\psi(s)$ is a reactance function, then

$$Z_{RC}(s) = \frac{1}{\sqrt{s}}\psi(\sqrt{s}) \tag{17}$$

is the driving-point impedance of an RC network.

Let us now consider the admittance of an RC network. By using (17), it can be expressed as

$$Y_{RC}(s) = \sqrt{s}\, \frac{1}{\psi(\sqrt{s})}.$$

But the reciprocal of a reactance function ψ is itself a reactance function. Hence, given a reactance function $\psi(s)$, to obtain an RC admittance we replace s by $\sqrt{s}$, then multiply by $\sqrt{s}$. For convenient reference we shall state this fact and its converse as

Theorem 6. If $Y_{RC}(s)$ is the admittance of an RC network, then

$$\psi(s) = \frac{1}{s} Y_{RC}(s^2) \tag{18}$$

is a reactance function. Conversely, if $\psi(s)$ is a reactance function, then

$$Y_{RC}(s) = \sqrt{s}\, \psi(\sqrt{s}) \tag{19}$$

is the driving-point admittance of an RC network.

Here we find a basic distinction between reactance functions and RC immittance functions. Whereas the reciprocal of a reactance function is again a member of the same class of functions, the reciprocal of an RC impedance is a member of the class of RC admittances, and vice versa.

With the preceding transformations we are in a position to translate all the properties of reactance functions into properties of RC immittance functions. The procedure for establishing these results is quite straightforward. To start with, let us apply (17) and (19) to the partial-fraction expansion of a reactance function given in (5). With appropriate changes in notation for the poles and residues, the results are

$$Z_{RC}(s) = k_\infty + \frac{k_0}{s} + \sum_i \frac{k_i}{s + \sigma_i}, \tag{20a}$$

$$Y_{RC}(s) = k_\infty s + k_0 + \sum_i \frac{k_i s}{s + \sigma_i}, \tag{20b}$$

where the k's and σ's are all real and positive. Note that we have used the same symbols for the residues and poles in both cases, but these are general expressions for classes of functions — the two are not related.

Equation (20b) is not a partial-fraction expansion of $Y_{RC}(s)$. It is, rather, an expansion of $Y_{RC}(s)/s$, after which the result is multiplied through by s. If we divide (20b) by s, we find that the form is identical with (20a). This shows that *an RC admittance function divided by s is an RC impedance function.* Conversely, *an RC impedance function multiplied by s is an RC admittance function.* We see that the poles of both these functions are negative real, and the residues of Z_{RC} and Y_{RC}/s are all positive real.

By differentiating the last two equations along the real axis ($s = \sigma$), we obtain a result that is the counterpart of the positive-slope property of a reactance function; that is, except at poles,

$$\frac{dZ_{RC}(\sigma)}{d\sigma} < 0, \tag{21a}$$

$$\frac{dY_{RC}(\sigma)}{d\sigma} > 0. \tag{21b}$$

Thus RC driving-point immittance functions for real values of s are monotonic between poles, with $Z_{RC}(\sigma)$ being strictly decreasing and $Y_{RC}(\sigma)$ being strictly increasing. Just as in the case of reactance functions, this implies that the zeros and poles of both must alternate, in this case along the real axis.

Sketches of typical RC driving-point functions for real values of s are shown in Fig. 9. In Fig. 9(a) note that the first pole near the origin may in fact move to the origin, making $Z_{RC}(0)$ infinite. Also, the last zero on the negative real axis may move out to infinity, causing $Z_{RC}(\infty)$ to become zero. Similarly, in Fig. 9(b) the first zero may be at the origin, causing $Y_{RC}(0)$ to be zero. Also, the final pole may move out to infinity, causing $Y_{RC}(\infty)$ to become infinite.

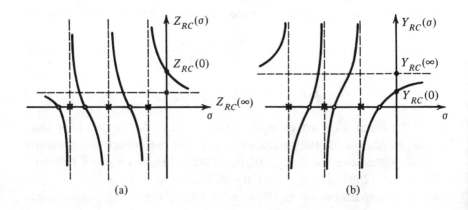

Fig. 9 Typical $Z_{RC}(\sigma)$ and $Y_{RC}(\sigma)$

Let us now collect all of these results and state them in the form of theorems. Theorems 7 and 8 for *RC* impedances and admittances, respectively, are the counterparts of Theorem 1 for reactance functions. Theorem 9 is the counterpart of Theorem 2.

Theorem 7. A rational function F(s) is the driving-point impedance of an RC network if an only if all of its poles are simple and restricted to the (finite) non-positive real axis, with positive real residues at all poles and with F(∞) real and non-negative.

Theorem 8. A rational function F(s) is the driving-point admittance of an RC network if and only if all of its poles are simple and restriced to the extended negative real axis, with all the residues of F(s)/s real and positive and with F(0) real and non-negative.

Theorem 9. A rational function F(s) is the driving-point impedance (alternatively, admittance) of an RC network if and only if all the poles and zeros are simple, lie on the negative real axis, and alternate with each other, the first critical point (pole or zero), starting at the origin and moving down the negative real axis, being a pole (alternatively, zero).

We have already sketched the proofs of all these theorems in the preceding discussion. You may organize the proofs as an exercise.

12.5 REALIZATION OF RC IMMITTANCES

We have now stated several sets of necessary and sufficient conditions for a rational function to be an *RC* immittance function. Generally, when it is desired to prove the sufficiency of a set of conditions for a given function to be the impedance or admittance of a network from a class of networks, it is done by showing that at least one network of the given class can be found that realizes the impedance or admittance. In the present case we drew a connection with reactance functions by showing that the given function could always be transformed into a reactance function. This function could then be realized as an *LC* network. The desired *RC* network would then be obtained by performing the inverse transformation, which amounts to replacing each *L* in the *LC* network with a *R* of equal value.

Alternatively, we can work on the given function itself, expressing it as a partial fraction just as we did for reactance functions. We have already obtained the desired forms in (20). Each term in these expressions is recognizable as the impedance or admittance of a simple RC structure. The series or parallel connection of these structures (depending on whether the function is to be impedance or admittance) gives the desired result. The networks have the same form as the Foster forms of lossless networks shown in Fig. 4. Hence they are referred to as Foster realizations of, or forms of, RC networks, although it was Cauer who first gave these results. Table 2 shows the realizations of the terms in (20).

Table 2   Representation of Partial Fraction Summands

	Term		
Z_{RC}	$k_\infty = R$	$k_0/s = \dfrac{1}{Cs}$	$\dfrac{ks}{s+\sigma} = \dfrac{1/C}{s+1/RC}$
	$R = k_\infty$ —⋀⋀⋀—	$C = 1/k_0$ —❘(—	*(R in parallel with C)* $C = 1/k$ $R = k/\sigma$
Y_{RC}	$k_\infty s = Cs$	$k_0 = \dfrac{1}{R}$	$\dfrac{ks}{s+\sigma} = \dfrac{s/R}{s+1/RC}$
	$C = k_\infty$ —❘(—	$R = 1/k_0$ —⋀⋀⋀—	*(R in series with C)* $R = 1/k$ $C = k/\sigma$

To illustrate, consider the function

$$Z(s) = \frac{2(s+2)(s+4)}{(s+1)(s+3)} = 2 + \frac{3}{s+1} + \frac{1}{s+3},$$

which is seen to satisfy the conditions of Theorem 8 for an RC impedance. The poles are negative real and simple, and the residues are positive, as the partial-fraction expansion shows. The constant term can be recognized as a 2 unit resistor. The term $3/(s+1)$ represents a parallel connected resistor and capacitor. By reference to Table 2, the values of C and R are found to be $C = \frac{1}{3}$ and $R = 3$. The last term has the same form as the second one and can be realized in the same fashion. The complete realization is given in Fig. 10(a). Now consider the reciprocal of the function under consideration; it is the admittance

$$Y(s) = \frac{(s+1)(s+3)}{2(s+2)(s+4)} = \frac{1}{16}\left(3 + \frac{2s}{s+2} + \frac{3s}{s+4}\right).$$

The right side was obtained by first expanding $Y(s)/s$ as a partial fraction and then multiplying by s. By reference to Table 2, the realization shown in Fig. 10(b) is obtained. You should verify that both networks have the same impedance.

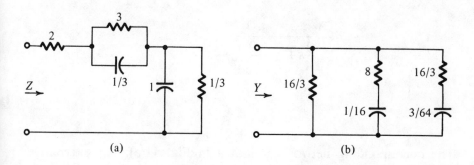

Fig. 10   RC networks realizing a given function

Since a one-to-one correspondence has been established between reactance functions and RC immittance functions through appropriate transformations, we should expect that whatever procedures can be used to obtain network realizations of a reactance function can also be used to obtain realizations of RC functions. The Foster forms have already been obtained. The ladder, or Cauer, forms can also be obtained by expanding Z_{RC} and Y_{RC} in continued fractions. We shall not give the detailed development in the general case, since it should be quite obvious. Instead, an illustrative example will be given, with the same function for which Foster form realizations were obtained above. There will be some characteristic differences in obtaining the continued fraction expansion of Z_{RC} or Y_{RC} compared with that of a reactance function, because Z_{RC} cannot have a pole at infinity and Y_{RC} cannot have a pole at the origin. Also (see Probs. 7-8), the smallest value of the real part in the closed right half-plane occurs at different values of s for Z_{RC} and Y_{RC}; respectively, at $s = \infty$ and $s = 0$.

Starting with the previously given $Z(s)$, a continued fraction expansion dealing with the behavior at infinity is obtained as follows:

$$Z(s) = \frac{2s^2 + 12s + 16}{s^2 + 4s + 3} = 2 + \cfrac{1}{\cfrac{s^2 + 4s + 3}{4s + 10}}$$

$$= 2 + \cfrac{1}{\cfrac{1}{4}s + \cfrac{1}{\cfrac{8s + 20}{3s + 6}}} = 2 + \cfrac{1}{\cfrac{1}{4}s + \cfrac{1}{\cfrac{8}{3}s + \cfrac{1}{\cfrac{3s + 6}{4}}}}$$

$$= 2 + \cfrac{1}{\cfrac{1}{4}s + \cfrac{1}{\cfrac{8}{3} + \cfrac{1}{\cfrac{3}{4}s + \cfrac{1}{\cfrac{2}{3}}}}}$$

The corresponding network is shown in Fig. 11(a). An alternative realization is obtained by starting with the admittance and dealing with the zero-frequency behavior. Thus

$$Y(s) = \frac{3 + 4s + s^2}{16 + 12s + 2s^2} = \frac{3}{16} + \cfrac{1}{\cfrac{128 + 96s + 16s^2}{14s + 5s^2}} = \frac{3}{16} + \cfrac{1}{\cfrac{64}{7}\cfrac{1}{s} + \cfrac{1}{\cfrac{98 + 35s}{352 + 112s}}}$$

$$= \frac{3}{16} + \cfrac{1}{\cfrac{64}{7}\cfrac{1}{s} + \cfrac{1}{\cfrac{49}{176} + \cfrac{1}{\cfrac{1936 + 616s}{21s}}}}$$

$$= \frac{3}{16} + \cfrac{1}{\cfrac{64}{7}\cfrac{1}{s} + \cfrac{1}{\cfrac{49}{176} + \cfrac{1}{\cfrac{1936}{21}\cfrac{1}{s} + \cfrac{1}{\cfrac{3}{88}}}}}$$

The corresponding network is shown in Fig. 11(b).

As a collateral concept, suppose that the current in each right-hand branch in Fig. 11 is to be regarded as an output when the input port is

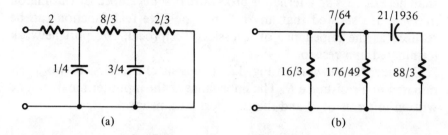

Fig. 11   RC (ladder) network realizing a given function

appropriately excited. Because of the behavior of a capacitor impedance at $s=0$ and ∞, in Fig. 11(a) there will be no output at infinity; so this network is called *low-pass*. Similarly, there will be no output at $s=0$ in Fig. 11(b), so this network is called *high-pass*.

12.6   RL ONE-PORT NETWORKS

What has been done for RC one-port networks could be duplicated for RL one-port networks. The starting point would again be a transformation, in this case converting a reactance function into an RL immittance function. It is immediately found that the class of RL impedance functions is identical with the class of RC admittance functions, and vice versa. Hence there is no need to duplicate the detailed development. In any theorem involving RC networks it is only necessary to replace the word "impedance" with the word "admittance" (or "admittance" with "impedance") to arrive at a valid theorem for RL networks. We shall not pursue this subject here.

12.7   RLC ONE-PORT NETWORKS

Up to this point we have accomplished the following. For a passive network with two kinds of elements, we have established necessary and sufficient conditions for the driving-point functions. Given a function satisfying these conditions, procedures have been discussed for finding a one-port network having the given function as its impedance or admittance. More generally, we have seen that positive realness is a necessary condition on the impedance or admittance of the most general network of the class under discussion. We have not, however, shown that this is a sufficient condition. This was shown initially by Brune in 1932, but we shall here discuss an alternative procedure first developed by Darlington in 1939. He showed that any rational, positive real function can be realized as the impedance of a lossless, reciprocal, two-port network terminated in a resistor.

Consider the network of Fig. 12. It consists of a lossless network terminated in a resistance R. The impedance at the input terminals can be written in terms of R and the two-port parameters as

$$Z = \frac{Rz_{11} + z_{11}z_{22} - z_{12}z_{21}}{R + z_{22}} = z_{11}\frac{R + 1/y_{22}}{R + z_{22}} \qquad (22a)$$

or, upon normalization of all impedances by R,

$$Z = z_{11}\frac{1 + 1/y_{22}}{1 + z_{22}}. \qquad (22b)$$

(See Chapter 5.) Note that the final form, in which all impedances have been normalized to R, is equivalent to taking the value of R to equal 1.

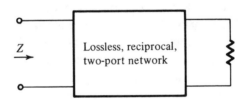

Fig. 12   Resistance terminated lossless two-port

Now suppose a rational positive real function $Z(s)$ is given. The even and odd parts of its numerator and denominator can be separated, and the function can be written in the usual form. Then this expression can be placed in the same form as (22b) in two possible ways, as follows:

$$Z(s) = \frac{m_1(s) + n_1(s)}{m_2(s) + n_2(s)}, \qquad (23)$$

$$Z = \frac{m_1}{n_2}\frac{1 + n_1/m_1}{1 + m_2/n_2} \qquad \text{(case A)}, \qquad (24a)$$

$$Z = \frac{n_1}{m_2}\frac{1 + m_1/n_1}{1 + n_2/m_2} \qquad \text{(case B)}. \qquad (24b)$$

For each of these two cases, formal identifications can be made by comparing these expressions with (22b). Thus,

Case A   Case B

$$z_{11} = \frac{m_1}{n_2}$$ $$z_{11} = \frac{n_1}{m_2}$$

(25)

$$z_{22} = \frac{m_2}{n_2}$$ $$z_{22} = \frac{n_2}{m_2}$$

$$y_{22} = \frac{m_1}{n_1}$$ $$y_{22} = \frac{n_1}{m_1}$$

Since Z is positive real, both $m_1 + n_1$ and $m_2 + n_2$ are Hurwitz polynomials. Hence the ratios m_1/n_1 and m_2/n_2, and their reciprocals, are reactance functions. In addition, using Theorem 11-7 (concerning the interchange of the even or odd parts of a numerator and denominator of a pr function), the ratios m_1/n_2 and n_1/m_2 are also found to be reactance functions. Thus all the functions in (25) are reactance functions.

There remains the task of determining z_{21} ($=z_{12}$) from the expressions in (25), so that a complete set of parameters for the lossless, reciprocal two-port in Fig. 12 will be available. To do this, observe that

$$z_{11}z_{22} - z_{21}^2 = \frac{z_{11}}{y_{22}} = \frac{n_1}{n_2} \quad \text{(case A)}, \tag{26a}$$

$$= \frac{m_1}{m_2} \quad \text{(case B)}. \tag{26b}$$

Since

$$z_{21} = \sqrt{z_{11}z_{22} - (z_{11}z_{22} - z_{21}^2)}$$

we get for z_{21}, by using (25) and (26),

$$z_{21} = \frac{\sqrt{m_1m_2 - n_1n_2}}{n_2} \quad \text{(case A)}, \tag{27a}$$

$$z_{21} = \frac{\sqrt{n_1n_2 - m_1m_2}}{m_2} \quad \text{(case B)}. \tag{27b}$$

Of course, once the z-parameters are known, the y-parameters can also be found. (See Table 1 in Chapter 5.) The complete results are tabulated in Table 3.

Table 3 Two-port parameter assignments in Darlington Synthesis of pr function

Condition	z-Parameters			y-Parameters		
	z_{11}	z_{22}	z_{21}	y_{11}	y_{22}	y_{21}
Case A: No pole or zero of $Z(s)$ at $s=0$	$\dfrac{m_1}{n_2}$	$\dfrac{m_2}{n_2}$	$\dfrac{\sqrt{m_1 m_2 - n_1 n_1}}{n_2}$	$\dfrac{m_2}{n_1}$	$\dfrac{m_1}{n_1}$	$\dfrac{\sqrt{m_1 m_2 - n_1 n_2}}{n_1}$
Case B: Pole or zero of $Z(s)$ at $s=0$	$\dfrac{n_1}{m_2}$	$\dfrac{n_2}{m_2}$	$\dfrac{\sqrt{n_1 n_2 - m_1 m_2}}{m_2}$	$\dfrac{n_2}{m_1}$	$\dfrac{n_1}{m_1}$	$\dfrac{\sqrt{n_1 n_2 - m_1 m_2}}{m_1}$

The question is: Do these impedance or admittance parameters satisfy realizability conditions for a lossless reciprocal, two-port? The first difficulty appears to be that z_{21} is not a rational function because of the indicated square root. However, if $m_1 m_2 - n_1 n_2$ in Case A or $n_1 n_2 - m_1 m_2$ in Case B is a perfect square, the apparent difficulty will disappear. Observe that $m_1 m_2 - n_1 n_2$ is the numerator of the even part of $Z(s)$. Because $Z(s)$ is a positive real function, zeros of its even part on the $j\omega$-axis must necessarily have even multiplicity. There is no such requirement, however, on any other zeros. Hence, unless some remedy can be found, it appears that z_{21} will generally not be rational.

A remedy can be had in the following way. Let the given $Z(s)$ be *augmented* by multiplying its numerator and denominator by a strictly Hurwitz polynomial $m_0 + n_0$; this certainly does not change the function. Thus,

$$Z = \frac{m_1 + n_1}{m_2 + n_2} \cdot \frac{m_0 + n_0}{m_0 + n_0} = \frac{\hat{m}_1 + \hat{n}_1}{\hat{m}_2 + \hat{n}_2}. \tag{28}$$

The new even part of $Z(s)$ will be

$$\mathrm{Ev}[Z(s)] = \frac{\hat{m}_1 \hat{m}_2 - \hat{n}_1 \hat{n}_2}{\hat{m}_2^2 - \hat{n}_2^2} = \frac{m_1 m_2 - n_1 n_2}{m_2^2 - n_2^2} \cdot \frac{m_0^2 - n_0^2}{m_0^2 - n_0^2}. \tag{29}$$

The new z_{21} for case A will be

$$z_{21} = \frac{\sqrt{\hat{m}_1 \hat{m}_2 - \hat{n}_1 \hat{n}_2}}{\hat{n}_2} = \frac{\sqrt{(m_1 m_2 - n_1 n_2)(m_0^2 - n_0^2)}}{m_0 n_2 + n_0 m_2}. \tag{30}$$

It is now clear how to make z_{21} a rational function: Set $m_0^2 - n_0^2$ equal to the product of all factors in $m_1 m_2 - n_1 n_2$ that are of odd multiplicity and thus cause z_{21} to be irrational in the first place. Since $m_0^2 - n_0^2 = (m_0 + n_0)(m_0 - n_0)$, the augmenting polynomial $m_0 + n_0$ is found by taking the left half plane zeros of $m_0^2 - n_0^2$.

The question arises as to the significance of cases A and B. When is one appropriate and when the other? We observe from Table 3 that the denominator of z_{21} (or y_{21}) is odd for case A and even for case B. Since z_{21} should be an odd rational function, the numerator of z_{21} should be even for case A and odd for case B. If $m_1 m_2 - n_1 n_2$ has s^2 as a factor, taking the square root will make the numerator of z_{21} odd, and so case B is appropriate. On the other hand, if $m_1 m_2 - n_1 n_2$ does not have s^2 as a factor, case A is appropriate. The only way in which s^2 can be a factor of $m_1 m_2 - n_1 n_2$ is for either m_1 or m_2 to have its constant term missing. This means that *case B applies when $Z(s)$ has a pole or a zero at $s=0$, and case A applies if $Z(s)$ has neither a pole nor a zero at $s=0$.*

To illustrate the preceding, let

$$Z(s) = \frac{s^3 + 4s^2 + 4s}{s^3 + 5s^2 + 8s + 4}.$$

This function has a zero at $s=0$; hence case B is appropriate. We form

$$n_1 n_2 - m_1 m_2 = (s^3 + 4s)(s^3 + 8s) - 4s^2(5s^2 + 4) = s^2(s^2 - 4)^2.$$

This is a perfect square, so that augmentation is not needed. Hence, from Table 3:

$$z_{21} = \frac{\sqrt{n_1 n_2 - m_1 m_2}}{m_2} = \frac{s(s^2 - 4)}{5s^2 + 4} = \frac{s}{5} - \frac{0.96s}{s^2 + 4/5}$$

Also,

$$z_{11} = \frac{n_1}{m_2} = \frac{s(s^2 + 4)}{5s^2 + 4} = \frac{s}{5} + \frac{0.64s}{s^2 + 4/5},$$

$$z_{22} = \frac{n_2}{m_2} = \frac{s(s^2 + 8)}{5s^2 + 4} = \frac{s}{5} + \frac{1.44s}{s^2 + 4/5}.$$

Whatever the given $Z(s)$, it is possible to make z_{21} an odd rational function, by augmenting the original function if necessary. Now let us consider the other realizability conditions. The real-part condition of (11-62a) and (11-62c) is satisfied identically with the equals sign when

$s = j\omega$. Since the functions are regular in the right half-plane, the maximum modulus theorem can be used to show that the real-part condition will be satisfied everywhere in the right half-plane.

There remains the residue condition of (11-58a) and (11-59). The residues of a function can be calculated as its numerator divided by the derivative of its denominator, evaluated at the zeros of its denominator. For the z-parameters the residues at finite nonzero poles are given in Table 4, in which the primes indicate the derivative with respect to s. Thus, upon forming $k_{11}k_{12} - k_{21}^2$, it is found that at all the finite nonzero poles the residue condition is satisfied; furthermore, it is satisfied with the equality sign.

Table 4   Residues at finite nonzero poles of z-parameters

Condition	k_{11}	k_{22}	k_{21}
Case A	$\left.\dfrac{m_1}{n_2'}\right|_{n_2=0}$	$\left.\dfrac{m_2}{n_2'}\right|_{n_2=0}$	$\left.\dfrac{\sqrt{m_1 m_2 - n_1 n_2}}{n_2'}\right|_{n_2=0}$
Case B	$\left.\dfrac{n_1}{m_2'}\right|_{m_2=0}$	$\left.\dfrac{n_2}{m_2'}\right|_{m_2=0}$	$\left.\dfrac{\sqrt{n_1 n_2 - m_1 m_2}}{m_2'}\right|_{m_2=0}$

It is also true that the residue condition is satisfied at a possible pole at infinity or at zero, but not always with an equality sign. (See Prob. 29.) A similar development can be carried out for the y-parameters, leading to similar results. The conclusion is that the residue condition is satisfied by both the z-parameters and the y-parameters at all their poles.

We now know that the z-parameters satisfy the conditions of a lossless, reciprocal two-port established in the last chapter. It remains only to present a synthesis procedure for such a two-port to complete the validation of

Theorem 10. A rational, positive real function can always be realized as the impedance or admittance of a passive, one-port network.

This is the sought converse of a result we already knew, namely: *The impedance and admittance of a passive, one-port network are each a rational, positive real function.* The truly striking feature of the realization is that the resistively terminated — a passive termination — two-port, realizing the desired impedance or admittance at its other port, is not only lossless (hence, passive), it is reciprocal as well. This implies that such lossless, but non-reciprocal, components as the gyrator will not be needed in a realization of the two-port. Another consequence of the reciprocity of the two-port is: Any impedance or admittance realized by a passive network with non-reciprocal components can be realized by another passive network without non-reciprocal components.

12.8 LOSSLESS, RECIPROCAL TWO-PORT SYNTHESIS

We have now established that, given a positive real function, it is possible to find a set of impedance or admittance parameters that satisfy realizability conditions of a lossless two-port terminated in a unit resistance. There remains the task of actually synthesizing the two-port.

One procedure for synthesizing lossless, reciprocal two-ports was developed by Cauer. It starts by expressing the z-parameters (alternatively, y-parameters) as partial fraction expansions. The terms from all z-parameters (alternatively, y-parameters) corresponding to a particular pole are lumped together; they are simple enough so that a lossless two-port realizing this set of parameters can be recognized. The set of two-ports so obtained is then connected in series (alternatively, in parallel). However, as the discussion of interconnecting two-ports in Chapter 5 described, in order to permit a series or parallel connection it may be necessary to use ideal transformers. Thus, these interconnected two-port structures may not be very desirable, as some ports of the constituent two-ports may be floating above ground.

The network in Fig. 13(a) will realize a typical set of terms from the z-parameter partial fraction expansions of the form

$$\frac{2s}{s^2 + \omega^2} \begin{bmatrix} k_{11} & k_{21} \\ k_{21} & k_{22} \end{bmatrix} \tag{31}$$

when $k_{21} \geqslant 0$. Because the residue condition is satisfied — the case of interest — the assignments to Z_a, Z_b, Z_c, and n fall into three distinct categories according to whether $|k_{21}| \leqslant \min\{k_{11}, k_{22}\}$ or $k_{11} < |k_{21}| \leqslant k_{22}$ or $k_{22} < k_{21} \leqslant k_{11}$. The assignments are given in Table 5. In the first case, for which $n = 1$, the ideal transformer, rather obviously, is not needed in the realization of (31). The nonzero impedances are each the parallel connection of an inductor and a capacitor. [When $k_{21} < 0$ the realization of (31) simply requires the reversal of the polarity on one side of the transformer; the assignments found in Table 5 continue to apply. (In

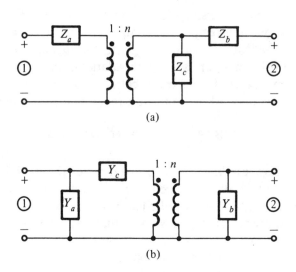

(a)

(b)

Fig. 13   Two-ports realizing (31) as (a) an impedance when $k_{21} \geqslant 0$ and (b) an admittance when $k_{21} \leqslant 0$

Table 5   Assignments for network of Fig. 13(a)

Conditions	Assignments			
	Z_a	Z_b	Z_c	n
$\|k_{21}\| \leqslant \min\{k_{11}, k_{22}\}$	$\dfrac{2(k_{11} - \|k_{21}\|)s}{s^2 + \omega^2}$	$\dfrac{2(k_{22} - \|k_{21}\|)s}{s^2 + \omega^2}$	$\dfrac{2\|k_{21}\|s}{s^2 + \omega^2}$	1
$k_{11} < \|k_{21}\| \leqslant k_{22}$	0	$\dfrac{2(k_{22} - n\|k_{21}\|)s}{s^2 + \omega^2}$	$\dfrac{2n\|k_{21}\|s}{s^2 + \omega^2}$	$\dfrac{\|k_{21}\|}{k_{11}}$
$k_{22} < \|k_{21}\| \leqslant k_{11}$	$\dfrac{2(k_{11} - \|k_{21}\|/n)s}{s^2 + \omega^2}$	0	$\dfrac{2n\|k_{21}\|s}{s^2 + \omega^2}$	$\dfrac{k_{22}}{\|k_{21}\|}$

this situation the transformer is needed in all three cases. Why?)] Tables similar to Table 5 can be composed when the function form in (31) is s or $1/s$—*corresponding to a pole at infinity or zero*—rather than $s/(s^2 + \omega^2)$. You should do so.

If we wish to realize a typical set of terms from the y-parameter partial fraction expansions of the form (31) when $k_{21} \leqslant 0$, then we would use the network in Fig. 13(b). The assignments are as given in Table 6. The various special considerations for the z-parameter case have their counterparts in this case. You should fill in the details.

Table 6 Assignments for network of Fig. 13(b)

Conditions	Assignments			
	Y_a	Y_b	Y_c	n
$\|k_{21}\| \leqslant \min\{k_{11},\, k_{22}\}$	$\dfrac{2(k_{11} - \|k_{21}\|)s}{s^2 + \omega^2}$	$\dfrac{2(k_{22} - \|k_{21}\|)s}{s^2 + \omega^2}$	$\dfrac{2\|k_{21}\|s}{s^2 + \omega^2}$	1
$k_{11} < \|k_{21}\| \leqslant k_{22}$	0	$\dfrac{2(k_{22} - \|k_{21}\|/n)s}{s^2 + \omega^2}$	$\dfrac{2n\|k_{21}\|s}{s^2 + \omega^2}$	$\dfrac{k_{11}}{\|k_{21}\|}$
$k_{22} < \|k_{21}\| \leqslant k_{11}$	$\dfrac{2(k_{11} - n\|k_{21}\|)s}{s^2 + \omega^2}$	0	$\dfrac{2n\|k_{21}\|s}{s^2 + \omega^2}$	$\dfrac{\|k_{21}\|}{k_{22}}$

Let us now briefly digress for the purpose of introducing a few additional descriptive terms. In doing so we will refer to the residue condition at $j\omega$-axis poles expressed by (11-60). When a network is lossless, all the poles of z_{ij} and y_{ij} are on the $j\omega$-axis; hence, the residue condition applies at all the poles. One of the implications of this fact for a lossless network is that it is impossible for z_{21} to have a pole that is not also a pole of z_{11} and z_{22}, nor for y_{21} to have a pole that is not also a pole of y_{11} and y_{22}. For if either k_{11} or k_{22} is zero when k_{21} is not, the residue condition will be violated. On the other hand, it is possible for z_{11} or z_{22} (or both) to have a pole not shared by the other parameters. We refer to such poles as *private poles* of z_{11} or z_{22}. A similar statement applies to the y-parameters.

We have seen that $|k_{21}|$ can be nonzero only if $\min\{k_{11},\, k_{22}\}$ is nonzero. Its largest value would be that corresponding to the second part of the residue condition holding with the equality sign; that is, $k_{11}k_{22} - k_{21}^2 = 0$. In this case we refer to the corresponding pole of the impedance matrix $\mathbf{Z}$ (and its elements, the z-parameters) or of the admittance matrix $\mathbf{Y}$ (and its elements, the y-parameters) as a *compact pole*. We also say that the network is compact at such a pole.

Now, observe that, if the poles giving rise to (31) are compact, then, by Table 5, Z_a and Z_b are zero in all cases. Similarly, by Table 6, Y_a and Y_b are zero in all cases. We leave to you the following task: In what way are the networks of Fig. 13 simplified when the associated driving-point functions have private poles?

If we had not shown the network of Fig. 13(a) as a three-terminal, two-port, but rather as a four-terminal two-port by isolating the two sides of the transformer, then the series connection of several networks each realizing (31) as an impedance, would need no additional transformers. On the other hand, the parallel connection of several two-ports of the type shown in Fig. 13(b), each realizing (31) as an admittance, requires neither a change in the two-port structure nor additional transformers.

The series (alternatively, parallel) connection of two-ports of the type shown in Fig. 13(a) [alternatively, Fig. 13(b)] is the two-port counterpart of the one-port Foster forms. Are there counterparts of the Cauer forms? We will not develop an answer to this question other than to observe that in their development one would expect alternatively to do a partial realization of a two-port impedance matrix and a two-port admittance matrix, each the residual from the previous step. This observation alone is important, for by acting in accordance with it we might find a realization requiring fewer ideal transformers than the synthesis procedure we have been discussing would demand.

To illustrate all that has been done in these last two sections, consider the pr impedance

$$Z(s) = \frac{s^4 + s^3 + 3s^2 + 2s + 1}{5s^3 + 5s^2 + 2s + 5}.$$

Suppose the z-parameters are now formed by using Table 1. The result will be as follows:

$$z_{11} = \frac{s^4 + 3s^2 + 1}{5s^3 + 2s} = \frac{(13/5)s^2 + 1}{5s^3 + 2s} + \frac{1}{5}s = \frac{1}{5}s + \frac{1/2}{s} + \frac{(1/50)s}{s^2 + 2/5}$$

$$z_{22} = \frac{5s^2 + 1}{5s^3 + 2s} = \frac{1/2}{s} + \frac{(1/2)s}{s^2 + 2/5}$$

$$z_{21} = \frac{2s^2 + 1}{5s^3 + 2s} = \frac{1/2}{s} - \frac{(1/10)s}{s^2 + 2/5}$$

Observe that z_{11} has a private pole at infinity and that the pole at the origin is compact with $k_{21} \geqslant 0$. The two-ports corresponding to these poles have simple realizations, as shown, respectively, in Figs. 14(a) and 14(b). The terms of the form $s/(s^2 + 2/5)$ constitute a compact pole but can be realized only by a two-port with a transformer because $k_{21}(= -1/20) < 0$ and $k_{11} < |k_{21}| \leqslant k_{22}$. By reference to Fig. 13(a) and Table 5, together with the discussion following, you can validate the realization given in Fig. 14(c). The series connection of these two-ports shown in Fig. 14(d) completes a realization of the impedance parameters.

It is possible to realize $\mathbf{Z}$ without an ideal transformer by a series connection of the two-port in Fig. 13(a) — realizing the private pole of z_{11} —

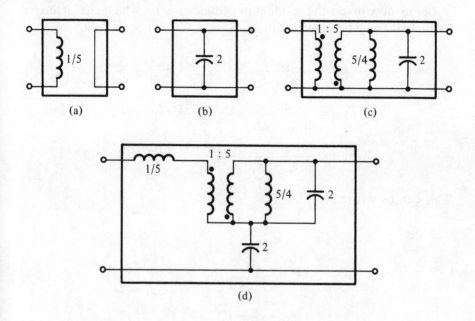

Fig. 14   Series realization of Z

and of a two-port $\hat{\mathcal{N}}$ realizing the residual z-parameters from an admittance point of view. This series connection is depicted in Fig. 15(a).

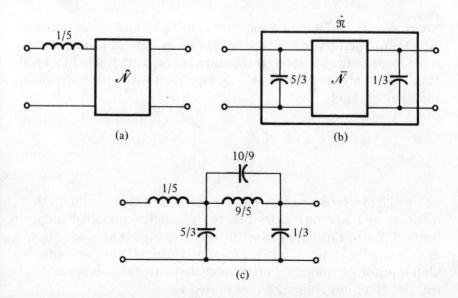

Fig. 15   Realization of impedance as lossless ladder terminated in R

Let us now invert the residual impedance matrix which characterizes $\hat{\mathcal{N}}$ to find the y-parameters for $\hat{\mathcal{N}}$. The result will be as follows:

$$y_{11} = \frac{z_{22}}{z_{11}z_{22} - z_{21}^2} = \frac{5(5s^2 + 1)}{9s} = \frac{25s}{9} + \frac{5}{9s},$$

$$y_{22} = \frac{z_{11}}{z_{11}z_{22} - z_{21}^2} = \frac{(13s^2 + 5)}{9s} = \frac{13s}{9} + \frac{5}{9s},$$

$$-y_{21} = \frac{z_{21}}{z_{11}z_{22} - z_{21}^2} = \frac{5(2s^2 + 1)}{9s} = \frac{10s}{9} + \frac{5}{9s}.$$

This can be written as

$$y_{11} = Y + \frac{5s}{3},$$

$$y_{22} = Y + \frac{s}{3},$$

$$-y_{21} = Y,$$

where

$$Y = \frac{10}{9}s + \frac{5}{9s}.$$

Notice that, in addition to a common term Y, y_{11} and y_{22} each have an extra term. These terms can each be realized by capacitors, one in shunt at the input and one in shunt at the output of $\hat{\mathcal{N}}$, as shown in Fig. 15(b). That leaves only the network $\overline{\mathcal{N}}$ — see Fig. 15(b) — with the short-circuit admittance matrix

$$\begin{bmatrix} Y & -Y \\ -Y & Y \end{bmatrix}$$

as unrealized. But it can be realized by a (trivial) ladder with no shunt branches and just one series branch, a parallel connected inductor (value 9/5) and capacitor (value 10/9). The complete network, then, is as shown in Fig. 15(c). It is in the form of a lossless ladder network. No ideal transformer appears. Furthermore, terminated in a unit resistor, it realizes the pr impedance $Z(s)$ we started with.

We conclude this section with comments on the topics of the last two sections. Refer to Fig. 12. Let us remove the reciprocity condition from the lossless two-port. In this case the decomposition of Z leads to $z_{12}z_{21} = (m_1m_2 - n_1n_2)/n_2$, case A, or $z_{12}z_{21} = (n_1n_2 - m_1m_2)/m_2$, case B, rather than to the specifications in (27). The problem of separating the product to get a z_{12} and z_{21} such that Z is realizable is left to you to consider. Clearly, when $z_{12} \neq z_{21}$ we have a new realization task, the resolution of which can be found in a lossless non-reciprocal synthesis procedure using the gyrator. See if you can develop such a procedure.

12.9 RC TWO-PORT REALIZABILITY

Let us start with the observation that what was said about lossless two-ports is also true for RC two-ports, by virtue of the transformations previously discussed and with appropriate and obvious modifications. Thus for RC two-ports, the z- and y-parameters will have all their poles on the extended non-positive real axis, and the residue condition will apply at these poles and to the constant term. Furthermore, no pole of z_{21} can fail to be a pole of both z_{11} and z_{22}, but z_{11} and z_{22} can each have private poles and/or a constant term; similarly for the y-parameters. Note: By reference to (20) the constant term refers to the values of the z-parameters at infinity and of the y-parameters at the origin.

For the impedance or the admittance of a one-port containing only two kinds of elements we found sets of necessary conditions that were also proved to be sufficient. In fact, actual procedures for realizing one or more networks from a given function were obtained. The case for a two-port is not as simple, since a set of three parameters is involved. Although necessary conditions on these parameters have been obtained, these conditions turn out to be generally sufficient for realizability only if we admit the inclusion of ideal transformers. We saw this in the previous section. The residue condition at each of the poles guaranteed the existence of a two-port of the form in Fig. 13(a) [alternatively, Fig. 13(b)] to realize each of the terms in the partial fraction expansion of Z (alternatively, Y). Unfortunately, most of the structures contained a transformer. If transformers are not permitted, a general set of sufficient conditions is not available.

Clearly, now, the synthesis procedures of the last section apply here to the RC case. The obvious change from (31) is as follows:

Term in **Z**   Term in **Y**

$$\frac{1}{s+\sigma}\begin{bmatrix} k_{11} & k_{21} \\ k_{21} & k_{22} \end{bmatrix} \qquad\qquad \frac{s}{s+\sigma}\begin{bmatrix} k_{11} & k_{21} \\ k_{21} & k_{22} \end{bmatrix} \qquad (32)$$

The corresponding changes to the assignment columns for impedances in Table 5 and admittances in Table 6 are rather obvious.

It is rather unlikely that ideal transformers can be avoided in the series connection of two-ports to realize **Z**. Even if they could be avoided in the constituent two-ports themselves $-0 \leqslant k_{21} \leqslant \min\{k_{11}, k_{22}\}$ at every pole of **Z**$-$they would almost assuredly be needed to achieve the interconnection. On the other hand, if $0 \leqslant -k_{21} \leqslant \min\{k_{11}, k_{22}\}$ at every pole of **Y**, then no ideal transformer is needed in the parallel connection of two-ports to realize **Y**. Also, as we saw by illustration in the last section, successive partial realization of a succession of residual impedance matrices and admittance matrices may lead to a transformerless realization of $\dot{Z}$ or **Y** where the above procedure would not. We have here made almost a fetish of transformerless synthesis because transformers are not appropriate additions to otherwise RC two-ports $-$ideal transformers destroy the possibility of fabrication as part of a hybrid integrated circuit.

We will now illustrate this discussion by realizing the following positive real admittance matrix:

$$\mathbf{Y}(s) = \begin{bmatrix} \dfrac{2s^2 + 4s + 1}{s+1} & -\dfrac{s}{s+1} \\[4mm] -\dfrac{s}{s+1} & \dfrac{s^2 + 4s + 2}{s+1} \end{bmatrix}.$$

Obviously the poles are on the extended negative real axis $-$at $s = \infty$ and $s = -1$. Furthermore, the residue condition holds at each pole as the partial fraction expansion

$$\mathbf{Y}(s) = \begin{bmatrix} 1 & 0 \\ 0 & 2 \end{bmatrix} + s\begin{bmatrix} 2 & 0 \\ 0 & 1 \end{bmatrix} + \frac{s}{s+1}\begin{bmatrix} 1 & -1 \\ -1 & 1 \end{bmatrix}$$

makes evident. In fact, the pole at $s = -1$ is compact with $k_{21} \leqslant 0$ and the pole at $s = \infty$ and the constant term are private to y_{11} and y_{22}. This means that the three two-ports associated with the three terms in this partial fraction expansion can be realized as RC two-ports, not augmented by ideal transformers. Thus, their parallel connection will realize $\mathbf{Y}(s)$ as an RC network. That network is shown in Fig. 16.

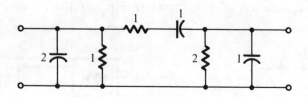

Fig. 16   RC network realization of Y(s) in example

Let us now examine an alternate synthesis procedure by which to realize this $\mathbf{Y}(s)$. Suppose we realize it as the parallel connection of a two-port realizing the private pole of $y_{11}(s)$ at $s = \infty$ and the private constant term of $y_{22}(s)$ and two-port $\mathcal{N}$. This situation is depicted in Fig. 17(a). Simple calculations show that the open-circuit impedance matrix of $\hat{\mathcal{N}}$ is

$$
\hat{\mathbf{Z}}(s) = \begin{bmatrix} \dfrac{s+2}{2(s+1)} & \dfrac{1}{2(s+1)} \\[4mm] \dfrac{1}{2(s+1)} & \dfrac{2s+1}{2s(s+1)} \end{bmatrix}
$$

$$
= \begin{bmatrix} \frac{1}{2} & 0 \\ 0 & 0 \end{bmatrix} + \frac{1}{s}\begin{bmatrix} 0 & 0 \\ 0 & \frac{1}{2} \end{bmatrix} + \frac{1}{s+1}\begin{bmatrix} \frac{1}{2} & \frac{1}{2} \\ \frac{1}{2} & \frac{1}{2} \end{bmatrix}.
$$

Let us now realize $\hat{\mathbf{Z}}(s)$ as a series connection of a two-port realizing the private constant term of $z_{11}(s)$ and the private pole of $z_{22}(s)$ at $s = 0$ and the two-port $\mathcal{N}$. This is illustrated in Fig. 17(b). The impedance matrix of $\mathcal{N}$,

$$\bar{\mathbf{Z}}(s) = \frac{1}{s+1} \begin{bmatrix} \tfrac{1}{2} & \tfrac{1}{2} \\ \tfrac{1}{2} & \tfrac{1}{2} \end{bmatrix}$$

is obviously that of a ladder with one shunt arm and no series arms, the shunt arm being a parallel connection of a resistor, $G=2$, and of a capacitor, $C=2$. When this is incorporated in the network of Fig. 17(b) we get the realization of $\mathbf{Y}(s)$ shown in Fig. 17(c).

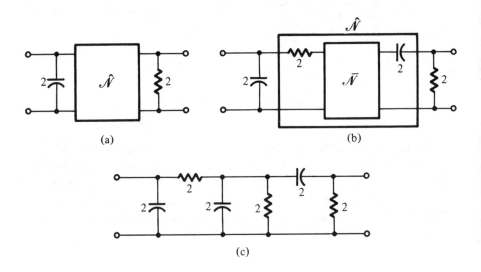

Fig. 17 Alternate RC network realization of $\mathbf{Y}(s)$ in example

12.10 TRANSFER FUNCTION, PASSIVE NETWORK SYNTHESIS

In the previous two sections we discussed the synthesis process for lossless and for RC two-ports specified by an impedance matrix or an admittance matrix. We saw that it is a tedious process to simultaneously realize all the z-parameters or y-parameters. It is often true, however, that what we must do is just realize some specific transfer function, such as voltage gain. In this case it will not be necessary to prespecify all the z-parameters or y-parameters, thereby introducing some flexibility into the synthesis process. With these thoughts in mind we shall switch to consideration of the network by which to realize some selected transfer functions. Bear in mind that the locations of transmission zeros of a network depend both on the types of elements contained in the network and on the structure of the network. Nothing definitive can be stated as to restriction on the locations of transmission zeros due to element types. For example, *RC* networks, which have only one type of reactive component, can have complex transmission zeros, as well as real ones, and can even have zeros in the right half-plane. But structure alone does place restrictions.

12.10.1 Ladder Networks

The most notable restriction is given in

Theorem 11. The transfer function of a passive ladder network without mutual coupling between branches is minimum-phase.

The graph of a general ladder network is shown in Fig. 18. The series and shunt branches need not be single elements but can be arbitrary two-terminal passive networks with no coupling between branches. The first and last shunt branches may or may not be present. By topological analysis methods (see Proj. II-1) it is easily shown that the transfer impedance can be written as

$$z_{21} = \frac{Y_2 Y_4 \ldots Y_{2m}}{\sum \text{products of tree admittances}}, \tag{33}$$

where the summation extends over all possible trees in the graph for the network. By nodal analysis of this ladder network you should be able to easily verify the numerator of (33). You should also, by nodal analysis, verify the denominator of (33) for at least $m = 1, 2, 3$.

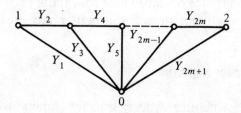

Fig. 18   General ladder network

The zeros of $z_{21}(s)$ will occur where the numerator has zeros that do not cancel with zeros of the denominator and where the denominator has poles that do not cancel with poles of the numerator. Every tree must contain node 0 and, hence, every admittance product in the summation must contain at least one of the shunt-branch admittances, Y_1, Y_3, ..., Y_{2m+1}. Hence the poles of these admittances must be the poles of the denominator expression. Some of the series branches may also be in a tree, but the poles of the admittances Y_2, Y_4, ... in these tree products cancel with the poles of the numerator expression $Y_2 ... Y_{2m}$. The conclusion is that the zeros of $z_{21}(s)$ can occur at the zeros of series-branch admittances Y_2, Y_4, ... and at the poles of shunt-branch admittances Y_1, Y_3, ... But the poles and the zeros of the admittance of a passive two-terminal network cannot lie in the right half-plane. Hence, the result follows.

Although the development was carried out for the z_{21} function, the result is true for other transfer functions also.

It was shown above that the transmission zeros of a ladder network can occur when a shunt-branch admittance has a pole (the branch is a short circuit) or a series-branch admittance has a zero (the branch is an open circuit). It is not true, however, that a transmission zero must occur at such points—only that these are the only points at which it can occur. You should convince yourself of this fact by devising examples where a series-branch admittance zero and a shunt-branch admittance pole are not zeros of transmission.

The foregoing becomes very useful in synthesis. Suppose a filter is to be designed with transmission zeros in the right half plane. We at least know that a ladder network cannot realize such zeros. But suppose all the transmission zeros are imaginary; is that sufficient to realize an LC ladder? Or suppose all the transmission zeros are on the extended negative real axis; is that sufficient to realize an RC ladder? The answer to these questions is yes, if the specified task is to realize a realizable driving point admittance or impedance with those prescribed transmission zeros. We shall not pursue the matter any further here. (See Proj. 1.)

12.10.2 Non-Ladder Networks

The simplest structures whose transfer functions can be non-minimum-phase are the bridged tee, the twin tee, and the lattice, shown in Fig. 19. Whether they are actually non-minimum-phase will depend upon the types of elements present and upon their numerical values; for example, the twin-tee network in Fig. 20 will be minimum phase for some values of the resistors and non-minimum-phase for other values, as shown by two particular cases in the figure.

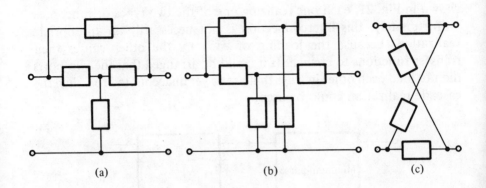

Fig. 19 Potentially non-minimum-phase networks: (a) bridged-tee,
(b) twin-tee, (c) lattice

Minimum-phase network:
transmission zeros at

$$s = -1 \pm j3, \; -\tfrac{9}{2}$$

for $G_1 = 4.28$

$G_2 = 2.22$

$G_3 = 1.43$

Non-minimum-phase network:
transmission zeros at

$$s = 1 \pm j3, \; -\tfrac{9}{2}$$

for $G_1 = 2.28$

$G_2 = 0.22$

$G_3 = 90$

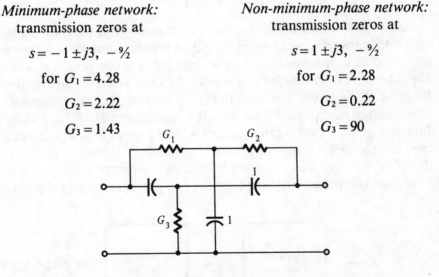

Fig. 20 Twin-tee that can be either minimum- or non-minimum-phase

12.10.3   Constant-Resistance Networks

We saw in (7-25) that a non-minimum-phase transfer function can be written as the product of a minimum-phase function and an all-pass function. This has significance in synthesis: If $F_m(s)$ and $F_a(s)$ can be realized separately, an interconnection of the two realizations will give the desired network. Consider, for example, the cascade of 2 two-ports shown in Fig. 21, each one realizing one of the two types of functions. Unfortunately, this interconnection is not necessarily an appropriate realization, because the loading of each by the other causes their transfer functions to change. If it could be arranged that the two-ports did not load each other in ways that are as yet unaccounted for, then the cascade realization could be used.

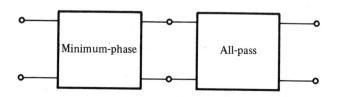

Fig. 21   Cascaded two-ports

One way of eliminating the loading is to make the two-ports *constant-resistance networks*, as shown in Fig. 22. *A constant-resistance network is defined as a two-port whose input impedance at one port is R when the other port is terminated in a resistor R.* Thus whatever the transfer function of the second two-port in Fig. 22 may be, the load it presents at the output port of the first two-port is a resistance R. If the transfer function of each two-port is realized with a termination R, they can then be cascaded without introducing any loading. What has just been described applies to any number of cascaded constant-resistance networks, and it applies whether or not the two-ports are minimum-phase.

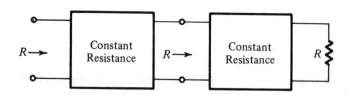

Fig. 22   Cascade of constant-resistance networks

By direct evaluation of the input impedance of various simple networks when terminated in R, it is found that the two-ports shown in Fig. 23 are constant resistance under the conditions $Z_a Z_b = R^2$; that is, when the impedances Z_a and Z_b are inverse of each other with respect to R^2 — equivalently, when the normalized impedances Z_a/R and Z_b/R are

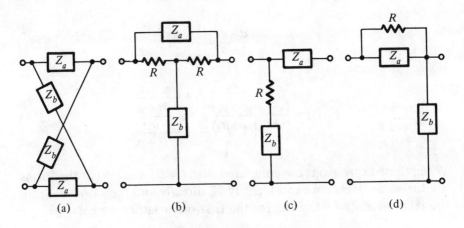

**Fig. 23   Some constant-resistance two-ports for $Z_a Z_b = R^2$:
(a) lattice, (b) bridged-tee, (c) right-ell; (d) left-ell**

inverses of each other. When each of these two-ports is terminated in R, the transfer function can be calculated. For concreteness we shall deal with the voltage gain $G_{21} = V_2/V_1$. It is found to be

$$G_{21} = \frac{R - Z_a}{R + Z_a} = \frac{1 - \dfrac{Z_a}{R}}{1 + \dfrac{Z_a}{R}} \text{ (for the lattice),} \qquad (34a)$$

$$G_{21} = \frac{R}{R + Z_a} = \frac{1}{1 + \dfrac{Z_a}{R}} \text{ (for the bridged-tee and ells).} \qquad (34b)$$

You should verify these. (See Prob. 34.)

Constant-resistance two-ports provide a means of realizing a given transfer function of any order. The function can be decomposed into a product of any number of simple transfer functions, each one can then be realized separately as a constant-resistance two-port and finally the set of two-ports can be connected in cascade. We shall now discuss this process in some detail.

Let us start with an all-pass function. Any all-pass function can be written as the product of the following first-order and second-order all-pass functions:*

---

* Notice that the numerator factor in the first-order case is written as $a - s$ rather than $s - a$. This amounts to changing the sign of the transfer function. Doing this will avoid a discontinuity of π radians in the phase function at $\omega = 0$.

$$F_{a1}(s) = \frac{a-s}{a+s} = \frac{1 - \dfrac{s}{a}}{1 + \dfrac{s}{a}}, \tag{35a}$$

$$F_{a2}(s) = \frac{(s^2 - a_1 s + a_0)}{(s^2 + a_1 s + a_0)} = \frac{1 - \dfrac{a_1 s}{s^2 + a_0}}{1 + \dfrac{a_1 s}{s^2 + a_0}} \tag{35b}$$

When these expressions are compared with (34a), we see that the forms are the same. Hence we can identify Z_a directly and then find Z_b from the relation $Z_a Z_b = R^2$. Thus for the first-order lattice we get

$$Z_a(s) = \frac{R}{a}s, \qquad\qquad Z_b(s) = \frac{1}{\dfrac{1}{aR}s}, \tag{36}$$

and for the second-order lattice,

$$Z_a(s) = \frac{a_1 R s}{s^2 + a_0}, \qquad\qquad Z_b(s) = \frac{R}{a_1}s + \frac{1}{\dfrac{a_1}{R a_0}s}. \tag{37}$$

Thus, the two-ports that realize first- and second-order all-pass functions take the form shown in Fig. 24.

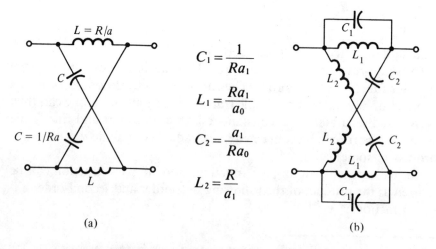

$$C_1 = \frac{1}{Ra_1}$$

$$L_1 = \frac{Ra_1}{a_0}$$

$$C_2 = \frac{a_1}{Ra_0}$$

$$L_2 = \frac{R}{a_1}$$

(a)   (b)

Fig. 24   Constant-resistance, all-pass lattices: (a) first order,
(b) second order

The lattice network has the disadvantage of not having a common ground for its two ports. This cannot be avoided in the first-order case because no common-terminal two-port can realize a zero on the positive real axis, as this lattice does. However, for the second-order all-pass lattice a common-terminal equivalent may exist. This will depend on the locations of the zeros. Bridged-tee and twin-tee equivalents of this lattice are discussed in Prob. 35.

With all-pass functions accounted for, there remains the realization problem for minimum-phase functions. We shall illustrate by an example the realization of a voltage gain by means of constant-resistance networks. The realization of a minimum-phase function in the general case will become evident from this example. Let the load resistance R equal 1 and suppose

$$G_{21}(s) = K\frac{s^2 - \dfrac{s}{2} + 1}{s^2 + 6s + 1} = \frac{s^2 - \dfrac{s}{2} + 1}{s^2 + \dfrac{s}{2} + 1}\left(K\frac{s^2 + \dfrac{s}{2} + 1}{s^2 + 6s + 1}\right),$$

where K is a gain constant that we shall take to be 1 in this example. The given function has been multiplied and divided by the quadratic *surplus factor* $s^2 + s/2 + 1$ in order to put the result in the form of an all-pass function times a minimum-phase function: $G_{21} = F_a F_m$. The all-pass function is immediately realized by the second-order lattice in Fig. 24(b). The angle of the transmission zero is 69°. Hence conditions for both the bridged-tee and twin-tee equivalents of the lattice, as discussed in Prob. 35, are satisfied.

To realize F_m by means of one of the other networks in Fig. 23, we must write this function in the form of (34b). Thus,

$$F_m(s) = \frac{s^2 + \dfrac{s}{2} + 1}{s^2 + 6s + 1} = \frac{1}{1 + \dfrac{11s/2}{s^2 + s/2 + 1}}.$$

From this we get

$$Y_a = \frac{1}{Z_a} = \frac{s^2 + \dfrac{s}{2} + 1}{\dfrac{11s}{2}} = \frac{2}{11}s + \frac{1}{11} + \frac{1}{(11/2)s}.$$

With $Z_a Z_b = R^2$ and $R = 1$, we get $Z_b = Y_a$. We see that the $Z_a(= 1/Y_a)$ branch is the parallel connection of a capacitor, an inductor, and a resistor. If we use Fig. 23(d) for the realization, the resistor $R(= 1)$ can be combined with the parallel resistor in the Z_a branch. The final realization is shown in Fig. 25, where one of the bridged-tee equivalents of the lattice has been used.

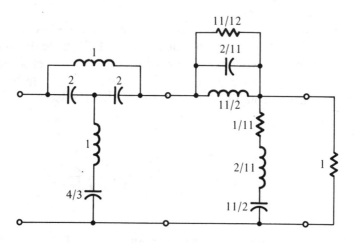

Fig. 25 Realization of $G_{21} = \dfrac{s^2 - s/2 + 1}{s^2 + 6s + 1}$

The minimum-phase part of the transfer function in the preceding example was realized by a left-ell network, which is a simple ladder. Although we shall not do so here, it can be proved that any minimum-phase transfer function can be realized by a constant-resistance ladder (a cascade of ell networks) by choosing a sufficiently small value of the constant K.* In some cases this may require the introduction of surplus factors by which both numerator and denominator are multiplied, leaving the function unchanged but permitting the identification in the form of (34b). Thus, the transfer function $G_{21}(s) = 1/(s^2 + 3s + 3)$ can be written as

$$G_{21}(s) = \frac{s+1}{s^2 + 3s + 3} \cdot \frac{1}{s+1} = \frac{1}{1 + \dfrac{s^2 + 2s + 2}{s+1}} \cdot \frac{1}{s+1}$$

$$= \frac{1}{1 + \left(s + 1 + \dfrac{1}{s+1}\right)} \cdot \frac{1}{1+s} = G_{21a}(s) G_{21b}(s).$$

---

* For a proof, see Norman Balabanian, *Network Synthesis*, Prentice-Hall, Englewood Cliffs, N.J., 1958.

The surplus factor $(s+1)$ converts the transfer function into a product of two functions, each of which can be put in the form of (34b).

The fact that all-pass functions have unit magnitude for all values of $s=j\omega$ is utilized in the design of transmission systems by permitting an independent design for the magnitude and for the angle of the transfer function. Thus a network is designed to realize a desired magnitude function without concern for the angle. From the designed network, the phase function is then determined. Finally, a number of constant-resistance all-pass lattices are cascaded with this network to correct for the angle. Further development of this idea will be left to books on synthesis.

12.10.4 RC Networks

A problem that often presents itself, notably as part of an active RC synthesis task, is the following: Given some transfer function, find an RC two-port realizing the function. Of course, the given function must be realizable as an RC function: poles on the negative real axis.

Suppose the function is the voltage gain, or the transfer impedance or admittance, of the two-port. Furthermore, suppose the desired two-port is obtained as yet another RC two-port terminated in a resistor, as shown in Fig. 26. These functions can be written in terms of the two-port impedance or admittance function of $\mathcal{N}$ as follows:

$$\frac{V_2}{V_1} = \frac{-y_{21}}{y_{22}} = \frac{z_{21}}{z_{11}} \tag{38a}$$

$$\frac{V_2}{I_1} = \frac{Rz_{21}}{z_{22}+R} \tag{38b}$$

$$\frac{I_2}{V_1} = \frac{Gy_{21}}{y_{22}+G} \tag{38c}$$

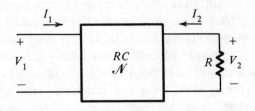

Fig. 26   Terminated two-port

In all cases, the given function is expressed in terms of two of the three impedance or admittance parameters: one transfer and one driving point. (For simplicity, the functions can be normalized to the value of R by setting $R = 1$.) It is possible to identify these two parameters by simple operations performed on the given transfer function. There is a slight variation of detail depending on whether the impedance or admittance parameters are involved because of the different behaviors at $s = 0$ and infinity. We shall illustrate the procedure for admittances.

Let the given function be $V_2/V_1 = F(s) = P(s)/Q(s)$, where P and Q are polynomials. For realizability, the zeros of Q must be negative real. Since y_{22}, as an RC admittance, should have poles and zeros that are negative real and alternate, let us divide numerator and denominator of $F(s)$ by an auxiliary polynomial $D(s)$ which is arbitrary save that it must have negative real zeros that alternate with those of the given $Q(s)$. [To be a little more precise, we note also (see the section "Realization of RC Immittances") that the zero of $D(s)$ having the least magnitude must exceed the magnitude of the zero of $Q(s)$ closest to the origin, in order for $Q(s)/D(s)$ to be an RC admittance.] Now y_{21} and y_{22} are easily identified.

To illustrate, suppose

$$\frac{V_2}{V_1} = \frac{(s+6)(s^2 + 2s + 2)}{(s+1)(s+3)(s+5)}$$

Choose $D(s) = (s+2)(s+4)$. Then, by comparison with (38a),

$$y_{22} = \frac{(s+1)(s+3)(s+5)}{(s+2)(s+4)}$$

$$-y_{21} = \frac{(s+6)(s^2 + 2s + 2)}{(s+2)(s+4)}$$

Clearly, y_{22} is a realizable RC admittance. There is no question of satisfying the residue condition on the admittances since y_{11} is not given; if an RC two-port is found realizing the functions y_{21} and y_{22}, the residue condition must necessarily be satisfied. In this illustration, one additional zero with magnitude >5 could have been added to $D(s)$ and the resulting Q/D would still have been an RC admittance.

The only difference when the given function is the transfer admittance in (38c) is that, to get y_{22} from the given Q/D, we must subtract G. It can be guaranteed that this subtraction need not lead to a nonpositive real function: multiply $D(s)$ by a sufficiently small constant.

Finally, to deal with the impedance functions in (38a) or (38b), the locations of the zeros of $D(s)$ must be appropriately modified. How?

12.10.4.1 Complex Transmission Zeros

How to proceed to the realization of a network from a given y_{21} and y_{22} (or z_{21} and z_{22}) depends on the locations of the transmission zeros. If these are all on the extended negative real axis, the necessary condition for a ladder network is satisfied. As alluded to in the preceding subsection, this is also sufficient to realize an RC ladder. (See Proj. 1.)

Of more value is the case of complex zeros. Specifically, let us treat the case of a single pair of complex transmission zeros. (A function having more complex zeros can always be decomposed into components each having a pair of zeros. This is amplified in the next chapter.) The simplest y_{21} function with a pair of complex zeros in the closed left half-plane can be written as

$$-y_{21}(s) = \frac{k\left(s^2 + \dfrac{\omega_n}{Q_n}s + \omega_n^2\right)}{s + \alpha} = k\left(s + k_0 - \frac{k_{21}s}{s + \alpha}\right) \tag{39a}$$

with $\omega_n/Q_n \geqslant 0$ and with both k_0 and $k_{21} > 0$ as follows:

$$k_0 = \frac{\omega_n^2}{\alpha}, \quad k_{21} = \frac{k(\alpha^2 - \alpha\omega_n/Q_n + \omega_n^2)}{\alpha}. \tag{39b}$$

Different realizations of this transfer admittance are possible depending on the location of the pole relative to that of the transmission zeros. The possibilities are shown in Table 7, complete with element values in terms of the quantities in (39).* The structures are either bridged-tee or twin-tee. A certain amount of element value flexibility is provided by an arbitrary parameter x; for the case $x = 1$, the two-ports are symmetrical.

From the two-ports in Table 7, the driving point admittances are determined to be

$$y_{11}(s) = k\left(s + k_0 + x\frac{k_{21}s}{s + \alpha}\right) = \frac{k[s^2 + (k_0 + \alpha + xk_{21})s + \omega_n^2]}{s + \alpha} \tag{40a}$$

$$y_{22}(s) = k\left(s + k_0 + \frac{1}{x}\frac{k_{21}s}{s + \alpha}\right) = \frac{k[s^2 + (k_0 + \alpha + k_{21}/x)s + \omega_n^2]}{s + \alpha} \tag{40b}$$

---

* For further discussion of the networks in Tables 7 and 8, see Chapter 7 of Norman Balabanian, *Network Synthesis*, Prentice-Hall, 1958.

Table 7   Realizations of $-y_{21} = \dfrac{k\left(s^2 + \dfrac{\omega_n}{Q_n}s + \omega_n^2\right)}{s+\alpha}$

---

x is an arbitrary positive number

(a) $\dfrac{\omega_n}{Q_n} \geqslant \alpha$

$C_1 = k, \quad G_1 = k(\omega_n/Q_n - \alpha)$

$G_2 = \dfrac{k}{\alpha}(x+1)(\alpha^2 + \omega_n^2 - \alpha\omega_n/Q_n)$

$C_2 = \dfrac{x+1}{x\alpha}G_2$

(b) $\dfrac{\omega_n}{Q_n} < \alpha$

$C_1 = \dfrac{\omega_n k/Q_n}{\alpha x}$

$G_1 = \dfrac{k\omega_n^2(x+1)}{\alpha}$

$C_2 = \dfrac{k(x+1)(\alpha - \omega_n/Q_n)}{\alpha}$

$G_2 = \dfrac{\alpha(x+1)}{x}C_2$

$C_3 = \dfrac{x+1}{x\alpha}G_1$

(c) $\dfrac{1}{Q_n} \geqslant \omega_n/\alpha$

$C_1 = \dfrac{k}{\alpha^2}(\alpha\omega_n/Q_n - \omega_n^2)$

$G_1 = \dfrac{k\omega_n^2}{\alpha}$

$G_2 = \dfrac{k(x+1)^2(\omega_n^2 + \alpha^2 - \alpha\omega_n/Q_n)}{x\alpha}$

$C_2 = \dfrac{x+1}{x\alpha}G_2$

Obviously, all poles are compact. But an interesting fact is that the constant terms in the numerator of all three admittances are the same. Note that one of the bridging elements in each of the bridged-tee networks in Table 7 will vanish if the negative of the pole of y_{21} equals twice the real part of the zeros (i.e., $\alpha = \omega_n / Q_n$).

Suppose now that y_{21} is a biquadratic function, with two poles instead of the one in (39), and that one of the driving point admittances is also specified. (If it isn't specified, an appropriate function can always be constructed; the poles would be the same as those of y_{21} and the zeros would alternate with the poles.) They would be of the following forms:

$$-y_{21}(s) = \frac{s^2 + \dfrac{\omega_n}{Q_n}s + \omega_n^2}{(s + \alpha_1)(s + \alpha_2)} \tag{41a}$$

$$y_{22}(s) = \frac{H(s + a)(s + b)}{(s + \alpha_1)(s + \alpha_2)} \tag{41b}$$

Note: H is a positive constant. From the properties of RC admittances,

$$a < \alpha_1 < b < \alpha_2 \tag{42}$$

Depending on the relative locations of the zeros of y_{22} and y_{21}, two appropriate components can be removed and the functions in (41) can be reduced to the form of those in (39) and (40). The realizations are shown in Table 8.

A very common situation is the one where the given function is the voltage gain $V_2 / V_1 = G(s)$ of a two-port. In the above, we showed how the two admittance functions y_{21} and y_{22} could be derived from $G(s)$. Specifically, suppose the given function has a single pair of complex zeros and two poles; thus

$$G(s) = K\frac{s^2 + \dfrac{\omega_n}{Q_n}s + \omega_n^2}{(s + a)(s + b)} = K\frac{s^2 + \dfrac{\omega_n}{Q_n}s + \omega_n^2}{s^2 + (a + b)s + ab} \tag{43}$$

In the special case $K = 1$ and $\omega_n^2 = ab$ (that is, the constant terms in numerator and denominator are the same), we can multiply the numerator and denominator by $k/(s + \alpha)$ and then identify the y_{21} and y_{22} functions as in (39) and (40b). Both k and α are arbitrary positive numbers except that α must be between a and b. Thus, in addition to

Table 8   Realizations of $-y_{21} = \dfrac{s^2 + \dfrac{\omega_n}{Q_n}s + \omega_n^2}{(s+\alpha_1)(s+\alpha_2)}, \; y_{22} = \dfrac{H(s+a)(s+b)}{(s+\alpha_1)(s+\alpha_2)}$

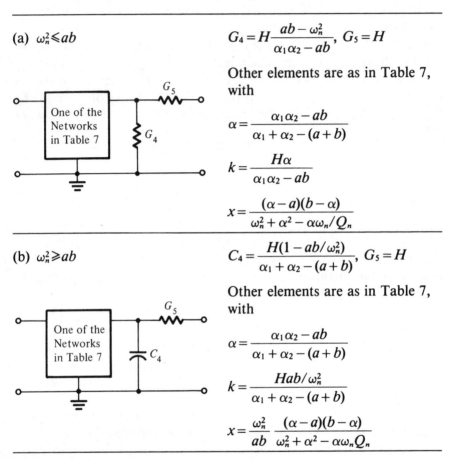

(a) $\omega_n^2 \leqslant ab$

$$G_4 = H\frac{ab - \omega_n^2}{\alpha_1\alpha_2 - ab}, \; G_5 = H$$

Other elements are as in Table 7, with

$$\alpha = \frac{\alpha_1\alpha_2 - ab}{\alpha_1 + \alpha_2 - (a+b)}$$

$$k = \frac{H\alpha}{\alpha_1\alpha_2 - ab}$$

$$x = \frac{(\alpha - a)(b - \alpha)}{\omega_n^2 + \alpha^2 - \alpha\omega_n/Q_n}$$

(b) $\omega_n^2 \geqslant ab$

$$C_4 = \frac{H(1 - ab/\omega_n^2)}{\alpha_1 + \alpha_2 - (a+b)}, \; G_5 = H$$

Other elements are as in Table 7, with

$$\alpha = \frac{\alpha_1\alpha_2 - ab}{\alpha_1 + \alpha_2 - (a+b)}$$

$$k = \frac{Hab/\omega_n^2}{\alpha_1 + \alpha_2 - (a+b)}$$

$$x = \frac{\omega_n^2}{ab}\frac{(\alpha - a)(b - \alpha)}{\omega_n^2 + \alpha^2 - \alpha\omega_nQ_n}$$

the degree of freedom in choosing x in Table 7, there are two other degrees of freedom — k and α — in the specification of element values. This freedom can be used to achieve other goals besides simple realizability, such as reducing the spread of element values or the sensitivity. In fact, there would be no reason why α could not be chosen equal to ω_n/Q_n in cases (a) and (c) in Table 7, thus resulting in one fewer component.

But in the more general case when $\omega_n^2 \neq ab$, the networks in Table 7 are inappropriate. Two approaches are possible to handle this situation. One of these is to use the networks in Table 8, arising from the admittance functions in (41). The ratio of these two functions still results in

(42). Secondly, it isn't necessary first to find the admittance functions before finding the network; we could assume a candidate network, then determine its voltage gain function in terms of the components and then compare coefficients with (42). Possible candidate networks should contain bridged-tees or twin-tees but possibly with different arrangements of R's and C's from the ones in Table 7.

Two possibilities are shown in Table 9. They are obtained from the bridged-tees in Table 7 by adding a resistor or capacitor to the shunt branch of the tee in cases (a) and (c) respectively. In addition, since α is an arbitrarily chosen quantity in the situation now under discussion, we might as well choose it to make one of the bridging elements disappear: G_1 in case (a) or C_1 in case (c). The table gives the general expression for $G(s)$ from (42) and shows the actual expression in terms of component values in the two cases. Some design formulas and constraints involving component values in terms of the general coefficients of $G(s)$ are also given.

Table 9   Bridged-tee realizations of $G(s) = K \dfrac{s^2 + \dfrac{\omega_n}{Q_n} + \omega_n^2}{s^2 + (a+b) + ab}$

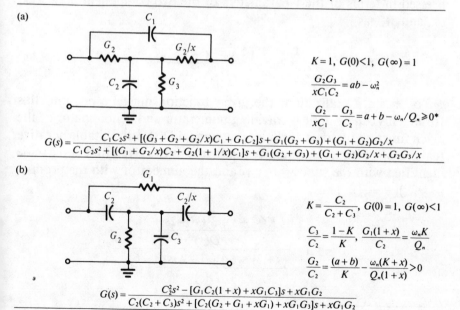

(a)

$$K = 1, \ G(0) < 1, \ G(\infty) = 1$$

$$\frac{G_2 G_3}{x C_1 C_2} = ab - \omega_n^2$$

$$\frac{G_2}{x C_1} - \frac{G_3}{C_2} = a + b - \omega_n/Q_n \geqslant 0^*$$

$$G(s) = \frac{C_1 C_2 s^2 + [(G_3 + G_2 + G_2/x)C_1 + G_1 C_2]s + G_1(G_2 + G_3) + (G_1 + G_2)G_2/x}{C_1 C_2 s^2 + [(G_1 + G_2/x)C_2 + G_2(1 + 1/x)C_1]s + G_1(G_2 + G_3) + (G_1 + G_2)G_2/x + G_2 G_3/x}$$

(b)

$$K = \frac{C_2}{C_2 + C_3}, \ G(0) = 1, \ G(\infty) < 1$$

$$\frac{C_3}{C_2} = \frac{1 - K}{K}, \ \frac{G_1(1 + x)}{C_2} = \frac{\omega_n K}{Q_n}$$

$$\frac{G_2}{C_2} = \frac{(a+b)}{K} - \frac{\omega_n(K + x)}{Q_n(1 + x)} > 0$$

$$G(s) = \frac{C_2^2 s^2 - [G_1 C_2(1 + x) + x G_1 C_3]s + x G_1 G_2}{C_2(C_2 + C_3)s^2 + [C_2(G_2 + G_1 + x G_1) + x G_1 G_3]s + x G_1 G_2}$$

---

* If $G(s)$ is to be realized as a common-terminal two-port then, according to the Fialkow-Gerst condition, the numerator coefficients must be no greater than the corresponding ones in the denominator. Thus, with $K = 1$, $a + b - \omega_n/Q_n$ can never be negative.

A bridged twin-tee is shown in Table 10. For the simplest special case when the parameters a, b, and x are all equal to zero, the network reduces to a "notch" twin-tee, with transmission zeros on the imaginary axis. For the simplest case of complex transmission zeros, only parameter x is nonzero. For this case, $G(j\omega_n) = x/(2+x)$; and since x depends only on Q_n for this case, the value of $G(j\omega_n)$ cannot be adjusted independently from the Q of the transmission zeros. The introduction of nonzero a and b parameters — which adds a branch in parallel with the shunt branch of each tee — permits the independent adjustment of $G(j\omega_n)$.*

The use of these tables will be illustrated by means of an example. Suppose the following short-circuit transfer admittance function is to be realized as an RC two-port.

$$-y_{21} = K\frac{(s^2+s+3)(s^2+2s+2)}{(s+2)(s+4)(s^2+25s/3+6)}$$

The desired two-port can be considered as a cascade of two two-ports as shown in Fig. 27. The y_{21} function of the overall network $\mathcal{N}$ can be expressed in terms of the y-parameters of the two component networks, $\mathcal{N}_a$ and $\mathcal{N}_b$, as

$$-y_{21} = \frac{(-y_{21a})(-y_{21b})}{y_{22a}+y_{11b}}$$

To obtain a realization, the given function must be put into this form. This can be done by dividing numerator and denominator of the given function by some auxiliary polynomial $D(s)$ with suitable negative real roots. Then the resulting denominator of the given function can be identified with the sum $y_{22a}+y_{11b}$ and the numerator with the product $(-y_{21a})(-y_{21b})$. Thus,

$$-y_{21} = \frac{\dfrac{K(s^2+s+3)(s^2+2s+2)}{D(s)}}{\dfrac{(s+2)(s+4)(s^2+25s/3+6)}{D(s)}}$$

---

* In order to ensure a second order $G(s)$, instead of a higher order that a network with three or more capacitors would lead to, the values of elements must be chosen such that the sum of the capacitances in the branches of each tee must be the same; similarly for the sum of the conductances. That is the reason for the specific selections of shunt branch capacitances and conductances.

Table 10 Bridged twin-tee realization of $G(s) = K\dfrac{s^2 + \dfrac{\omega_n}{Q_n}s + \omega_n^2}{(s+a)(s+b)}$

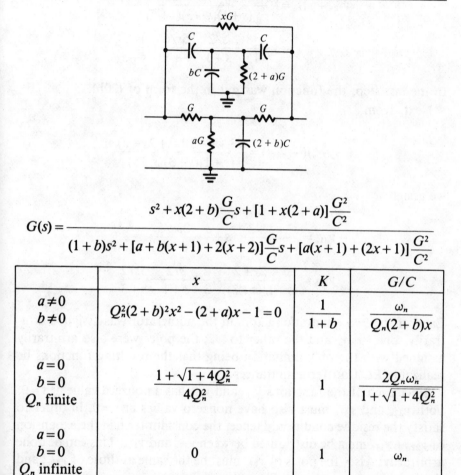

$$G(s) = \frac{s^2 + x(2+b)\dfrac{G}{C}s + [1 + x(2+a)]\dfrac{G^2}{C^2}}{(1+b)s^2 + [a + b(x+1) + 2(x+2)]\dfrac{G}{C}s + [a(x+1) + (2x+1)]\dfrac{G^2}{C^2}}$$

	x	K	G/C
$a \neq 0$ $b \neq 0$	$Q_n^2(2+b)^2x^2 - (2+a)x - 1 = 0$	$\dfrac{1}{1+b}$	$\dfrac{\omega_n}{Q_n(2+b)x}$
$a = 0$ $b = 0$ Q_n finite	$\dfrac{1 + \sqrt{1 + 4Q_n^2}}{4Q_n^2}$	1	$\dfrac{2Q_n\omega_n}{1 + \sqrt{1 + 4Q_n^2}}$
$a = 0$ $b = 0$ Q_n infinite	0	1	ω_n

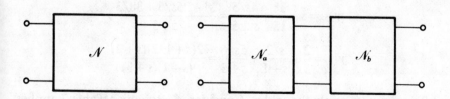

Fig. 27   Cascaded two-ports

The polynomial $D(s)$ must be chosen so that the denominator of the preceding function is an RC admittance function. One possibility is

$$y_{22a} + y_{11b} = \frac{(s+2)(s+4)(s^2+25s/3+6)}{(s+1)(s+3)(s+5)}$$

$$= s + \frac{48}{15} + \frac{s/2}{s+1} + \frac{5s/6}{s+3} + \frac{4s/5}{s+5}.$$

In the last step, the function was put in the form of (20b).
Next, from

$$(-y_{21a})(-y_{21b}) = \frac{(s^2+s+3)(s^2+2s+2)}{(s+1)(s+3)(s+5)},$$

we assign

$$-y_{21a} = \frac{s^2+s+3}{s+5} = s + \frac{3}{5} - \frac{23s/5}{s+5},$$

$$-y_{21b} = \frac{s^2+2s+2}{(s+1)(s+3)} = \frac{2}{3} + \frac{s/2}{s+1} - \frac{5s/2}{s+3}.$$

Each of the two quadratic factors in the numerator was assigned arbitrarily, one to $\mathcal{N}_a$ and the other to $\mathcal{N}_b$; the poles were also arbitrarily assigned with the only limitation being that the resulting functions be realizable RC transfer admittances.

Since each of the functions y_{21a} and y_{21b} has a nonzero value at $s=0$, both y_{22a} and y_{11b} must also have nonzero values at $s=0$, in order to satisfy the residue condition. Hence, the constant term in the expansion of $y_{22a} + y_{11b}$ must be distributed between y_{22a} and y_{11b}. This can be done arbitrarily. Also, the poles of y_{22a} must be the same as those of y_{21a}; and similarly for y_{11b} and y_{21b}. Thus, we might have

$$y_{22a} = s + \frac{38}{15} + \frac{4s/5}{s+5} = \frac{s^2 + 25s/3 + 38/3}{s+5},$$

$$y_{11b} = \frac{2}{3} + \frac{s/2}{s+1} + \frac{5s/6}{s+3} = \frac{2(s+1/2)(s+2)}{(s+1)(s+3)}.$$

We can now apply the tables. Consider $\mathcal{N}_a$, to which Table 7 applies, first. The two corresponding functions from above can be written as

$$-y_{21a} = s + \frac{3}{5} - \frac{23s/5}{s+5} = \frac{s^2 + s + 3}{s+5},$$

$$y_{22a} = \left(s + \frac{3}{5} + \frac{4}{23}\frac{23s/5}{s+5}\right) + \frac{29}{15}.$$

The last term of y_{22a} can be realized as a resistor of $^{15}/_{29}$ units across the output port of $\mathcal{N}_a$. Comparing $-y_{21a}$ and the remainder of y_{22a} with (39) and (40) leads to the identification of the following values:

$k=1$	$\alpha=5$	$x=23/4$
$k_0=3/5$	$k_{21}=23/5$	$\omega_n/Q_n=1$
		$\omega_n^2=3$

From these values we find that $\omega_n/Q_n=1<5=\alpha$ and $\omega_n/Q_n=1>3/5=\omega_n^2/\alpha$. Hence, either of the last two networks in Table 7 will be appropriate. Since the one in (c) has fewer elements than the one in (b), that is the one we shall choose. The component values can be found by substituting numerical values given above into the expressions in (c) of Table 7. The result is shown on the left of the dashed line in Fig. 28. As for $\mathcal{N}_b$, the y-parameters are

$$-y_{21b} = \frac{s^2 + 2s + s}{(s+1)(s+3)},$$

$$y_{11b} = \frac{2(s+1/2)(s+2)}{(s+1)(s+3)}.$$

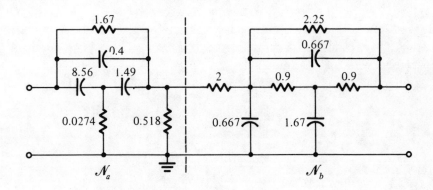

Fig. 28   Realization of example (normalized values of C and R)

These are of a form appropriate for Table 8. A comparison with the generic functions in that table leads to the following values:

$$a = 1/2 \qquad\qquad \omega_n/Q_n = 2 \qquad\qquad H = 2$$
$$b = 2 \qquad\qquad \omega_n^2 = 2$$

From these values, we find that $\omega_n^2 = 2 > 1 = ab$. Hence, the network in (b) of Table 8 is the appropriate one. From the formulas given there we find

$$\alpha = 4/3, \; k = 2/3, \; x = 1.$$

Now we find that $\omega_n/Q_n = 2 > 4/3 = \alpha$; hence, the bridged tee in (a) of Table 7 is the appropriate one to embed in the network in (b) of Table 8. With the element values calculated from table 7, the final realization is shown on the right in Fig. 28.

CHAPTER 13
Active RC Synthesis

The networks treated throughout this book have been lumped, linear, and time-invariant. The preceding two chapters were devoted to the synthesis of passive and reciprocal networks within this general class. In this chapter we shall drop the "passive" and "reciprocal" designations.

From a practical point of view, an inductor is a very undesirable component. It is bulky and heavy, it deviates from the ideal significantly (especially at low frequencies), and it is impossible to fabricate as an integrated circuit component, which is the increasingly desired form of construction for most circuits. It is, therefore, highly desirable to synthesize networks without inductors. But RC networks alone cannot realize complex poles. Hence, what is needed is to combine active and/or nonreciprocal devices with RC networks. The result of such a combination is referred to as an *active RC network*.

But which specific active and/or nonreciprocal device should be combined with R and C components to achieve an active RC network? One of the earliest devices used as a basic building block was the negative converter. However, this led to unacceptably high sensitivity and has been largely abandoned. Because of the ease and low cost of fabrication of operational amplifiers, this has become the most popular building block by far. Synthesis procedures use op-amps either directly or as the constituents in the construction of other devices used as the basic active building blocks.

13.1 INDUCTANCE SIMULATION

The classical method of synthesis (of filters, amplitude and delay equalizers, etc.) results in a lossless (LC) network terminated at each end in a resistor—whose value can be zero or infinity. The great disadvantage of this method is the appearance of inductors. However, the *LC* network also has a large advantage—at least when the structure is a ladder—namely, the low sensitivity to changes in the element values. This advantage can be preserved if somehow the inductors can be replaced by active network equivalents. We shall now discuss a number of ways in which this can be done.

13.1.1 Gyrator-Capacitor Simulation

As discussed in Chapter 1, the gyrator shown in Fig. 1 is a device with the following voltage-current equations.

$$\begin{bmatrix} V_1 \\ V_2 \end{bmatrix} = \begin{bmatrix} 0 & -r \\ r & 0 \end{bmatrix} \cdot \begin{bmatrix} I_1 \\ I_2 \end{bmatrix} . \tag{1}$$

When loaded at one port by a capacitor C, as in Fig. 1(b), the behavior at the other port is that of an inductor $L = r^2C$.

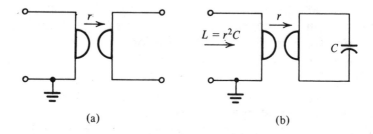

(a)   (b)

Fig. 1   Gyrator-capacitor simulation of an inductor

What is shown in Fig. 1 is a common terminal (grounded) gyrator; so the equivalent inductor has one of its terminals effectively grounded. If a floating inductor is desired, one would imagine that a floating gyrator (non-common terminal) would be used in the configuration of Fig. 1(a). However, floating gyrators are not easy to implement, for practical reasons. Hence, a different arrangement, using only grounded gyrators, is necessary. Such a configuration was given in Prob. 2 of Chapter 1 and is shown here in Fig. 2. The floating inductor is obtained at the expense of an extra gyrator.

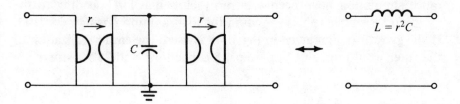

Fig. 2 Floating inductor simulation

The approach taken in the method of simulation under discussion is as follows. Given a synthesis task (say the design of a filter), first obtain an *LC* realization using classical synthesis methods. Then replace grounded inductors by the structure of Fig. 1(a) and floating inductors by the structure of Fig. 2.

13.1.2 Example

The following transfer function is that of an elliptic band-pass filter.

$$F(s) = \frac{3.98 \times 10^{-3}(s^2 + .882)(s^2 + 1.134)}{(s^2 + .0308s + 1)(s^2 + .0131s + .958)(s^2 + .0137s + 1.044)}. \quad (2)$$

A resistively-terminated *LC* realization of the filter is shown in Fig. 3. Two of the inductors in Fig. 3 are grounded and two are floating. Inductance simulation by gyrators will require a total of six gyrators. The

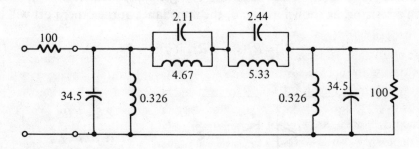

Fig. 3 Passive realization of filter example: *R* in kΩ, *L* in H, *C* in nF

resulting structure is shown in Fig. 4. The capacitors used in the inductance simulation have been arbitrarily chosen as $1\,nF$, leading to the gyration resistance values shown in the diagram upon using $r = \sqrt{L/C}$. If the gyrator design given in Fig. 1-18 is used, the entire realization of the filter would utilize 12 op-amps, 8 capacitors, and 24 resistors.

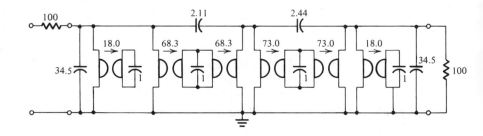

Fig. 4   Gyrator-capacitor simulation of inductors in example:
R in kΩ, C in nF

13.1.3   General Converter-Resistor Simulation of Inductor Subnetwork

A second approach to the replacement of inductors is to use general converters with appropriate values of $f(s)$. Recall from Chapter 1 that the voltage-current relations of a general converter are

$$\begin{bmatrix} V_1 \\ I_2 \end{bmatrix} = \begin{bmatrix} 0 & 1 \\ -f(s) & 0 \end{bmatrix} \begin{bmatrix} I_1 \\ V_2 \end{bmatrix} \tag{3}$$

where $f(s)$ is an arbitrary function. If a general converter is terminated in a resistor, as shown in Fig. 5, the impedance at the other port will be

$$Z_{in} = Rf(s) = KRs, \text{ if } f(s) = Ks. \tag{4}$$

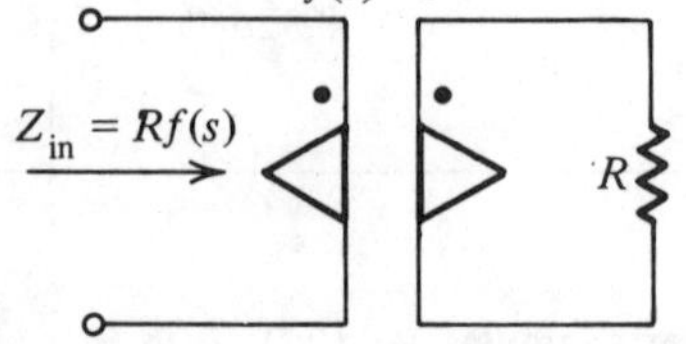

$f(s) : 1$

$Z_{in} = Rf(s)$

R

$Z_{in} = KRs$

if $f(s) = Ks$

Fig. 5   Inductance simulation by a general converter-resistor combination

Thus, the structure in Fig. 5 will simulate an inductor.

But rather than dealing with each inductor separately, let us consider a connected subnetwork of inductors. This subnetwork is to be replaced by a similar subnetwork of resistors suitably combined with general converters.

In Fig. 6(a) is shown an $(n+1)$-terminal network of resistors, $\mathcal{N}_R$. Let the impedance matrix of this network considered as a common-terminal n-port be $\mathbf{Z}_R$, a matrix of constants. Now suppose a general converter is connected between the common terminal and each of the other terminals, with $f(s) = Ks$ for each GC. Using the general converter relationship (3), we can write

$$\mathbf{V}_L = \mathbf{V}_R, \tag{5a}$$

$$\mathbf{I}_L = \frac{1}{f(s)}\mathbf{I}_R. \tag{5b}$$

Letting the impedance matrix of the overall network in Fig. 6(b) be $\mathbf{Z}_L(s)$, we find that

$$\mathbf{Z}_L(s) = f(s)\mathbf{Z}_R = Ks\mathbf{Z}_R, \text{ if } f(s) = Ks. \tag{6}$$

Thus, $\mathbf{Z}_L(s)$ has nonzero elements only where $\mathbf{Z}_R$ has nonzero elements. $\mathbf{Z}_L(s)$ is the impedance matrix of a subnetwork of inductors having the identically same structure as that of $\mathcal{N}_R$.

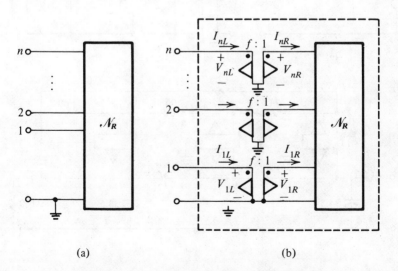

(a)   (b)

Fig. 6   Resistive $(n+1)$-port connected to general converters

The synthesis procedure is the converse of the preceding. From a given LC design, a connected $(n+1)$-terminal subnetwork of inductors is identified; each inductor L_i is replaced by a resistor $R_i = L_i/K$. Then a general converter with $f(s) = Ks$ is connected between one of the terminals (considered the common terminal) and each of the other terminals. In the LC design, the original inductor subnetwork is then replaced by this new structure.

13.1.4 Example

The procedure will be illustrated by the LC filter considered in the preceding section and shown in Fig. 3. All inductors in this diagram form a single 4-terminal connected subnetwork, as shown in Fig. 7(a). Hence, three general converters will be required, and Fig. 7(a) is replaced by Fig. 7(b). The complete network is shown in Fig. 7(c), where $K = 3 \times 10^{-4}$. Suppose the general converter design given in Fig. 1-20 is used, in which $f(s) = Z_1 Z_2 / Z_3 Z_4$. Either Z_3 or Z_4 can be chosen as a capacitor, and the remaining three impedances as resistors. With the first choice, $f(s) = R_1 R_2 C_3 s / R_4$; so $K = R_1 R_2 C_3 / R_4$. With the easily real-

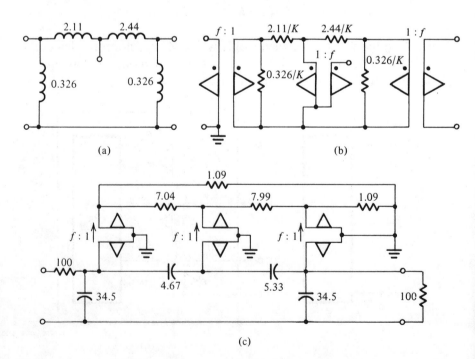

Fig. 7   General converter-resistor simulation of L-subnetwork: R in kΩ, C in nF

izable values $R_1 = R_2 = 10k\Omega$, $R_4 = 1k\Omega$, and $C = 3nF$, the value of K equals 3×10^{-4}. This was the value used in Fig. 7(c). Count the number of components and compare with the previous realization.

13.2 DIRECT GENERAL CONVERTER REALIZATION

The approach treated in the preceding section required, first, that a given transfer function be realized as a classical LC network, after which the inductors would be replaced by active/nonreciprocal components together with R's or C's. We shall now consider a realization procedure which uses the properties of a general converter with a specific conversion function $f(s)$ directly in the synthesis procedure.

The starting point is a transfer function. Let a transfer voltage ratio be written in a form that shows the coefficients of the numerator and denominator polynomials. Thus,

$$G(s) = \frac{V_2}{V_1} = \frac{\sum\limits_{i=0}^{n} a_i s^i}{\sum\limits_{i=0}^{n} b_i s^i} \tag{7}$$

The denominator coefficients must of necessity be positive if the corresponding network is to be stable. But, generally, the numerator coefficients need not all be positive. Nevertheless, let us assume that the condition (called the Fialkow-Gerst condition) $b_i \geqslant |a_i|$ is satisfied. This condition can always be satisfied by multiplying the numerator by a sufficiently small constant. Although this would sacrifice some output voltage level, this could later be restored by amplification, if necessary. Let us initially assume that those numerator coefficients that are not zero are positive; we shall later remove this restriction.

For a two-port $\mathcal{N}$ and for two two-ports in parallel, as shown in Fig. 8, the transfer voltage ratio can be written in terms of the admittance parameters as

$$\frac{V_2}{V_1} = \frac{-y_{21}}{y_{22}} \tag{8a}$$

$$\frac{V_2}{V_1} = \frac{(-y_{21a}) + (-y_{21b})}{y_{22a} + y_{22b}}. \tag{8b}$$

It is a simple matter to rewrite the numerator and denominator of $G(s)$ in (7) as follows:

$$G(s) = \frac{a_0 + a_1 s + \sum\limits_{i=2}^{n} a_i s^i}{b_0 + b_1 s + \sum\limits_{i=2}^{n} b_i s^i}. \tag{9}$$

By comparing this with (8b), the following identifications can be made:
For Network $\mathcal{N}_a$

$$-y_{21a} = a_0 + a_1 s \tag{10a}$$

$$y_{22a} = b_0 + b_1 s \tag{10b}$$

$$G_a(s) = \frac{-y_{21a}}{y_{22a}} = \frac{a_0 + a_1 s}{b_0 + b_1 s} \tag{10c}$$

and for Network $\mathcal{N}_b$

$$-y_{21b} = s^2 \sum_{i=2}^{n} a_i s^{i-2} \tag{11a}$$

$$y_{22b} = s^2 \sum_{i=2}^{n} b_i s^{i-2} \tag{11b}$$

$$G_b(s) = \frac{\sum\limits_{i=2}^{n} a_i s^{i-2}}{\sum\limits_{i=2}^{n} b_i s^{i-2}} \tag{11c}$$

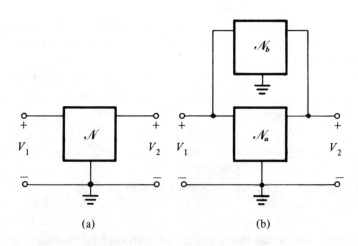

(a)   (b)

Fig. 8   Parallel connection of two-ports

If each of the two networks $\mathcal{N}_a$ and $\mathcal{N}_b$ can be realized, then the realization of the original function will consist of their parallel connection.

The transfer function of $\mathcal{N}_a$ is only of first order. The simple inverted "ell" network shown in Fig. 9 can realize it. The element values can be found in terms of the coefficients of the voltage ratio by writing the transfer function of Fig. 9 in literal form and then comparing coefficients with (10c). The results are

$$G_s = a_0 \qquad\qquad G_p = b_0 - a_0$$
$$C_s = a_1 \qquad\qquad C_p = b_1 - a_1 \tag{12}$$

Under the assumption of positive coefficients and $b_i \geqslant a_i$, none of the element values will be negative; however, any of them could be zero.

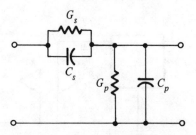

Fig. 9   Realization of first-order transfer function

Next consider $G_b(s)$ in (11c); this has the same form as the original transfer function except that its order has been reduced by 2. But the forms of y_{21b} and y_{22b} in (11) each differ by a factor s^2 from those of the original y_{21} and y_{22}, obtained respectively by equating numerators and denominators of (7a) and (8a). If this factor can be removed without changing the transfer function $G_b(s)$, then the realization of $\mathcal{N}_b$ could be carried out in the same manner as the original network, that is, a parallel realization. This process can be continued until the transfer function is exhausted and the desired network would be the parallel connection of a number of subnetworks.

Clearly removal of the s^2 factor will require bringing an active component into play—otherwise an RC network would realize the general transfer function under discussion.

Consider a two-port terminated in a current general converter as shown in Fig. 10 and let this entire structure be the previous network $\mathcal{N}_b$. The admittance representation of the overall network, including the general converter, is

$$\begin{bmatrix} I_{1b} \\ I_{2b} \end{bmatrix} = \begin{bmatrix} y_{11b} & y_{12b} \\ y_{21b} & y_{22b} \end{bmatrix} \begin{bmatrix} V_{1b} \\ V_{2b} \end{bmatrix} \tag{13}$$

But $V_{2c} = V_{2b}$ and $I_{2c} = f(s)I_{2b}$. So the admittance representation of only the two-port $\mathcal{N}_c$ will be

$$\begin{bmatrix} I_{1c} \\ I_{2c} \end{bmatrix} = \begin{bmatrix} y_{11b} & y_{12b} \\ y_{21b}/f(s) & y_{22b}/f(s) \end{bmatrix} \begin{bmatrix} V_{1c} \\ V_{2c} \end{bmatrix} \tag{14}$$

Now if $f(s)$ is proportional to s^2, we will have succeeded in removing the s^2 factor from y_{21b} and y_{22b}.

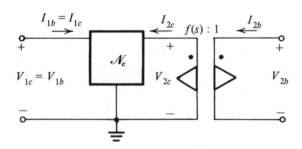

Fig. 10   Network cascaded with a current general converter

Suppose the network of Fig. 1-20 is again used as the general converter design, this time letting Z_3 and Z_4 both be capacitors and Z_1 and Z_2 resistors. Then,

$$f(s) = (R_1R_2C_3C_4)s^2 = Ks^2 \tag{15}$$

with $K = R_1R_2C_3C_4$.
Using this $f(s)$ in (14), we obtain

$$-y_{21c} = \frac{-y_{21b}}{Ks^2} = \frac{1}{K}\sum_{i=2}^{n} a_i s^{i-2} \tag{16a}$$

$$-y_{22c} = \frac{y_{22b}}{Ks^2} = \frac{1}{K}\sum_{i=2}^{n} b_i s^{i-2} \tag{16b}$$

$$G_c(s) = G_b(s) = \dfrac{\dfrac{1}{K}\displaystyle\sum_{i=2}^{n} a_i s^{i-2}}{\dfrac{1}{K}\displaystyle\sum_{i=2}^{n} b_i s^{i-2}} \tag{16c}$$

Thus, aside from a constant multiplier, y_{21c} and y_{22c} have the same form as the original y_{21} and y_{22} functions, and $G_c(s)$ has the same form as the original $G(s)$ but is of lower order. The cycle can now be repeated with $\mathcal{N}_c$; it can be realized as the parallel combination of a first-order network and another network which, in turn, can be handled in the same way that $\mathcal{N}_b$ was above.

One point remains to be cleared up; the possibility of negative numerator coefficients. From (12) it is clear that this will cause some of the series elements in the inverted ells to become negative. Figure 11 shows how to handle this by a unity gain inverting amplifier. It isn't necessary to use a separate amplifier for each first order function having negative numerator coefficients as the synthesis proceeds; a single amplifer for the entire network will be sufficient. The general realization is shown in Fig. 12 together with expressions for the element values in terms of the coefficients. When a numerator coefficient is positive, the corresponding switch will be in the upper position; when it is negative, in the lower position.

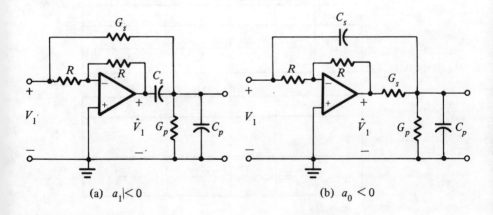

(a) $a_1 < 0$ (b) $a_0 < 0$

Fig. 11 **Realization of negative numerator coefficients:** $\hat{V}_1 = -V_1$

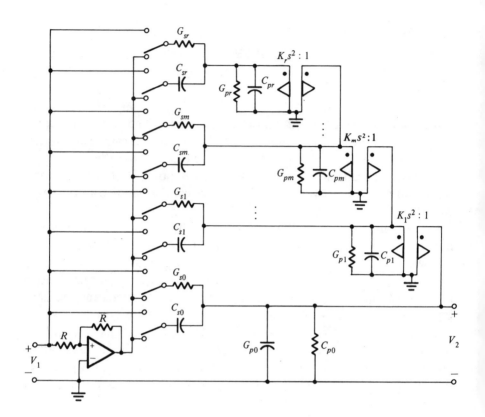

mth Section

K_m	G_{sm}	C_{sm}	G_{pm}	C_{pm}
$\displaystyle\prod_{\substack{j=0 \\ (K_0=1)}}^{m} K_j$	$\dfrac{\|a_{2m}\|}{K_m}$	$\dfrac{\|a_{2m+1}\|}{K_m}$	$\dfrac{b_{2m} - \|a_{2m}\|}{K_m}$	$\dfrac{b_{2m+1} - \|a_{2m+1}\|}{K_m}$

Last (rth) Section

Order n	G_{sr}	C_{sr}	G_{pr}	C_{pr}
Even $r = n/2$	$\dfrac{a_n}{K_r}$	0	$\dfrac{b_n - \|a_n\|}{K_r}$	0
Odd $r = \dfrac{n-1}{2}$	$\dfrac{\|a_{n-1}\|}{K_r}$	$\dfrac{\|a_n\|}{K_r}$	$\dfrac{b_{n-1} - \|a_{n-1}\|}{K_r}$	$\dfrac{b_n - \|a_n\|}{K_r}$

Fig. 12   Realization of a general transfer function

13.2.1 Example

As an example, consider the following transfer function which represents a fifth order elliptic low-pass filter.

$$G(s) = \frac{1 + 1.35s^2 + 0.4205s^4}{1 + 3.125s + 4.527s^2 + 7.588s^3 + 3.837s^4 + 4.394s^5}.$$

The numerator coefficients are all positive; hence, no inverting amplifier will be needed. Odd powers are absent from the numerator; hence, there will be no series capacitors. The complete realization is shown in Fig. 13.

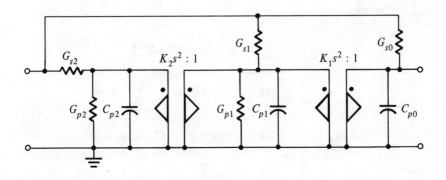

Units	G_{s0}	G_{s1}	G_{s2}	G_{p1}	G_{p2}	G_{p0}	C_{p1}	C_{p2}	K_1, K_2
mS nF	0.1	0.135	0.0420	0.3177	0.3417	15.625	37.94	21.94	2.5×10^{-9}

Fig. 13   Realization of fifth order filter

In the construction of the general converters (both the same), it was assumed that $R_1 = R_2 = 10$ kΩ and $C_3 = C_4 = 5$ nF. Hence, $K_1 = K_2 = 2.5 \times 10^{-9}$. If we take $K_1 = K_2 = 1$ in the normalized design, then the actual element values will be obtained from the normalized ones by multiplying conductances by 10^{-4} and capacitances by 5×10^{-9}.

13.2.2 Sensitivity Considerations

As the element values of a realized network vary, the transfer function will vary. This variation can be expressed in terms of the movement of the poles and zeros or in terms of changes in the coefficients in the numerator and denominator. If the coefficients can be expressed in terms of the element values, then the calculation of the coefficient sensitivities can be easily carried out.

From the general realization in Fig. 12 it is not difficult to carry out an analysis and to write the transfer function in terms of the element values. The results are: For n even,

$$\frac{V_2}{V_1} = \frac{\pm K_r G_{sr} s^n + \displaystyle\sum_{m=0}^{(n-2)/2} K_m(\pm G_{sm} \pm sC_{sm})s^{2m}}{K_r(G_{sr} + G_{pr})s^n + \displaystyle\sum_{m=0}^{(n-2)/2} K_m[(G_{sm} + G_{pm}) + s(C_{sm} + C_{pm})]s^{2m}}$$

and for n odd

$$\frac{V_2}{V_1} = \frac{\displaystyle\sum_{m=0}^{(n-1)/2} K_m(\pm G_{sm} \pm sC_{sm})s^{2m}}{\displaystyle\sum_{m=0}^{(n-1)/2} K_m[(G_{sm} + G_{pm}) + s(C_{sm} + C_{pm})]s^{2m}}.$$

(K_m is defined in Fig. 12.) By comparing coefficients with those in (7), the a_i and b_i coefficients can be written in terms of the element values as follows:

	a_i	b_i
i even $m = i/2$	$\pm K_m G_{sm}$	$K_m(G_{sm} + G_{pm})$
i odd $m = (i-1)/2$	$\pm K_m C_{sm}$	$K_m(C_{sm} + C_{pm})$

$$(18)$$

It is now a simple matter to compute the sensitivity of any coefficient to any of the element values. Since each coefficient depends on only one or two elements—and conversely, each element influences only one or two coefficients—the variation of any one element will affect at most two coefficients. The sensitivity of any one coefficient will equal zero with respect to all but one or two element values. Furthermore, these one or two nonzero sensitivities will be no greater than one. Thus,

$$S_e^{a_i} \leqslant 1 \tag{19a}$$

$$S_e^{b_i} \leqslant 1 \tag{19b}$$

where the element e stands for any one of the following: G_{sm}, G_{pm}, C_{sm}, C_{pm}, K_1, K_2, ..., K_m where $m = i/2$ or $(i-1)/2$.

13.3 BIQUADS

The synthesis approach of the preceding section handled a given transfer function of any order as a single unit. In contrast, a more popular method is to factor the numerator and denominator of the given transfer function and to group each quadratic factor in the denominator with a quadratic or lower order factor of the numerator. Each grouping is a *biquadratic* function, and the entire transfer function is made up of the product of the biquadratic factors. Now if a realization is obtained for each biquadratic function such that the output impedance is very low (and the input impedance very high) then the cascade of all these realizations gives a synthesis of the entire function. A network that realizes a biquadratic function is called a *biquad*. Of course, a large number of useful transfer functions are no more than biquadratic anyway, so that methods of realizing biquadratic functions would be important in their own right.

The product of biquadratic functions, realized as a cascade of biquads, is conceptually the easiest to visualize. However, it turns out that there is a disadvantage of this configuration from the point of view of sensitivity, which is improved by other methods of coupling the biquads. This, in turn, implies other ways of decomposing the given function. These questions will be briefly mentioned in Section 4.

13.3.1 Some Specific Biquadratic Functions

A biquadratic function can be written in general form as follows:

$$G(s) = K \frac{s^2 + \dfrac{\omega_n}{Q_n} s + \omega_n^2}{s^2 + \dfrac{\omega_0}{Q} s + \omega_0^2}, \tag{20}$$

where ω_0 is the natural frequency of the pole-pair and Q is its Q-factor. Similarly for the zeros. A number of special cases of this function are of particular interest; they are listed in Table 1.

The historical literature of biquad design presents a wide selection of different configurations, each using from one to four amplifiers, usually operational amplifiers, employed in a number of different RC network configurations. Various attempts have been made to classify the

Table 1   Biquadratic function types

Type	$G(s)$	Zeros
Low-pass	$\dfrac{K}{s^2 + \dfrac{\omega_0}{Q}s + \omega_0^2}$	∞, ∞
High-pass	$\dfrac{Ks^2}{s^2 + \dfrac{\omega_0}{Q}s + \omega_0^2}$	$0, 0$
Band-pass	$\dfrac{Ks}{s^2 + \dfrac{\omega_0}{Q}s + \omega_0^2}$	$0, \infty$
All-pass	$K\dfrac{s^2 - \dfrac{\omega_0}{Q}s + \omega_0^2}{s^2 + \dfrac{\omega_0}{Q}s + \omega_0^2}$	Right-half plane images of the poles
Low-band notch $(\omega_n > \omega_0)$		$\pm j\omega_n, \ \omega_n > \omega_0$
Band-reject $(\omega_n = \omega_0)$	$K\dfrac{s^2 + \omega_n^2}{s^2 + \dfrac{\omega_0}{Q}s + \omega_0^2}$	$\pm j\omega_n, \ \omega_n = \omega_0$
High-band notch $(\omega_n < \omega_0)$		$\pm j\omega_n, \ \omega_n < \omega_0$

different structures, with some success. For our purpose, an exhaustive treatment of biquad structures is not appropriate. We shall instead treat only the most advantageous configurations from the point of view of sensitivity, spread in component values, total required capacitance, etc. At that, we shall consider only representative cases and will not treat the many different variations.

13.3.2   Single-Amplifier Negative Feedback Biquad

The most general configuration for a negative feedback biquad using a single op-amp is shown in Fig. 14. Feedback is to the inverting terminal of the op-amp only; it is through an RC network $\mathcal{N}_1$ shown as a three-port. The RC two-port $\mathcal{N}_2$ can be as simple as a straight-through connection or quite extensive, with a limitation mentioned below. The op-amp gain A is assumed finite at the start.

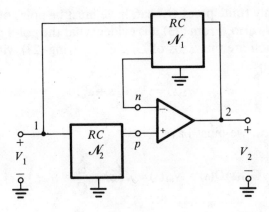

Fig. 14   Single amplifier negative feedback biquad

The over-all voltage gain function can be written in terms of the parameters of $\mathcal{N}_1$ and $\mathcal{N}_2$. For our purposes, the useful parameters are appropriately defined voltage gain functions. Thus, $G_{p1} = V_p/V_1$ is the left-to-right voltage gain of $\mathcal{N}_2$; $G_{n1} = V_n/V_1$ with $V_2 = 0$, and $G_{n2} = V_n/V_2$ with $V_1 = 0$ are both voltage gain functions of $\mathcal{N}_1$ with a terminal 2 and terminal 1 grounded, respectively. In terms of those functions, analysis yields

$$G = \frac{V_2}{V_1} = \frac{G_{p1} - G_{n1}}{G_{n2} + 1/A}. \tag{21}$$

Now G_{n1} and G_{n2} must have the same poles since they refer to the same network; hence they can be written as

$$G_{n1}(s) = \frac{N_{n1}(s)}{D(s)}, \quad G_{n2}(s) = \frac{N_{n2}(s)}{D(s)}. \tag{22}$$

Substituting into (21) yields

$$G = \frac{G_{p1}D - N_{n1}}{N_{n2} + D/A} \xrightarrow[A \to \infty]{} \frac{G_{p1}D - N_{n1}}{N_{n2}}. \tag{23}$$

We shall place the following limitation on $\mathcal{N}_2$:

$$G_{p1}(s)D(s) = \text{polynomial}. \tag{24}$$

That is, the only finite poles G_{p1} can have must be poles of the transfer functions of $\mathcal{N}_1$ also. From (23) it is evident that the poles of the overall transfer function are the zeros of G_{n2}. Comparing (23) with (20) yields

$$N_{n2}(s) = s^2 + \frac{\omega_0}{Q}s + \omega_0^2. \tag{25}$$

As for the zeros, we must have

$$G_{p1}(s)D(s) - N_{n1}(s) = K\left(s^2 + \frac{\omega_n}{Q_n}s + \omega_n^2\right). \tag{26}$$

There remains the task of finding suitable RC networks $\mathcal{N}_1$ and $\mathcal{N}_2$ satisfying the preceding expressions. From (25) it is clear that $\mathcal{N}_1$ must have a pair of complex transmission zeros between terminals n and 2, with terminal 1 grounded. In Tables 12-7 to 12-10 a number of such networks were given. An appropriate one of these can be selected and element values chosen to give transmission zeros at the appropriate places.

To form the three-port $\mathcal{N}_1$ from its generating network just discussed, any grounded branch can be opened to form a new terminal which is then connected to the input source. This process does not affect the locations of the zeros of $\mathcal{N}_{n2}$. There is flexibility in the specific branch, or combination of branches, to use in this process. Additional flexibility results from the fact that the branch can be considered as the parallel combination of two branches (two parallel resistors or two parallel capacitors), only one of which is treated in this manner. Further flexibility comes from the selection of $\mathcal{N}_2$ to satisfy (24) and (26).

13.3.2.1 Generic Bridged-Tee Example

To illustrate the process for finding appropriate networks $\mathcal{N}_1$ and $\mathcal{N}_2$ we shall treat an example. However, we shall leave the question of transmission zeros open and examine the variations required to deal with the zeros for the specific biquadratic functions in Table 1.

In Tables 12-7 to 12-10 there are two types of networks: bridged-tees and (possibly bridged) twin-tees. Let us first deal with the former. Given a voltage gain function in the form of (20), let us select case (b) in Table 12-9 as the basis for $\mathcal{N}_1$, with the further simplification that $C_3 = 0$. [This reduces to case (c) in Table 12-7 with $C_1 = 0$.] From the table, the voltage gain function in the notation of this chapter is

$$G_{n2}(s) = \frac{N_{n2}(s)}{D(s)} = \frac{s^2 + G_1(1+x)s/C_2 + xG_1G_2/C_2^2}{s^2 + [G_2 + G_1(1+x)]s/C_2 + xG_1G_2/C_2^2}. \quad (27)$$

The numerator of this expression is to be the denominator of (20). Thus, we can identify ω_0 and Q as

$$\omega_0 = \frac{\sqrt{xG_1G_2}}{C_2} \quad (28a)$$

$$Q = \frac{\sqrt{xG_1G_2}}{G_1(1+x)} \quad (28b)$$

The only grounded branch in this bridged-tee is G_2. Thus, a fraction f of G_2 is opened to form terminal 1, as illustrated in Fig. 15, leaving $(1-f)G_2$ still in place. Clearly, $0 < f \leqslant 1$.

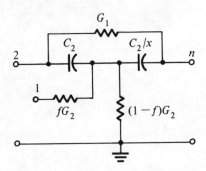

Fig. 15   The formation of $\mathscr{N}_1$ for use in Fig. 14

From Fig. 15 we now determine the voltage gain G_{n1}, with terminal 2 grounded. The result is

$$G_{n1} = \frac{fG_2s/C_2}{s^2 + [G_2 + G_1(1+x)]s/C_2 + xG_1G_2/C_2^2} = \frac{N_{n1}(s)}{D(s)}. \quad (29)$$

As expected G_{n1} has the same poles as G_{n2}. We now use the numerator of (29) as N_{n1} in (26), together with the denominator. Thus,

$$G_{p1}(s)D(s) - f\frac{G_2s}{C_2} = \text{numerator of } G(s). \quad (30)$$

Now the voltage gain function $G_{p1}(s)$ of $\mathscr{N}_2$ is chosen to satisfy (30).

Suppose, for example, that $G(s)$ is a band-pass function. According to Table 1, its numerator is proportional to s. So $\mathcal{N}_2$ is a trivial network; its input terminal is left open and its output terminal (connected to the noninverting terminal of the op-amp) is grounded. The fraction f can be adjusted, within the limits 0 through 1, to achieve the desired multiplying constant.

For a second order low-pass or high-pass function $G(s)$, the zeros are both at ∞ or both at the origin, respectively; namely, on the extended negative real axis. So, if $f = 0$, then according to the preceding chapter, each corresponding $\mathcal{N}_2$ can be realized by a ladder, as shown in Fig. 16. The voltage gain functions for the two cases are

$$\text{Low-pass, Fig. 16(a): } G_{p1}(s) = \frac{\dfrac{G_a G_b}{C_a C_b}}{s^2 + \left(\dfrac{G_b}{C_b} + \dfrac{G_a + G_b}{C_a}\right)s + \dfrac{G_a G_b}{C_a C_b}}. \tag{31a}$$

$$\text{High-pass, Fig. 16(b): } G_{p1}(s) = \frac{s^2}{s^2 + \left(\dfrac{G_b}{C_b} + \dfrac{G_a + G_b}{C_a}\right)s + \dfrac{G_a G_b}{C_a C_b}}. \tag{31b}$$

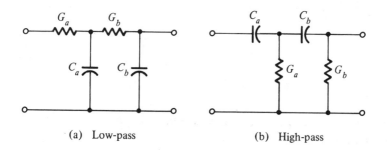

(a) Low-pass   (b) High-pass

Fig. 16 Low-pass and high-pass ladders

The denominators of these functions are the same; to satisfy (24), both must equal $D(s)$. By comparing coefficients, the following identifications of the components in Fig. 16 are made in terms of the components in Fig. 15:

$$G_a = G_2, \ G_b = G_1, \ C_a = C_2, \ C_b = C_2/x. \tag{32}$$

So, low-pass, high-pass and band-pass designs have been identified. The results are shown in Fig. 17. In the low-pass and high-pass cases,

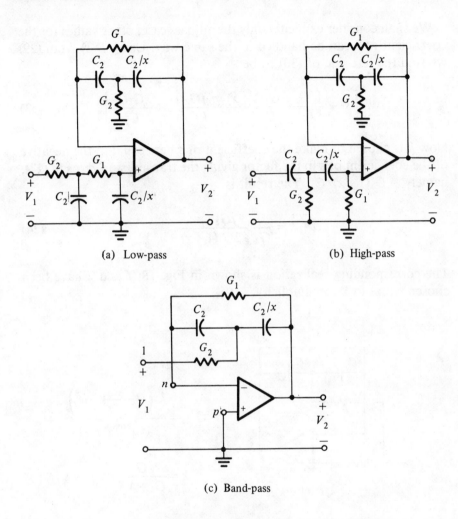

(a) Low-pass   (b) High-pass

(c) Band-pass

Fig. 17   Single amplifier realizations of low-pass, high-pass, and band-pass functions

because the fraction f in Fig. 15 was set to zero, no part of conductance G_2 goes to the input terminal of the biquad.

Others of the second order functions from Table 1, such as the all-pass and notch functions can be handled by the preceding general approach. From (30) it is clear that, if G_{p1} is a constant, the left side will be a quadratic when $\mathcal{N}_1$ is the network in Fig. 15. Because of the subtraction involved, the coefficient of the first power of s can be controlled; it can be made to vanish or to become negative. G_{p1} can be made a constant by choosing $\mathcal{N}_2$ to be simply a resistive voltage divider, say with $G_{p1} = k$.

We shall consider explicitly only the all-pass case; other values for the coefficient of s can be handled in the same way. Using $D(s)$ from (29) we find the left side of (30) to be

$$k \left[s^2 + \left\{ \frac{G_2 + G_1(1+x)}{C_2} - \frac{fG_2}{kC_2} \right\} s + \frac{xG_1G_2}{C_2^2} \right]. \tag{33}$$

Now k is chosen to make the coefficient of s here equal to the negative of the coefficient of s in the factor giving the transmission zeros in (27), namely $-G_1(1+x)/C_2$. The result is

$$k = \frac{fG_2}{G_2 + 2G_1(1+x)}. \tag{34}$$

The corresponding realization is shown in Fig. 18; f and x have been chosen equal to 1 for simplicity.

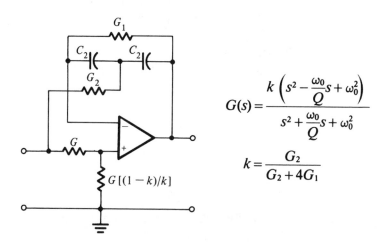

$$G(s) = \frac{k \left(s^2 - \dfrac{\omega_0}{Q}s + \omega_0^2 \right)}{s^2 + \dfrac{\omega_0}{Q}s + \omega_0^2}$$

$$k = \frac{G_2}{G_2 + 4G_1}$$

Fig. 18   All-pass realization

In all of the specific designs of Fig. 17 and 18, the pole frequency and Q are given by (28). Four components must be selected to satisfy only these two equations. Clearly this freedom permits achieving other goals; among these can be the setting of the impedance level, the reducing of sensitivity and/or the spread of element values, and others.

Note that only one specific bridged tee network has been used in these designs. Other bridged-tee structures, some derived from those in Table

12-7, cases (a) and (c), and Table 12-9, could be used with no more than some small variations in detail from what was done here. A number of these will be suggested as problems.

13.3.2.2 A Generic Twin-Tee Example

The designs in the preceding example were all based on a bridged-tee. Thus, all of these designs belong to a single class. Another class of biquads is based on the (bridged) twin-tee given in Table 12-10. For simplicity, we shall assume that $a = b = 0$ so that the shunt branch of each tee has only a single component. From Table 12-10, with $a = b = 0$, the voltage gain function is

$$G_{n2}(s) = \frac{s^2 + 2x\frac{G}{C}s + (1 + 2x)\frac{G_2}{C^2}}{s^2 + (4 + 2x)\frac{G}{C}s + (1 + 2x)\frac{G^2}{C^2}}. \tag{35}$$

The grounded branches are the shunt branches of each tee. Terminal 1 can be formed by opening a fraction f_1 of the branch with conductance $2G$ and a fraction f_2 of the branch with capacitance $2C$. The resulting biquad is shown in Fig. 19.

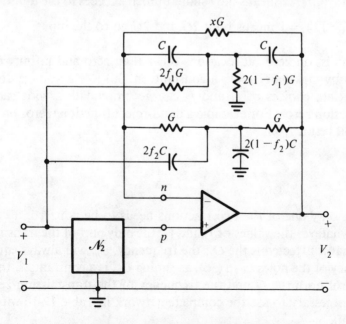

Fig. 19   Single-amplifier, negative-feedback biquad
generated by a bridged twin-tee

Using (35) and the expression for G_{n1} found from Fig. 19, the voltage gain function in (23) becomes

$$G(s) = \frac{\left[s^2 + (4+2x)\dfrac{G}{C}s + (1+2x)\dfrac{G^2}{C^2}\right]G_{p1}(s) - 2(f_1 + f_2)\dfrac{G}{C}s}{s^2 + \dfrac{2xG}{C}s + (1+2x)\dfrac{G^2}{C^2}}. \quad (36)$$

To ensure a biquadratic $G(s)$, $G_{p1}(s)$ must be either 0 ($\mathcal{N}_2$ not present and op-amp terminal p grounded), or a constant ($\mathcal{N}_2$ a simple voltage divider), or a biquadratic having a denominator proportional to the polynomial multiplying G_{p1} in (36).

Low-pass, high-pass, and band-pass designs are obtained by selecting $\mathcal{N}_2$ exactly as for the design based on a bridged-tee in Fig. 17. In the band-pass case, where $\mathcal{N}_2$ is the trivial network with port one open and port two short, the following choices of extreme values of f_1 and f_2 lead to 3 variations:

$f_1 = 1, f_2 = 0$ means only shunt branch $2G$ goes to the input.

$f_1 = 0, f_2 = 1$ means only shunt branch $2C$ goes to the input.

$f_1 = 1, f_2 = 1$ means both $2G$ and $2C$ go to the input.

Transmission zeros at locations other than zero and infinity can be realized by making $G_{p1} = k$, a constant, in (36) ($\mathcal{N}_2$ a voltage divider). Appropriate choices of f_1 and f_2 can accommodate a wide range of transmission zeros. For example a band-reject function (zeros on the $j\omega$ axis) will result from

$$k = \frac{f_1 + f_2}{2 + x}. \quad (37)$$

Clearly, only one of the two fractions needs to be nonzero.

But whatever the values of f_1 and f_2, the only part of the transmission zeros that is affected is the Q_n; the frequency, ω_n, will always equal the frequency of the poles ω_0 in (36), assuming G_{p1} is a constant, k. In order to control both the Q and the frequency of the transmission zeros, it will be necessary to use the complete network in Table 12-10 with $a \neq 0$ and $b \neq 0$.

13.3.2.3 Sensitivity Analysis

One of the measures by which to compare the performance of the many different designs that realize a given transfer function is the sensitivity to variations in component values. In the second section, the most convenient quantities for assessing sensitivities were the coefficients. For biquads it has become standard to deal with the sensitivity of the pole Q and frequency. The design of a biquad involves passive components (G or R and C) and active components. To find the sensitivities of ω_0 and Q to these components, it is necessary to have the expression for the realized voltage gain function in terms of all Gs and Cs and the op-amp gain A.

In the foregoing, the op-amp gain A has been assumed infinite. Thus, although the passive sensitivities can be determined from the results obtained above, in order to find the sensitivites to the op-amp gain, it is necessary to return to (23) and assume A is finite. The pole frequency and Q will depend in different ways on A for each of the different generic designs.

To illustrate the analysis for the sensitivities, we shall treat the general biquad of Fig. 14 with $\mathcal{N}_1$ realized by the specific bridged-tee in Fig. 15, but with $f = 0$ or 1. Thus, conductance G_2 goes either to ground or to the input terminal. (This is for simplicity because only one component is involved rather than the two that would result if G_2 were split.)

Using $N_{n2}(s)$ and $D(s)$ from (27), and with finite A, the denominator of $G(s)$ in (23) becomes

$$\left(1 + \frac{1}{A}\right)\left(s^2 + \left[\frac{G_1}{C_2} + \frac{G_1}{(C_2/x)} + \frac{G_2}{C_2(A+1)}\right]s + \frac{G_1 G_2}{C_2(C_2/x)}\right). \quad (38)$$

We shall assume here that A is independent of frequency. The effect of the frequency dependence of op-amp gain will be considered in a later section. From the preceding expression the sensitivity of the pole frequency and Q are found to be

$$S_A^{\omega_0} = 0, \quad S_A^Q = \frac{G_2}{\omega_0 C_2}\frac{Q}{A}. \quad (39)$$

Clearly, the pole frequency does not depend on op-amp gain; and the sensitivity of Q to A is proportional to Q/A. The higher the Q, the higher the sensitivity; but, even so the sensitivity is low for high gain op-amps. This can be assured by proper selection of the values of G_2 and C_2.

As for the passive component sensitivities, they are easily computed. Note that the capacitance of one of the capacitors is C_2/x; so one of the desired sensitivities is $S^\Omega_{C_2/x}$. It can be seen by direct evaluation that $S^y_{C_2/x} = -S^y_x$, where y is any function of C_2/x. The results are:

$$
\begin{array}{ll}
S^{\omega_0}_{G_1} = \frac{1}{2} & S^Q_{G_1} = -\frac{1}{2} \\[2mm]
S^{\omega_0}_{G_2} = \frac{1}{2} & S^Q_{G_2} = \frac{1}{2} \\[2mm]
S^{\omega_0}_{C_2} = -\frac{1}{2} & S^Q_{C_2} = \dfrac{1}{1+x} \qquad (40) \\[4mm]
S^{\omega_0}_{C_2/x} = -\frac{1}{2} & \\[2mm]
& S^Q_{C_2/x} = -\left(\dfrac{1-x}{1+x}\right)
\end{array}
$$

The passive sensitivities are all seen to be quite small.

13.3.3   Single-Amplifier Positive Feedback Biquads

The biquads considered in the previous section had the general structure shown in Fig. 14. Feedback was to the inverting terminal of the op-amp only, so all of those biquads were in the category of negative feedback biquads. A second general category is illustrated by the structure of Fig. 20. The main feedback is to the non-inverting terminal, although at least resistive feedback is needed to the inverting terminal for stability.*

Observe that the structure within dashed lines is nothing but a positive gain amplifier, with gain $K = (G_1 + G_2)/G_1 \geqslant 1$. This results in the simplified structure shown in Fig. 20(b), which is a structure first proposed in 1954 by Sallen and Key and now carries their name.

Assuming an ideal op-amp with gain A, the expression for the voltage gain function can be written as follows:

$$
G = \frac{V_2}{V_1} = K\frac{G_{p1}}{1 - KG_{p2} + K/A}, \qquad (41)
$$

where $G_{p1} = V_p/V_1$ with terminal 2 grounded ($V_2 = 0$) and $G_{p2} = V_p/V_2$ with terminal 1 grounded ($V_1 = 0$). Since G_{p1} and G_{p2} relate to the same

---

* This is not the most general structure for this category because right half-plane transmission zeros cannot be realized. For generality, the inverting terminal also should be excited by the input. But because of the complexity of the resulting expressions, we shall not treat this case.

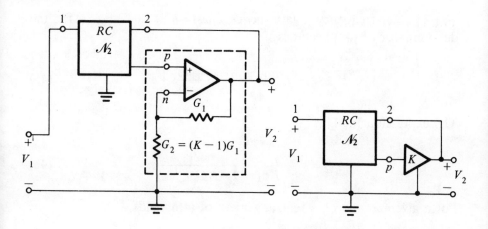

Fig. 20   Positive feedback biquad structure

RC network, their poles (all on the extended negative real axis) will be the same. Thus,

$$G_{p1}(s) = \frac{N_{p1}(s)}{D(s)}, \quad G_{p2}(s) = \frac{N_{p2}(s)}{D(s)} \tag{42}$$

Using these in (41) leads to

$$G = K \frac{N_{p1}}{D - K N_{p2} + KD/A} \xrightarrow[A \to \infty]{} K \frac{N_{p1}}{D - K N_{p2}}. \tag{43}$$

The transmission zeros are determined solely by the zeros of N_{p1} while the poles of G are determined by both zeros and poles of G_{p2}. The pole frequency, ω_0, will be insensitive to amplifier gain K and to op-amp gain A if these quantities do not appear in the expression for ω_0. We know that D is a second-degree polynomial. If N_{p2} contains only the first power of s, the even powers of s in the denominator of the right side in (43) will not be influenced by N_{p2}. Hence, ω_0 will not depend on K (or A); so we shall choose a structure to achieve this.*

In accordance with this discussion, let G_{p2} be the following band-pass function:

$$G_{p2}(s) = \frac{b_1 s}{s^2 + c_1 s + \omega_0^2}. \tag{44}$$

---

* It is also possible for ω_0 to be independent of K or A if the even part of $N_{p2}(s)$ is proportional to the even part of $D(s)$. We shall not treat this approach.

The "center-frequency" gain is $G_{p2}(j\omega_0) = b_1/c_1$. Using (44), the denominator of (43) becomes

$$s^2 + (c_1 - Kb_1)s + \omega_0^2 = s^2 + \frac{\omega_0}{Q}s + \omega_0^2. \tag{45}$$

The expression for Q is

$$Q = \frac{\omega_0}{c_1 - Kb_1} = \frac{\omega_0/c_1}{1 - KG_{p2}(j\omega_0)}. \tag{46}$$

For a given ω_0 and Q, a rearrangement of (46) yields

$$K\frac{b_1}{c_1} = 1 - \frac{\omega_0}{c_1 Q}. \tag{47}$$

If, in addition, the amplifier gain is fixed (say $K = 1$), then (47) places a limitation on the voltage gain function of network $\mathcal{N}_2$.

The design procedure is clear. The first step is to find an RC grounded two-port having a voltage gain function of the form of (44) — band-pass — with the component values chosen to make the constant term in the denominator equal to the desired ω_0^2. Then K in (47) is chosen to give the desired Q. The freedom in choosing the component values can be used so that the spread in values is not excessive while at the same time the sensitivites of Q to these values is reduced.

Terminal 1 is then created by opening any combination of grounded branches. Clearly, the choice of the original two-port must contain a sufficient number of grounded branches to permit the desired transmission zeros in G_{p1}.

13.3.3.1 A Generic Example

Second order low-pass and high-pass ladders were shown in Fig. 16. A series capacitor gives a zero at the origin, while a shunt capacitor gives a zero at infinity. For the second order band-pass case, with one zero at the origin and one at infinity, it is clear that there must be at least one series capacitor and one shunt one. The simplest cases are shown in Fig. 21. More flexibility can be achieved by adding components in parallel with one or both of the grounded branches in each ladder. These variations are left for you to work out.

For concreteness, let us select Fig. 21(b) and open a fraction of each grounded branch to form terminal 1. The resulting design is shown in

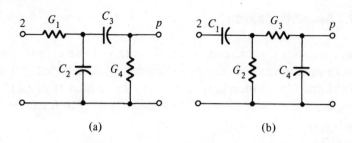

Fig. 21   Band-pass ladders

Fig. 22. Clearly, with the fractions f_1 and f_2 in the range 0 to 1, not all types of biquadratic functions can be realized by this design. For example, zeros on the $j\omega$-axis are not realizable. Using the ladder in 21(a) rather than that in 21(b), or loading one of the shunt branches in each of the ladders, permits some additional zeros but still does not permit the realization of imaginary zeros. What are required are *three* parameters of the nature of f_1 and f_2 so that the three coefficients in the numerator of $G(s)$ can be independently adjusted. More complex ladders are needed or structures like bridged twin-tees, with additional branches going to ground at the input, output, or center. Further variations will not be pursued here.

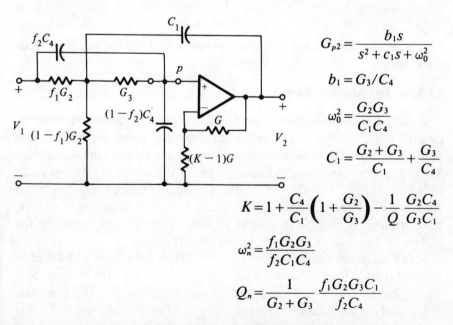

$$G_{p2} = \frac{b_1 s}{s^2 + c_1 s + \omega_0^2}$$

$$b_1 = G_3/C_4$$

$$\omega_0^2 = \frac{G_2 G_3}{C_1 C_4}$$

$$C_1 = \frac{G_2 + G_3}{C_1} + \frac{G_3}{C_4}$$

$$K = 1 + \frac{C_4}{C_1}\left(1 + \frac{G_2}{G_3}\right) - \frac{1}{Q}\frac{G_2 C_4}{G_3 C_1}$$

$$\omega_n^2 = \frac{f_1 G_2 G_3}{f_2 C_1 C_4}$$

$$Q_n = \frac{1}{G_2 + G_3}\frac{f_1 G_2 G_3 C_1}{f_2 C_4}$$

Fig. 22   Generic biquad design

13.3.3.2 Sensitivity Analysis

In the approach used above, we deliberately chose a feedback network $\mathcal{N}_2$ in such a way that the pole frequency was independent of op-amp gain A and closed loop gain K. Hence, the sensitivity of ω_0 to these quantities is zero: $S_K^{\omega_0} = 0$, $S_A^{\omega_0} = 0$. The sensitivity of Q to K can be found from (46); it is

$$S_K^Q = \frac{b_1 K Q}{\omega_0} = \frac{c_1}{\omega_0} Q - 1. \tag{48}$$

Since the poles of G_{p2} in (44) are not complex, $c_1/\omega_0 \geqslant 2$; for large values of Q, then, approximately

$$S_K^Q \geqslant 2Q. \tag{49}$$

As for the passive component sensitivities, for the design in Fig. 22 they can be determined from the information given there. They are found to be of the order of Q, considerably higher than the values found in (40) for a negative feedback design.

That leaves the sensitivity of Q to A. To find that, we return to (43) and, assuming a finite A, we substitute (44). The resulting sensitivity is found to be

$$S_A^Q = \frac{1}{b_1 \omega_0} \frac{Q}{A}. \tag{50}$$

This is of the same order as the one given in (39) for the negative feedback design.

13.3.4 Two Amplifier Biquads

Clearly a single-amplifier biquad, using close to a canonic number of passive components, is cheaper than a biquad using more than one amplifier. So why look for designs using more than one amplifier? There must be something to compensate for the added expense of additional amplifiers. Possible motivations include: reduced sensitivity and such practical considerations as reduced spread in component values, easier tuning, prototype structures yielding different gain functions for different input nodes or for different output nodes.

Many different designs using two amplifiers have been published in the literature. However, except for one case, the quest for reduced sensitivity has not been very successful. We shall discuss only this one case. It is based on the Antoniu network shown in Fig. P-5 of Part II. In that network, if either component 3 or component 4 is taken as the load and the remaining components are resistors, the result is a gyrator. (The network in Fig. 1-18 is the latter case.) Now if component 4 is made a capacitor, what appears at the input terminals is a grounded inductor whose value is

$$L = \frac{CG_3}{G_1G_2G_5} = \frac{C}{G^2}. \tag{51}$$

Now suppose an ell structure is connected across the equivalent inductance, as shown in Fig. 23, and the output is taken across the inductor. The voltage gain function will be

$$\frac{V_2}{V_1} = \frac{sY_AC/G^2}{(Y_A + Y_B)Cs/G^2 + 1}. \tag{52}$$

We would like to choose Y_A and Y_B so as to make the denominator a quadratic in s. There are a number of possibilities, the simplest of which results in the following:

$$\begin{aligned} Y_A &= G_A \\ Y_B &= Cs \end{aligned} \qquad \frac{V_2}{V_1} = \frac{\dfrac{G_A}{C}s}{s^2 + \dfrac{G_A}{C}s + \dfrac{G_1G_2G_5}{G_3C^2}} \tag{53a}$$

$$\begin{aligned} Y_A &= Cs \\ Y_B &= G_B \end{aligned} \qquad \frac{V_2}{V_1} = \frac{s^2}{s^2 + \dfrac{G_B}{C}s + \dfrac{G_1G_2G_5}{G_3C^2}} \tag{53b}$$

These represent a band-pass and high-pass function, respectively, in which G_A or G_B affects only the Q and not the pole frequency. There is a major problem in the design of Fig. 23. Cascading of biquads will not

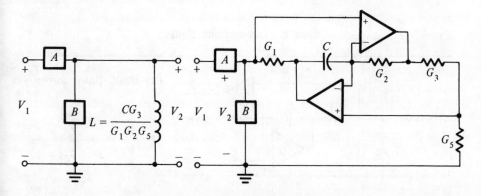

Fig. 23   Design with simulated inductance

be possible without severe loading problems because the gyrator input is not a low impedance point. However, it was found in Problem 5 of Part II that the voltage at the output of op-amp 1 is proportional to the voltage input to the gyrator; specifically with a proportionality constant $(G_3 + G_5)/G_3$. With $G_3 = G_5$, this ratio equals 2. Hence, taking the output voltage at the output of op-amp 1 yields the same voltage gain function, only multiplied by 2.

The complete band-pass and high-pass designs are given as (a) and (b) in Table 2, assuming $G_1 = G_2 = G_3 = G_5 = G$ and $G_A = G/Q$, $G_B = G/Q$, respectively.

Now let us examine other choices for Y_A and Y_B in Fig. 23, or other variations that will lead to different transmission zeros. Examining (52) and the specific components in (53a) reveals that the pole Q can be controlled independently from the numerator coefficient by adding a resistor in parallel with C in the inductor simulation. But the function still remains band-pass. For the case of (53b), the added zero at $s=0$ came from $Y_A = Cs$. This zero can be made to occur at a nonzero value of s by placing a resistor in parallel with C in the series arm. However, no choices of RC admittances Y_A and Y_B can yield complex transmission zeros. For these, a different approach is needed.

A solution to the problem is provided by examining Fig. 24. A grounded two-port is shown in Fig. 24(a). If the ground connection is opened, a new terminal g can be formed. Assume that both terminals 1 and g are excited; then, the output voltage V_2 will be given by

$$V_2(s) = G_{21}(s) V_1(s) + G_{2g}(s) V_g(s). \tag{54}$$

Since G_{21} and G_{2g} refer to the same network, they have the same poles. The original voltage gain function was G_{21}, with terminal g grounded,

Table 2   Two-amplifier biquads

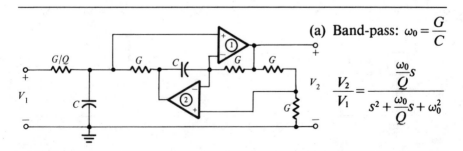

(a) Band-pass: $\omega_0 = \dfrac{G}{C}$

$$\frac{V_2}{V_1} = \frac{\dfrac{\omega_0}{Q}s}{s^2 + \dfrac{\omega_0}{Q}s + \omega_0^2}$$

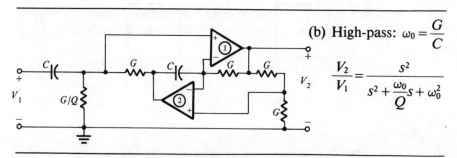

(b) High-pass: $\omega_0 = \dfrac{G}{C}$

$$\frac{V_2}{V_1} = \frac{s^2}{s^2 + \dfrac{\omega_0}{Q}s + \omega_0^2}$$

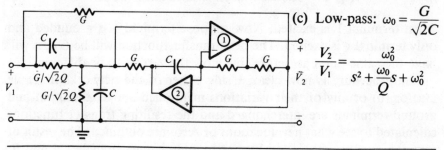

(c) Low-pass: $\omega_0 = \dfrac{G}{\sqrt{2}C}$

$$\frac{V_2}{V_1} = \frac{\omega_0^2}{s^2 + \dfrac{\omega_0}{Q}s + \omega_0^2}$$

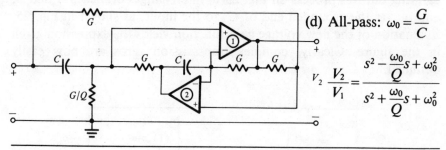

(d) All-pass: $\omega_0 = \dfrac{G}{C}$

$$\frac{V_2}{V_1} = \frac{s^2 - \dfrac{\omega_0}{Q}s + \omega_0^2}{s^2 + \dfrac{\omega_0}{Q}s + \omega_0^2}$$

(e) Low-pass notch: $\omega_0 = \dfrac{G}{C}$

$$\omega_n \geqslant \omega_0$$

$$C_A = \frac{1}{2}\left[1 - \left(\frac{\omega_0}{\omega_n}\right)^2\right]C$$

$$C_B = \frac{1}{2}\left[1 + \left(\frac{\omega_0}{\omega_n}\right)^2\right]C$$

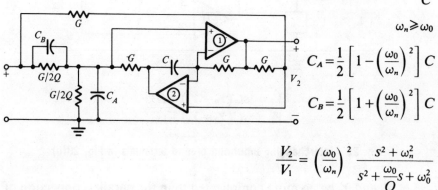

$$\frac{V_2}{V_1} = \left(\frac{\omega_0}{\omega_n}\right)^2 \frac{s^2 + \omega_n^2}{s^2 + \dfrac{\omega_0}{Q}s + \omega_0^2}$$

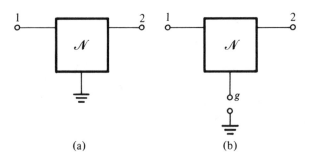

Fig. 24   Common-terminal three-port from two-port

when terminal 1 is excited. Now suppose terminal 1 is grounded and only terminal g is excited. The new transfer function will be G_{2g}; it will have the same poles as before, but now the zeros can be different.

The procedure is now clear. Using either of the networks in Table 2(a) or (b) or any of their variations mentioned above, the input and ground terminals are interchanged and the resulting transfer functions calculated to see what new locations of zeros are obtained. The result of carrying out this process on Fig. 23(b) interchanges branches A and B, and moves the grounded end of G_5 to the input, as shown in Fig. 25. Evaluation of the new voltage gain function yields the expression given in the figure. Clearly, complex transmission zeros are now easily obtained.

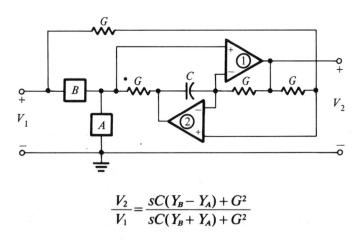

$$\frac{V_2}{V_1} = \frac{sC(Y_B - Y_A) + G^2}{sC(Y_B + Y_A) + G^2}$$

Fig. 25   Interchanging input and ground terminals in Fig. 23(b)

Let Y_A and Y_B be no more complicated than the parallel connection of a resistor and capacitor. That is,

$$Y_A = sC_A + G_A, \tag{55a}$$

$$Y_B = sC_B + G_B. \tag{55b}$$

The voltage gain function then becomes

$$\frac{V_2}{V_1} = \frac{C_B - C_A}{C_B + C_A} \frac{s^2 + \dfrac{G_B - G_A}{C_B - C_A} + \dfrac{G^2}{C(C_B - C_A)}}{s^2 + \dfrac{G_B + G_A}{C_B + C_A} + \dfrac{G^2}{C(C_B + C_A)}}. \tag{56}$$

By selecting appropriate values for the conductances and capacitances a variety of transmission zeros are obtained. Three designs are given in Table 2(c), (d), and (e). They occur for the following choices:

(c) Low-pass $(Y_A = Y_B = sC + G/\sqrt{2}Q)$:

$$\frac{V_2}{V_1} = \frac{G^2/2C^2}{s^2 + \dfrac{G}{\sqrt{2}QC}s + \dfrac{G^2}{2C^2}}. \tag{57a}$$

(d) All-pass $(Y_A = G/Q$ and $Y_B = sC)$:

$$\frac{V_2}{V_1} = \frac{s^2 - \dfrac{G}{QC}s + \dfrac{G^2}{C^2}}{s^2 + \dfrac{G}{QC}s + \dfrac{G^2}{C^2}}. \tag{57b}$$

(e) Low-band notch $\left(Y_A = \dfrac{G}{2Q} + s\dfrac{(\omega_n^2 - \omega_0^2)}{2\omega_n^2}C\right.$ and

$Y_B = \dfrac{G}{2Q} + s\dfrac{(\omega_n^2 + \omega_0^2)}{2\omega_n^2}C\Big)$:

$$\frac{V_2}{V_1} = \left(\frac{\omega_0}{\omega_n}\right)^2 \frac{s^2 + \omega_n^2}{s^2 + \dfrac{G}{CQ}s + \dfrac{G^2}{\omega_n^2}}. \tag{57c}$$

Additional variations are possible to achieve other transmission zeros, but we shall not pursue the matter any further.

The question of sensitivity remains to be examined. No new principles are involved in the sensitivity analysis so we shall not elaborate the details. Direct evaluation shows that the S^{ω_0} to passive components are all as low as they can get — no greater than $1/2$ in magnitude — and the passive S^Q are also low. As for the active sensitivities, $S_A^{\omega_0}$ is low and S_A^Q approximately equals $2Q/A$ for both op-amp gains. These are no greater than any other biquad design. All in all, then, the biquads in Table 2 are as good a design as can be obtained from the point of view of sensitivity.

The only remaining question is: Would the inclusion of more op-amps lead to a design which can better these sensitivities or yield other practical advantages? In the following section we shall describe a design procedure requiring three (and, in some cases, four) op-amps.

13.3.5 Three-Amplifier Biquads: State Variable Approach

A particularly interesting and flexible biquad structure results from the introduction of state variables as intermediate variables linking the input and output. In fact, the procedure is general and can be applied to transfer functions of any order; however, we shall deal with biquadratic functions only.

In this case there will be two state variables. Assuming a single input voltage and a single output voltage, the state and output equations can be written as follows in the Laplace transform domain:

$$s \begin{bmatrix} X_1 \\ X_2 \end{bmatrix} = \begin{bmatrix} a_{11} & a_{12} \\ a_{21} & a_{22} \end{bmatrix} \begin{bmatrix} X_1 \\ X_2 \end{bmatrix} + \begin{bmatrix} b_{11} \\ b_{12} \end{bmatrix} V_1 \tag{58a}$$

$$V_2 = [c_{11} \quad c_{12}] \begin{bmatrix} X_1 \\ X_2 \end{bmatrix} + [d] V_1 \tag{58b}$$

The first of these can be solved for the vector $\mathbf{X}$ and substituted into the second. From this, the transfer function is obtained; thus,

$$\frac{V_2}{V_1} = d + [c_{11} \quad c_{12}] \begin{bmatrix} s-a_{11} & -a_{12} \\ -a_{21} & s-a_{22} \end{bmatrix}^{-1} \begin{bmatrix} b_{11} \\ b_{12} \end{bmatrix} \tag{59}$$

$$= d + \frac{a_1 s + a_0}{s^2 + b_1 s + b_0},$$

where

$$b_1 = -(a_{11} + a_{22}) \tag{60a}$$

$$b_0 = a_{11}a_{22} - a_{12}a_{21} \tag{60b}$$

$$a_1 = c_{11}b_{11} + c_{12}b_{21} \tag{60c}$$

$$a_0 = c_{11}(a_{12}b_{21} - b_{11}a_{22}) + c_{12}(a_{21}b_{11} - b_{21}a_{11}) \tag{60d}$$

In addition to d — the value of the transfer function at infinity which represents a direct contribution to the output by the input without influence from the state variables — the second order transfer function is specified by four coefficients (a_1, a_0, b_1, b_0). In (60) these four are expressed in terms of 8 quantities, the elements of the **A**, **B**, and **C** matrices. There is, therefore, flexibility in choosing four of these eight quantities. This means that the state equations resulting in a given transfer function are not unique. We shall make two specific choices of the four arbitrary parameters and thus obtain two different variations of the structure being developed. Clearly, other choices, leading to different variations, are possible.

13.3.5.1 Three-Amplifier Biquad Design 1

As a first selection, we shall choose

$$\begin{aligned} a_{11} = b_{11} = 0 \\ a_{12} = b_{21} = 1 \end{aligned} \tag{61}$$

Then, from (60),

$$\begin{aligned} b_1 = -a_{22} && a_1 = c_{12} \\ b_0 = -a_{21} && a_0 = c_{11} \end{aligned} \tag{62}$$

The state equations can now be written directly in terms of the coefficients of the transfer function as

$$\begin{bmatrix} sX_1 \\ sX_2 \end{bmatrix} = \begin{bmatrix} 0 & 1 \\ -b_0 & -b_1 \end{bmatrix} \begin{bmatrix} X_1 \\ X_2 \end{bmatrix} + \begin{bmatrix} 0 \\ 1 \end{bmatrix} V_1 \tag{63a}$$

$$V_2 = [a_0 \quad a_1] \begin{bmatrix} X_1 \\ X_2 \end{bmatrix} + [d] V_1$$

(63b)

Suppose that, in addition to the state variables X_1 and X_2, we also consider sX_1 and sX_2 to be variables. (In the time domain, these are the corresponding derivatives.) Then there will be a total of 6 variables. To (63) we can add the trivial equations

$$X_1 = \frac{1}{s}(sX_1),$$

$$-X_2 = \frac{-1}{s}(sX_2).$$

(64)

It is now possible to draw a signal-flow graph (see Proj. II-3) from the equations in (63) and (64), as shown in Fig. 26. In order to realize this diagram by a network, it will be necessary to have components that realize the operations of integration ($1/s$) and summation represented by nodes sX_2 and V_2 in the diagram.

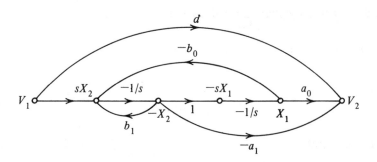

Fig. 26   Signal-flow graph representing (63) and (64)

Integrators and summers are standard components of analog computers. They can be realized with operational amplifiers. Figure 27 shows both inverting and noninverting integrators. The transfer functions of these two networks, assuming infinite gain op-amps are:

Fig. 27(a): $\dfrac{V_2}{V_1} = \dfrac{-1/RC}{s}.$

(65a)

Fig. 27(b): $\dfrac{V_2}{V_1} = \dfrac{2/RC}{s}.$

(65b)

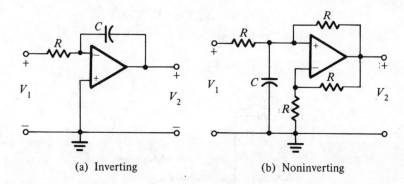

(a) Inverting   (b) Noninverting

Fig. 27   Integrators

In the noninverting integrator the capacitor is connected to ground; this is desirable if the network is to be realized by an integrated circuit. However, this network is rather sensitive to manufacturing tolerances of the components.

As for a summer, Fig. 28 shows one that algebraically adds a number of terms. Assuming an infinite gain op-amp is used, the output is given by

$$V_0 = \frac{(1+RG_n)}{G_p} \sum_{i=1}^{k} G_{ip} V_{ip} - R \sum_{i=1}^{m} G_{in} V_{in}, \qquad (66a)$$

where

$$G_p = \sum_{i=1}^{k} G_{ip} \text{ and } G_n = \sum_{i=1}^{m} G_{in}. \qquad (66b)$$

The subscripts p and n in these equations and in Fig. 28 stand for "positive" and "negative."

Note that the signal-flow graph in Fig. 26 has two feedback loops and that two integrators are involved. This is characteristic of all the variations of the structure under discussion.

Using the integrators and summers just described, the signal-flow graph of Fig. 26 representing the second-order transfer function of (59) can be realized by the network shown in Fig. 29. For convenience the normalized values of some of the elements have been set equal to unity. The input is between terminal 1 and ground. Outputs can be taken from the output of any of the op-amps. The voltages at various points can be identified with state variables as follows:

$$V_3 = -X_2 = -sX_1$$
$$V_4 = X_1 \qquad\qquad (67)$$
$$V_5 = sX_2$$

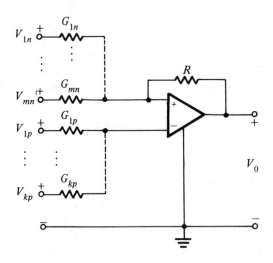

Fig. 28   Summing network

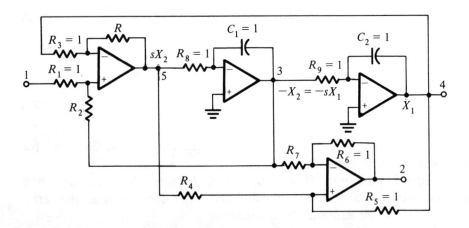

Fig. 29   Realization of a second-order function

Suppose the final summer is temporarily neglected and we concentrate on the part of the network which is redrawn in Fig. 30. The following equations can be written:

$$V_3 = -\frac{1}{s}V_5 \tag{68a}$$

$$V_4 = -\frac{1}{s}V_3 \tag{68b}$$

$$V_5 = \frac{R_2(1+R)}{1+R_2}\left(V_1 + \frac{1}{R_2}V_3\right) - RV_4. \tag{68c}$$

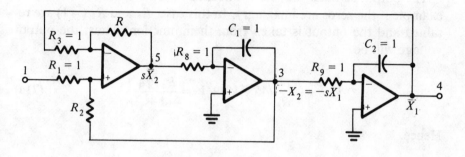

Fig. 30   Basic feedback network

Solving these for V_3, V_4, and V_5 leads to the following transfer functions:

$$\frac{V_3}{V_1} = G_{bp} = \frac{-R_2(1+R)}{1+R_2}\frac{s}{s^2 + \dfrac{1+R}{1+R_2}s + R} \tag{69a}$$

$$\frac{V_4}{V_1} = G_{lp} = \frac{R_2(1+R)}{1+R_2}\frac{1}{s^2 + \dfrac{1+R}{1+R_2}s + R} \tag{69b}$$

$$\frac{V_5}{V_1} = G_{hp} = \frac{R_2(1+R)}{1+R_2}\frac{s^2}{s^2 + \dfrac{1+R}{1+R_2}s + R} \tag{69c}$$

Thus, if the desired transfer function is any one of these functions (corresponding to a band-pass, low-pass, and high-pass function, respectively) then the output summer is not needed and the output is taken at node 3, 4, or 5, respectively. Observe that only this part of the network influences the poles. It is the part of the structure that leads to the designation "three-amplifier biquad." The pole frequency and the Q are given by

$$\omega_0 = \sqrt{R},\tag{70a}$$

$$Q = \frac{1+R_2}{1+R}\sqrt{R}.\tag{70b}$$

Thus, the frequency is set by adjusting resistor R. When that is done, the Q is set by adjusting R_2.

The output summer may not be needed in some other cases also; for example if the zeros are imaginary. In this case, R_4 and R_5 $(=1)$ are retained and the output is taken from their junction. Thus, the output voltage will be

$$V_0 = \frac{R_4}{1+R_4}(V_4 - V_5) + V_5 = \frac{R_4 V_4 + V_5}{1+R_4}.\tag{71a}$$

Hence,

$$\frac{V_0}{V_1} = \frac{R_2(1+R)}{(1+R_2)(1+R_4)}\frac{s^2 + R_4}{s^2 + \dfrac{1+R}{1+R_2}s + R}.\tag{71b}$$

It is clear that the zeros are set simply by adjusting R_4. [It should be noted that an implication of not using the output summer is: The Thévenin equivalent output resistance is not insignificant; the normalized value is $R_4/(1+R_4)$.]

Finally, for the general biquadratic function, the output is V_2 in Fig. 29. Using (66a) we get

$$V_2 = \frac{(1+R_7)}{R_7(1+R_4)}(R_4 V_4 + V_5) - \frac{1}{R_7}V_3.\tag{72}$$

Using (69), the transfer function becomes

$$\frac{V_2}{V_1} = \frac{R_2(1+R)(1+R_7)}{R_7(1+R_2)(1+R_4)}\frac{s^2 + \dfrac{1+R_4}{1+R_7}s + R_4}{s^2 + \dfrac{1+R}{1+R_2}s + R}.\tag{73}$$

The resonant frequencies and the Q-factors of both the poles and zeros are each independently adjustable by a single resistor. However, there is no independent adjustment of the overall multiplier.

As given in (73), the zeros are in the left half-plane. Some modification of the network is necessary if the zeros are to be in the right half-plane. One possibility is to return R_4 and R_5 to the inverting terminal of the output summer. In this case the transfer function will become

$$\frac{V_2}{V_1} = \frac{-R_2(1+R)}{R_4(1+R_2)} \frac{s^2 - R_4 s + R_4/R_7}{s^2 + \dfrac{1+R}{1+R_2}s + R}. \qquad (74)$$

Other possibilities also exist.

13.3.5.2 Three Amplifier-Biquad Design 2

To arrive at the realization in Fig. 29, we made arbitrary choices of four of the elements in the matrices appearing in the state equations. A different choice will lead to a variation of this network. Instead of the selection in (61), let us make the following choices:

$$a_{11} = b_{11} = 0$$
$$a_{12} = 1/k_1 \qquad (75)$$
$$b_{21} = -k_2$$

Then, from (60), the remaining parameters will be

$$
\begin{aligned}
a_{22} &= -b_1 & c_{12} &= -a_1/k_2 \\
a_{21} &= -k_1 b_0 & c_{11} &= -k_1 a_0/k_2
\end{aligned} \qquad (76)
$$

These will reduce to the previous set if $k_1 = -k_2 = 1$. But leaving k_1 and k_2 arbitrary leads to some useful results.

With these choices, the state equations become

$$\begin{bmatrix} sX_1 \\ sX_2 \end{bmatrix} = \begin{bmatrix} 0 & 1/k_1 \\ -k_1 b_0 & -b_1 \end{bmatrix} \begin{bmatrix} X_1 \\ X_2 \end{bmatrix} + \begin{bmatrix} 0 \\ -k_2 \end{bmatrix} V_1 \qquad (77a)$$

$$V_2 = [-k_1 a_0/k_2 \quad -a_1/k_2] \begin{bmatrix} X_1 \\ X_2 \end{bmatrix} + [d] V_1 \qquad (77b)$$

If we solve the first row in (77a) for X_1 and the second row for X_2, we get

$$X_1 = \frac{1}{k_1 s} X_2, \tag{78a}$$

$$X_2 = \frac{-k_1 b_0}{s + b_1} X_1 - \frac{k_2}{s + b_1} V_1. \tag{78b}$$

A signal-flow graph representing (78) and (77b) is shown in Fig. 31. We have assumed that the integrator operating on X_2 is inverting; hence, an additional inverter is needed to restore the sign.

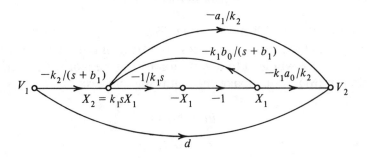

Fig. 31   Alternate signal-flow graph

The network realizing this signal-flow graph is shown in Fig. 32. The first integrator is referred to as a *lossy* (or *leaky*) *integrator*. (The network was first called a biquad by Thomas in 1971.[*])

The voltages at various points can be identified as follows:

$$\begin{aligned}
V_3 &= X_2 \\
V_5 &= -V_4 = X_1
\end{aligned} \tag{79}$$

From these, the following equations can be written from Fig. 32:

$$V_3 = -\frac{G_3 V_5}{s + G_1} - \frac{G_4 V_1}{s + G_1} \tag{80a}$$

$$V_5 = G_2 V_3 / s \tag{80b}$$

---

[*] L. C. Thomas, "The biquad: part I—some practical design considerations," *IEEE Transactions on Circuit Theory*, vol. CT-18, 1971, pp. 350-357.

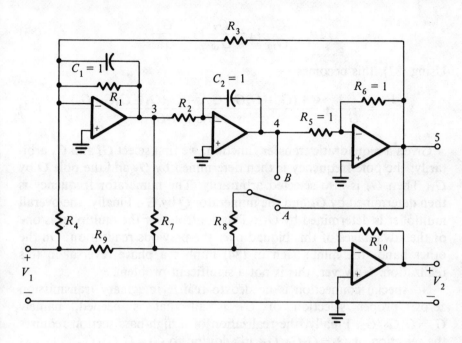

Fig. 32   Alternate state variable biquad

Comparing these with (78) leads to the following, in view of the identifications in (79):

$$G_1 = b_1 \qquad\qquad G_4 = k_2$$
$$G_3 = k_1 b_0 \qquad\qquad G_2 = 1/k_1 \tag{81}$$

Note that G_2 and G_4 are fixed by the values of k_1 and k_2, respectively.

Solving for V_3 and V_5 in the two equations in (80) leads to the following transfer functions:

$$\frac{V_3}{V_1} = \frac{-G_4 s}{s^2 + G_1 s + G_2 G_3} \tag{82a}$$

$$\frac{V_5}{V_1} = -\frac{V_4}{V_1} = \frac{-G_2 G_4}{s^2 + G_1 s + G_2 G_3} \tag{82b}$$

Thus, for band-pass and low-pass filter realizations, the output summer is not needed.

Since $V_5 = -V_4$, the position of the switch in Fig. 32 will determine the sign of the constant term in the numerator. The voltage from the output summer will be

$$V_2 = -\frac{G_9}{G_{10}}V_1 - \frac{G_7}{G_{10}}V_3 \pm \frac{G_8}{G_{10}}V_5. \tag{83}$$

Using (82), this becomes

$$\frac{V_2}{V_1} = \frac{-G_9}{G_{10}} \cdot \frac{s^2 + (G_1 - G_2G_7/G_9)s + G_2(G_3 \pm G_4G_8/G_9)}{s^2 + G_1s + G_2G_3}. \tag{84}$$

Given a biquadratic transfer function, we first select G_2 and G_4 arbitrarily; the pole frequency is then determined by G_3 and the pole Q by G_1. Then G_9 is also selected arbitrarily. The numerator frequency is then determined by G_8 and the numerator Q by G_7. Finally, the overall multiplier is determined by G_{10}. This control over the multiplier is one of the advantages of this biquad over the previous realization. On the other hand, the minus sign in (84) implies a phase reversal in this realization. However, this is not a significant problem.

No special connection is needed to realize imaginary transmission zeros; proper selection of G_7 is all that is needed, namely $G_7 = G_1G_9/G_2$. Finally, the realization of a high-pass section requires the selection of $G_8 = G_3G_9/G_4$, in addition to $G_7 = G_1G_9/G_2$.

13.3.5.3 Sensitivity Analysis

Since expressions for the pole Q and ω_0 in terms of the R and C values in the realizations shown in Fig. 29 and Fig. 32 are easily written, the passive component sensitivities are readily calculated. They are found to be quite small; for some components zero, for others $\pm \frac{1}{2}$. (See Exercise 15.) These value are as small as can be expected for any realization.

To find the sensitivities to op-amp gains, it is necessary to assume finite gains and recalculate $G(s)$. The coefficient of s and the constant term in the quadratic denominator are nominally ω_0/Q and ω_0^2 for infinite A_i. For finite A_i in the Thomas design of Fig. 32, they become

$$\frac{\omega_0}{Q} \frac{1 + \dfrac{2Q+1}{A_1} + \dfrac{Q+1}{A_2} + \dfrac{3Q+1}{A_3}}{\left(1 + \dfrac{1}{A_1}\right)\left(1 + \dfrac{1}{A_2}\right)}, \tag{85a}$$

$$\omega_0^2 \frac{\dfrac{1}{1+2/A_3} + \dfrac{2}{A_1A_2} + \dfrac{1}{QA_2}\left(1 + \dfrac{1}{A_1}\right)}{\left(1 + \dfrac{1}{A_1}\right)\left(1 + \dfrac{1}{A_2}\right)}. \tag{85b}$$

The realized values of ω_0 and Q are different from their nominal values for infinite gains. The sensitivities can be calculated from the realized values of ω_0 and Q determined from (85). Assuming high Q ($Q \gg 1$) and high gains ($A_i \gg Q$), it is found that

$$S_{A_i}^Q \propto 1/A_i \tag{86a}$$

$$S_{A_3}^Q \propto 1/A_3 \tag{86b}$$

$$S_{A_1}^Q \cong 2Q/A_1 \tag{86c}$$

$$S_{A_2}^Q \cong Q/A_2 \tag{86d}$$

All of these are acceptably small; in the case of the last two, the sensitivities are proportional to Q. Similar results for the sensitivities hold for the design of Fig. 29.

13.4 CASCADE DESIGN

The preceding section has described a number of different designs for realizing a biquadratic voltage gain function. The output of each of the designs is taken from an op-amp and thus is from a low-impedance point. The biquads can thus be cascaded without much mutual loading or coupling.

Given a voltage gain function of order higher than 2, the realization procedure is conceptually straightforward and simple. Decompose the given function into biquadratics. (Obviously, if the order is odd, there will be a first order function in addition to the biquadratics. This can be realized by an RC network, so it introduces no complications. To avoid the necessity of making special reference to this case, we shall assume the order of the given function is even.) Then realize each biquadratic function by one or another biquad. Then connect the biquads in cascade.

Although conceptually straightforward, a number of practical problems are presented by this procedure. Let the given function be written as

$$G(s) = K \frac{P(s)}{D(s)}. \tag{87}$$

Both $P(s)$ and $D(s)$ can be factored into their quadratic factors. (Of course, the "quadratic factors" in the numerator can be simply second, first or zero order powers of s.) Let us designate each resulting biquadratic function as

$$G_i(s) = K_i \frac{P_i(s)}{D_i(s)}, \tag{88}$$

where

$$\Pi K_i = K \tag{89a}$$

$$\Pi P_i(s) = P(s) \tag{89b}$$

$$\Pi D_i(s) = D(s) \tag{89c}$$

The gain constants K_i are arbitrary, subject only to the condition that their product equals the given K.

A number of questions now arise: (a) How should gain constant values K_i be assigned? (b) How should pole-pairs be matched with zeros to form each biquadratic factor? (c) After these are done and the biquads are designed, in what order should the biquads be cascaded? None of these questions is significant from a realizability standpoint. However, a number of practical considerations intrude.

For example, the maximum voltage output of a real op-amp and, hence, of the incorporating biquad, is limited by the value of the op-amp bias voltage. Thus, the maximum input voltage before the biquad output saturates is the bias voltage divided by the gain. The range of input voltages over which a network will operate in accordance with its design assumptions (for example, linearity) is the *dynamic range*. Now if a K_i is made too large, the output from biquad i may exceed the dynamic range of the next biquad in the cascade, even though the overall K equals the given value. Thus, K_i must be distributed among the biquads in such a way that none of the biquads saturates at any frequency in the operating range of the network. This means none should saturate at the frequency of its maximum output, but should almost saturate. In fact, the optimum would be to make the maximum output from each biquad equal to the maximum output of the network as a whole, although these maxima would normally occur at different frequencies.

Another practical problem is noise. To make sure that the signal is least degraded by noise, the signal level should be as high as possible at the output of each biquad. Since the magnitude of the biquad output varies with frequency, two factors come into play here. If the maximum magnitude of an output voltage is much greater than the minimum magnitude, then near the frequency of this minimum magnitude, the relative impact of the noise will be great. So it would be best if the output voltage magnitude from any biquad not have significant peaks and valleys; that is, $|G_i(j\omega)|$ should be as flat as possible. Clearly, how the zeros of $G(s)$ are associated with the poles will have a great effect on $|G_i(j\omega)|$. Furthermore, the same considerations would apply to the voltage gain function from the input to any point before the final output. So the order of the biquads in the cascade should be such that, not only should each $|G_i(j\omega)|$ be as flat as possible, but also the product of the G_i's from the first one to any other one in the cascade should have as flat a magnitude as possible.

There are other practical considerations which can influence the matching of zeros to poles or the order of cascading the biquads. It is possible, of course, that the requirements stemming from satisfying one criterion conflict with those demanded by another criterion. In this case, a compromise is made, weighted by the value attached to satisfying each criterion.

In order to answer the questions about gain constant, pole-zero matching, and order of cascading, an exhaustive (and exhausting) search is carried out. All possible combinations of pole-zero pairings for the given function are made and the "flatness" of $|G_i(j\omega)|$ — as measured by the ratio of maximum to minimum magnitude — determined. The "flattest" pairings are then selected. Then a similar process is carried out for all possible biquad orders. The "flatness" of the gain functions from input to the output point of each biquad are calculated for each biquad order and the "flattest" order is selected. Finally, starting with the input biquad, each K_i is selected so that

$$\max |G_1(j\omega)| = \max |G_1(j\omega)G_2(j\omega)| = \ldots = \max |G(j\omega)|$$

No significant principles are involved in the details of carrying out this process; hence, we shall not pursue the matter any further.

The decomposition of a given voltage gain function into biquadratics, the design of biquads realizing each biquadratic, and the subsequent cascade connection of the biquads has the virtue of simplicity and straightforwardness. Furthermore, there is very little interaction among the biquads so that variation of component values affects only one pair of poles (and zeros). In the sense that this permits independent tuning and adjustment of each biquad and assures the insensitivity of the location of all but a single pair of poles to changes in a component value can be viewed as an advantage. However, changes in the location of a single pair of poles, especially those close to the $j\omega$-axis (high Q), have a major effect on $|G(j\omega)|$. Hence, the cascade design, even with its advantages, has the disadvantage of high sensitivity of the overall transfer function.

There would be a smaller disruption in the *pattern* of poles, and thus a smaller change in the overall $|G(j\omega)|$, if the change in a component value moved *all* poles (rather than just a pole-pair). This is the case for a passive ladder where every component influences all poles, and the sensitivity is known to be low.

A number of active *RC* structures have been proposed utilizing biquads that are coupled by feedback in different ways, rather than decoupled in a cascade connection. The signal-flow graphs of two of these structures for the case of four biquads are shown in Fig. 33 and carry the fanciful names: (a) leapfrog feedback and (b) follow-the-leader feedback. Both of them exhibit considerably lower sensitivity than a cascade design of the same function. Because a thorough description would require considerable space, we shall reluctantly not pursue the designs further here.

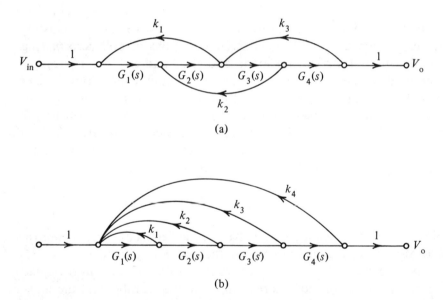

(a)

(b)

Fig. 33 Coupled biquads

13.5 EFFECT OF OP-AMP FREQUENCY DEPENDENCE ON REALIZATIONS

A real operational amplifier is itself a complex electronic network. In all of the synthesis techniques utilizing op-amps, we have assumed that the op-amp gain is infinite over an infinite band of frequencies. Even when we calculated sensitivities of Q and ω_0 to op-amp gain, taken to be finite, we still assumed an infinite bandwidth. But real amplifiers have finite bandwidth and the gain is a function of frequency. In order to stabilize an op-amp, it is necessary to introduce compensating networks to modify and shape the frequency characteristics. As a result, we shall assume that a well-designed, frequency-compensated op-amp has the following expression for the gain as a function of frequency (see Exercise II-59):

$$A(s) = \frac{A_o \omega_a}{s + \omega_a} \tag{90}$$

where A_o is the gain—the value of $A(s)$ as $s \to 0$—and ω_a is the low-frequency 3-dB bandwidth. The quantity $A_o \omega_a$, called the dc gain bandwidth product, is also essentially the frequency at which $|A(j\omega)| = 1$; it is sometimes designated ω_t. Typical numerical values in available op-amps are

$$A_o: 30{,}000 \text{ to } 200{,}000$$

$$\omega_a: 60 \text{ to } 500 \text{ rad/sec} \tag{91}$$

$$\omega_t = A_o \omega_a: 2 \times 10^6 \text{ to } 10^8 \text{ rad/sec}$$

In the synthesis procedures described in the preceding sections, the op-amp appears in a number of configurations: it may be a component of a more complex active device, like a gyrator or general converter; it may be used to form an inverting or noninverting amplifier or integrator; or it may be embedded in a more extensive RC network, as in the single-amplifier, negative feedback biquads. The frequency dependence of the op-amp open-loop gain and the finiteness of the gain-bandwidth product will have profound influences on any realization using op-amps.

Let's examine the influence of (90) on the inverting and noninverting amplifiers in Fig. 34. Under the reasonable assumption that $A_o \gg 1 + R_b/R_a$, the voltage gain functions are found to be the following:

Noninverting
Amplifier:
$$G(s) = \frac{V_2}{V_1} = \frac{A_o \omega_a}{s + A_o \omega_a / K_o}, \tag{92a}$$

Inverting
Amplifier:
$$G(s) = \frac{V_2}{V_1} = -\left(1 - \frac{1}{K_o}\right) \frac{A_o \omega_a}{s + A_o \omega_a / K_o}, \tag{92b}$$

where $K_o = 1 + R_b/R_a$. When $s = 0$, these reduce to the expected values. Both of these expressions are similar to (90) for the op-amp alone. The main difference is that the 3 dB bandwidth has been increased by a factor A_o/K_o, which is usually $\gg 1$.

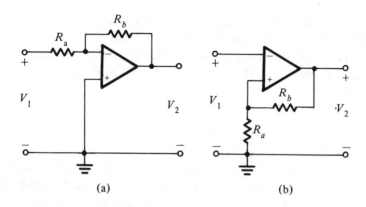

Fig. 34 Amplifiers: (a) inverting, (b) noninverting

Now consider the integrator shown with its voltage gain function in Fig. 35. For infinite $A(s)$, this function is $-1/RCs$, which has a pole at $s=0$. Now let $A(s)$ be given by (90); the voltage gain function becomes

$$G(s) = \frac{-A_o\omega_a/RC}{s^2 + A_o\omega_a s + \omega_a/RC}, \tag{93}$$

under the assumption that $A_o\omega_a \gg 1/RC$. Instead of a single pole at the origin, the integrator gain now has two poles whose approximate values are found to be

$$s_{1,2} = -\frac{1}{A_o RC}, \; -A_o\omega_a. \tag{94}$$

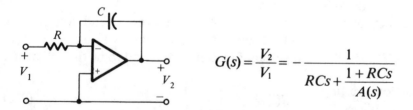

$$G(s) = \frac{V_2}{V_1} = -\frac{1}{RCs + \dfrac{1+RCs}{A(s)}}$$

Fig. 35 Integrator

For the typical numerical values in (91) and for RC of the order of microseconds or more, the first pole is very near the origin and the second one is far out on the negative real axis. Thus, the frequency dependence of the op-amp has shifted the location of the nominal pole slightly and has added another real pole so far away that its effect on the integrator performance is negligible. This is the general way in which the frequency dependence of A influences the transfer functions in other op-amp networks as well.

In order to examine the effect of the frequency dependence of A on the voltage gain functions of biquads, let us consider the single-amplifier biquads treated in Sec. 13.3.2. The voltage gains of the negative feedback case and the positive feedback case were given in (23) and (43) before A was allowed to go to infinity. Comparing these expressions, we see that they both have the following form:

$$G(s) = \frac{\text{Numerator}}{P_1(s) + P_2(s)/A(s)} = \frac{\text{Numerator}}{s^2 + \dfrac{\omega_0}{Q}s + \omega_0^2 + P_2(s)/A(s)}, \tag{95}$$

where P_1 and P_2 are quadratic polynomials. When A is infinite, the denominator is just $s^2 + \omega_0 s/Q + \omega_0^2$. But when (90) is inserted for $A(s)$, the denominator becomes a cubic; the voltage gain function now has 3 poles.

For the sake of concreteness and in order to pursue the details of the analysis, let us consider the generic bridged-tee example leading to the designs in Fig. 17. The polynomials P_1 and P_2 in (95) are N_{n2} and D as given in (27). Hence, using (27) and (90) and the expression for ω_0 and Q in (28), the cubic polynomial in the denominator whose roots are the poles of the voltage gain function becomes

$$\text{Denominator} =$$

$$\left(s^2 + \frac{\omega_0}{Q}s + \omega_0^2\right) + \frac{(s + \omega_a)}{A_o \omega_a}\left[s^2 + \left(\frac{\omega_0}{Q} + \frac{G_2}{C_2}\right)s + \omega_0^2\right]. \tag{96}$$

For values of $|s| \gg \omega_a$,

$$\frac{1}{A(s)} = \frac{s + \omega_a}{A_o \omega_a} \rightarrow \frac{s}{A_o \omega_a} = \frac{s}{\omega_t}. \tag{97}$$

Using this relation and expanding expressions, (96) becomes

$$\text{Denominator} =$$

$$\frac{s^3}{\omega_t} + \left[\frac{1}{\omega_t}\left(\frac{\omega_0}{Q} + \frac{G_2}{C_2}\right) + 1\right]s^2 + \left[\frac{\omega_0^2}{\omega_t} + \frac{\omega_0}{Q}\right]s + \omega_0^2. \tag{98}$$

Let $\hat{\omega}_0$ and $\hat{Q}$ be the new (shifted) values of ω_0 and Q. The cubic in (98) can be factored in terms of a quadratic representing $\hat{\omega}_0$ and $\hat{Q}$ and a linear factor as follows:

$$\text{Denominator} = \left(\frac{s}{\omega_t} + \frac{\omega_0^2}{\hat{\omega}_0^2} \right) \left(s^2 + \frac{\hat{\omega}_0}{\hat{Q}} s + \hat{\omega}_0^2 \right). \tag{99}$$

Note that the extra pole introduced by this process is located approximately at $s = -\omega_t$, which is far out on the axis. Hence, it will have little effect on the frequency response in the pass band.

Expanding this expression and equating the coefficients of s^2 and s in (98) and (99) leads to two equations in the unknowns $\hat{\omega}_0$ and $\hat{Q}$, as follows:

$$\frac{\hat{\omega}_0^2}{\omega_t} + \frac{\omega_0^2}{\hat{\omega}_0 \hat{Q}} = \frac{\omega_0^2}{\omega_t} + \frac{\omega_0}{Q} \tag{100a}$$

$$\frac{\hat{\omega}_0}{\omega_t \hat{Q}} + \frac{\omega_0^2}{\hat{\omega}_0^2} = \frac{1}{\omega_t} \left(\frac{\omega_0}{Q} + \frac{G_2}{C_2} \right) + 1 \tag{100b}$$

Let $\hat{\omega}_0 = \omega_0 + \Delta\omega_0$; so

$$\frac{\hat{\omega}_0}{\omega_0} = 1 + \frac{\Delta\omega_0}{\omega_0}. \tag{101}$$

Using (101) and such approximations as $1/(1+\epsilon) \cong 1 - \epsilon$, when $\epsilon \ll 1$, (100b) becomes

$$\frac{\Delta\omega_0}{\omega_0} \left(\frac{\omega_0}{\hat{Q}} - 2\omega_t \right) = \frac{G_2}{C_2} + \frac{\omega_0}{Q} - \frac{\omega_0}{\hat{Q}}.$$

Since the difference between Q and $\hat{Q}$ is not a primary factor in this expression for the changes in ω_0, we shall set $\hat{Q} = Q$ here. For $\omega_0 \ll 2\omega_t Q$, the preceding expression becomes

$$\frac{\Delta\omega_0}{\omega_0} = -\frac{G_2}{2C_2\omega_t}. \tag{102}$$

Recall from (39) that G_2/C_2 is proportional to the sensitivity of Q to A_o. Since this sensitivity is to be small, so should G_2/C_2. (For example, for $A_o = 10^5$, $\omega_0 = 10^5$ (a high value) and $Q = 100$ (also a high value),

$S_A^Q = 10^{-8}G_2/C_2$. Thus G_2/C_2 could be a convenient 10^4 or 10^5 to yield an acceptably low sensitivity.)

To get a different perspective, let us substitute (39) into (102) to get

$$\frac{\Delta\omega_0}{\omega_0} = -\frac{1}{2Q}\frac{\omega_0}{\omega_t}A_0 S_{A_o}^Q. \tag{103}$$

Even though the open loop gain appears as a multiplier, since $S_{A_o}^Q$ is inversely proportional to A_o, the product $A_o S_{A_o}^Q$ can be quite small. It is evident that the relative change in pole frequency is proportional to this frequency. If an upper limit on this relative change is specified, this will limit the maximum pole frequency that can be realized with a biquad utilizing an op-amp in the configuration under discussion. A similar conclusion is true for other configurations.

Now let us return to (100a); using the approximation in (101) this becomes

$$\frac{\hat{Q}}{Q} = \frac{1}{1 + \left(1 - \dfrac{2Q\omega_0}{\omega_t}\right)\dfrac{\Delta\omega_0}{\omega_0}}. \tag{104}$$

Since $2Q\omega_0/\omega_t$ can be of the same order as 1, neither of the terms in the denominator can be neglected, in general. An interesting condition is observed from (104). In the vicinity of $2Q\omega_0 = \omega_t$ (which corresponds to a very high Q) $\hat{Q} \cong Q$; so the frequency dependence of the op-amp gain has very little influence on Q in this case. This is a surprising result. In fact, for $2Q\omega_0 > \omega_t$, the realized Q becomes *greater* than the desired one; this is the phenomenon of *Q-enhancement*.

Although the details will vary slightly for other negative feedback designs and for positive feedback designs, the overall conclusions will be similar to what has just been discussed. In fact, any other biquad design, whose voltage gain function can be written in the form of (95) will lead to similar results. For example, under the assumption of identical op-amps, the 3 amplifier biquad shown in Fig. 33 (not counting the summer) has a voltage gain function exactly of the form of (95). Hence, the results apply to this biquad also, including the phenomenon of Q-enhancement.

Question Set: Part IV

EXERCISES

1. Verify the angle condition (11-20) for the driving point impedances of the one-ports in Fig. E-1.

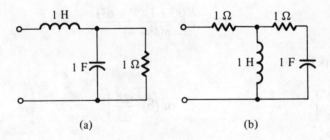

(a)   (b)

Fig. E-1

2. It is claimed that the functions below are not positive real for $n > N_0$. Verify this claim and determine the value of N_0 for each function.

(a) $F(s) = \left[\dfrac{s+1}{s+2} \right]^n$,

(b) $F(s) = \left[\dfrac{s+10}{s+11} \right]^n$.

3. Let

$$Z(s) = \frac{s^2 + s + 1}{s^2 + s + 4}.$$

The even part of this positive real function has a (double) zero on the $j\omega$-axis. Hence, this function maps this point on the $j\omega$-axis to a point on the jX-axis in the Z-plane. Verify that the derivative dZ/ds at this point is real and positive.

4. Let

$$Y_{RC}(s) = \frac{(s+1)(s+3)(s+8)}{(s+2)(s+4)(s+10)}.$$

To obtain a realization for Y_{RC} it is suggested that the first branch across the terminals be a resistor of $\frac{1}{2}\,\Omega$. The remaining admittance will be $Y_{RC}-2$. Is this a pr function?

5. Find one or more realizations of the following reactance functions:

(a) $Z(s) = \dfrac{10s(s^2+1)(s^2+4)}{(s^2+1/4)(s^2+2)}$ (b) $Z(s) = \dfrac{2(s^2+1)(s^2+25/4)}{s(s^2+9/4)(s^2+9)}$

6. Consider the rational function

$$Y(s) = \frac{K(s^2+1)(s^2+\alpha^2)}{s(s^2+4)}.$$

for which

(a) $\left.\dfrac{dY}{ds}\right|_{s=j1} = \dfrac{1}{2}$ or (b) $\left.\dfrac{dZ}{ds}\right|_{s=j2} = 2.$

Find a realization as a ladder network and as one of the Foster forms for each case.

7. The admittance of a passive RC network has zeros at $s=0$, -1, and -3. At each of these points the slope of $Y(\sigma)$ equals 2. For large values of $s=\sigma$, $Y(\sigma)$ approaches 4. Find a ladder network and a network in one of the Foster forms to realize this function.

8. Verify whether the following polynomials are Hurwitz:

(a) $P(s) = s^4 + 7s^3 + 6s^2 + 4s + 1$

(b) $P(s) = 2s^4 + 4s^3 + 7s^2 + 7s + 3$

(c) $P(s) = s^7 + 3s^6 + 6s^5 + 6s^4 + 6s^3 + 6s^2 + 5s + 3$

(d) $P(s) = 2s^5 + 9s^4 + 16s^3 + 15s^2 + 7s + 2$

9. For each of the one-ports shown in Fig. E-9, find the inverse network. Verify that the driving-point admittance of the inverse is the same as the driving-point impedance of the given network.

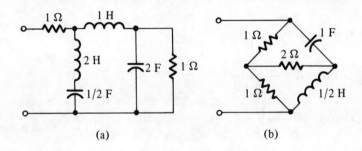

(a)   (b)

Fig. E-9

10. Find the z- or y-parameters of the lossless two-port which, when terminated in a resistance, realizes the following impedance functions. Specify whether the Darlington case A or case B applies.

(a) $Z(s) = \dfrac{s^2 + s + 4}{s^2 + s + 1}$

(b) $Z(s) = \dfrac{s^3 + s^2 + 2s + 1}{s^2 + s + 1}$

(c) $Z(s) = \dfrac{s^2 + 5s + 1}{s^3 + 5s^2 + 2s + 1}$

(d) $Z(s) = \dfrac{s^4 + 2s^3 + 3s^2 + s + 1}{s^4 + s^3 + 3s^2 + 2s + 1}$

(e) $Z(s) = \dfrac{s^3 + 2s^2 + 5s}{s^3 + 3s^2 + 4s + 35/8}$

(f) $Z(s) = \dfrac{s^4 + s^3 + 3s^2 + 2s + 6}{s^3 + 3s^2 + 7s}$

11. Find a two-port network terminated in a 100Ω resistor whose voltage gain function is given by each of the following all-pass functions. In each case involving a lattice, determine if a common-terminal equivalent exists and, if it does, convert it.

(a) $G_{21}(s) = \dfrac{s^2 - 2s + 2}{s^2 + 2s + 2}$

(b) $G_{21}(s) = \dfrac{s^2 - 3s + 5}{s^2 + 3s + 5}$

(c) $G_{21}(s) = \dfrac{(s^2 - s + 1)(s - 5)}{(s^2 + s + 1)(s + 5)}$

12. Find a two-port network terminated in a 50Ω resistor whose voltage gain function is given by each of the following nonminimum-phase functions. Select any convenient value of K. Convert any lattices to common-terminal equivalent networks where possible.

(a) $G_{21}(s) = K\dfrac{s^2 - s + 2}{(s+1)^2}$

(b) $G_{21}(s) = K\dfrac{s-2}{s^2 + 4s + 3}$

(c) $G_{21}(s) = K\dfrac{s^2 - 3s + 5}{s^2 + 7s + 5}$

13. RC ladder networks are to be obtained that realize each of the following transfer voltage ratio (voltage gain) functions. (Note that the poles must be real; so $Q \leqslant \frac{1}{2}$.)

(a) $G_1(s) = \dfrac{K}{s^2 + \dfrac{\omega_o}{Q}s + \omega_o^2}$ (low-pass; zeros at ∞, ∞)

(b) $G_2(s) = \dfrac{Ks^2}{s^2 + \dfrac{\omega_o}{Q}s + \omega_o^2}$ (high-pass; zeros at 0, 0)

(c) $G_3(s) = \dfrac{Ks}{s^2 + \dfrac{\omega_o}{Q}s + \omega_o^2}$ (band-pass; zeros at 0, ∞)

Since transmission zeros of ladder networks occur when a series-branch admittance is zero or a shunt-branch admittance is infinite; a zero at $s=0$ will be obtained only for a capacitor series branch. Similarly, a zero at infinity will be obtained only for a capacitor shunt branch.

(a) On this basis, draw canonic RC ladder networks—that is, having the least number of components to give the desired order transfer functions—to realize each of the functions.

(b) Express K, Q, and ω_o in terms of the component values.

(c) Find the values of the sensitivity of each of the quantities K, Q, and ω_o to each of the component values.

14. The following sets of elements of the admittance matrix of an RC two-port are given. Find RC two-ports realizing each set, using appropriate tables in Chapter 12.

(a) $-y_{21}(s) = \dfrac{s^2 + 3s + 6}{s^2 + 4s + 3}$ $\qquad$ (b) $-y_{21}(s) = \dfrac{s^2 + 2s + 2}{(s+2)(s+5)}$

$y_{22}(s) = \dfrac{2s^2 + 5s + 2}{s^2 + 4s + 3}$ $\qquad$ $y_{22}(s) = \dfrac{s^2 + 5s + 4}{(s+2)(s+5)}$

15. Taking the open-loop op-amp gains A_i to be finite in the 3-amplifier biquads discussed in Chapter 13, find expressions for the voltage gain function in terms of all the gain, resistance, and capacitance parameters. Using these expressions, evaluate the sensitivities of pole Q and ω_o to all component values, including op-amp gains.

16. Taking the open-loop gains A_i in the 3-amplifier biquads discussed in Chapter 13 to be identical but frequency dependent, as in (13-90), find expressions for the voltage gain function of the biquads.

17. For the result of Exercise 16, follow a procedure similar to the one carried out in Section 13.5 to determine the variation in pole frequency and Q due to the finiteness of the op-amp gain bandwidth product.

18. Repeat exercise 16 for the positive feedback biquad whose voltage gain function is given in (13-41) with $G_{p2}(s)$ as in (13-44).

19. Let a biquadratic voltage gain function be realized directly by the general-converter realization method described in Section 13.2.
    (a) Find expressions for the pole frequency and Q in terms of the components values.
    (b) From these determine the sensitivity of ω_o and Q to component values, including the general converter parameter K.

20. Suppose the general-converter network in Fig. 1-20 is used in the realization of Exercise 19, with branches 3 and 4 being capacitors and branches 1 and 2 being resistors. Assume identical op-amps with finite, frequency-independent gain A.
    (a) Find an expression for K in the general-converter function $f(s) = Ks^2$.
    (b) From the result of (a), determine the sensitivities s_A^K.
    (c) Using this information, find the sensitivites S_A^Q and $S_A^{\omega_o}$ for the realization of the biquadratic function in Exercise 19.

21. In Exercise 20, suppose the op-amp gains have the frequency dependence given in (13-90).
    (a) Find an expression for $f(s)$.
    (b) Discuss the impact on the realization procedure of Section 13.2.

22. Assume the function given in (13-2) is a voltage gain function. Obtain a realization of this function in the form of Fig. 13-12. Compare the number of components with the realization given in Fig. 13-7.

23. Choose the bridged-tee network in case (a) of Table 12-9 as the generating network for a single amplifier, negative feedback biquad.
    (a) Write expressions for the pole Q and ω_o, assuming infinite op-amp gain.
    (b) Repeat (a) assuming finite op-amp gain.
    (c) Determine the sensitivities of ω_o and Q to the various network parameters in each case.

24. Let $G(s) = N(s)/D(s)$ be a biquadratic function. A number of possible polynomials $N(s)$ and $D(s)$ are listed next:

$N(s)$	$D(s)$
(1) 10	(1) $s^2 + s + 25$
(2) $5s$	(2) $s^2 + 0.1s + 100$
(3) $2s^2$	(3) $s^2 + 0.05s + 1$
(4) $s + 1$	(4) $s^2 + (\sqrt{2}/10)s + 2$
(5) $s^2 + 2$	
(6) $s^2 + s + 16$	
(7) $s^2 - s + 25$	

Form $G(s)$ from the possible combinations of $N(s)$ and $D(s)$ above.
(a) Obtain single-amplifier, negative feedback designs for $G(s)$. Where possible, use the bridged-tee and twin-tee generic RC networks in Figs. 13-17 to 13-19. Where not possible, find modifications of these RC networks or find other generating networks to obtain a design. Use the flexibility available in selecting component values to reduce the sensitivities of the pole ω_0 and Q to any parameter values on which they depend, including op-amp gain.
(b) Repeat (a) for a single-amplifier, positive-feedback design.
(c) Repeat (a) for a two-amplifier design.
(d) Repeat (a) for designs obtained from the state-variable approach.
(e) For each design find the spread of conductance (or resistance) values. (A large spread of values is not easy to fabricate, so it is not desirable.)

25. Show that the voltage gain function of the network of Fig. E-25 is the all-pass function

$$G(s) = K \frac{\alpha - s}{\alpha + s}.$$

Give values of K and α.

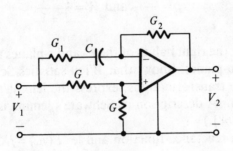

Fig. E-25

26. Assume the function given in (13-2) is a voltage gain function. Obtain a realization as a cascade of biquad sections using any convenient pole-zero matching.

27. Consider the following pairs of y-parameters:

(1) $-y_{21} = \dfrac{s^2 + 0.1s + 1}{s + 2}$ (2) $-y_{21} = \dfrac{s^2 + 0.1s + 1}{(s + 0.2)(s + 1)}$

$y_{22} = \dfrac{(s + 1)(s + 3)}{s + 2}$ $\overset{\bullet}{y_{22}} = \dfrac{2(s + 0.15)(s + 0.5)}{(s + 0.2)(s + 1)}$

(3) $-y_{21} = \dfrac{s^2 + 0.6s + 4}{(s + 2)(s + 6)}$ (4) $-y_{21} = K \dfrac{s^2 + 6s + 9}{(s + 1)(s + 2)}$ (K arbitrary)

$y_{22} = \dfrac{5(s + 1)(s + 5)}{(s + 2)(s + 6)}$ $y_{22} = \dfrac{(s + 0.5)(s + 1.5)}{(s + 1)(s + 2)}$

(a) Verify that each pair is realizable by an RC two-port.

(b) Realize any that are realizable as a ladder network by a process similar to that in Problem 33 by using an appropriate transformation.

(c) Realize, using an appropriate Table in Chapter 12, those that cannot be realized by a ladder.

PROBLEMS

1. Let $F(s)$ be a positive real function. Prove the angle property, namely that $|\arg F(s)| \leq |\arg s|$ for $0 \leq |\arg s| \leq \pi/2$. Hint: Make the following bilinear transformations:

$$p = \frac{s-1}{s+1} \text{ and } W = \frac{F-1}{F+1}.$$

Observe how the right halves of the F- and s-planes are mapped into the W- and p-planes. Show that $W(p)$ satisfies Schwarz's lemma. Then, by the transformations, express the lemma's conclusions in terms of $F(s)$. (A description of Schwarz's lemma is to be found in [6, pp. 267-268].)

2. Let $F(s)$ be a reactance function and let $F(j\omega) = jX(\omega)$. Prove that

$$\frac{dX(\omega)}{d\omega} \geq \left| \frac{X}{\omega} \right|.$$

Hint: Use energy functions.

3. Prove that a bilinear transformation of a bounded real function is a positive real function.

4. Let $Z = (m_1 + n_1)/(m_2 + n_2)$ be a positive real function. Prove that

$$P(s) = m_1(s) + an_1(s) + bm_2(s) + cn_2(s)$$

is a Hurwitz polynomial, where a, b, and c are positive constants.

5. Let $P(s)$ be a Hurwitz polynomial. Prove that $F(s)$ is a positive real function, where

$$F(s) = \frac{1}{P(s)} \frac{dP(s)}{ds}.$$

6. Let $Z(s) = P(s)/Q(s)$ be a positive real function. Prove that the following function is also positive real:

$$\hat{Z}(s) = \frac{dP(s)/ds}{dQ(s)/ds}.$$

7. Using the partial fraction expansions in (12-20), show that

   (a) $\text{Im}[Z_{RC}(j\omega)]>0$ (<0) for $\omega<0$ (>0)

   (b) $\text{Im}[Y_{RC}(j\omega)]<0$ (>0) for $\omega<0$ (>0)

   (c) $\text{Re}[Z_{RC}(j\omega)]$ is a monotonically decreasing function of ω for $\omega\geq0$.

   (d) $\text{Re}[Y_{RC}(j\omega)]$ is a monotonically increasing function of ω for $\omega\geq0$.

8. From the result of Problem 7, show that

   (a) $\text{Re}[Z_{RC}(0)]>\text{Re}[Z_{RC}(\infty)]$ or $Z_{RC}(0)>Z_{RC}(\infty)$,

   (b) $\text{Re}[Y_{RC}(0)]<\text{Re}[Y_{RC}(\infty)]$ or $Y_{RC}(0)<Y_{RC}(\infty)$.

9. The result of Problem 7 can be described as a mapping of the upper half of the s-plane into the lower half of the Z-plane and a mapping of the lower half of the s-plane into the upper half of the Z-plane. Use this to obtain an alternate proof of: $dZ_{RC}(s)/ds$ is negative on the real axis.

10. Using the approach of Problem 9, show that, for the impedance $Z_{RL}(s)$ of a passive RL network, $dZ_{RL}(s)/ds$ is real and positive on the real axis.

11. Let $Z_1(s)$ and $Z_2(s)$ be RC impedance functions. Prove that $Z_1(s)/Z_2(s)$ is a positive real function.

12. Let $P(s)$ be a polynomial whose zeros are all imaginary. Prove that

$$F(s) = \frac{P(s)}{dP(s)/ds}$$

   is a reactance function.

13. Let $Y_{RC}(s)$ be the admittance of a passive RC network. Prove that the residues of $Y_{RC}(s)$ are negative at all poles except the pole at infinity.

14. Let $P(s)$ be a polynomial whose zeros are all real and negative. Prove that each of the following two functions is the admittance of a passive RC network:

   (a) $F_1(s) = \dfrac{P(s)}{dP(s)/ds}$

   (b) $F_2(s) = \dfrac{s\,dP(s)/ds}{P(s)}$

15. Let $P(s)$ be a polynomial whose zeros are all real and negative. If K is a real, positive constant, prove that all the zeros of

$$F(s) = \frac{s\,dP(s)/ds}{ds} + KP(s)$$

are real and negative.

16. (a) Let $F(s) = P(s)/Q(s)$ be an RC impedance function. Prove that

$$F(s) = \frac{dP(s)/ds}{dQ(s)/ds}$$

is also an RC impedance function.

(b) Repeat (a) after replacing the word impedance by admittance.

17. It is desired to prove Theorem 12-4 on Hurwitz polynomials. In the first place, to prove that *if $P(s) = m(s) + n(s)$ is Hurwitz, then $m(s)/n(s)$ is a reactance function* note that the factors of a Hurwitz polynomial are of the form $(s^2 + as + b)$ or $(s + c)$, where a, b, and c are real and positive. Write

$$P(s) = (s^2 + as + b)\hat{P}(s) = (s^2 + as + b)(\hat{m} + \hat{n})$$
$$= [(s^2 + b)\hat{m} + as\hat{n}] + [(s^2 + b)\hat{n} + as\hat{m}].$$

Then, the ratio of the even and odd parts can be written as

$$\frac{m}{n} = \frac{(s^2 + b)\hat{m} + as\hat{n}}{(s^2 + b)\hat{n} + as\hat{m}} = \left[\frac{\hat{n}}{\hat{m}} + \frac{as}{s^2 + b}\right]^{-1} + \left[\frac{s^2 + b}{as} + \frac{\hat{m}}{\hat{n}}\right]^{-1}.$$

Show that m/n will be a reactance function provided $\hat{m}/\hat{n}$ is also. Repeat this procedure, with $\hat{P} = \hat{m} + \hat{n}$ until all the factors of $P(s)$, both quadratic and linear, are exhausted.

In the second place, it must be proved that *if $P(s) = m(s) + n(s)$ and $m(s)/n(s)$ is a reactance function, then $P(s)$ is a Hurwitz polynomial, except for a possible even factor.* The zeros of $P(s)$ occur when

$$P(s) = m(s) + n(s) = n(s)\left[\frac{m(s)}{n(s)} + 1\right] = 0.$$

Prove that, since m/n is a reactance function, $m/n = -1$ cannot occur in the right half of the s-plane.

18. Suppose that a network having a driving-point impedance $Z_1(s) = F(s)$ is given. It is desired to find a second network whose driving-point admittance $Y_2(s)$ is equal to $F(s)$. Such networks are called *inverse networks*. Discuss the conditions under which the inverse of a given network may be found using the concept of duality.

19. In the text, the **Z**-matrix of a two-port was shown to be positive real. Now, show that the **Y**-matrix of a two-port is positive real.

20. Show that the residue condition is satisfied with the "equals" sign — compact poles — at all the finite, nonzero poles of the y-parameters of a lossless two-port terminated in a unit resistance, as given in Table 12-4.

21. Show that the matrix of rational functions

$$\begin{bmatrix} z_{11}(s) & z_{12}(s) \\ z_{21}(s) & z_{22}(s) \end{bmatrix}$$

is a positive real matrix if and only if the matrix of real parts

$$\begin{bmatrix} r_{11}(\sigma,\omega) & r_{12}(\sigma,\omega) \\ r_{21}(\sigma,\omega) & r_{22}(\sigma,\omega) \end{bmatrix}$$

is positive definite or semidefinite in $\sigma \geq 0$.

22. Prove that the real part condition (11-63b), (11-63c) in the case of a reciprocal two-port, is sufficient for the **Z**-matrix of the two-port to be positive real. Establish the corresponding result for the **Y**-matrix also.

23. Let $y_{11} = y_{22}$ and $y_{21} = y_{12}$ be two real rational functions. Suppose the lattice shown in Fig. P-23 is to have these functions as its y-parameters. Show that the branch impedances Z_a and Z_b will be positive real if (a) y_{11} is positive real and (b) the real part condition $(\text{Re } y_{11})^2 - (\text{Re } y_{21})^2 \geq 0$ is satisfied for Re $s \geq 0$. If in (b) it is only known that the real part condition is satisfied on the $j\omega$-axis, what additional conditions must be placed on the given functions y_{11} and y_{21} before the theorem will again be true?

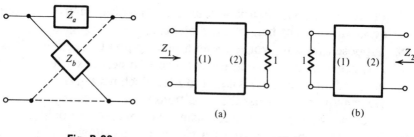

Fig. P-23   **Fig. P-25**

24. Consider a passive, reciprocal two-port. Show that at a zero of z_{11} on the $j\omega$-axis, z_{21} is imaginary. Hence show that any $j\omega$-axis poles of the voltage gain

$$g_{21}(s) = \frac{V_2(s)}{V_1(s)} \bigg|_{I_2 = 0}$$

are simple and with imaginary residues. Repeat for the current gain $h_{21}(s)$.

25. Fig. P-25(a) shows a lossless two-port terminated in a unit resistance at port 2. In Fig. P-25(b) the termination is at port 1. In the first instance, the impedance is

$$Z_1(s) = \frac{m_1(s) + n_1(s)}{m_2(s) + n_2(s)}.$$

(a) Find expressions for Z_2 appropriate to the Darlington case A and case B.

(b) State the relationship between Z_1 and Z_2 when (1) $m_1 = m_2$ and (2) $n_1 = n_2$.

26. Let $Z(s)$ be the impedance of a lossless two-port terminated in a unit resistance. Show that

(a) if $Z(s)$ has a pole at $s = 0$, then the z-parameters of the lossless two-port have a noncompact pole there;

(b) if $Z(s)$ has a zero at $s = 0$, then the y-parameters have a non-compact pole there;

(c) if $Z(s)$ has neither a pole nor a zero at $s = 0$, then both the z- and y-parameters will have a compact pole there;

(d) the conclusions of (a) through (c) remain true if the point $s = 0$ is replaced by the point $s = \infty$.

27. Darlington's realization theorem shows that $Z(s)$ can be realized as a reactive two-port terminated in a resistance at one port. However,

the two-port will generally require transformers in the realization. An alternative which does not is given next. Let a positive real function be written as

$$Z(s) = \frac{m_1(s) + n_1(s)}{m_2(s) + n_2(s)},$$

where m_1 and m_2 are even polynomials and n_1 and n_2 are odd. The zeros of the polynomial $m_1 m_2 - n_1 n_2$ have quadrantal symmetry. Let $H(s)$ be a Hurwitz polynomial formed from the left half-plane zeros of $m_1 m_2 - n_1 n_2$; that is,

$$H(s)H(-s) = m_1(s)m_2(s) - n_1(s)n_2(s)$$

and

$$H(s) = m(s) + n(s).$$

(a) Prove that

$$
Z = \begin{bmatrix}
\dfrac{n^2 + m_1 m_2}{m_2 n_2} & \sqrt{R_2}\,\dfrac{m}{n_2} & \sqrt{R_3}\,\dfrac{n}{m_2} \\[2ex]
\sqrt{R_2}\,\dfrac{m}{n_2} & R_2\,\dfrac{m_2}{n_2} & 0 \\[2ex]
\sqrt{R_3}\,\dfrac{n}{m_2} & 0 & R_3\,\dfrac{n_2}{m_2}
\end{bmatrix}
$$

is the impedance matrix of a reactive three-port which, when terminated in resistances at two of its ports, as shown in Fig. P-27, realizes $Z(s)$ as the impedance at the remaining port. (The major element of the proof is in proving the residue condition.)

(b) Prove that

$$
Y = \begin{bmatrix}
\dfrac{n^2 + m_1 m_2}{m_1 n_1} & \dfrac{m}{\sqrt{R_2}\,n_1} & \dfrac{n}{\sqrt{R_3}\,m_1} \\[2ex]
\dfrac{m}{\sqrt{R_2}\,n_1} & \dfrac{m_1}{R_2 n_1} & 0 \\[2ex]
\dfrac{n}{\sqrt{R_3}\,m_1} & 0 & \dfrac{n_1}{R_3 m_1}
\end{bmatrix}
$$

is the admittance matrix of the above reactive three-port.
(c) Realize the following impedances in the above form. (The Darlington realization requires transformers.)

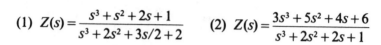

$$(1)\ Z(s) = \frac{s^3 + s^2 + 2s + 1}{s^3 + 2s^2 + 3s/2 + 2} \qquad (2)\ Z(s) = \frac{3s^3 + 5s^2 + 4s + 6}{s^3 + 2s^2 + 2s + 1}$$

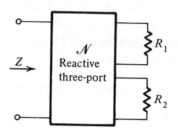

Fig. P-27

28. Prove that the inverse of a positive real matrix is positive real.
29. A transfer impedance function is to be realized by a cascade of the units shown in Fig. E-14 of Part II, in which each of the two-ports $\mathcal{N}_a$ and $\mathcal{N}_b$ are to be RC.
   (a) Develop a procedure which will permit the identification of RC-realizable functions z_{21b} and z_{21a} and other functions of the networks in the cascade.
   (b) Illustrate the procedure using the following function:

$$z_{21} = K \frac{(s^2 + 1)(s^2 + 4)}{(s^2 + 2s + 2)(s^2 + 3s + 6)}$$

30. Let $Z(s)$ be a rational positive real function.
   (a) Prove that

$$F(s) = \frac{kZ(s) - sZ(k)}{kZ(k) - sZ(s)}$$

   is also positive real, where k is a real, positive constant.
   (b) Show that the numerator and denominator have a common factor $(s + k)$ if and only if $Z(-k) = -Z(k)$.
   (c) When $Z(s)$ is expressed in terms of $F(s)$, the result is

$$Z(s) = Z(k) \frac{s + kF(s)}{k + sF(s)}.$$

Show that if $Z(-k) \neq -Z(k)$, then the numerator and denominator of the expression for $Z(s)$ will have a common factor $(s+k)$.

(d) Illustrate the above with the following positive real functions:

(1) $Z(s) = \dfrac{s^2+s+1}{s^2+s+4}$ (2) $Z(s) = \dfrac{s^3+2s^2+s+1}{s^3+s^2+2s+1}$

31. (a) Two positive real functions $F_1(s)$ and $F_2(s)$ are said to be *complementary functions* if their sum is equal to a positive constant K. Suppose that $F_1(s)$ and K are given. Determine the restrictions on $F_1(s)$ and K such that $F_1(s)$ will have a complementary function. If $F_1(s)$ and $F_2(s)$ are complementary and represent driving-point impedance functions, this means that the series connection of the two corresponding networks has a constant input impedance. In case $F_1(s)$ and $F_2(s)$ are admittance functions, then the parallel connection of the corresponding networks will have a constant input admittance. We refer to such pairs of networks as being complementary.

(b) Let $Z_1(s)$ be the driving-point impedance function of an *RC* network and assume that it is regular at the origin. Show that its complementary function $Z_2(s)$ will be an *RL* impedance function regular at infinity.

(c) Find complementary networks for each of the networks shown in Fig. P-31.

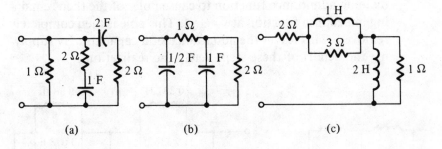

(a)   (b)   (c)

Fig. P-31

32. The Cauer ladders (shown in Fig. 12-8) realizing a reactance function are obtained by removing the entirety of a pole at ∞ or at 0, alternately from a function and from the reciprocal of the remainder after its removal. This process can be varied in a number of ways: (1) by removing the entirety of any other pole alternately

from a function and from the reciprocal of the remainder until the function is exhausted and (2) by removing a pole partially, thus shifting a pole of the reciprocal of the remainder into a desired position and then removing this pole entirely from the remainder.
(a) Consider the following reactance function:

$$Y(s) = \frac{2(s^2 + 1)(s^2 + 25/4)}{s(s^2 + 9/4)(s^2 + 9)}.$$

Fig. P-32(a) shows a realization in which the poles at $s = \pm j3$ are entirely removed; then the pole of the reciprocal of the remainder at infinity is partially removed so as to cause a pole of the reciprocal of *its* remainder to occur at $s = \pm j2$. That pole is then completely removed. The remaining function represents an inductor. Carry out this process and determine the component values.

(b) Consider the following reactance function:

$$Y(s) = \frac{s(s^2 + 2)(s^2 + 4)}{(s^2 + 1)(s^2 + 3)}.$$

The realization shown in Fig. P-32(b) is obtained as follows: The pole of Y at infinity is partially removed so as to cause poles of the reciprocal of the remainder at $s = \pm j3$. This is then entirely removed as a parallel tuned circuit in the series arm. Again there is a partial removal of the pole at infinity of the remaining admittance function to cause poles of the then remaining impedance function at $s = \pm j4$. This pole is then completely removed. This leaves the admittance of a capacitor. By supplying the details of these steps verify the realization.

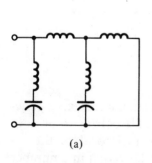

(a)

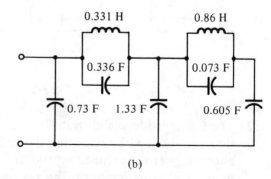

(b)

Fig. P-32

33. A symmetrical lattice has series and cross branch impedances Z_a and Z_b, respectively. Show that when it is terminated in a resistance R, the input impedance equals R if $Z_a Z_b = R^2$. Verify that for this constant-resistance case the voltage gain function is

$$G_{21}(s) = \frac{1 - Z_a(s)/R}{1 + Z_a(s)/R}.$$

34. Verify that the bridged-tee in Fig. 12-23(b) and the ell-networks in (c) and (d) are each constant-resistance networks when terminated in a resistance R if $Z_a Z_b = R^2$. Verify also that under this condition the voltage gain function is

$$G_{21}(s) = \frac{1}{1 + Z_a(s)/R}.$$

35. Fig. P-35(a) shows a symmetrical lattice.
    (a) Find the y-parameters and show that the Fialkow-Gerst condition (defined in Project 2 of Part II) will be satisfied under any one of the three conditions

    (1) $L_2/L_1 \geqslant 1$ or (2) $C_1/C_2 \geqslant 1$ or (3) $(L_2/L_1) + (C_1/C_2) \geqslant 1$.

    (b) Figures P-35(b) and (c) show two bridged-tee networks. Show that the first has the same y-parameters as the lattice under condition (1) above, and hence is equivalent to the lattice. Show also that the second one has the same y-parameters as the lattice under condition (2) above.
    (c) If the y-parameters of the lattice are expanded in partial fractions, the result will have the form

    $$y_{11} = y_{22} = k_\infty s + \frac{k_o}{s} + \frac{ks}{s^2 + \omega_o^2}$$

    $$= \left(k_\infty s + \frac{\alpha ks}{s^2 + \omega_o^2} \right) + \left(\frac{k_o}{s} + \frac{(1-\alpha)ks}{s^2 + \omega_o^2} \right),$$

    $$y_{12} = y_{21} = k_\infty s + \frac{k_o}{s} - \frac{ks}{s^2 + \omega_o^2}$$

    $$= \left(k_\infty s - \frac{\alpha ks}{s^2 + \omega_o^2} \right) + \left(\frac{k_o}{s} - \frac{(1-\alpha)ks}{s^2 + \omega_o^2} \right),$$

On the right side a fraction of the finite pole has been combined
with the pole at infinity and the rest of it is combined with the
pole at the origin. Show that each of the tee networks in the
twin-tee shown in Fig. P-35(d) has one of the sets of
y-parameters within the above parentheses. Determine the
range of values of α and show that this range of values exists if
condition (3) above is satisfied. Thus under this condition the
twin-tee is equivalent to the lattice.

(d) Determine the angle of the transmission zeros of the bridged-
tees and twin-tees determined by the three conditions in part
(a).

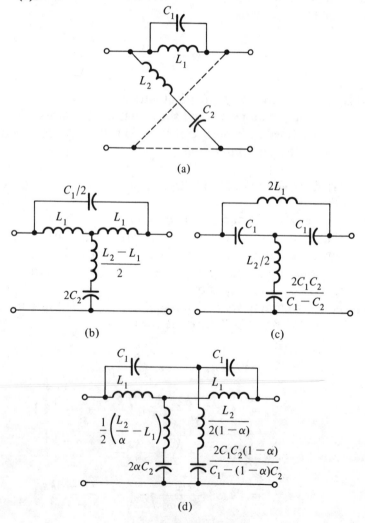

Fig. P-35

36. In the networks in Problem 35, replace each L_i by an R_i; the networks are thereby RC. Make the appropriate transformation to convert the admittances in part (a) to RC admittances. Find the angle of the transmission zeros for each of the RC bridged-tees and twin-tees.

37. A filter $\hat{\mathcal{N}}$ is to be designed to realize a given $|G(j\omega)|^2 = |V_2/V_i|^2$ between two given resistive terminations, as shown in Fig. P-37(a). Suppose $\hat{\mathcal{N}}$ is realized as a two-port $\mathcal{N}$ across whose input terminals its complementary network $\mathcal{N}_c$ is connected, as shown in Fig. P-37(b). In particular,

$$Y(s) + Y_c(s) = K \rightarrow \text{Re } Y(j\omega) + \text{Re } Y_c(j\omega) = K.$$

(a) Show how $|I_2/V_1| = G|V_2/V_1|$ for two-port $\mathcal{N}$ can be obtained from the given voltage gain function and, from this, $|I_{2c}/V_1| = G_c|V_{2c}/V_1|$ for the complement.

(b) Outline a procedure for finding an LC network for both $\mathcal{N}$ and $\mathcal{N}_c$.

(c) Carry out a synthesis if the given function is one of the following:

$$(1) \quad |G(j\omega)|^2 = \frac{1}{1+\omega^6} \qquad (2) \quad |G(j\omega)|^2 = \frac{1}{1+\omega^8}$$

(d) Obtain an active RC realization instead.

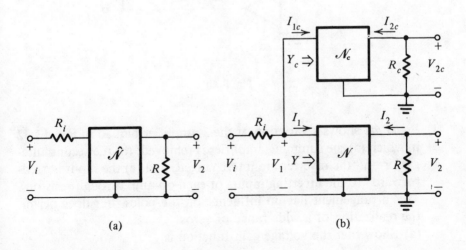

(a)   (b)

Fig. P-37

38. Assuming identical op-amps with gains given by (13-90), find the expressions for the voltage gain function in each of the 3-amplifier biquads shown in Figs. 13-32 and 13-29. (Assume the summing amplifier is removed.)

39. In order to compensate for the phenomenon of Q-enhancement in the 3-amplifier biquad design, a capacitor C_c is connected across the resistor in the second integrator. Show that, for identical op-amps with gain-bandwidth product $\omega_t = A_o\omega_a$, a value $C_c = 4/\omega_t R$ eliminates the Q-enhancement. Determine the effect of this capacitor on the realized voltage gain function for infinite-gain op-amps.

40. In the 3-amplifier biquad in Fig. 13-33 suppose the combination of the integrator followed by the inverter is replaced by the structure in Fig. P-40.

   (a) Find the voltage gain function.

   (b) Assuming identical op-amps, evaluate the effect of the frequency dependence of op-amp gain A on Q and ω_o, showing that this is an improvement over the original design.

   Note: This biquad was proposed by Ackerberg and Mossberg in 1975.

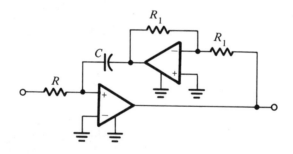

Fig. P-40

41. Fig. P-41 shows a variation of the 3-amplifier biquad in Fig. 13-32 in which (a) the summing amplifier is removed, (b) the second integrator and the inverter are interchanged, and (c) the input is "fed-forward" to the inverting inputs of each op-amp through resistors. This arrangement has no influence on the poles, but does permit the realization of a wide range of zeros.

   (a) Show that the voltage gain function is

$$G(s) = \frac{V_2}{V_1} = -\frac{\dfrac{R_i}{R_3}s^2 + \dfrac{\omega_0}{Q}\left(\dfrac{R_i}{R_3} - \dfrac{QR}{R_1}\right)s + \dfrac{R}{R_2}\omega_0^2}{s^2 + \dfrac{\omega_0}{Q}s + \omega_0^2}$$

where $\omega_0 = 1/RC$.

(b) Specify the values of R_1, R_2, and R_3 in order to obtain the following results:

(1) low-pass function
(2) high-pass function
(3) band-pass function
(4) all-pass function
(5) notch and band-reject functions

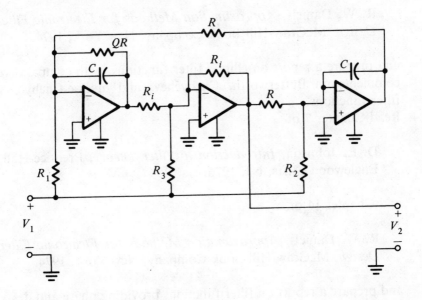

Fig. P-41

PROJECTS

1. Read Chapters 5 and 7 of

   N. Balabanian, *Network Synthesis*, Prentice-Hall Englewood Cliffs, NJ, 1958.

and prepare a report, containing examples, on transfer function synthesis by LC and RC ladder networks. The report should state and present verification of realizability conditions.

2. Read Chapter 8 of

> G. C. Temes and J. W. LaPatra, *Introduction to Circuit Synthesis and Design*, McGraw-Hill Book Company, New York, 1977.

and prepare a report, containing examples, on synthesis of networks containing distributed components, uniform LC (lossless) and RC structures.

3. Read Chapters 4 and 5 of

> R. W. Daniels, *Approximation Methods for Electronic Filter Design*, McGraw-Hill Book Company, New York, 1974.

and prepare a report on elliptic filter functions, with comparative comments on Butterworth, Chebychev, and inverse-Chebychev filter functions.

4. Read Chapter 7 of

> D. E. Johnson, *Introduction to Filter Theory*, Prentice-Hall, Englewood Cliffs, NJ, 1976.

and Chapter 14 of

> R. W. Daniels, *Approximation Methods for Electronic Filter Design*, McGraw-Hill Book Company, New York, 1974.

and prepare a report on filter functions providing phase and delay approximations.

FORTRAN and APL Programs

In this appendix, we list computer subroutines (1) to find the inverse of a matrix, if it exists, and (2) to perform a row echelon decomposition of a matrix. We provide both FORTRAN and APL code in the latter case, but only FORTRAN for the former case because matrix inversion is a primitive APL operation.

A.1 INVERSION

The single-precision FORTRAN subroutine MINV invokes Gauss elimination with partial pivoting to realize the inverse of an $N \times N$ matrix. The magnitude of a pivot element must exceed the tolerance value (TOL) set to the value two orders of magnitude greater than N times the unit round-off (EPS) for the computer times the maximum magnitude norm (NORM) of the matrix. Information needed to invoke MINV is contained in the comment cards at the beginning of the code presented next.

```
      SUBROUTINE MINV(A,AINV,FLAG,MA,MAINV,N)
      INTEGER FLAG
      REAL NORM
      DIMENSION A(MA,N),AINV(MAINV,N)
C
C     * IF THE N BY N MATRIX A IS INVERTABLE, THEN ON RETURN FLAG IS 1     *
C     * AND AINV IS THE N BY N MATRIX INVERSE OF A. (A IS THE N BY N       *
C     * UNIT MATRIX.) IF THE N BY N MATRIX A IS NOT INVERTABLE, THEN       *
C     * ON RETURN FLAG IS 0. (A AND AINV ARE NOT DEFINED.)                 *
C     *                                                                    *
C     * MA AND MAINV ARE THE ROW DIMENSIONS OF THE STORAGE SPACE FOR A     *
C     * AND AINV. (MA AND MAINV MUST NOT BE LESS THAN N.)                  *
C
```

```
C-----COMPUTE TOLERANCE PARAMETER
      EPS=1.0
   10 EPS=EPS/2.0
      EPSP1=EPS+1.0
      IF (EPSP1.GT.1.0) GOTO 10
      NORM=0.0
      DO 30 I=1,N
        DO 20 J=1,N
          NORM=MAX1(NORM, ABS(A(I.J)))
   20   CONTINUE
   30 CONTINUE
      TOL=1.0E2*N*EPS*NORM
C-----INITIALIZE AINV
      DO 50 I=1,N
        DO 40 J=1,N
          AINV(I,J)=0.0
   40   CONTINUE
        AINV(I,I)=1.0
   50 CONTINUE
C-----BEGIN INVERSION PROCEDURE
      DO 180 L=1,N
C-----SEARCH FOR PIVOT IN COLUMN L
      P=TOL
      K=0
      DO 60 I=L,N
        Q=ABS(A(I,L))
        IF (P.GE.Q) GOTO 60
        P=Q
        K=I
   60 CONTINUE
      IF (K.GT.0) GOTO 70
      FLAG=0
      RETURN
C-----PIVOT OF MAGNITUDE GREATER THAN TOL IN ROW K
   70    IF (K.EQ.L) GOTO 100
C-----INTERCHANGE ROWS K AND L, BRINGING PIVOT IN COLUMN L TO ROW L
      DO 80 J=L,N
        R=A(K,J)
        A(K,J)=A(L,J)
        A(L,J)=R
   80    CONTINUE
      DO 90 J=1,N
        R=AINV(K,J)
        AINV(K,J)=AINV(L,J)
        AINV(L,J)=R
   90    CONTINUE
C-----PERFORM ELIMINATION IN COLUMN L
  100    LP1=L+1
      R=A(L,L)
      A(L,L)=1.0
      IF (L.EQ.N) GOTO 120
      DO 110 J=LP1,N
        A(L,J)=A(L,J)/R
  110    CONTINUE
  120    DO 130 J=1,N
        AINV(L,J)=AINV(L,J)/R
  130    CONTINUE
      DO 170 I=1,N
        IF (I.EQ.L) GOTO 170
```

```
             R = A(I,L)
             A(I,L) = 0.0
             IF (L.EQ.N) GOTO 150
             DO 140 J = LP1,N
                A(I,J) = A(I,J) − R*A(L,J)
   140       CONTINUE
   150       DO 160 J = 1,N
                AINV(I,J) = AINV(I,J) − R*AINV(L,J)
   160       CONTINUE
   170    CONTINUE
   180 CONTINUE
         FLAG = 1
         RETURN
         END
```

A.2 ROW ECHELON DECOMPOSITION

The single-precision FORTRAN subroutine MECH invokes Gauss elimination with partial pivoting to realize the row echelon decomposition of an $M \times N$ matrix. The magnitude of a pivot element must exceed a tolerance set to the value two orders of magnitude greater than M times the unit round-off (EPS) for the computer times the maximum magnitude norm of the column (vector) in which the pivot resides. The vector WORK is used in the column-by-column evaluation of the norms and storage of the tolerances. Information needed to invoke MECH is contained in the comment cards at the beginning of the code presented next.

```
      SUBROUTINE MECH(A,M,MM,N,PIV,WORK)
      INTEGER PIV
      DIMENSION A(MM,N),PIV(M),WORK(N)
C
C     * UPON EXECUTION OF MECH, THE M BY N MATRIX A IS REPLACED BY      *
C     * ITS ROW ECHELON FORM. (MM IS THE ROW DIMENSION OF THE STORAGE  *
C     * SPACE FOR A.) THE M VECTOR OF INTEGERS PIV CONTAINS THE LIST    *
C     * OF SUCCESSIVE PIVOT COLUMNS. IF THE NUMBER OF PIVOTS IS LESS    *
C     * THAN M, THEN ZEROS ARE RIGHT CATENATED TO THE LIST OF PIVOTS    *
C     * TO FILL PIV. THE N VECTOR WORK IS USED AS WORKING STORAGE       *
C     * SPACE IN, COLUMN-BY-COLUMN, EVALUATING THE MAXIMUM MAGNITUDE    *
C     * NORMS OF AND TOLERANCES ASSOCIATED WITH THE COLUMNS OF A.       *
C
C-----COMPUTE TOLERANCE PARAMETERS FOR EACH COLUMN
      EPS = 1.0
   10 EPS = EPS/2.0
      EPSP1 = EPS + 1.0
      IF (EPSP1.GT.1.0) GOTO 10
      DO 30 J = 1,N
         WORK(J) = 1.0
         DO 20 I = 1,M
            WORK(J) = MAX1(WORK(J),ABS(A(I,J)))
   20    CONTINUE
         WORK(J) = 1.0E2*M*EPS*WORK(J)
   30 CONTINUE
```

```
C-----BEGIN DECOMPOSITION PROCEDURE
      NPR = 1
      DO 130 L = 1,N
C-----SEARCH FOR PIVOT IN COLUMN L
      P = WORK(L)
      K = 0
      DO 40 I = NPR,M
      Q = ABS(A(I,J))
      IF (P.GE.Q) GOTO 40
      P = Q
      K = I
   40 CONTINUE
      IF (K.GT.0) GOTO 60
C-----NO PIVOT IN COLUMN L IN ROWS NPR THROUGH M, SET THESE ELEMENTS TO
C-----ZERO (IDENTICALLY) AND SEARCH NEXT COLUMN FOR PIVOT.
      DO 50 I = NPR,M
      A(I,L) = 0.0
   50 CONTINUE
      GOTO 130
C-----PIVOT OF MAGNITUDE GREATER THAN WORK(L) IN ROW K
   60 PIV(NPR) = L
      IF (K.EQ.NPR) GOTO 80
C-----INTERCHANGE ROWS K AND NPR, BRINGING PIVOT IN COLUMN L TO ROW NPR
      DO 70 J = L,N
      R = A(K,J)
      A(K,J) = A(NPR,J)
      A(NPR,J) = R
   70 CONTINUE
C-----PERFORM ELIMINATION IN COLUMN L
   80 LP1 = L + 1
      R = A(NPR,L)
      A(NPR,L) = 1.0
      IF (L.EQ.N) GOTO 100
      DO 90 J = LP1,N
      A(NPR,J) = A(NPR,J)/R
   90 CONTINUE
  100 DO 120 I = 1,M
      IF (I.EQ.NPR) GOTO 120
      R = A(I,L)
      A(I,L) = 0.0
      IF (L.EQ.N) GOTO 120
      DO 110 J = LP1,N
      A(I,J) = A(I,J) - R*A(NPR,J)
  110 CONTINUE
  120 CONTINUE
      IF (NPR.EQ.M) GOTO 150
      NPR = NPR + 1
  130 CONTINUE
      DO 140 I = NPR,M
      PIV(I) = 0
  140 CONTINUE
  150 RETURN
      END
```

The relative tolerances can easily be changed to absolute tolerances or mixed (relative with absolute) tolerances; change the code in line 24. For example,

$$WORK(J) = 1.0E2*M*EPS*MAX1(1.0E-13, WORK(J))$$

is the code for mixed tolerances which we have found to give reliable performance when using MECH in the analysis of electrical networks. The absolute tolerance threshold is set by the value, here $1.0E$-13, to which WORK(J) is compared. This threshold setting value must be thoughtfully selected, often following experiments with the program using the subroutine, such that MECH functions reliably — provides a computationally correct row echelon decomposition for a well chosen set of test problems.

The APL function ECHELON listed next returns a matrix which is the row echelon decomposition of its right argument. The mixed tolerances generated in the first row can be easily changed to absolute tolerances or relative tolerances. As in MECH, Gauss elimination with partial pivoting is used.

```
      ▼ Z←ECHELON A;C;D;E;I;J;K;L;M;M;N;N;P;T
[1]      T←(⍴M)×1E‾14×1E‾13ΓΓ/|Z←A[(M←ι0),M←K←ι1⍳K;(N←ι0),N←ι1⍳K←⍴A]
[2]    L1:→L2×ι(⍴M)<I←EιP←Γ/T[J],E←|,Z[M;J←N[1]]
[3]      Z[I;]←Z[I;]÷Z[I←M[I];J]
[4]      Z[;N]←Z[;N]−(Z[;J]×I≠K)∘.×Z[I;N]
[5]      M←M,I,0⍴M←(I≠M)/M
[6]      N←N,J
[7]    L2:N←1⍳N
[8]      →L1×ι(0<⍴M)/\0<⍴N
[9]      R←N
[10]     Z←Z[M,M;]
      ▼
```

APPENDIX B
Bibliography

This bibliography is not intended to be exhaustive; the entries listed constitute some references for the subjects treated or cited in this text.

B.1 MATHEMATICAL BACKGROUND

B.1.1 Complex Variable Theory

[1] Hille, E., *Analytic Function Theory*, Ginn and Co., New York, vol. I, 1959.

[2] Knopp, K., *Theory of Functions*, Dover Publications, New York, vol. I, 1945, vol. II, 1947.

[3] LePage, W. R., *Complex Variables and the Laplace Transform for Engineers*, McGraw-Hill Book, Co., New York, 1961.

[4] A. I. Markushevich, *Theory of Functions of a Complex Variable*, Chelsea Publishing Co., New York, 1977.

[5] E. B. Saff and A. D. Snider, *Fundamentals of Complex Analysis*, Prentice-Hall, Englewood Cliffs, NJ, 1976.

[6] R. A. Silverman, *Introductory Complex Analysis*, Dover Publications, New York, 1972.

[7] M. R. Spiegel, *Theory and Problems of Complex Variables*, McGraw-Hill Book Co., New York, 1964.

B.1.2 Computer Programming

[8] G. B. Davis and T. R. Hoffmann, *FORTRAN: A Structured, Disciplined Style*, McGraw-Hill Book Co., New York, 1978.

[9] W. R. Lepage, *Applied APL Programming*, Prentice-Hall, Englewood Cliffs, NJ, 1978.

[10] N. Wirth, *Systematic Programming: An Introduction*, Prentice-Hall, Englewood Cliffs, NJ, 1973.

B.1.3 Laplace Transform Theory

[11] G. Doetsch, *Handbuch der Laplace Transformation*, Birkhauser, Basel, vol. I, 1950.

[12] W. R. Lepage, *Complex Variables and the Laplace Transform for Engineers*, McGraw-Hill Book Co., New York, 1961.

[13] M. R. Spiegel, *Theory and Problems of Laplace Transforms*, McGraw-Hill Book Co., New York, 1965.

B.1.4 Linear Algebra and Matrix Theory

[14] S. Barnett, *Matrices in Control Theory*, Van Nostrand Reinhold Co., London, 1971.

[15] R. Bellman, *Introduction to Matrix Analysis*, McGraw-Hill Book Co., New York, 1960.

[16] D. G. B. Edelen and A. D. Kydoniefs, *An Introduction to Linear Algebra for Science and Engineering*, American Elsevier Publishing Co., New York, 1972.

[17] F. R. Gantmacher, *The Theory of Matrices*, Chelsea Publishing Co., New York, vol. I, 1959, vol. II, 1959.

[18] R. J. Goult, R. F. Hoskins, J. A. Milner, and M. J. Pratt, *Computational Methods in Linear Algebra*, John Wiley & Sons, New York, 1974.

[19] A. Jennings, *Matrix Computation for Engineers and Scientists*, John Wiley & Sons, London, 1977.

[20] S. Lipschutz, *Linear Algebra*, McGraw-Hill Book Co., New York, 1968.

[21] M. C. Pease III, *Methods of Matrix Algebra*, Academic Press, New York, 1965.

[22] F. M. Stewart, *Introduction to Linear Algebra*, D. Van Nostrand Co., Princton, NJ, 1963.

[23] R. P. Tewarson, *Sparse Matrices*, Academic Press, New York, 1973.

B.1.5 Numerical Analysis

[24] R. Beckett and J. Hurt, *Numerical Calculations and Algorithms*, McGraw-Hill Book Co., New York, 1967.

[25] G. Dahlquist and A. Björck, *Numerical Methods*, Prentice-Hall, Englewood Cliffs, NJ, 1974.

[26] I. A. Dodes, *Numerical Analysis for Computer Science*, North-Holland, New York, 1978.

[27] G. E. Forsythe and C. B. Moler, *Computer Solution of Linear Algebraic Systems*, Prentice-Hall, Englewood Cliffs, NJ, 1967.

[28] G. E. Forsythe, M. A. Malcolm, and C. B. Moler, *Computer Methods for Mathematical Computations*, Prentice-Hall, Englewood Cliffs, NJ, 1977.

[29] C. W. Gear, *Numerical Initial Value Problems in Ordinary Differential Equations*, Prentice-Hall, Englewood Cliffs, NJ, 1971.

[30] F. W. Hamming, *Introduction to Applied Numerical Analysis*, McGraw-Hill Book Company, New York, 1971.

[31] P. Henrice, *Discrete Variable Methods in Ordinary Differential Equations*, John Wiley & Sons, New York, 1962.

[32] A. S. Householder, *The Theory of Matrices in Numerical Analysis*, Dover Publications, New York, 1975.

[33] E. Isaacson and H. B. Keller, *Analysis of Numerical Methods*, John Wiley & Sons, New York, 1966.

[34] L. G. Kelly, *Handbook of Numerical Methods and Applications*, Addison-Wesley Publishing Co., Reading, MA, 1967.

[35] J. C. Nash, *Compact Numerical Methods for Computers: Linear Algebra and Function Minimisation*, John Wiley & Sons, New York, 1979.

[36] F. Scheid, *Theory and Problems of Numerical Analysis*, McGraw-Hill Book Co., New York, 1968.

[37] L. F. Shampine and M. K. Gordon, *Computer Solution of Ordinary Differential Equations: The Initial Value Problem*, W. H. Freeman and Co., San Francisco, 1975.

[38] J. H. Wildinson, *Rounding Errors in Algebraic Processes*, Prentice-Hall, Englewood Cliffs, NJ, 1963.

B.2 NETWORK ANALYSIS

B.2.1 Linear Graph Theory

[39] S.-P. Chan, *Introductory Topological Analysis of Electrical Networks*, Holt, Rinehart and Winston, New York, 1969.

[40] N. Deo, *Graph Theory with Applications to Engineering and Computer Science*, Prentice-Hall, Englewood Cliffs, NJ, 1974.

[41] W. H. Kim and R. T.-W. Chien, *Topological Analysis and Synthesis of Communication Networks*, Columbia University Press, New York, 1962.

[42] W. Mayeda, *Graph Theory*, Wiley-Interscience, New York, 1972.

[43] E. Minieka, *Optimization Algorithms for Networks and Graphs*, Marcel Dekker, New York, 1978.

[44] S. Seshu and N. Balabanian, *Linear Network Analysis*, John Wiley & Sons, New York, 1963.

[45] S. Seshu and M. B. Reed, *Linear Graphs and Electrical Networks*, Addison-Wesley Publishing Co., Reading, MA, 1961.

[46] P. Slepian, *Mathematical Foundations of Network Analysis*, Springer-Verlag, New York, 1968.

B.2.2 Network Equations

[47] M. Athans, M. L. Dertouzos, R. N. Spann, and S. J. Mason, *Systems, Networks, and Computation*, McGraw-Hill Book Co., New York, 1974.

[48] N. Balabanian and T. A. Bickart, *Electrical Network Theory*, John Wiley & Sons, New York, 1969.

[49] D. A. Calahan, *Computer-Aided Network Design*, McGraw-Hill Book Co., New York, 1968.

[50] L. O. Chua and P.-M. Lin, *Computer-Aided Analysis of Electronic Circuits*, Prentice-Hall, Englewood Cliffs, NJ, 1975.

[51] C. A. Desoer and E. S. Kuh, *Basic Circuit Theory*, McGraw-Hill Book Co., New York, 1969.

[52] E. A. Guillemin, *Theory of Linear Physical Systems*, John Wiley & Sons, New York, 1963.

[53] S. C. Gupta, J. W. Bayless, B. Peikari, *Circuit Analysis*, Matrix Publishers Inc., Portland, OR, 1977.

[54] L. P. Huelsman, *Basic Circuit Theory with Digital Computations*, Prentice-Hall, Englewood Cliffs, NJ, 1972.

[55] K. E. Koenig, Y. Tokad, and H. K. Kesavan, *Analysis of Discrete Physical Systems*, McGraw-Hill Book Co., New York, 1968.

[56] B. Peikari, *Fundamentals of Network Analysis and Synthesis*, Prentice-Hall, Englewood Cliffs, NJ, 1974.

[57] R. L. Ramey and E. J. White, *Matrices and Computers in Electronic Circuit Analysis*, McGraw-Hill Book Co., New York, 1971.

[58] P. H. O'N. Roe, *Networks and Systems*, Addison-Wesley Publishing Co., Reading, MA, 1966.

[59] R. A. Rohrer, *Circuit Theory: An Introduction to the State Variable Approach*, McGraw-Hill Book Co., New York, 1970.

[60] S. Seshu and N. Balabanian, *Linear Network Analysis*, John Wiley & Sons, New York, 1959.

[61] O. Wing, *Circuit Theory with Computer Methods*, McGraw-Hill Book Co., New York, 1978.

B.3 NETWORK PROPERTIES

B.3.1 Multiterminal and Multiport Representations

[62] N. Balabanian, *Network Synthesis*, Prentice-Hall, Englewood Cliffs, NJ, 1958.

[63] N. Balabanian and T. A. Bickart, *Electrical Network Theory*, John Wiley & Sons, New York, 1969.

[64] W. Cauer, *Synthesis of Communications Networks*, McGraw-Hill Book Co., New York, translation second German edition, 1958.

[65] E. A. Guillemin, *Synthesis of Passive Networks*, John Wiley & Sons, New York, 1957.

[66] W. H. Kim and H. E. Meadows, Jr., *Modern Network Analysis*, John Wiley & Sons, New York, 1971.

[67] E. S. Kuh and R. A. Rohrer, *Theory of Linear Active Networks*, Holden-Day, San Francisco, 1967.

[68] S. Seshu and N. Balabanian, *Linear Network Analysis*, John Wiley & Sons, New York, 1959.

[69] M. E. Van Valkenburg, *Introduction to Modern Network Synthesis*, John Wiley & Sons, New York, 1960.

B.3.2 Scattering Parameters

[70] N. Balabanian and T. A. Bickart, *Electrical Network Theory*, John Wiley & Sons, New York, 1969.

[71] H. J. Carlin and A. B. Giordano, *Network Theory*, Prentice-Hall, Englewood Cliffs, NJ, 1964.

[72] W. H. Kim and H. E. Meadows, Jr., *Modern Network Analysis*, John Wiley & Sons, New York, 1971.

[73] E. S. Kuh and R. A. Rohrer, *Theory of Linear Active Networks*, Holden-Day, San Francisco, 1967.

B.3.3 Frequency- and Time-Domain Representations

[74] N. Balabanian and T. S. Bickart, *Electrical Network Theory*, John Wiley & Sons, New York, 1969.

[75] R. W. Daniels, *Approximation Methods for Electronic Filter Design*, McGraw-Hill Book Co., New York, 1974.

[76] E. A. Guillemin, *The Mathematics of Circuit Analysis*, John Wiley & Sons, New York, 1949.

[77] E. A. Guillemin, *Theory of Linear Physical Systems*, John Wiley & Sons, New York, 1963.

[78] F. F. Kuo, *Network Analysis and Synthesis, second edition*, John Wiley & Sons, New York, 1966.

[79] J. D. Rhodes, *Theory of Electrical Filters*, John Wiley & Sons, London, 1976.

B.3.4 Sensitivity

[80] H. W. Bode, *Network Analysis and Feedback Amplifier Design*, D. Van Nostrand Co., New York, 1945.

[81] K. Geher, *Theory of Network Tolerances*, Akademiai Kiado, Budapest, 1971.

[82] I. M. Horowitz, *Synthesis of Feedback Systems*, Academic Press, New York, 1963.

[83] L. P. Huelsman, *Theory and Design of Active RC Circuits*, McGraw-Hill, New York, 1968.

[84] E. S. Kuh and R. A. Rohrer, *Theory of Linear Active Networks*, Holden-Day, San Francisco, 1967.

[85] S. K. Mitra, *Analysis and Synthesis of Linear Active Networks*, John Wiley & Sons, New York, 1969.

[86] G. S. Moschytz, *Linear Integrated Networks*, Van Nostrand Reinhold Co., New York, 1974.

[87] P. Penfield, Jr., R. Spence, and S. Duinker, *Tellegen's Theorem and Electrical Networks*, M.I.T. Press, Cambridge, MA, 1970.

[88] G. C. Temes and J. W. LaPatra, *Introduction to Circuit Synthesis and Design*, McGraw-Hill Book Co., New York, 1977.

[89] J. G. Truxal, *Automatic Feedback Control System Synthesis*, McGraw-Hill Book Co., 1955.

B.4 COMPUTER-AIDED DESIGN

[90] M. Athans, M. L. Dertouzos, R. N. Spann, and S. J. Mason, *Systems, Networks, and Computation*, McGraw-Hill Book Co., New York, 1974.

[91] D. A. Calahan, *Computer-Aided Network Design, revised edition*, McGraw-Hill Book Co., New York, 1972.

[92] L. O. Chua and P.-M. Lin, *Computer-Aided Analysis of Electronic Circuits*, Prentice-Hall, Englewood Cliffs, NJ, 1975.

[93] S. W. Director, *Circuit Theory: A Computational Approach*, John Wiley & Sons, New York, 1975.

[94] S. W. Director, *Computer-Aided Circuit Design: Simulation and Optimization*, Dowden, Hutchinson & Ross, Stroudsburg, PA, 1973.

[95] J. K. Fidler and C. Nightingale, *Computer Aided Circuit Design*, John Wiley & Sons, New York, 1978.

[96] B. Peikari, *Fundamentals of Network Analysis and Synthesis*, Prentice-Hall, Englewood Cliffs, NJ, 1974.

[97] P. Penfield, Jr., R. Spence, and S. Duinker, *Tellegen's Theorem and Electrical Networks*, M.I.T. Press, Cambridge, MA, 1970.

B.5 NETWORK SYNTHESIS

B.5.1 Energy Functions and Positive Real Functions

[98] N. Balabanian, *Network Synthesis*, Prentice-Hall, Englewood Cliffs, NJ, 1958.

[99] N. Balabanian and T. A. Bickart, *Electrical Network Theory*, John Wiley & Sons, New York, 1969.

[100] E. A. Guillemin, *Synthesis of Passive Networks*, John Wiley & Sons, New York, 1957.

[101] G. C. Temes and J. W. LaPatra, *Introduction to Circuit Synthesis and Design*, McGraw-Hill Book Co., New York, 1977.

[102] M. E. Van Valkenburg, *Introduction to Modern Network Synthesis*, John Wiley & Sons, New York, 1960.

[103] L. Weinberg, *Network Analysis and Synthesis*, McGraw-Hill Book Co., New York, 1962.

B.5.2 Passive Synthesis

[104] N. Balabanian, *Network Synthesis*, Prentice-Hall, Englewood Cliffs, NJ, 1958.

[105] N. Balabanian and T. A. Bickart, *Electrical Network Theory*, John Wiley & Sons, New York, 1969.

[106] P. M. Chirlian, *Integrated and Active Network Analysis and Synthesis*, Prentice-Hall, Englewood Cliffs, NJ, 1967.

[107] E. A. Guillemin, *Synthesis of Passive Networks*, John Wiley & Sons, New York, 1957.

[108] D. E. Johnson, *Introduction to Filter Theory*, Prentice-Hall, Englewood Cliffs, NJ, 1976.

[109] S. Karni, *Network Theory: Analysis and Synthesis*, Allyn and Bacon, Boston, 1966.

[110] G. C. Temes and J. W. LaPatra, *Introduction to Circuit Synthesis and Design*, McGraw-Hill Book Co., New York, 1977.

[111] G. C. Temes and S. K. Mitra, *Modern Filter Theory and Design*, Wiley-Interscience, New York, 1973.

[112] M. E. Van Valkenburg, *Introduction to Modern Network Synthesis*, John Wiley & Sons, New York, 1960.

[113] L. Weinberg, *Network Analysis and Synthesis*, McGraw-Hill Book Co., New York, 1962.

B.5.3 Active RC Synthesis

[114] P. M. Chirlian, *Integrated and Active Network Analysis and Synthesis*, Prentice-Hall, Englewood Cliffs, NJ, 1967.

[115] G. Daryanani, *Principles of Active Network Synthesis and Design*, John Wiley & Sons, New York, 1976.

[116] S. S. Haykin, *Active Network Theory*, Addison-Wesley Publishing Co., Reading, MA, 1970.

[117] S. S. Haykin, *Synthesis of RC Active Filter Networks*, McGraw-Hill Book Co., London, 1969.

[118] L. P. Huelsman, *Active Filters: Lumped, Distributed, Integrated, Digital, and Parametric*, McGraw-Hill Book Co., New York, 1970.

[119] L. P. Huelsman, *Theory and Design of Active RC Circuits*, McGraw-Hill Book Co., New York, 1968.

[120] D. E. Johnson, *Introduction to Filter Theory*, Prentice-Hall, Englewood Cliffs, NJ, 1976.

[121] S. K. Mitra, *Analysis and Synthesis of Linear Active Networks*, John Wiley & Sons, New York, 1969.

[122] G. S. Moschytz, *Linear Integrated Networks: Fundamentals*, Van Nostrand Reinhold Co., New York, 1974.

[123] G. S. Moschytz, *Linear Integrated Networks: Design*, Van Nostrand Reinhold Co., New York, 1975.

[124] R. W. Newcomb, *Active Integrated Circuit Synthesis*, Prentice-Hall, Englewood Cliffs, NJ, 1968.

[125] A. S. Sedra and P. O. Bracket, *Filter Theory and Design: Active and Passive*, Matrix Publishers, Portland, OR, 1978.

[126] K. L. Su, *Active Network Synthesis*, McGraw-Hill Book Co., New York, 1965.

[127] G. C. Temes and J. W. LaPatra, *Introduction to Circuit Synthesis and Design*, McGraw-Hill Book Co., New York, 1977.

[128] G. C. Temes and S. K. Mitra, *Modern Filter Theory and Design*, Wiley-Interscience, New York, 1973.

[129] J. V. Wait, L. P. Huelsman, and G. A. Korn, *Introduction to Operational Amplifier Theory and Applications*, McGraw-Hill Book Co., New York, 1975.

INDEX